AZO AND DIAZO CHEMISTRY
ALIPHATIC AND AROMATIC COMPOUNDS

AZO AND DIAZO CHEMISTRY
ALIPHATIC AND AROMATIC COMPOUNDS

BY

HEINRICH ZOLLINGER

PROFESSOR
IN THE EIDGENÖSSISCHE TECHNISCHE HOCHSCHULE, ZURICH
SWITZERLAND

TRANSLATED BY HARRY E. NURSTEN

LECTURER IN THE UNIVERSITY OF LEEDS
GREAT BRITAIN

INTERSCIENCE PUBLISHERS, INC., NEW YORK
INTERSCIENCE PUBLISHERS, LTD., LONDON
1961

INTERSCIENCE PUBLISHERS, INC., 250 FIFTH AVENUE, NEW YORK 1, NEW YORK
FOR GREAT BRITAIN AND NORTHERN IRELAND:
INTERSCIENCE PUBLISHERS LTD., 88/90 CHANCERY LANE, LONDON W. C. 2

PRINTED IN SWITZERLAND BY GASSMANN S. A. SOLEURE
1961

Preface

The chemistry of diazo and azo compounds possesses a surprising number of facets and a glance at the historical development of this field, reaching as it does into both aliphatic and aromatic chemistry, shows in how many directions progress has been made.

The discoveries of azobenzene (Mitscherlich, 1834) and azoxybenzene (Zinin, 1841) took place in the early days of organic chemistry. Immediately after the beginning of the classic period of this subject, characterized by the work of Kekulé and Couper, Griess started his attack on the aromatic diazo compounds (1858). His researches form the origin from which the chemistry of the azo dyestuffs grew to reach its flood tide at about the end of the nineteenth century. The problems of azo chemistry were tackled in the most intensive manner both scientifically and technologically not only in industrial laboratories, but also in the universities. Of the many famous names those of Hantzsch, Bamberger, Sandmeyer, Duisberg and Green stand out particularly.

On the other hand, the development of aliphatic diazo compounds after Curtius's discovery of diazoacetic ester (1883) set in only slowly and hesitantly. Two reasons are probably responsible for this marked contrast to the aromatic analogues. Azo coupling permits introduction of the aromatic azo group into organic molecules and the aryldiazo compounds are therefore the most important starting material for the preparation of aromatic azo derivatives but, since in most reactions of the diazoalkanes nitrogen is liberated, alkyldiazo residues can only be rarely introduced in this way. However, for alkylation several reagents other than diazoalkanes can be used and the splitting off of nitrogen does lead in part to highly reactive, unstable intermediates, which frequently give rise to complex products, difficult to interpret.

Although it was anticipated to some extent by men such as Staudinger, it is no accident that the systematic and fruitful exploitation of the potentialities of the diazoalkanes did not begin before the nineteen thirties. Only then had the necessary development taken place in physical organic chemistry to enable the behaviour of diazoalkanes to be understood. It is only necessary to recall the Arndt–Eistert synthesis which, although already it had been recognized in principle by Wolff at the turn of the century, did not become established until 1935.

In spite of being known for over a hundred years, the aliphatic azo compounds were investigated in detail only when the required theoretical framework was available. The study of their decomposition, of interest both technologically and from the point of view of mechanism, presupposes a knowledge of radical reactions in general.

Now that the fundamental principles underlying several of the reactions and properties of diazo and azo compounds, both aliphatic and aromatic, are becoming clear, the time seems ripe to examine these classes of compounds from a common viewpoint. Apart from a few brief references to the reactions of diazo-alkanes in the book on aromatic diazo compounds by Hantzsch and Reddelien, this has not been done so far.

Hence in this book the varied properties of diazoalkanes, of aliphatic and aromatic diazonium ions, of azoalkanes, and of aromatic azo derivatives are to be presented alongside one another. In view of the apparently great differences between, for example, aliphatic and aromatic diazonium ions or azomethane and azobenzene, this may seem questionable at first sight, but the newer results obtained essentially through the methods of physical organic chemistry allow the common roots to become apparent. Based on these fundamentals, the great range of characteristics exhibited by the classes of compounds covered by the title of this book can be understood.

The presentation of the subject is based on lectures delivered during my former activity in the University of Basle on azo dyestuffs as well as on aliphatic and aromatic diazo compounds. The chapters dealing with aromatic diazotization, with the equilibria, isomerization, and reactions of aryldiazonium ions, with azo coupling, and with the properties and metal complexes of aromatic azo compounds have been taken from my book, *Chemie der Azofarbstoffe*, published in 1958 by the Birkhäuser Verlag, but thoroughly revised, brought up to date and, in part, rewritten. In contrast to that book, this one is not a monograph solely concerned with dyestuffs chemistry and so there is no need to discuss dyestuffs technology and dyeing as such. On the contrary, reactions of aromatic diazo compounds which play no part in actual azo dyestuffs chemistry, as, for example, that due to Sandmeyer, do find a place in this volume.

With the varied reactions of diazoalkanes, the first aim has been to differentiate them according to mechanism into characteristic groups. A series of recent researches of fundamental importance, like those of R. Huisgen and J. D. Roberts, enable such a classification to be carried out and the connection with the behaviour of the aromatic diazo compounds to be traced. The work on the mechanism of the reactions of aliphatic amines with nitrous acid is still fluid and has caused me to present the different views alongside one another, but otherwise in this book older, superseded theories are only mentioned in exceptional instances. Apart from classic pieces of work, attention has been focused mainly on the newest investigations. It has frequently proved necessary to omit considerable supporting data in order to keep the book within sensible limits.

In accordance with my personal inclinations kinetics and mechanisms take pride of place. To make these aspects more readily understandable, the fundamental considerations underlying them are explained in some detail where appropriate. It also seemed desirable in some chapters, such as those treating spectra or metal complexes, to state the general principles of these lesser known fields of study.

A great number of friends, colleagues and students in the University of Basle, in Switzerland, Germany, Great Britain, Holland and the United States of America have contributed in many ways to the preparation of this book. In particular I wish to mention Professor R. Huisgen, Professor E. Heilbronner and Dr. H. Suhr, who have read parts of the manuscript critically and have made several valuable suggestions, and also Dr. H. E. Nursten, who is responsible for the translation into English. Not only has he been most careful to reproduce my thoughts faithfully, but through his familiarity with the field he has contributed materially to the final version. Miss B. Thüring has taken part in preparing the manuscript and she has compiled the list of references. Dr. Nursten and Mrs. E. Suhr kindly volunteered to read the proofs. Lastly, it gives me special pleasure to be able to say that my wife's help and understanding has made it possible to write this book in addition to my other activities.

I thank all of them for their cooperation and participation.

Binningen, Switzerland, April, 1960.   HEINRICH ZOLLINGER

CONTENTS

1. Methods of Preparing Diazo Compounds

1.1 Introduction

In 1858, at a time when modern organic chemistry was just beginning, Peter Griess discovered the aromatic diazo compounds. One of the newest advances had been the concept of the quadrivalence of carbon, and structural theory, especially that of aromatic compounds, did not yet exist. Elementary analysis was almost the only means which the organic chemist possessed for obtaining information about the structure of natural products or those of chemical reactions. Griess chose the term 'diazo' for his new compounds, because originally he thought that two hydrogen atoms of the benzene ring had been replaced by the two nitrogen atoms (868). Recently, several accounts have appeared of the history of the discovery of diazo compounds (432, 2168, 2183).

The thoroughness and extent of the work of Griess in this field probably provide the reason why Mène (1424) is rarely mentioned in this connection. Independently of Griess and possibly even before him, Mène obtained diazoaminobenzene through the action of nitrous fumes on aniline.

The fact that practically all aromatic amines are readily converted into diazo compounds contributed greatly to Griess's success. The original method by which he diazotized picramic acid (867) consisted of passing nitrous gases, prepared by the reduction of nitric acid with starch or arsenious acid, into an alcoholic solution of the amine.

His intention had been to replace the amino group of picramic acid with a hydroxyl one. Kolbe had drawn Griess's attention to the corresponding reaction of aminobenzoic acid with nitrous fumes. Because Kolbe allowed the gases to act at higher temperatures in water, the diazo compound formed as intermediate eluded him and he obtained only its decomposition product, hydroxybenzoic acid. That Griess was able to isolate the intermediate depended, on the one hand, on the lower temperature and, on the other, on the relatively high stability of the diazo compound from picramic acid. His supposition that the use of alcohol in place of water plays an important part is without significance according to present knowledge of the decomposition of diazo compounds.

Griess's method was soon replaced by simpler procedures, but it retained some interest for the isolation of diazonium salts. Only after more than thirty years was it displaced for this purpose by Knoevenagel's diazotization with esters of nitrous acid (see § 1.4).

In preparative chemistry, the diazonium salts themselves are required usually only as intermediates. Because of their comparatively poor stability, their isolation is almost always avoided, the solutions or suspensions in which they are formed being used as such for the next step. For these purposes, methods based on sodium nitrite are suitable and they are described in § 1.3. Sodium nitrite as source of the nitrosating agent was first employed by Martius (*1372*).

In some ways comparable with Griess's method are those of Witt (*2177*) and Möhlau (*1455*). Witt dissolved the amine in concentrated nitric acid and added a reducing agent, for example, sodium metabisulphite ($Na_2S_2O_5$), to convert nitric into nitrous acid in an amount equivalent to that of the amine used. Möhlau treated a solution of anilinium nitrate with zinc and acid, the first step being the reduction of the nitrate ion.

As shown in § 3.3, *aliphatic diazonium salts* are incapable of existence because the $\diagdown\!C\!-\!N\!=$ bond is not stabilized by resonance. Stable derivatives, the so-called *diazoalkanes* (1.1), are formed by splitting off a proton from the α-carbon atom of the alkyldiazonium ion. Diazoalkanes were first prepared in 1883 by

$$XCH_2\!-\!N_2^{\oplus} \xrightarrow{\text{Base}} X\overset{\ominus}{C}H\!-\!N_2^{\oplus} + H^{\oplus} \qquad (1.1)$$

Curtius (*504*) using this route, but diazotization is only suitable in special cases for their preparation. For this reason, the next sections of this chapter are concerned with the methods of preparing aromatic diazo compounds only and a separate section (1.6) is devoted to the diazoalkanes.

1.2 Diazotization with Alkali Nitrite in Aqueous Solution

Usually, diazotization can be carried out by allowing sodium nitrite to act on a solution of the amine in mineral acid at temperatures[1] of about $0°$. The overall equation for this process is:

$$Ar\!-\!NH_2 + 2\,HX + NaNO_2 \longrightarrow Ar\!-\!N_2X + NaX + 2\,H_2O \qquad (1.2)$$
$$(X = Cl,\ Br,\ NO_3,\ HSO_4,\ \text{etc.})$$

Of course, in aqueous solution the reactants and the products exist wholly or partly in their ionized forms: $H^{\oplus}X^{\ominus}, Na^{\oplus}NO_2^{\ominus}, Na^{\oplus}X^{\ominus}$, the diazonium salts are practically completely ionized and the amine is in equilibrium with the corresponding ammonium ion, $Ar\cdot\overset{\oplus}{N}H_3$. The question of which of these various particles are involved in the substitution proper will be dealt with in Chapter 2. Although it is generally desirable to introduce ionized forms into equations, this is inappropriate for the overall equation for the diazotization process, as will become apparent in the discussion of the reaction mechanism (Chapter 2) and from the following remarks.

---

[1] Temperatures are in degrees Centigrade throughout the text.

According to equation (1.2) two equivalents of mineral acid are essential for smooth reaction and usually even an excess of at least half an equivalent of acid is added at the beginning. During the diazotization and at its completion, the solution should react distinctly acid to Congo Red, corresponding to a pH of below 2. This is necessary for several reasons:

1. At higher pH values the equilibrium ammonium ion $\leftrightarrows$ amine changes in favour of the free base which, unless it contains carboxy or sulpho groups, is much less soluble in water.

2. At low concentrations of hydrogen ions, the diazo compound formed reacts with the free base of as yet unattacked amine to produce the diazoamino compound.

3. As described more fully in § 2.3, with increasing pH the reactive forms of the diazotizing agent are converted into ineffective ones, namely, free nitrous acid, HNO_2, and the nitrite ion, $NO_2^\ominus$. From the discussion of the mechanism of diazotization it will also become apparent why the reaction proceeds better, that is faster, in hydrochloric than in sulphuric acid. With very slow diazotizations for instance, because of high dilution as in nitrite titrations, the use of hydrobromic acid (i.e. HCl + KBr) commends itself. This depends on the catalytic effect of halogen ions and has nothing to do with the acid concentration.

An increased hydrogen ion concentration, that is a considerably greater amount of acid than the theoretical two equivalents of equation (1.2), is necessary in the diazotization of weakly basic amines. The classic example of this is the preparation of p-nitrodiazobenzene: p-nitroaniline is dissolved in hot 5–10 N HCl to convert it into the anilinium ion and the solution is either cooled quickly or poured on to ice. In this way the anilinium chloride is precipitated before hydrolysis to the base can occur. On immediate addition of nitrite, smooth diazotization can be obtained. The diazo solution formed should be practically clear and should not become cloudy on standing in the dark. Some pratice is necessary and details can be found in textbooks (709d, 1776e). Fierz-David and Blangey give a useful review of the principal variations of the methods of diazotization.

In contrast to the acid, *sodium nitrite* in general should not be added in excess. On the one hand, as far as the ratio amine to nitrite is concerned, diazotization is practically a quantitative reaction. In consequence, it provides the most important method for determining aromatic amines by titration. On the other hand, an excess of nitrous acid exerts a very unfavourable influence on the stability of diazo solutions, as was shown particularly by Gies and Pfeil (791). It is therefore important to measure the amount of nitrite required for a reaction as exactly as possible. Hence the azo chemist takes the following precautions:

1. Determination of the content of diazotizable amine by titration with nitrite.

2. Use of standard solutions of sodium nitrite.

3. Testing for excess of nitrous acid at the end of the reaction. For this purpose starch–potassium iodide papers are best used and these indicate nitrite

in acid solution by turning blue *instantaneously*. With some practice, the nitrite reaction is clearly distinguished from the coloration caused by certain diazo compounds, such as those bearing nitro substituents. The latter react only after $\frac{1}{2}$ to 2 seconds. Often the difference becomes more marked after dilution of the diazo solution with concentrated hydrochloric acid. A properly carried out diazotization should exhibit on completion a very weak nitrite reaction, corresponding to an excess of about 10^{-4} mol./l. Other indicators for nitrite have been described (*1776e*) and of these only the so-called Sulphone reagent (I) (*709c, 2702*), which gives a blue-green coloration with nitrite, is employed occasionally.

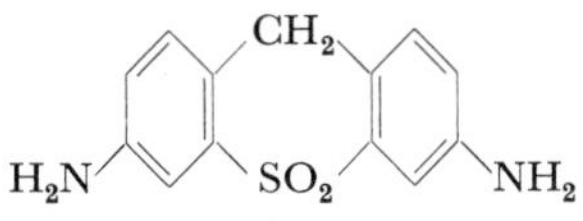

I

4. If nitrite is present in greater excess, it must be destroyed. Urea or sulphamic acid convert it into nitrogen, as shown in equations (1.3) and (1.4), probably via *N*-nitroso compounds. The decomposition is usually more rapid with sul-

$$CO\begin{smallmatrix}NH_2\\\\NH_2\end{smallmatrix} + 2\ HNO_2 \longrightarrow CO_2 + 2\ N_2 + 3\ H_2O \qquad (1.3)$$

$$SO_2\begin{smallmatrix}OH\\\\NH_2\end{smallmatrix} + HNO_2 \longrightarrow H_2SO_4 + N_2 + H_2O \qquad (1.4)$$

phamic acid. According to Grimmel and Morgan (*888*), the following side reaction with the diazo compound is possible in strongly acid solution:

$$Ar-N_2^{\oplus} + H_2N-SO_3^{\ominus} + H_2O \longrightarrow ArNH_3^{\oplus} + N_2 + HSO_4^{\ominus} \qquad (1.5)$$

A kind of diazo exchange (cf. § 8.4), leading to the intermediate, metastable diazoamino compound, $Ar \cdot N : N \cdot NH \cdot SO_3^{\ominus}$, must be involved.

Diazotization is normally carried out at 0°. A low temperature is advantageous for two reasons. First, the solubility of free nitrous acid is greater, which means that there is less danger of the nitrous gases escaping from the acid medium. Secondly, the moderate stability of most diazo compounds demands it. These two factors usually outweigh the lower rate of reaction and the poorer solubility of the starting material, which are in themselves undesirable. In cases where the diazo compound is relatively stable, higher temperatures of diazotization may be used, such as 10° to 15° for sulphanilic acid. On the large scale, selected diazotizations are carried out at 30°, 40°, and even higher, thus, for example, 2-amino-5-benzamido-1, 1'-diphenyl sulphone and its derivatives, which are important components for fast-to-light acid dyes for wool, are diazo-tized at 40° to 45°.

In general, the temperature is kept at 0° most easily by addition of ice *to* the reaction mixture. In this way, the considerable heats of reaction obtained in diazotizations are dealt with more safely and effectively than with external cooling.

A great number of publications about heats of reaction of diazotizations by Swientoslawski and his collaborators as well as by Wojeiechowski (*1776d, u, v*) appeared between 1910 and 1935. In the light of the more recent ideas on the mechanism of diazotization and of diazo equilibria, no significance can any longer be attached to these researches. The heat of reaction of the formation of *p*-chlorobenzenediazonium chloride is about 28 kcal./mole.

$$H_3\overset{\oplus}{N}-\!\!\left\langle\!\!\!\bigcirc\!\!\!\right\rangle\!\!-SO_3^{\ominus} \underset{+\,H^{\oplus}}{\overset{+\,OH^{\ominus}}{\rightleftarrows}} H_2N-\!\!\left\langle\!\!\!\bigcirc\!\!\!\right\rangle\!\!-SO_3^{\ominus} \qquad (1.6)$$

$$\text{II} \qquad\qquad\qquad\qquad \text{III}$$

Monoaminoarylsulphonic acids exist in acid solution as zwitterions (II in the case of sulphanilic acid), which are relatively insoluble in contrast to the corresponding bases (such as III). For this reason, in such cases the 'indirect method' of diazotization is often employed. The aminoarylsulphonic acid is dissolved as the anion (III) by means of the required amount of sodium carbonate or hydroxide, nitrite is added to the approximately neutral solution, which is then run into mineral acid. Indirect diazotization is particularly recommended for the aminosulphonic acids of greater molecular weight but, contrary to some statements in the literature, the three anilinesulphonic acids themselves can be diazotized directly in suspension, the reaction proceeding quite smoothly after some practice.

The diazotization of aminosulphonic acids, as well as that of amines with sparingly soluble salts, can be improved by the presence of dispersing agents. Most cationic textile auxiliary products may be used for this purpose. For example, the hydrochloride of *N*-diethylaminoethyloleoylamide [Sapamine CH (Ciba); IV] (*986, 2550, 2554*) is recommended for use in the preparation of the diazo components for a series of azoic dyes.

$$C_{17}H_{33}-CO-NH-CH_2-CH_2-N(C_2H_5)_2 \cdot HCl$$

$$\text{IV}$$

Easily oxidized amines, such as derivatives of *o*-aminonaphthols, are diazo-tized in a weakly acid medium (so-called neutral diazotization) in the presence of zinc or copper salts (*2503, 2535, 2536*). The process, which is due to Sand-meyer, has significance for the manufacture of diazo components for metal–complex dyes, in particular those derived from 1,2,4 acid, 1-amino-2-naph-thol-4-sulphonic acid. The metal ions are thought to restrain the oxidizing action of nitrous acid relative to its *N*-nitrosating effect.

1.3 Diazotization in Concentrated Acids

As the amines become more weakly basic, the normal method of diazotization becomes progressively more difficult. The equilibrium between amine and ammonium salt increasingly favours the former which, usually because of its poor solubility in water, is prevented from taking part in the reaction. The researches into the mechanism of diazotization have demonstrated that the important step is the addition of nitrosating agent to the *base* of the amine. Thus the acidity for each diazotization should be so chosen, that the equilibrium concentration of base corresponds to that of its saturated solution. This rule leads to the use of higher concentrations of aqueous mineral acid for weakly basic amines.

The position is complicated by several factors. The significance of the equilibria in which nitrous acid takes part will be detailed in the discussion of the mechanism of diazotization. In addition, in more concentrated acids, nitrous acid undergoes undesirable side reactions. In hydrochloric acid containing more than 20% HCl, nitrous acid begins to exert an unfavourable oxidizing effect according to equation (1.7). When nitrite solution is added dropwise to sulphuric

$$2\,NO_2^{\ominus} + 2\,Cl^{\ominus} + 4\,H^{\oplus} \longrightarrow 2\,NO + Cl_2 + 2\,H_2O \qquad (1.7)$$

or nitric acid of concentration greater than 25%, the rate of evolution of nitrous gases is greater than that of nitrosation.

For these reasons, there are limits to the extent to which the acid concentration can be increased *gradually* as the basicity of the amines decreases.

However, diazotization can be carried out without difficulties in 90 to 96% sulphuric acid. It has already been mentioned that nitrous fumes are given off as soon as nitrite is added to sulphuric acid of somewhat lower concentration, but *solid* sodium nitrite can be dissolved in 90 to 96% sulphuric acid at 0 to 10° smoothly and without evolution of gas. Nitrosylsulphuric acid, HSO_4NO, is formed. Directions for the preparation of 2 N nitrosylsulphuric acid are given by Fierz-David and Blangey (*709e*), but from acid of this strength sodium hydrogen sulphate crystallizes after some time so that it is best to prepare a stock solution of N sodium nitrite in 96% sulphuric acid, which is quite stable at room temperature.

The nitrosylsulphuric acid method is particularly suitable for the diazotization of polynitroanilines and aminoanthraquinones. Such amines may be added directly to the nitrosylsulphuric acid, but it is preferable to run the appropriate amount of nitrosylsulphuric acid into a solution of the amine in 96% sulphuric acid. In general, these diazotizations can be carried out at room temperature. The end point is determined in the usual manner with iodide paper, but after dilution of a few drops with ice. On completion, the whole is diluted with ice. The test with iodide paper fails in the case of polynitrodiazonium salts. Compounds such as a 2,6-dinitrobenzenediazonium salt decompose on dilution with water, forming nitrous acid and the original amine. Nitrous acid can also result from nucleophilic substitution by hydroxyl ions of nitro groups *ortho* or *para* to the diazonium residue.

Often diazotization in nitrosylsulphuric acid is very slow (*266*), because the concentration of the free amine is exceedingly small. The improvements due to Schoutissen (*1834*) and Misslin (*1451*, see also *1059, 1060*) are probably brought about by altering the ammonium–amine equilibrium in favour of the base. After dilution with concentrated phosphoric or acetic acid, respectively, amines, such as *p*-aminobenzaldehyde, which cannot be diazotized in nitrosylsulphuric acid alone, become reactive.

In several cases the use of nitrosylsulphuric acid may be avoided, if 1-naphthalenesulphonic acid is added to moderately concentrated sulphuric acid (20 to 60%). This greatly reduces the evolution of nitrous fumes compared with a solution of pure sulphuric acid of the same hydrogen ion concentration. It has not yet been investigated whether the phenomenon is due to the formation of naphthalene-α-nitrosylsulphonate, $C_{10}H_7 \cdot SO_3 \cdot NO$, or whether it is only a solubility effect. In any case, the region of total acidity of 4 to 12 N has thus become available for diazotization and technically crude sulphonation mixtures are used after dilution with water, for example, a solution of total acidity 4 N, of which 2·7 N is due to sulphuric acid. A further advantage of the method lies in the stabilizing effect which the naphthalenesulphonic acid exerts on the diazo compounds formed (see § 7.10).

1.4 Diazotization in Organic Solvents

The obstacle to diazotization with nitrite in organic solvents is the poor solubility of the salts of nitrous acid. An observation by Griess (*872*) was later developed by Knoevenagel (*1239*). In place of nitrous gases or alkali nitrite as nitrosating agent esters of nitrous acid were used, especially ethyl and amyl nitrite. With these, diazotizations can be carried out in alcohol, acetic acid, dioxane, and other media.

Knoevenagel's method is very important in the isolation of diazo compounds. The alcoholic diazo solution is diluted with ether, when the diazo compound is usually precipitated in a pure form.

An interesting claim has been made (*2569, 2570*) that treatment of amines in dimethylformamide with alkyl nitrites *in the absence of* acid replaces the amino group by hydrogen via the diazo compound.

Recently Cade and Pilbeam (*2310*) investigated diazotization in tetrahydrofurane as solvent. The use of nitrosylsulphuric acid in a mixture of glacial acetic and propionic acid has been exploited by J.B.Dickey (*2598–2600*), the addition of propionic acid depressing the melting point of glacial acetic acid to 0° or below.

1.5 Preparation of Aromatic Diazo Compounds by Other Methods

In the literature are described several methods of preparing aromatic diazo compounds in ways other than by the diazotization reaction. Saunders (*1776f*) has tabulated most of them.

The various processes, which Bamberger in particular developed for the preparation of diazotates, are relevant here. Bamberger had hoped to prove unequivocally the structure of the two isomeric diazotates through their methods of formation. It is now known that this is not possible and that, because of the various diazo equilibria, these special methods can come into consideration as routes to the diazonium salts. Saunders (*1776k*) treats the diazotate methods separately. The only one to obtain importance is the rearrangement of nitrosoacylarylamines, originally due to Bamberger (*146, 180*). In a series of papers, Huisgen *et al.* (*1111, 1121, 1125, 1126, 1128*) were able not only to elucidate the mechanism of the reaction, but also to indicate, by means of the rearrangement of cyclic nitrosoacylarylamines (V), the nature of the isomerism of *cis*- and *trans*-diazoacylates (diazoacetates etc., see § 7.5).

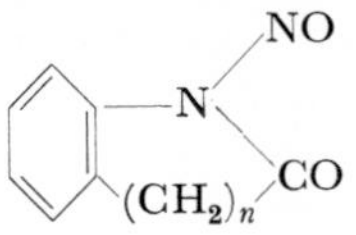

$$\text{V}$$

Recently, Tedder (*2014–2018*; see also *1513*) described an interesting way of introducing a diazonium group into aromatic systems. Phenols are treated with two equivalents of nitrous acid and give, via the intermediate nitroso compound, the diazonium salt in satisfactory yield according to equation (1.8). With aromatic compounds, such as benzenesulphonic acid, in which nitrosation is not facilitated by a hydroxyl group, prior mercuration offers a way out (1.9).

$$\text{ArH} + 2\,\text{HNO}_2 + \text{HX} \longrightarrow \text{ArN}_2^{\oplus}\,\text{X}^{\ominus} + 2\,\text{H}_2\text{O} + 2\,\text{O} \qquad (1.8)$$

$$\text{ArH} \xrightarrow{+\,\text{Hg}^{\oplus\oplus}} \text{ArHg}^{\oplus} \xrightarrow{+\,\text{HNO}_2} \text{ArNO} \xrightarrow{+\,\text{HNO}_2} \text{ArN}_2^{\oplus} \qquad (1.9)$$

The formation of diazonium compounds by reactions of nitroso compounds with nitric oxide was first observed by Bamberger (*164*). Gowenlock and Lüttke (*849*) discussed its mechanism.

Noteworthy is also the so-called self-diazotization discovered by Sihlbohm (*1892–1894*): several nitroaniline derivatives on treatment with hydrochloric acid in acetic acid solution form the corresponding chlorodiazobenzenes. 2,5-Dinitroaniline will serve as example (1.10). This method had already been discovered in principle by Meldola and Eyre (*1409*) in 1901 (see § 7.3).

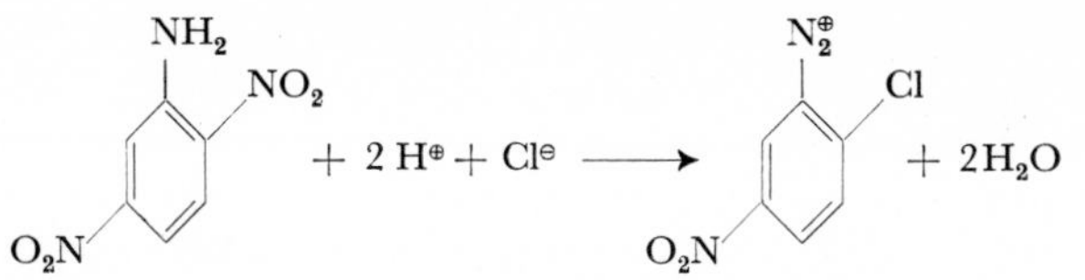

$$\text{(structure)} + 2\,H^{\oplus} + Cl^{\ominus} \longrightarrow \text{(structure)} + 2H_2O \qquad (1.10)$$

1.6 Preparation of Diazoalkanes

Primary aliphatic amines generally yield an alcohol by replacement of the amino group when they are treated with nitrous acid under diazotization conditions. Although the transient formation of unstable alkyldiazonium ions is involved, these are not discussed here but in the chapter on the reactions of aliphatic diazo compounds (§§ 6.1 and 6.5).

However, the first aliphatic diazo compound, diazoacetic ester, was prepared by Curtius (*504*) by direct nitrosation (i.e. diazotization) of aminoacetic ester, but this method can only be used for those amines which carry at the α-carbon atom strongly negative substituents, such as COR (*35, 1800*), COOR (*506*), SO_3H (*1607*), or CF_3 (*801*).

Curtius's original procedure consisted of dissolving the ethyl ester of glycine, or its hydrochloride, in water and adding sodium nitrite, sulphuric acid, and ether. On shaking, the diazo compound formed dissolves in the ether layer, which is separated, dried, and purified in one of several ways. Diazoacetic ester, $N_2:CH \cdot COOC_2H_5$, is formed in good yield (80 to 94%). It is a slightly yellow oil with an intense smell, which can be distilled without danger under reduced pressure or in steam. Apart from Curtius's procedure (*506*), there are several examples of checked preparations recorded in the literature (*784, 891*).

Usually, especially for the preparation of the important diazomethane, the diazo group has to be introduced indirectly. In principle most syntheses of diazomethane and its homologues start with a nitroso compound of the general formula $HR \cdot N(NO) \cdot X$, which, on treatment with a suitable base, yields the diazoalkane $R:N_2$ (the formulation of diazoalkanes is discussed in §§ 3.3 and 6.1).

For diazomethane two methods are in general use. Franchimont (*750*) observed that nitrosomethylurethan evolved a yellow gas when treated with alkali and von Pechmann (*1597, 1598*), after investigating the reaction carefully, established the structure CH_2N_2 for diazomethane. He recognized its close relationship to diazoacetic ester and the differences between it and aromatic diazo compounds. The preparation, of which Eistert (*662, 663*) gives details, follows equation (1.11).

$$CH_3N\begin{array}{l} NO \\ \\ COOR \end{array} + KOH \longrightarrow CH_2N_2 + KHCO_3 + ROH \qquad (1.11)$$

Nitrosomethylurea (*2137*) may be used in place of the urethan (1.12) and probably provides the most popular method for preparing diazomethane solutions.

$$CH_3N\diagonalmatrix{NO \\ CO-NH_2} + KOH \longrightarrow CH_2N_2 + KOCN + H_2O \qquad (1.12)$$

Following Arndt (55), nitrosomethylurea is added to aqueous potassium hydroxide and ether at 5° in a flask fitted with a condenser set for distillation. On heating the mixture to the boiling point of ether, the yellow diazomethane distils together with the ether and is collected in ice-cooled ether contained in another flask. On completion, the ether distils colourless.

Diazomethane must be prepared very carefully for two reasons. First, it is extremely toxic, so that its preparation must always be carried out in a well ventilated fume-cupboard. The main danger is due to the fact that one may work with it for some time without noticeable effects, but later symptoms similar to asthma develop, followed by an allergic oversensitivity. Secondly, diazomethane is explosive. Under no circumstances should all the ether be distilled from the reaction vessel: an excess must always be present. Sharp glass corners facilitate the explosive decomposition of diazomethane, so the ends of glass tubes should be rounded in a flame and ground-glass joints should be replaced by cork or rubber. When drying ethereal solutions of diazomethane, only potassium hydroxide pellets with a smooth surface should be used. Explosions may be caused not only by the product but also by the nitroso compounds, and especially nitrosomethylurethan in contact with concentrated alkali is dangerous.

With regard to the stability of the starting material, de Boer and Backer (274) recommend the use of N-methyl-N-nitrosotoluene-p-sulphonamide, p-CH_3·C_6H_4·$SO_2N(NO)CH_3$, treated with potassium hydroxide and diethylene-glycol monoethyl ether in water and ether. The glycol reacts with the sulphonic acid formed, yielding the corresponding ester.

Other nitroso compounds which have been used for the preparation of diazo-methane are 4-methyl-4-(methylnitrosamino)-2-pentanone (VI) (6–8, 1688) and 1-methyl-1-nitroso-3-nitroguanidine (VII) (1383, 1384).

$$(CH_3)_2\,C-CH_2-COCH_3 \qquad\qquad CH_3-N-C-NH-NO_2$$
$$\underset{ON-N-CH_3}{|} \qquad\qquad\qquad\qquad \underset{NO\ \ NH}{|\ \ \|}$$

VI   VII

In all the above cases, diazomethane is formed from a compound containing an N-methyl-N-nitrosamino group, but preparations are also known in which an alkane derivative is treated with a nitroso compound. Equations (1.13) (2590) and (1.14) (1492) will serve as examples. In (1.14) nitrosyl chloride may be used instead of nitrous oxide (1497).

$$2\,CH_3NH_2 + CH_3N(NO)-CO-CO-N(NO)CH_3 \longrightarrow$$
$$2\,CH_2N_2 + CH_3NH-CO-CO-NHCH_3 \qquad (1.13)$$

$$CH_3Li + \overset{\ominus}{N}=\overset{\oplus}{N}=O \longrightarrow CH_2N_2 + LiOH \qquad (1.14)$$

In principle most of these methods can be adapted for the preparation of the homologues of diazomethane. Adamson and Kenner's synthesis (*6–8, 1688*) of diazoalkanes from 4-methyl-4-(alkylnitrosamino)-2-pentanones is recommended especially. The starting material is obtained easily by reaction of mesityl oxide with an alkylamine and nitrosation of the resulting secondary amine. Huisgen (*1127, 1128*) has described the formation of diazoalkanes from *N*-nitrosolactams.

Disubstituted derivatives of diazomethane are made preferably by oxidation of ketohydrazones (1.15). Introduced by Curtius (*517–519*), the method has been evaluated thoroughly by Staudinger (*1931, 1933–1935, 1937*, cf. *897*). Instead of mercuric oxide, silver oxide or manganese dioxide may also be used (*1843*). Using this method, benzilmonohydrazone (VIII) is readily converted into azibenzil (IX) (*1514*). The latter, on treatment in acetone solution with aqueous methanolic sodium hydroxide, leads to phenyldiazomethane (X) in considerably better yield than by other methods (*2203*).

$$\begin{matrix} R \\ \\ R \end{matrix}\!\!\!>\!\!C{=}N{-}NH_2 \xrightarrow{+\ HgO} \begin{matrix} R \\ \\ R \end{matrix}\!\!\!>\!\!CN_2 \qquad (1.15)$$

$$C_6H_5{-}CO{-}\underset{\underset{N{-}NH_2}{\|}}{C}{-}C_6H_5 \xrightarrow{+\ HgO} C_6H_5{-}CO{-}\underset{\underset{N_2}{\|}}{C}{-}C_6H_5$$

$$\text{VIII} \qquad\qquad\qquad\qquad \text{IX} \qquad\qquad (1.16)$$

$$\Big\downarrow +\ NaOH$$

$$C_6H_5{-}COONa + C_6H_5{-}CHN_2$$

$$\text{X}$$

A method for the synthesis of crystalline diazodiphenylmethane has been described by J. B. Miller (*2344*).

Gaseous diazomethane is prepared most conveniently by Staudinger's procedure (*1938*), in which an alcoholic solution of chloroform is added to a hot solution of potassium hydroxide and hydrazine hydrate in ethanol (1.17).

$$CHCl_3 + H_2NNH_2 + 3\ KOH \longrightarrow CH_2N_2 + 3\ KCl + 3\ H_2O \qquad (1.17)$$

A summary of experimental details of recommended preparations and reactions of diazoalkanes has been given by Gutsche (*895*). Diazoketones, $R \cdot CO \cdot CHN_2$, are made by the action of diazomethane on acyl halides and their preparation is discussed in § 5.6.

2. The Mechanism of Diazotization

2.1 Historical Development

It is surprising that for some thirty years after the first investigation by Hantzsch and Schümann (*977*), the fundamental aspects of the diazotization process attracted only sporadic interest compared with the other theoretical problems of azo chemistry, such as the diazo equilibria, isomerism, and the mechanism of the coupling reaction.

The researches into the mechanism of diazotization are based on Bamberger's supposition (*149*) that the reaction corresponds to the formation of nitroso-alkylarylamines. The N-nitrosation of secondary amines finishes at the nitros-amine stage, because in their case protolysis is not possible, but primary nitroso-arylamines in a medium moderately to strongly acid are quickly transformed into diazo compounds. The process probably takes place through a prototropic rearrangement into the diazohydroxide, which is attacked by a hydroxonium ion to yield the diazonium salt (2.1).

$$\text{Ar—NH}_2 \xrightarrow[\text{X—NO}]{\text{slow}} \text{Ar—NH—NO} \xrightarrow{\text{fast}} \text{Ar—N} = \text{N—OH} \xrightarrow[\text{H}_3\text{O}^\oplus]{\text{fast}} \text{Ar—}\overset{\oplus}{\text{N}} = \text{N} \quad (2.1)$$

Nitrosamine formation occurs also with ammonia and primary aliphatic amines, but the resultant diazonium ions are unstable. Normally they rapidly undergo nucleophilic substitution by bases (H_2O and $OH^\ominus$) with liberation of molecular nitrogen and the intermediate appearance of carbonium ions. With aliphatic amines which carry a strongly negative substituent at the α-carbon atom, the alkyldiazonium ion can stabilize itself as the diazoalkane by loss of a proton (see § 1.6).

As described more fully in the discussion of the constitution of the aryldiazo-nium salts and of the diazoalkanes (§§ 3.2 and 3.3), with $HN^{15}O_2$ it can be shown that the two nitrogen atoms of these compounds are not equivalent (*433, 438, 1068*). In the aryldiazonium ion the heavy nitrogen appears in the β-posi-tion, in agreement with formation according to mechanism (2.1), but in the preparation of diazoacetic ester from glycine ester some N^{15} goes into the α-po-sition, though in minor amount. As subsequent rearrangements were ruled out, Clusius and Lüthi (*438*) proposed as explanation that, in parallel to N-nitro-sation according to mechanism (2.1), some reaction was occurring according to (2.2).

$$\text{ROOC—CH}_2\text{—NH}_2 \xrightarrow[\text{—H}_2\text{O}]{+\,\text{HN}^{15}\text{O}_2} \text{ROOC—CH—NH}_2 \xrightarrow{\text{—H}_2\text{O}} \left(\text{ROOC—CH—N} \atop \text{N}^{15} \right)$$

(with N^{15}O below the middle structure)

$$(2.2)$$

$$\tfrac{1}{2}\,\text{ROOC—CH}=\overset{\oplus}{\text{N}}=\overset{\ominus}{\text{N}}^{15} \qquad \tfrac{1}{2}\,\text{ROOC—CH}=\overset{\oplus}{\text{N}}^{15}=\overset{\ominus}{\text{N}}$$

The nitrosation of phenylhydrazine leads to azidobenzene (phenyl azide) presumably by a mechanism similar to (2.2), 7% $\text{Ar·N}:\overset{\oplus}{\text{N}}{}^{15}:\overset{\ominus}{\text{N}}$ being formed apart from $\text{Ar·N}:\overset{\oplus}{\text{N}}:\overset{\ominus}{\text{N}}{}^{15}$ (442). However, 2,4-dinitrophenylhydrazine and benzoic acid hydrazide on treatment with HN^{15}O_2 yield only that azido compound in which the end nitrogen is tagged (439). This result shows that neighbouring electrophilic groups direct the attack by nitrous acid to the β-nitrogen atom, the nitroso derivative produced decomposing spontaneously into water and azido compound with a marked γ-nitrogen.

In all the investigations into the mechanism of diazotization since Bamberger's it has been assumed, quite rightly, that in aqueous solution the formation of the nitrosamine is considerably slower than the steps which follow. Direct experimental proof of this hypothesis has been provided only recently by Ridd (1704).

As far back as 1899, Hantzsch and Schümann (977) showed that diazotization is a second-order reaction. As it was carried out in those days in relatively acid media, it was assumed only too readily that the ammonium form of the amine reacts with free, undissociated nitrous acid. This corresponds to the kinetic equation (2.3).

$$\frac{\text{d}\,(\text{Ar—N}_2^{\oplus})}{\text{dt}} = \text{k}\,(\text{Ar—}\overset{\oplus}{\text{NH}}_3)\,(\text{HNO}_2) \qquad\qquad (2.3)[1]$$

That the reaction is of the second order has been confirmed in the main by several researches (276, 277, 1689, 1837, 1854, 2003–2005) and, essentially, all these appear to be based on the views originally developed by Hantzsch. Although Bamberger had already propounded the hypothesis that the first step of diazotization is nitrosation, Taylor's investigations (2010–2012) into the nitrosation and deamination of aliphatic amines seem not to have been considered in this connection. The velocity of reaction of all the aliphatic amines examined, as well as that of the decomposition of ammonium nitrite, was always found to be proportional to the stoichiometric concentration of amine, but

---

[1] In this book, square brackets in kinetic equations signify the effective concentrations of the species bracketed, these being the equilibrium forms actually taking part in the rate-determining step. Parentheses are used for stoichiometric concentrations. Thus (Ar·NH_2) is the total amount of an amine present in the system, even if it existed predominantly as $\text{Ar·}\overset{\oplus}{\text{NH}}_3$, but $[\text{Ar·NH}_2]$ would represent the concentration of only that part of the total amount of amine which is not combined with a proton. Parentheses are also employed in cases, such as that of equation (2.3) of this chapter, where the reactive equilibrium forms have not been determined.

dependent on the *square* of the concentration of nitrite. The reaction here was therefore of the third order.

Schmid (*1805*) was the first to observe a reaction of the third order in the diazotization of aromatic amines in the presence of sulphuric acid and he set up the kinetic equation (2.4). In subsequent work (*1806, 1807, 1810*), he investigated the course of reaction in dilute hydrochloric or hydrobromic acid, which could be expressed using an extra term as in equation (2.5).

Diazotization in dilute sulphuric acid:

$$v = \frac{k \; (Ar\overset{\oplus}{N}H_3) \; (HNO_2)^2}{(H^{\omega})} \qquad (2.4)$$

Diazotization in dilute hydrochloric or hydrobromic acid:

$$v = \frac{k \; (Ar\overset{\oplus}{N}H_3) \; (HNO_2)^2}{(H^{\omega})} + k_c \; (Ar\overset{\oplus}{N}H_3) \; (HNO_2) \; (Cl^{\ominus}) \qquad (2.5)$$

Schmid's work marks the start of a change in the way in which the mechanism of diazotization was regarded although, at first, it seems surprising that Schmid did not discuss further the contrast between his result of a reaction of third order and Hantzsch's second-order reaction. Hughes, Ingold, and Ridd (*1103, 1105–1110*) rightly drew attention to this discrepancy. However, interest was so focused on the reason for the presence of *two* molecules of nitrous acid in the kinetic equation that this aspect was left to be clarified by later work.

Several theories were developed to explain the appearance of the second molecule of nitrite. Schmid supposed that amine nitrite is formed first and that it then reacts with nitrous acid to yield the diazo compound. The researches of Earl and Hills (*647, 648, 650, 651*) on the stability of amine nitrites throw doubt on such a mechanism, which has been taken over only by Hodgson (*1058*). Other explanations (*1–4*) will not be discussed here.

2.2 Experimental Methods

All the more recent work on the kinetics of diazotization has been based on the determination of the concentration of the diazo compound formed. To a portion of the reaction mixture is added an excess of an aqueous solution of an azo coupling component, usually a naphtholsulphonic acid, buffered with alkali. The rise in pH stops the diazotization process, but any diazo compound already present couples practically quantitatively and the azo dye produced is best estimated colorimetrically.

This method has been employed by Tassilly (*2003–2005*), Boeseken, Brandma, and Schoutissen (*276*), as well as by the two most successful workers in this field, H. Schmid (*1805*) and J. H. Ridd (*1103, 1105–1110, 1704*). Ridd in particular has concerned himself with the errors brought about by side reactions, namely, the decomposition of nitrous acid and of diazo compounds and the formation of diazoamino bodies.

Rosenberger and Shoemaker (*2351*) have recently proposed to determine the concentrations of diazonium compounds by measurement of optical density at 380 mμ.

Of methods of estimation other than the colorimetric, only polarographic determination of the increase in the concentration of diazo compound, as worked out by Elofson, Edsberg, and Mecherly (*1389*) some years ago, can be considered to be up to present standards of research into reaction kinetics. The other methods hardly retain any importance. Hantzsch and Schümann (*977*) measured the decrease in the concentration of nitrous acid by means of zinc iodide–starch solution and Schümann (*1854*), as well as Earl and Laurence (*650*), followed the reaction conductometrically. The latter authors ascertained that dilatometric determination of the kinetics of diazotization in methanol is possible and yet other techniques have been described by Earl and Ralph (*651*), J. and K. Rostowzewa (*1736, 1737*), and Ueno and Suzuki (*2059*).

2.3 The Mechanism of Diazotization in Dilute Perchloric Acid

The more recent work finds its origin in the developments in theoretical organic chemistry which occurred in the 'thirties. By means of the electronic theory of G. N. Lewis and M. Kossel, the consistent application of the ionic theory and that of equilibria to organic chemistry, and with some help from thermodynamics and quantum theory, L. Pauling, C. K. Ingold, and others began to classify the many compounds and reactions according to fundamental principles, a process which is well known to have yielded a rich harvest.

It has already been pointed out that nitrosation is probably the first step in diazotization. Ingold (*1108, 1152*) describes the reaction as N-nitrosation and classifies it as an electrophilic substitution together with related processes, such as the formation of p-nitrosophenol, an example of C-nitrosation. The nitrosating agent is an electrophilic particle which attacks an ion or molecule with relatively high electron density (lone electron pairs in mesomeric forms) at one, or more, atoms. It was probably Kenner (*5,1205,1206*) who first applied these ideas to diazotization and he realized that in aniline itself the electron density at the nitrogen is greater than in the anilinium ion, so that the base is the more reactive. On the other hand, the nitrous acidium ion (I), the addition product of nitrous acid and a proton, is a more powerful electrophilic reagent than the HNO_2 molecule. He therefore represented the first step of diazotization as follows

$$\text{Ar-NH}_2 + \text{ON-}\overset{\oplus}{\text{O}}\text{H}_2 \longrightarrow \text{Ar}\overset{\oplus}{\text{NH}}_2\text{-NO} + \text{H}_2\text{O} \qquad (2.6)$$
$$\text{I} \qquad\qquad\qquad \text{II}$$

The second nitrite ion, which appears in Schmid's equation (2.4), was supposed to act as base in removing a proton from the nitrosamine cation (II). This leads to a kinetic equation, which corresponds to Schmid's, but for the distribution of protons

$$\frac{d\,(Ar{-}N_2^{\oplus})}{dt} = k\,[Ar{-}NH_2]\,[H_2O^{\oplus}{-}NO]\,[NO_2^{\ominus}] \tag{2.7}$$

Hodgson (*1058*) and Earl (*649*) thought that the fact that diazotization can occur in a neutral medium or even in the crystalline state speaks against Kenner's ideas, but such criticism has no foundation. Although the equilibrium of the system $NO_2^{\ominus}{\rightleftharpoons}HO{\cdot}NO{\rightleftharpoons}H_2\overset{\oplus}{O}{\cdot}NO$ will certainly lie well over to left at the neutral point, it is not impossible for the nitrous acidium ions to be sufficiently reactive for the merest traces to provide the main route for nitrosation. Ridd (*1108, 1704*) has pointed out the real weakness of Kenner's mechanism, namely, the necessity for removing the proton from the nitrosamine cation by a nitrite ion. One would expect water to be basic enough to convert the cation quickly into the uncharged nitrosamine. The splitting off of the proton may be difficult only in concentrated sulphuric acid, as experiments by Blangey (*267*) lead one to suppose.

Although Kenner's hypothesis abides by the views of theoretical organic chemistry, it can hardly be brought into agreement with Schmid's experimental data with respect to the active form of the electrophilic reagent. All the same, it provides a considerable contribution to the understanding of the reaction, not least because Kenner recognized the importance of the free amine, in spite of the fact that diazotization is normally carried out in fairly strongly acid solution and that in many recipes it is clearly stated that the amine must first be converted into the corresponding ammonium ion.

Recent research has concentrated exclusively on the reactive form of the electrophilic component. Schmid's observation of the dependence of the reaction velocity on the square of the concentration of nitrous acid was interpreted by Hammett (*914 f*) as due to the intermediate formation of dinitrogen trioxide, N_2O_3. Similarly, Hammett regards the second factor of Schmid's equation for diazotization in the presence of hydrochloric or hydrobromic acid as the result of the formation of nitrosyl halide. Dewar (*567*) accepted these views in his textbook.

Schmid's equations can now be written as follows

Diazotization in sulphuric acid:

$$\frac{d\,(Ar{-}N_2^{\oplus})}{dt} = k\,[Ar{-}NH_2]\,[N_2O_3] \tag{2.8}$$

Diazotization in hydrochloric (or hydrobromic acid):

$$\frac{d\,(Ar{-}N_2^{\oplus})}{dt} = k\,[Ar{-}NH_2]\,[N_2O_3] + k_c\,[Ar{-}NH_2]\,[NOCl] \tag{2.9}$$

as the equilibrium concentrations of N_2O_3 and $NOCl$ are respectively governed by the following relations

$$[N_2O_3] = K_{N_2O_3}\,(HNO_2)^2 \tag{2.10}$$

$$[NOCl] = K_{NOCl}\,(HNO_2)\,(H^{\oplus})\,(Cl^{\ominus}) \tag{2.11}$$

We now know that Hammett's explanation is correct in all its aspects. This is especially noteworthy because Hammett arrived at his conclusions not through extensive experimentation in his laboratory, but by the consistent application of the newer theories of organic chemistry to kinetic results already published by others. This is not the only example of such anticipation of views now generally accepted to be found in Hammett's book, and it is worth remembering that Hammett expressly postulates the diazonium ion as the reactive form of the diazo compound in coupling, in contrast to the then current opinion that the diazohydroxide is the effective species.

Although Hammett convincingly explained the nitrosation of aliphatic amines and the diazotization of aniline under the conditions employed by Schmid and others, one point remained unsatisfactory, namely, the kinetic equation of second order, obtained by Hantzsch and the workers who followed him, for diazotization in more weakly acid medium. Comparison of experimental details shows that apparently at concentrations of free mineral acid below 0·05 mol./l. the reaction is of second order, but it becomes of third order at higher concentrations of acid.

Before describing the surprising solution to this problem found by Hughes, Ingold, and Ridd (*1106*), it is important to recall briefly the investigation of the forms of nitric acid active in aromatic nitration carried out by the school of Ingold and Hughes (*263, 795–799, 813, 814, 907, 1101, 1102*). From these researches it can be seen most clearly that, depending on the nature of the nucleophilic component and on the conditions of reaction, a whole series of nitrating agents can take part in the substitution proper. The different species are the products of equilibria which may set in rapidly or slowly. In certain cases, the reaction leading to the actual nitrating agent may become rate-determining. Then the substitution in the aromatic ring which follows takes place more quickly and the overall reaction is independent of the concentration of the nucleophilic component.

For nitration, the active forms can be arranged in order according to their reactivity:

$$O_2N^{\oplus} > O_2N \cdot NO_3 > O_2N \cdot NO_2 > O_2N \cdot OH$$

One can see that the electrophilic reactivity of the particle O_2NX increases as the strength of the base $X^{\ominus}$ decreases. This is the same as saying that it increases with the strength of the acid HX. Although the implication is that the nitronium ion $(NO_2^{\oplus})$ forms the 'best' nitrating agent, reaction paths often involve one of the other species, which under the given conditions of medium etc. is present in considerably greater equilibrium concentration.

In a manner analogous to that applied to nitrating agents, the forms active in halogenation (*539, 540, 1153e, 1988*) and other electrophilic substitutions can be arranged in order according to their reactivity. As regards nitrosation and diazotization, the following entities, listed in order of decreasing activity, must be considered:

ON$^{\oplus}$	nitrosonium ion
ON$\cdot\overset{\oplus}{O}H_2$	nitrous acidium ion
ON$\cdot$Br and ON$\cdot$Cl	nitrosyl bromide and chloride
ON$\cdot$NO$_2$	dinitrogen trioxide (nitrous anhydride)
ON$\cdot$OOC$\cdot$CH$_3$	nitrosyl acetate
ON$\cdot$OH	nitrous acid.

Of course the list is not exhaustive. For the following discussion it is important to note that in dilute aqueous solution a covalent bond cannot be formed between nitrosonium and perchlorate ions. Nitrosyl perchlorate is completely ionized not only in solution, but even in the crystalline state (*1591d*). According to Ridd (*1108, 1704*), nitrosyl perchlorate cannot therefore appear as such in a reaction mechanism, but Schmid (*1812*) comes to a different conclusion in some recent work, which is referred to below.

Ridd, who studied the nature of the reagent in nitrosation, points out that it is not possible to tie down each of the reactive particles listed by means of a single kinetic equation.

For those forms, such as N$_2$O$_3$ or $\overset{\oplus}{N}$O, which are produced by dissociation of an N—O link of nitrous acid, *two* kinetic equations exist in theory for the overall reaction, depending on whether the formation of the nitrosating agent or its reaction with the amino compound is the rate-determining step. On the other hand, it can be assumed that the formation of the nitrous acidium ion is more rapid than its nitrosating action, as it is produced by proton transfer in aqueous solution and such reactions are known to be exceptionally fast.

Table 2.1

Kinetic Equations for Nitrosation in Perchloric Acid Solution
(after Ridd) (*1106, 1704*)

Nitrosating agent	Rate-determining step	
	Formation of the nitrosating agent	Nitrosation of the amine
$\overset{\oplus}{N}O$	$v = k\,[HNO_2]\,[H^{\oplus}]$ $v = k\,[HNO_2]^2$	$v = k\,[ArNH_2]\,[HNO_2]\,[H^{\oplus}]$
H$_2$O$^{\oplus}$—NO	—	$v = k\,[ArNH_2]\,[HNO_2]\,[H^{\oplus}]$
O$_2$N—NO	$v = k\,[HNO_2]^2$	$v = k\,[ArNH_2]\,[HNO_2]^2$
HO—NO	—	$v = k\,[ArNH_2]\,[HNO_2]$

For diazotization in an aqueous system, which contains only the aromatic amine, an alkali nitrite or nitrous acid, as well as perchloric acid, only four particles, $NO^{\oplus}$, $H_2O^{\oplus} \cdot NO$, N_2O_3, and HNO_2, need be considered; the nitrite ion is disregarded, as it can hardly be thought of as an electrophilic reagent. The kinetic equations thus left for discussion are given in Table 2.1.

For the case where the formation of the nitrosonium ion is rate-determining, two equations appear, depending on whether the reagent is formed by dissociation of nitrous acidium ions (2.12) or from nitrous anhydride (2.13).

$$HNO_2 \xrightarrow{\;+\,H^{\oplus}\;} H_2O^{\oplus}\text{-}NO \longrightarrow \overset{\oplus}{N}O + H_2O \qquad (2.12)$$

$$2\,HNO_2 \xrightarrow{\;-\,H_2O\;} N_2O_3 \longrightarrow \overset{\oplus}{N}O + NO_2^{\ominus} \qquad (2.13)$$

The most important fact which emerges from Table 2.1 is that of the seven types of mechanism possible two pairs exhibit identical kinetics and therefore cannot be distinguished on this basis.

For the diazotization of aniline in dilute perchloric acid, Ridd's kinetic experiments not only reconcile the previous inexplicable divergence between Hantzsch's reaction of second order and Schmid's of third order, but determine unambiguously the reactive form of nitrous acid.

In the first place, Ridd found that with the perchloric acid concentration increasing from 0·002 to 0·05 N, there was a continuous change in the reaction from second to third order. As the medium becomes more acid, conditions favour the anilinium ion, the concentration of the form of the amine which actually takes part in the nitrosation falls, and with it the velocity of the nitrosating step in the reaction. It must be concluded that at low acidity, the formation of the nitrosating agent is rate-determining, but at higher hydrogen ion concentrations the substitution at the amine nitrogen gains in importance.

Secondly, Ridd obtained the surprising result that, although diazotization proceeds as a reaction of second order at relatively high pH, the rate is not linearly proportional to both the concentration of amine and to that of nitrite, as Hantzsch has supposed. In fact, the rate depends on the square of the nitrite concentration and is independent of that of the amine. The work of Hantzsch and Ridd is probably the outstanding example of the importance of the rule of chemical kinetics, often disregarded, which states that one must determine always, not only the order of a reaction, but also the order with respect to each of the reactants.

Thirdly, Ridd was able to show that under these conditions the rate of diazotization is independent of acidity, as long as it is realized that the hydrogen ion concentration does affect the equilibria in which the reactants take part (nitrite ion $\rightleftharpoons$ HNO_2 and free aniline $\rightleftharpoons$ anilinium ion). There is no catalysis by acid.

With the help of these results and Table 2.1, the mechanism of diazotization is unambiguously determined as

$$N_2O_3 + ArNH_2 \longrightarrow Ar\overset{\oplus}{-}NH_2\text{--}NO + NO^{\ominus} \qquad\qquad (2.14\,a)$$

$$Ar\overset{\oplus}{-}NH_2\text{--}NO \xrightarrow{\text{fast}} Ar\overset{\oplus}{-}N{\equiv}N + H_2O \qquad\qquad (2.14\,b)$$

In relation to this mechanism Hughes, Ingold, and Ridd (*1106, 1107*) make three points:

1. At high pH, where dinitrogen trioxide formation is rate-determining, the diazotization becomes of zeroth order, if a great excess of nitrous acid over the amine is present. This demonstrates at the same time that step (2.14b), the decomposition of $Ar \cdot \overset{\oplus}{N}H_2 \cdot NO$ into $Ar \cdot \overset{\oplus}{N}_2$, is considerably faster than both (2.14a) and the formation of dinitrogen trioxide, as the rate no longer depends on the concentration of amine. The original hypothesis propounded by Bamberger (*149*) is thus proved.

2. In the region of the second-order reaction, the diazotization of aniline, *o*-, *m*-, and *p*-toluidine proceed at the same rate. This is due to the fact that these amines all react sufficiently rapidly with the nitrosating agent for its rate of formation only to be rate-determining.

The influence of substituents in the benzene nucleus on the rate of diazotization of aniline in the region of third-order kinetics has been determined by Ueno and Suzuki (*2059*) as well as by Okano and Ogata (*1550*). The rate constants follow Hammett's equation (*914c*). Recently Larkworthy measured the reactivities of some aromatic amines towards dinitrogen trioxide (*2335*) and he has also studied the diazotization of weakly basic amines in dilute perchloric acid (*2336*).

3. Schmid's experiments in dilute sulphuric acid show that diazotization is a reaction of third order also at relatively high acid concentrations of up to $0 \cdot 3\,\text{N}$. It can therefore be assumed that dinitrogen trioxide is still the nitrosating agent and that under these conditions nitrosylsulphuric acid ($ON \cdot SO_4H$ or $ON \cdot SO_4^{\ominus}$) has still no part to play.

2.4 Other Mechanisms of Diazotization

The discussion of the various nitrosating agents in the previous section suggests the investigation of conditions of reaction under which the nitrous acidium ion and/or the nitrosonium ion could participate in the substitution step. This leads to reaction in more concentrated perchloric acid. Later, the mechanism in the presence of chloride and bromide ions will be considered.

Ridd (*1107, 1704*) noted that in the diazotization of *o*-chloroaniline at pH 1·69 the rate of reaction is considerably greater than expected on the basis of the dinitrogen trioxide mechanism. Analysis of his results showed that in parallel to the reaction with dinitrogen trioxide another process was occurring at a rate directly proportional to the concentration of nitrous acid, not to its square. This process is also directly dependent on the concentration of the free amine and on that of the hydrogen ion and thus obeys the kinetic equation (2.15).

$$\frac{d\,(Ar-N_2^{\oplus})}{dt} = k\,[Ar-NH_2]\,[HNO_2]\,[H^{\oplus}] \qquad (2.15)$$

With the help of Table 2.1, it can be decided whether this corresponds to diazotization with a nitrosonium or a nitrous acidium ion. For the $\overset{\oplus}{N}O$-mechanism, increasing concentrations of amine should lead to a reaction of second order independent of the amine. As such an effect was not observed, it must be concluded that in the above diazotization of o-chloroaniline a part of the amine reacts with dinitrogen trioxide, the rest with the nitrous acidium ion. Which mechanism is of greater moment depends on how strongly basic the amine is and on the acidity and the other properties of the medium. Steric factors may also be significant.

Whilst in the diazotization of aniline at a pH of about 5, dinitrogen trioxide is practically the sole reagent, under no conditions so far investigated is the nitrous acidium ion mechanism the only effective one.

Already in the 'thirties, Schmid (*1806, 1807, 1810*) had shown that in the presence of chloride or bromide ions a second term enters the kinetic equation. Bearing in mind that it is the free amine which undergoes diazotization, the reaction corresponding to the extra term must be written as follows

$$\frac{d\,(ArN_2^{\oplus})}{dt} = k\,[Ar \cdot NH_2]\,[HNO_2]\,[H^{\oplus}]\,[Cl^{\ominus} \text{ or } Br^{\ominus}] \qquad (2.16)$$

It is apparent that reaction occurs between the free amine and a nitrosyl halide, which is formed in a relatively rapid step from halide ion and an electrophilic nitrosating reagent before the main process. Diazotization catalysed by halide is found also in conditions under which formation of dinitrogen trioxide becomes measurably slow. Evidently nitrosyl halides are not derived from the latter.

Using an excess of amine in the bromide-catalysed diazotization, in the same manner as in the investigation of the dinitrogen trioxide mechanism, the formation of NOBr can be made to become rate-determining. According to Schmid and Ridd, the rate of reaction is then directly proportional to undissociated nitrous acid, the concentration of hydrogen ion, and that of halide ion. One can conclude that the slow step consists of nucleophilic substitution in the nitrous acidium ion, not the nitrous anhydride:

$$HNO_2 + H^{\oplus} \underset{}{\overset{\text{fast}}{\rightleftharpoons}} H_2O^{\oplus}-NO \qquad (2.17\,a)$$

$$H_2O^{\oplus}-NO + Br^{\ominus} \xrightarrow{\text{slow}} NOBr + H_2O \qquad (2.17\,b)$$

The kinetics can also be reconciled with an interaction between nitrosonium and bromide ions but, according to Ridd (*1704*), such a mechanism is less likely.

As the reaction with bromide thus requires the prior addition of a proton to HNO_2, it can be supposed that other nitrosating agents, especially N_2O_3, are

formed analogously. Nitrous anhydride results by interaction, not of two molecules of HNO_2, but of nitrous acidium and nitrite ions:

$$H_2O^{\oplus}-NO + NO_2^{\ominus} \longrightarrow ON-NO_2 + H_2O \qquad (2.18)$$

According to Hughes, Ingold, and Ridd (*1108, 1109*), the catalysis of diazotization by carboxylate ions, such as acetate or phthalate, depends on the attack
of the particles formed (nitrosyl acetate etc.) on the nitrite ions and not on their
power to nitrosate amines. Thus the formation of dinitrogen trioxide is catalysed and the diazotization only indirectly.

Under the reaction conditions used by Ridd, nitrosonium ions play no part
in diazotization. They are present only at higher acidities. Based on the work of
Singer and Vample (*1898*), Bunton and Stedman (*384*) have investigated
spectroscopically the equilibria occurring in solutions of nitrous acid in aqueous
perchloric acid of increasing concentration. They were able to confirm the
steps preliminary to Ridd's mechanism of diazotization by proving the forma-
tion of N_2O_3 as well as that of a cation ($NO^{\oplus}$ or $H_2NO_2^{\oplus}$) (see also *2055*). Additional evidence comes from a recent study of the rate of oxygen exchange be-
tween nitrous acid and water by Bunton, Llewellyn, and Stedman (*383*). The
rate of formation of N_2O_3 obtained in this way is similar to that calculated from
the rate of diazotization.

With the help of the acidity functions it should prove possible to differentiate
between the reactions of nitrosonium and nitrous acidium ions. In the case of
nitrosation by $H_2NO_2^{\oplus}$, the rate of reaction should follow Hammett's acidity
function H_0, since this measures the protonation of a neutral particle by $H^{\oplus}$
(*2368, 2369*). In the $H_2NO_2^{\oplus}$ mechanism the catalysis by acid consists solely of
the addition of a proton to HNO_2. On the other hand, Deno *et al.* (*2370*), as
well as Turney and Wright (*2055*), have shown that in more concentrated perchloric acid the dehydration of the nitrous acidium to the nitrosonium ion is
determined by the acidity function J_0. So far the possibilities of this approach
have been utilized only for oxidations with nitrous acid, namely that of formic
(*548*) and of ascorbic acid (*2371, 2375*), but not for diazotization. From the
recently discovered linear dependence of the rate on H_0, Ridd (*2439*) concludes
that in 57–61% perchloric acid the amine is rapidly nitrosated to $Ar-NH_2^{\oplus}-NO$,
which is converted into the products by a process involving a slow proton-transfer
to the medium.

De la Mare and Ridd (*541*, pp. 94–95) reviewed all the experimental evidence
for the state of nitrous acid in different solvents and conditions.

The fundamentals of the mechanism discovered to date can be summarized
as on the next page, the brackets indicating that the nitrosamine and the diazohydroxide have not been proved experimentally to be intermediates.

Ridd (*1706*) has found a rate-determining proton-transfer in the kinetics
of diazotization of aniline in 60% sulphuric acid. It can be supposed that
$Ar \cdot \overset{\oplus}{N}H_2 \cdot NO$ is a *quasi*-stationary intermediate, the rate of conversion of which
into nitrosamine or diazohydroxide is of the same order of magnitude as the
back-reaction to its formation.

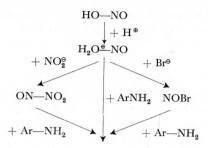

The comparison of the actual rate constants is of interest as regards the practical consequences of bromide catalysis: the nitrous acidium ion reacts eight

$$Ar—\overset{\oplus}{N}H_2—NO$$

$$(Ar—NH—NO)$$

$$(Ar—N = N—OH)$$

$$Ar—\overset{\oplus}{N}\equiv N$$

times as quickly with bromide, and seven times as fast with nitrite as with o-chloraniline (1107, 1152).

It can be supposed that under suitable conditions the nitrous acidium ion would react with other bases, such as a bisulphate or nitrate ion, but from the experiments of Schmid and Woppmann (1813) with diazotization in nitric acid of up to 0·2 M, it seems that at these concentrations the amine is attacked by the nitrous acidium ions themselves and not by nitrosyl nitrate (ON·NO₃).

Based on his kinetic results, Schmid (1808, 1809) has discussed what part of the total process at different conditions of acidity is due to each of the reactive species N₂O₃, H₂Ȯ·NO, and NOCl or NOBr. Schmid and Sami (1812) have shown that the diazotization of aniline in rather concentrated acid (up to 3 M HNO₃ or 4 M HClO₄) departs from the simple kinetic behaviour here described. It seems that results obtained in relatively concentrated strong acid must be interpreted with care. Such systems deviate in many ways from the relationships which apply to strong electrolytes in very dilute aqueous solution (914a).

Nitrosation has been presented most comprehensively by Seel (1875), who has drawn up a general scheme for the reactions of nitrous acid. He showed that the same laws apply not only to C-nitrosations and diazotizations, but also to the reactions in which nitrous acid acts as an oxidizing agent. From his general scheme for nitrosation, which embraces all the reactive forms of nitrous acid theoretically possible, Seel can derive as special cases every reaction so far found kinetically. His work is an excellent example of how a large number of apparently contradictory results from several laboratories can lead back to a relatively simple principle. Seel's reaction scheme includes apart from that of Hughes,

Ingold, and Ridd some other hypotheses about related reactions of nitrous acid. In the scheme, HX is the compound to be nitrosated, Y is a nitrosonium ion carrier (e.g. $Cl^{\ominus}$, $NO_2^{\ominus}$), and the bracketed formulas signify intermediates the concentrations of which are *quasi*-stationary.

$$ON-OH \underset{-H^{\oplus}}{\overset{+H^{\oplus}}{\rightleftarrows}} ON-\overset{\oplus}{O}H_2 \underset{-Y}{\overset{+Y}{\rightleftarrows}} \left(ON \overset{OH_2}{\underset{Y}{<}}\right)^{\oplus} \underset{+H_2O}{\overset{-H_2O}{\rightleftarrows}} ON-Y^{\oplus}$$

$$+HX \downarrow \qquad\qquad +HX \downarrow \qquad\qquad\qquad\qquad\qquad / \quad +HX$$

$$\left(ON \overset{OH}{\underset{XH}{<}}\right) \qquad \left(ON \overset{OH_2}{\underset{XH}{<}}\right)^{\oplus}$$

$$-H_2O \downarrow \qquad\qquad -H_2O \downarrow$$

$$ON-X \underset{-H^{\oplus}}{\longleftarrow} ON-\overset{\oplus}{X}H \longleftarrow \underset{-Y}{\left(ON \overset{Y}{\underset{XH}{<}}\right)^{\oplus}}$$

Seel's scheme for nitrosation

The reaction between nitrous and hydrazoic acid shows many similarities to diazotization (*2358, 2359*). Dahn, Bunton, and co-workers (*2371–2376*) demonstrated that the oxidation of ascorbic by nitrous acid starts with a nitrosation which exhibits mechanistic characteristics analogous to those of diazotization.

A review on nitrous acid and nitrosations has been published recently (*2056*).

2.5 Application to the Technique of Diazotization

In practice, difficulties on the preparative or industrial scale from too slow a diazotization occur relatively rarely. Unsatisfactory results are usually due to other causes, among which are important especially solubilities, particularly those of weakly basic amines, and also the decomposition of the diazo compounds formed.

All the same, some conclusions about the optimum conditions for diazotization can be drawn from the results of the investigations of the mechanism of the reaction. As regards the amine, Ridd, Schmid, and others have found that the free base is active, not the anilinium ion. If this were the only consideration, strongly acid media would have to be avoided, but the formation of the actual nitrosating agents (N_2O_3, $H_2\overset{\oplus}{N}O_2$, NOCl, etc.) is favoured by increasing the hydrogen ion concentration. Depending on the pH, nitrosation proceeds via a different derivative of nitrous acid because, on the one hand, the rate of formation of these derivatives varies in different ways with pH and, on the other, the derivatives exhibit different rates of nitrosation of the amine. Thus it is impossible to generalize about the optimum conditions for diazotization. However, the following points may be made:

1. The more weakly basic the amine, the more strongly acid should the medium be. Each amine has an optimum pH region for diazotization. For strongly basic amines it lies at pH 1–3.

2. In aqueous media, the equilibrium leading to the formation of N_2O_3 is less favourable than that for NOCl or NOBr (*1376, 1377, 1811, 1813*). Hence nitrosyl bromide is a better diazotizing agent than the chloride, which in turn is better than nitrous anhydride. Use is made of these facts in the analytical determination of amines. The titration with nitrite occurs more readily in presence of hydrochloric than sulphuric acid and it is advantageous to add potassium bromide which makes possible the formation of NOBr in place of NOCl.

3. For the same reason, increased halide ion concentration is helpful. Addition of sodium chloride instead of hydrochloric acid raises only the concentration of halide, not that of hydrogen ions.

4. Through the proper choice of acidity, certain compounds bearing two amino groups can be selectively nitrosated or diazotized. For example, in compounds of type (III) at a pH below 3 only the aromatic amino group reacts with

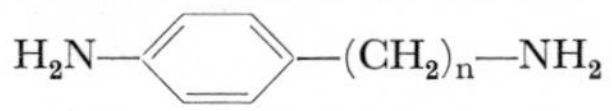

$$H_2N-\langle\ \rangle-(CH_2)_n-NH_2$$

III

nitrous acid, because the aliphatic one is much more basic and so its equilibrium lies much farther over in favour of the ammonium form (*1263*). Similarly, advantage was taken of the difference in basic strength of the two amino groups of *O*-glycylserine for a selective nitrosation leading to the synthesis of azaserine (*O*-diazoacetylserine) (*774, 775, 1461, 1527*).

5. A knowledge of the fundamentals of the kinetics of diazotization is essential for the design of a system for *continuous* operation, such as that recently described (*2573*). Here the control of the addition of the diazotizing reagent is important and it is carried out by means of determinations of the redox potential, based on the method of Elofson *et al.* (*1389*).

6. The electrophilic nature of nitrosating reagents is increased by complex formation with Lewis acids, as shown by the addition product of dinitrogen trioxide with boron trifluoride. Physical and chemical properties suggest (*2303*) that the structure of this complex is best represented as $(F_3B \leftarrow NO_2)^{\ominus} NO^{\oplus}$.

3. Diazo Equilibria

3.1 Nomenclature

Griess (*870*, *875*) had already observed that the diazo compounds obtained in acid solution are converted by alkalis into salts of alkalis. The reaction is reversible. The compounds which Hantzsch (*923*) termed *syn*-diazotates exhibit apparently the same reactions as diazonium ions into which they are instantaneously transformed by excess of acid. Clearly the reaction depends on an acid–base equilibrium.

However, complications appear in this protolytic system. In 1894 Schraube and Schmidt (*1842*, *2526*) discovered that the action of cold aqueous sodium hydroxide brought about a change in solutions of *p*-nitrodiazobenzene which did not correspond to that observed by Griess with diazobenzene. The salt, later described by Hantzsch as an *anti*-diazotate, was no longer capable of coupling and was transformed by acid back into the starting product only very slowly. Later, the interconversion of the two isomers was realized with many diazotates. The classic researches of Hantzsch and Bamberger were concerned mainly with the constitution of the isomers and were published mostly between 1894 and 1906. The investigation of the acid–base equilibria which Hantzsch carried out at this time and later were to some extent subsidiary to the central problem.

This book does not follow the classic method of presentation, but divides the subject into two. The present chapter deals with the protolytic equilibria, which set in rapidly, and the consideration of the isomers themselves will be left to the next one. As proposed by Hantzsch (*931*), substances in which the diazo group is present as a cationic substituent will be described as diazonium compounds, whereas those in which an atom or a group is *covalently* attached to the β-nitrogen of the residue $Ar \cdot N_2$ will be designated diazo derivatives. The distinction between a diazonium cyanide and a diazocyanide will serve as an example. The former, $\{Ar \cdot N_2^{\oplus} \, CN^{\ominus}\}$, is a salt, whilst in the latter, $Ar \cdot N_2 \cdot CN$, there is a homopolar bond between the diazo and the cyano group. The choice of the term diazonium by Hantzsch in analogy to ammonium is fortunate in the context of the modern Brönsted–Lewis nomenclature (see next section). Just as the ammonium ion is the conjugate acid of ammonia, so is the diazonium ion an acid in relation to the other two equilibrium forms, the diazohydroxide and the diazotate.

In this sense the description applies also to the aliphatic diazo compounds. Diazomethane is the conjugate base of the unstable methyldiazonium ion.

However, an essential difference exists in that the conjugate base of an alkyldiazonium ion is formed by dissociation of a proton (Brönsted acid), whereas the aryldiazonium ion is a Lewis acid, which is converted into its conjugate base by addition of a hydroxyl ion.

Saunders (*1776x*) and Hantzsch (*943*) have rightly pointed out that in principle there is no difference between the diazo derivatives, for example, a diazohydroxide, a diazocyanide, and a diazoamino compound, and the azo compounds, such as azobenzene, so that the former could equally well be described as azohydroxide, azocyanide, etc.

3.2 Constitution of the Aromatic Diazonium Ion

Griess designated the class of substances discovered by him in 1858 'diazo' compounds because he thought that *two* hydrogen atoms of the benzene nucleus had been replaced by nitrogen (*868*). He supposed that they had the composition $C_6H_4N_2$ and that, as weak bases, they could form salts of the type $C_6H_4 \cdot N_2 \cdot HX$. Kekulé (*1201*) realized that the diazo compounds were structurally analogous to their most important derivatives, the azo compounds, and he therefore described their constitution with the formula $C_6H_5 \cdot N:N \cdot X$. The fact that the diazo compounds are much less stable than the azo bodies was thought to detract from Kekulé's formulation. Blomstrand (*268, 269*) proposed the structure $C_6H_5 \cdot \overset{\text{N}}{\underset{\text{|||}}{N}} \cdot X$ and, in analogy to the ammonium salts, the name 'azoammonium'. Later, but independently, Strecker (*1968*) and Erlenmeyer (*682*) expressed similar views. Other formulas, which are now only of historical interest, are to be found in Saunders's book (*1776w*).

In 1895, Blomstrand's formula, which had been largely disregarded, was rediscovered practically simultaneously by Bamberger (*155*) and Hantzsch (*931*), who recognized how well it meets the experimental facts.

Since then, except for making the ionic nature of the N—X bond explicit, the principle of Blomstrand's formula has only been seriously challenged once, namely, by Dilthey (*592*), who introduced a three-membered ring as in formula (I). This structure is discussed below.

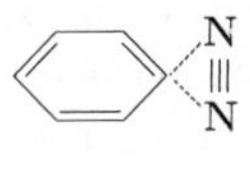

I

According to the current conception of acids and bases, originated by Brönsted and Lewis, the diazonium ion must be described as a *Lewis* acid. It is able to add a base, such as a hydroxyl ion, or, expressed in another way, it possesses electrophilic character, since in one of its limiting forms (IIb) one atom, the β-nitrogen, is deficient in electrons.

$$\text{Ar}\overset{\oplus}{-}\text{N}\equiv\overset{-}{\text{N}} \longleftrightarrow \text{Ar}\overset{-}{-}\text{N}=\overset{\oplus}{\text{N}}$$

$$\text{II a} \qquad\qquad\qquad \text{II b}$$

Diazonium salts the anions of which are derived from strong acids give neutral solutions in water and Goldschmidt (*822*) had already shown cryoscopically that they are completely dissociated. The conductivity determinations by Hantzsch (*531*) confirmed this. Thus, according to Lewis's definition, the diazonium ion is an acid but, more precisely, it is a *strong* acid, and therefore differs in this from the ammonium ion.

The only modification which current ionic theory requires of Blomstrand's original formula is that the anion X is not joined to the α-nitrogen atom of the diazonium radical by means of a line or a point as symbol of a covalent bond. As in any salt-like compound, the gegenion is not bound to a specific atom, but to the diazonium ion as a whole. A formulation of the relationship between the two ions has meaning only for the solid; in solution there is no actual bond between them.

In the ionic notation, the distinction between Kekulé's and Blomstrand's formulas disappears, as both can be regarded as limiting forms of the same substance (II a–II b). Stephenson and Waters (*1952*) have stressed that therefore it is incorrect to speak of diazo ions $(\text{Ar}\cdot\text{N}:\overset{\oplus}{\text{N}})$ as well as of diazonium ions $(\text{Ar}\cdot\overset{\oplus}{\text{N}}\equiv\text{N})$, although this has been done, even after the introduction of the concept of mesomeric limiting structures (*692, 941, 955, 1048, 1835*). The apparent difference in the reactivity of the two diazo groups in *p*-tetrazobenzene and in tetrazotized benzidine is due to other causes, as shown later (see § 11.4).

The consistent application of the ionic theory also leads to the abandonment of Hantzsch's hypothesis that, on addition of alkali to an acid diazo solution, 'diazonium hydroxide' $([\text{Ar}\cdot\text{N}\equiv\text{N}]^{\oplus}\text{OH}^{\ominus})$ is formed first and that this then 'rearranges' to the diazohydroxide $(\text{Ar}\cdot\text{N}:\text{N}\cdot\text{OH})$. The diazonium ion is present in solution together with some gegenion, say, chloride and, when alkali, for example, sodium hydroxide, is run in, the concentration of $\text{Na}^{\oplus}$ and $\text{OH}^{\ominus}$ is raised, but it must not be supposed that in alkaline solution the hydroxyl ion and no longer the chloride ion 'belongs' to the diazonium one. That in Hantzsch's day such a misconception was possible is not surprising, as the ionic theory was only in its early stages, but it is astonishing that the diazonium hydroxide is still accepted uncritically into many of the current textbooks.

Recently, with the help of isotopic tracers, it became possible to prove *directly* that, contrary to Dilthey's view, the two nitrogen atoms of the diazonium ion are not equivalent. Clusius and Hoch (*433*) prepared phenylhydrazine by diazotizing aniline with nitrite made from heavy nitrogen ($\text{NaN}^{15}\text{O}_2$), followed by reduction of the diazonium salt formed. On disproportionation, the phenylhydrazine yielded products with an isotope distribution derived exactly from equation (3.1).

$$2\ \text{C}_6\text{H}_5\text{NH}-\text{N}^{15}\text{H}_2 \longrightarrow \text{C}_6\text{H}_5\text{NH}_2 + \text{C}_6\text{H}_6 + \text{NN}^{15} + \text{N}^{15}\text{H}_3 \qquad (3.1)$$

In accordance with this result, Holt and Bullock (*1068*) started with N^{15}-aniline and NaN^{14}O$_2$, coupled to α-naphthol, and reduced the colouring matter formed, to find practically the whole of the heavy nitrogen in the recovered aniline.

The presence of a triple bond in diazonium salts is supported by the appearance of a characteristic band in the infra-red at 2260 cm^{-1} (4·42 μ) (*74, 2144*). The comparable cyano group possesses an absorption band in the same region at 2245 cm^{-1} (4·45 μ). Conclusions about the structure of diazonium salts drawn from considerations of the ultra-violet and visible spectra can no longer be accepted (*1464, 1468*). The infra-red spectra of diazobenzenes with hydroxy groups in *ortho* or *para* position, the so-called quinone diazides, diazo oxides, or diazophenols, exhibit a band corresponding to that of the carbonyl group in tropolone. Le Fèvre et al. (*1313*, see also *2144*) attribute this fact to the presence in these diazo compounds of a mesomeric system with the limiting forms (IIIa–IIIb), but consider cyclic structures to be absent. Investigations by Le Fèvre (*30, 32*) using determinations of dipole moments and ultra-violet spectra back up these conclusions. The quinonoid structure (IIIb) was postulated by Wolff (*2187*) along time ago and has been raised on several occasions (*31, 1045, 1050, 2074*). The zwitterionic form (IIIa) corresponds in principle

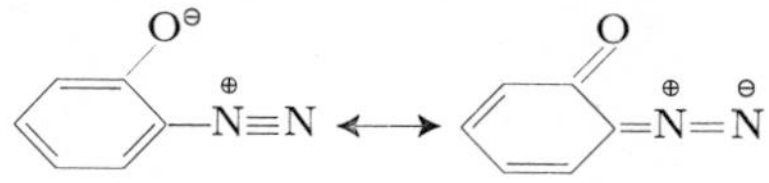

$$
\begin{array}{ccc}
\text{IIIa} & \longleftrightarrow & \text{IIIb}
\end{array}
$$

to Bamberger's formulation (IV), which was propounded at a time when one was unaccustomed to the ionic concept and particularly to that of zwitterions (*157*, see also *1229*). However, the recent researches rule out the covalent struc-

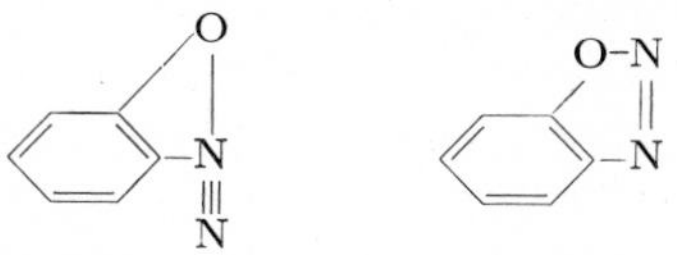

$$
\begin{array}{cc}
\text{IV} & \text{V}
\end{array}
$$

ture (V), advanced by Hantzsch and Morgan (*962, 1465, 1469, 1471*), but, according to Le Fèvre (*1313*), a heterocyclic ring, analogous to that in (V), must be present in *o*-diazothiophenols (§ 7.4, formula XXIV).

It can be concluded therefore that for diazophenols both Wolff's quinonoid structure and Bamberger's formula, when modified to the zwitterion, are equally correct, as they are limiting forms representing one and the same substance.

The diazonium group is an extremely strongly acidifying substituent; Schoutissen (*1839, 1840*) roughly equates its effect with that of two nitro residues. For this reason, the hydroxy group of diazophenols is strongly acid and, as illustration, the dissociation constant of the *p*-hydroxybenzenediazonium ion (pK 3·40) is about a million times greater than that of phenol itself (*1331*). In this connection, the *p*-acetamidobenzenediazonium ion is of interest, as with alkali it is not converted into the diazohydroxide and diazotate. Under the influence of the diazonium group, it behaves as a Brönsted acid, loses a proton from the acetamido nitrogen, and becomes converted into compound (VI), which is an analogue of the diazophenols (cf. § 3.5).

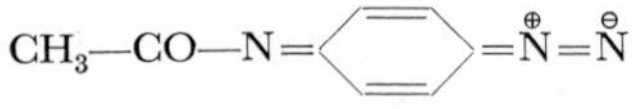

$$CH_3-CO-N=\!\!\underset{}{\bigcirc}\!\!=\overset{\oplus}{N}=\overset{\ominus}{N}$$

VI

Diazocyclopentadiene (VII), prepared by Doering and De Puy (*618*), also corresponds to the diazophenols (IIIa–IIIb). Structure (VIIa) is mesomeric with (VIIb) which involves the cyclopentadiene anion, a *quasi*-aromatic system. Diazocyclopentadiene provides a link between the aromatic diazo compounds of this section and the aliphatic ones considered in the next.

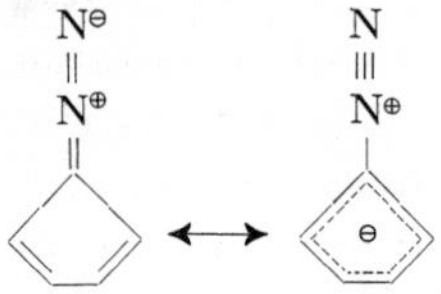

VIIa   VIIb

3.3 Constitution of Diazoalkanes

As explained in §§ 1.6 and 6.1, electron-releasing substituents in the aromatic nucleus greatly reduce the tendency of aryldiazonium ions to lose molecular nitrogen. The extreme stability which an *o*- or *p*-phenolate group confers on an aryldiazonium ion has even given rise to the special terms diazo oxide and quinone diazide mentioned above. The high stability of such compounds is due to the mesomerism (IIIa–IIIb) (§ 3.2). The importance of the limiting structure (IIIa), in which the potential nitrogen molecule is less strongly bound to the benzene ring, is diminished by (IIIb), but even an unsubstituted phenyl group is able to stabilize a diazonium ion through mesomerism between the π-electrons of the nucleus and the $-N_2^{\oplus}$ group, leading to limiting forms (VIIIb) and (VIIIc).

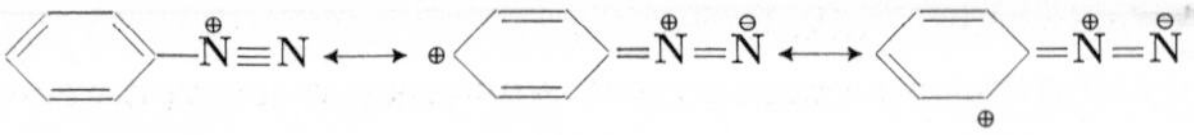

VIIIa   VIIIb   VIIIc

Such mesomerism cannot occur in the methyldiazonium ion, and decomposition, that is, the splitting off of molecular nitrogen, follows. The residual carbonium ion reacts with the solvent or loses a proton (cf. §§ 6.1 and 6.5).

Apart from hyperconjugation, tetrahedral carbon is unable to take part in mesomerism. Stabilization of an $-\overset{\oplus}{N}_2$ group bound to an sp^3-hybridized carbon atom is only possible if the carbon atom goes over into the trigonal sp^2-state. This happens when a substituent is split off leaving behind the electron pair of the broken bond, which implies, in the case of the methyldiazonium ion, the loss of a proton with formation of diazomethane (3.2). In this compound, meso-

$$CH_3-\overset{\oplus}{N}\equiv N + B \longrightarrow H_2\overset{}{C}-\overset{\oplus}{N}\equiv N + BH^{\oplus} \tag{3.2}$$

merism can occur (IX) just as in the aryldiazonium ion. Limiting structures with only a sextet of electrons on a nitrogen atom (e.g. IXc) or on a carbon atom have only minor significance for the ground state of a molecule.

$$H_2\overset{\ominus}{C}-\overset{\oplus}{N}\equiv N \longleftrightarrow H_2C=\overset{\oplus}{N}=\overset{\ominus}{N} \longleftrightarrow H_2\overset{\ominus}{C}-N=\overset{\oplus}{N}$$

$$\text{IXa} \qquad\qquad \text{IXb} \qquad\qquad \text{IXc}$$

This interpretation of the stability of diazoalkanes makes it clear why aliphatic amines with electron-attracting substituents in the α-position are converted into their diazo analogues by nitrous acid: such substituents ensure that in the intermediate alkyldiazonium ion a proton can split off more quickly than the C—N bond is able to dissociate. The diazoalkane derivative formed obtains additional stabilization from a —M substituent, because such a group can take over the negative charge of forms such as (IXa). The limiting structure (Xc) for diazoacetic ester provides an illustration.

$$\begin{array}{ccc} \overset{O}{\underset{\parallel}{}} & \overset{O}{\underset{\parallel}{}} & \overset{O^{\ominus}}{\underset{\mid}{}} \\ RO-C-\overset{\ominus}{C}H-\overset{\oplus}{N}\equiv N \longleftrightarrow RO-C-CH=\overset{\oplus}{N}=\overset{\ominus}{N} \longleftrightarrow RO-C=CH-\overset{\oplus}{N}\equiv N \\ \text{Xa} & \text{Xb} & \text{Xc} \end{array}$$

It would follow that it should be possible to obtain diazomethane by direct diazotization of methylamine, if the reaction could be carried out in a medium sufficiently alkaline to enable a proton to be removed from the primary product, the methyldiazonium ion. The right conditions may obtain in the preparation from methylamine and dinitrosodimethyloxamide (2590), mentioned in § 1.6, but alternatively dinitrosodimethyloxamide can be considered to be an analogue of nitrosomethylurea from which an alkali (methylamine here) liberates diazomethane. In the classic method of making diazoalkanes, the amine is first converted into the nitroso derivative, which is stable to acid and only decomposed subsequently by means of alkali.

Because of the different reactivity of diazoalkanes compared with aromatic diazo compounds, the cyclic formula (XI), proposed by Curtius (508) and von Pechmann (1597), remained accepted for very much longer. Angeli (37, 39) and Thiele (2032) advanced open structures and Langmuir (1296, 1297), who pointed out the steric similarities between the diazoalkanes, ketenes, and azides, introduced the zwitterionic form (XII). All evidence in favour of optical acti-

vity, expected by some on the basis of open structures, was disproved by Weissberger (*2123, 2124*).

$$
\begin{array}{cc}
\underset{H}{\overset{R}{>}}\hspace{-0.3em}C\hspace{-0.3em}\underset{N}{\overset{N}{\|}} & \underset{H}{\overset{R}{>}}\hspace{-0.3em}\overset{\ominus}{C}\hspace{-0.2em}-\hspace{-0.2em}\overset{\oplus}{N}\hspace{-0.2em}\equiv\hspace{-0.2em}N
\end{array}
$$

$$\qquad\qquad\text{XI}\qquad\qquad\qquad\qquad\qquad\qquad\text{XII}$$

Results obtained by means of electron diffraction by Boersch (*275*) brought
the final decision, as they can only be accounted for by the linear arrangement
(XII). Cox, Thomas, and Sheridan (*474*) redetermined the atomic distances and
angles recently (C—H:1·08 Å; C—N:1·32 Å; N—N:1·12 Å; H—C—H:127°).
Clusius (*438*) using N^{15} has shown that the two nitrogen atoms are not equivalent, also in agreement with structure (XII). The infra-red spectra of diazoalkanes can only be interpreted on the basis of a linear formula (*487, 734, 1447,
1676*), and the correctness of (XII) thus cannot be doubted. Diazoalkanes exhibit a characteristic band at 2010 to 2070 cm^{-1} (4·82 to 4·97 μ), which is assigned
to the N—N link. In α-diazoketones it is shifted to somewhat shorter wavelengths
(2060 to 2130 cm^{-1}, 4·69 to 4·85 μ). The position of the carbonyl band of
α-diazoketones (1620 to 1690 cm^{-1}, 5·90 to 6·17 μ) is not distinctive. A comparison of the infra-red spectra of aliphatic diazo compounds with those of aryldiazonium salts, azido compounds, nitriles, isocyanates, ketenes, and allenes has
been carried out by Yates and his co-workers (*2202*).

3.4 Acid–Base Equilibria of Aliphatic Diazo Compounds

As alkyldiazonium ions (XIII) are not stable, the equilibrium system (3.3) of
this ion with its conjugate bases, the alkyldiazohydroxide (XIV) and the alkyl-
diazotate (XV), cannot be studied. However, the methyldiazotate anion can
be isolated. Hantzsch (*970*, see also *2031*) obtained it as long ago as 1902 by
the action of extremely concentrated potassium hydroxide on nitrosomethyl-
urethan. This type of compound has become better known and more accessible
through Huisgen's researches (*1111, 1127*) on the removal of acyl groups from
nitrosoacylarylamines. Under the influence of bases, alkyldiazotates are converted into diazoalkanes (XVI). It must be supposed, that the reaction proceeds via the slight traces of the methyldiazonium ion present even under alkaline conditions, the strong alkali subsequently removing a proton (see equation 3.3). So far isomerism corresponding to that between the *syn*- and *anti*-
diazotates of the aromatic series has not been discovered for methyldiazotate.

$$
\begin{array}{ccccc}
 & \overset{+\,OH^{\ominus}}{\rightleftharpoons} & & \overset{-\,H^{\oplus}}{\rightleftharpoons} & \\
\text{R—CH}_2\text{—N}_2^{\oplus} & & \text{R—CH}_2\text{—N}{=}\text{N—OH} & & \text{R—CH}_2\text{—N}{=}\text{N—O}^{\ominus} \\
\quad\text{XIII} & & \text{XIV} & & \text{XV}
\end{array}
\qquad (3.3)
$$

$$-H^{\oplus}\;\Big\updownarrow$$

$$\text{R—}\overset{\ominus}{C}\text{H—N}_2^{\oplus}$$

$$\text{XVI}$$

Of great interest are the equilibria of diazoalkanes (XVI) with acids and bases. As Huisgen (*1114*) showed in a review some years ago, most of the heterolytic reactions can be systematized, if the diazoalkanes are regarded in turn as bases, as Brönsted, and as Lewis acids. The amphoteric character of the diazoalkanes is readily deduced from their different limiting structures; the scheme (3.4) illustrates these equilibria for diazomethane.

$$
\begin{array}{ccc}
A-CH_2-\overset{\oplus}{N}\equiv N & & H_2C=\overset{\oplus}{N}=N-A \\[2pt]
\quad +A^{\oplus}\Big\updownarrow \quad (3.4a) & & \quad +A^{\oplus}\Big\updownarrow \quad (3.4b) \\[6pt]
H_2\overset{\ominus}{C}-\overset{\oplus}{N}\equiv N \longleftrightarrow & H_2C=\overset{\oplus}{N}=\overset{\ominus}{N} \longleftrightarrow & H_2\overset{\ominus}{C}-N=\overset{\oplus}{N} \\
\text{XVIIa} & \text{XVIIb} & \text{XVIIc} \qquad (3.4)
\end{array}
$$

$$
\begin{array}{cc}
\quad +B^{\ominus}\Big\updownarrow \quad (3.4d) & \quad +B^{\ominus}\Big\updownarrow \quad (3.4c)
\end{array}
$$

$$
BH + \left[H\overset{\ominus}{C}=\overset{\oplus}{N}=N \longleftrightarrow HC-N=\overset{\ominus}{N} \right] \qquad H_2C=N-\overset{\ominus}{N}-B
$$

$$
\qquad \text{XVIIIa} \qquad\qquad \text{XVIIIb}
$$

$$
+H^{\oplus}\Big\updownarrow \quad (3.4e)
$$

$$
H\overset{\ominus}{C}=\overset{\oplus}{N}=NH \longleftrightarrow HC\equiv\overset{\oplus}{N}-\overset{\ominus}{NH}
$$

$$
\text{XIXa} \qquad\qquad \text{XIXb}
$$

The pair of electrons associated with the negative charge gives basic character in (XVIIa) to the carbon atom, in (XVIIb) to the β-nitrogen, and equilibria (3.4a) and (3.4b) follow, respectively. The electrophilic (acidic) nature of diazomethane comes from (XVIIc) and analogous limiting forms: the β-nitrogen possesses only an electron sextet and thus is able to react with a base (3.4c).

As the three equilibria (3.4a), (3.4b), and (3.4c) lead to most of the heterolytic reactions of diazoalkanes, they are discussed later, in §§ 5.2, 5.3, and 5.4. Here only the sequence of equilibria (3.4d) to 3.4e) ending in *isodiazomethane* will be considered. Normally this tautomerism greatly favours the diazomethane, as was recently shown in an investigation of the rotational fine structure of the infra-red spectrum by Mills and Thompson (*1447*). Eugen Müller (*1483, 1490, 1491, 1493, 1496*), the discoverer of isodiazomethane, found that organic compounds of alkali metals, such as tritylsodium and phenyl- or methyl-lithium, convert diazomethane according to equation (3.5) into explosive compounds of formula [CHN$_2$]M, which are salts of the mesomeric anion common to diazomethane and isodiazomethane (XVIII). If from these salts the acid is liberated in a suitable manner at $-50°$, the proton adds not to the carbon atom but to the nitrogen, and isodiazomethane is obtained as a pale yellow, very explosive liquid.

$$
CH_2N_2 + LiR \longrightarrow [CHN_2]\,Li + RH
$$

$$
\Big\downarrow H^{\oplus} \qquad\qquad (3.5)
$$

$$
\text{XIX}
$$

With hydroxyl ions isodiazomethane yields diazomethane immediately and quantitatively. Water and carboxylic acids give formylhydrazine and *N*-formyl-*N'*-acylhydrazines, respectively (3.6). It is hardly possible to bring these reactions into accord with any structure other than (XIX).

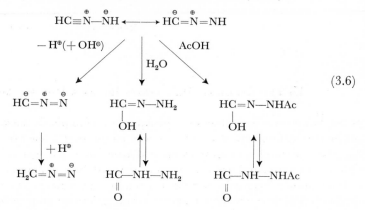

(3.6)

Although thermodynamically diazomethane is the favoured tautomer, that isodiazomethane is formed preferentially from the common anion can be explained kinetically. Even if the equilibrium (3.4d) lies further over to the side of the acid than (3.4e), the rate of proton addition is greater at the nitrogen than at the carbon atom. Similar circumstances are known to obtain in other prototropic systems, for instance, that of nitromethane derivatives.

Because of these results, Eugen Müller (*1482a*) supposes that in Staudinger's diazomethane synthesis (*1939*) from chloroform and hydrazine in the presence of alkali isodiazomethane acts as an intermediate (3.7).

$$HCCl_3 + H_2N\!-\!NH_2 \xrightarrow[-2\,HCl]{} \underset{Cl}{\overset{H}{>}}C\!=\!N\!-\!NH_2 \xrightarrow[-HCl]{} HC\!\equiv\!\overset{\oplus}{N}\!-\!\overset{\ominus}{NH} \qquad (3.7)$$

$$\downarrow (OH^{\ominus})$$

$$H_2C\!=\!\overset{\oplus}{N}\!=\!\overset{\ominus}{N}$$

The preparation of the so-called isodiazoacetic ester from diazoacetic ester by means of alcoholate in ether in the absence of moisture is also based on equilibrium (3.4d) (*505, 507, 969*). However, Curtius's work (*513, 514*) makes it probable that this compound is a dimer, corresponding to a dihydrotetrazine derivative rather than to Eugen Müller's isodiazomethane. It would therefore be better if it were designated pseudodiazoacetic ester. The mechanism (3.8), proposed by Huisgen (*1114*) for its formation, consists of the loss of a proton to give a base, which interacts with a second molecule of diazoacetic ester acting as an acid in a manner reminiscent of azo coupling (3.8b). A second azo coupling (3.8c) yields the pseudodiazoacetic ester.

$$ROOC\!-\!CH\!=\!\overset{\oplus}{N}\!=\!\overset{\ominus}{N} + RO^{\ominus} \rightleftharpoons ROOC\!-\!\overset{\ominus}{C}\!=\!\overset{\oplus}{N}\!=\!\overset{\ominus}{N} \longleftrightarrow ROOC\!-\!\overset{}{C}\!-\!N\!=\!\overset{\ominus}{N} \qquad (3.8a)$$

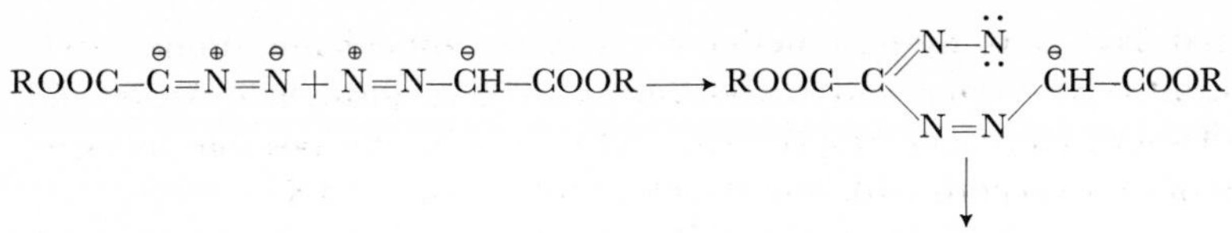

$$\text{ROOC—}\overset{\ominus}{\text{C}}\text{=}\overset{\oplus}{\text{N}}\text{=}\overset{\ominus}{\text{N}} + \overset{\oplus}{\text{N}}\text{=N—}\overset{\ominus}{\text{CH}}\text{—COOR} \longrightarrow \text{ROOC—C}\underset{\text{N=N}}{\overset{\text{N—}\ddot{\text{N}}}{\diagdown\diagup}}\text{CH—COOR} \quad (3.8\,b)$$

$$\downarrow$$

$$\text{ROOC—C}\underset{\text{N=N}}{\overset{\text{N—N}^{\ominus}}{\diagdown\diagup}}\text{CH—COOR} \quad (3.8\,c)$$

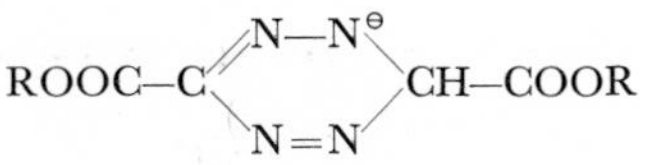

3.5 The Aromatic Diazonium Ion as a Dibasic Acid

In the last section were discussed the equilibria of aliphatic diazo compounds, the experimental study of which is prevented by irreversible side reactions. In contrast, the stability of most aromatic diazonium ions is such as to make possible the experimental determination of the acid–base equilibria.

It has already been said that the diazonium ion is a Lewis acid. By combination with a hydroxyl ion the diazohydroxide is formed and, in turn, becomes the diazotate on losing a proton. The two steps comprised by this equilibrium system are the subject of this section and can be represented by equation (3.9), from which the water molecules stoichiometrically necessary have been omitted.

$$\text{Ar—N}_2^{\oplus} \underset{\text{H}^{\oplus}}{\overset{\text{OH}^{\ominus}}{\rightleftarrows}} \text{Ar—N=N—OH} \underset{\text{H}^{\oplus}}{\overset{\text{OH}^{\ominus}}{\rightleftarrows}} \text{Ar—N=N—O}^{\ominus} \quad (3.9)$$

The system is formally analogous to that of the 'classic' dibasic acids, such as sulphuric or oxalic.

For the first step the equation (3.10) holds.

$$K_1' = \frac{[\text{Ar—N}_2\text{—OH}]}{[\text{ArN}_2^{\oplus}]\,[\text{OH}^{\ominus}]} \quad (3.10)$$

This becomes, on introduction of the equilibrium constant K_W of water

$$(K_w = [\text{H}^{\oplus}]\,[\text{OH}^{\ominus}]/[\text{H}_2\text{O}]), \quad K_1' = \frac{[\text{Ar—N}_2\text{—OH}]\,[\text{H}^{\oplus}]}{[\text{Ar—N}_2^{\oplus}]\cdot K_w} \quad (3.11)$$

K_W can be combined with the constant K_1' $(K_1 = K_1'\cdot K_W)$ to give

$$K_1 = \frac{[\text{Ar—N}_2\text{—OH}]\,[\text{H}^{\oplus}]}{[\text{Ar—N}_2^{\oplus}]} \quad (3.12)$$

In the same way, the second step can be expressed as

$$K_2 = \frac{[\text{Ar—N}_2\text{—O}^{\ominus}]\,[\text{H}^{\oplus}]}{[\text{Ar—N}_2\text{—OH}]} \quad (3.13)$$

According to (3.12), the diazonium ion as a Lewis acid is in equilibrium with its conjugate base, the diazohydroxide, and, according to (3.13), the diazohydroxide, this time as acid, is in equilibrium with its conjugate base, the *syn*-diazotate. This treatment refers exclusively to those parts of the reactions which occur moderately or very rapidly, i.e. 'reversibly'. The conditions must be so chosen that losses of diazo compounds, through decomposition or rearrangement (*syn-*→*anti*-diazotate), remain negligibly small.

Hantzsch (*531, 681*) investigated this system long ago on the supposition that it corresponds to that of the common dibasic acids. From conductivity measurements he deduced basic dissociation constants for the diazohydroxides, but it is now known that his assumptions were incorrect. In fact, at the turn of the century it was practically impossible to reach the right solution. On the one hand, Hantzsch did not have at his disposal the current potentiometric technique for protolytic equilibria, on the other hand, the system (3.9) is a special case for a dibasic acid, the principle of which was not grasped until 1943.

Wittwer and Zollinger (*2178*) determined the neutralization curves of aqueous solutions of diazonium salts under standard conditions of ionic strength etc. and found that the acidity depended on the degree of neutralization in a manner different to that expected of a dibasic acid. The curve obtained did not exhibit two steps, with an intermediate region of a few pH units in which the monobasic acid is stable, as is the case, for instance, with oxalic acid (Figure 3.1). On the contrary, there was only one step, but it extended over two equivalents of base per diazonium ion.

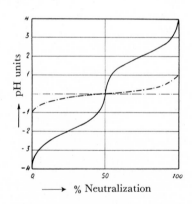

Figure 3.1

Neutralization curves of dibasic acids (*2178*)

———— $K_1 = 10^4 K_2$ ---------- $K_1 \ll K_2$

With the usual type of dibasic acid, the equilibrium constant for the second step is always smaller than that for the first ($K_1 > K_2$), but the diazonium ion represents another kind of acid, in which the second constant is *greater* than the first ($K_2 > K_1$). It was Schwarzenbach (*1858*) who first discovered such abnor-

mal equilibria in acids and he explained under what circumstances the phenomenon can occur.

The condition $K_2 > K_1$ has far-reaching consequences. Consider the diazonium ion during neutralization: *one* hydroxyl ion is taken up but, unlike the
oxalate ion, it cannot rest after the first stage, and the diazohydroxide formed
must lose a proton *immediately* to yield the diazotate, a second hydroxyl ion
acting as proton acceptor. In other words, *the diazohydroxide is not a stable intermediate and does not exist in aqueous solution in any appreciable concentration*. It follows
that the diazohydroxide cannot be isolated from aqueous solution and that, if
to a solution containing 1 mole of a diazonium salt is added 1 mole of a strong
base, about 1 mole diazohydroxide is *not* formed, as would be expected with a
'normal' dibasic acid, but $\frac{1}{2}$ mole diazotate results together with $\frac{1}{2}$ mole unchanged diazonium ion.

From the neutralization curves determined for three diazo compounds, it
becomes apparent that K_2 is considerably greater than K_1 ($K_2 \gg 10^3 K_1$). For
this reason, the constants K_1 and K_2 can no longer be determined separately
and only their product $K_1 \cdot K_2$ can be measured. The conversion of the diazonium ion into the *syn*-diazotate obeys the equation (3.14) and therefore from

$$pH = \frac{pK_1 + pK_2}{2} + \frac{1}{2} \log \frac{[Ar-N_2-O^\ominus]}{[Ar-N_2^\oplus]} \qquad (3.14)$$

the pH value at the mid-point of the curve only the point of inversion corresponding to half neutralization of *both stages simultaneously* can be obtained. By
means of the value of the term $(pK_1 + pK_2)/2$, it is possible to calculate the concentrations of diazonium and diazotate ions at every pH. However, for the
exact determination of the concentration of diazohydroxide, the separate values of pK_1 and pK_2 are necessary and it has already been stated that they are
not available to experiment. One can only estimate the relative concentration,
which is always greatest at $pH = (pK_1 + pK_2)/2$. Even then, with the diazo
compounds so far investigated, the diazohydroxides are present in less than 1%
of the total, analytical diazo concentration.

The conversion of diazonium ion into *syn*-diazotate takes place in the weakly
alkaline region of pH 7 to 10 with diazo compounds bearing strongly negative
substituents, for example, nitrodiazobenzene, and with the others at higher
alkalinity, the diazoanisoles and diazotoluenes requiring a pH greater than 12.
The investigation of the process is made difficult in the case of the strongly acid
diazo compounds (nitrodiazobenzenes) by the irreversible formation of the *anti*-
diazotate. Such equilibria will be discussed in § 4.2 in connection with the isomerism of diazo compounds.

The results obtained by Wittwer and Zollinger have recently been confirmed
and extended by Lewis and Suhr (*1334*), who have shown that the position of
the diazonium–diazotate equilibrium can also be determined spectroscopically.
Examples chosen from their 16 determinations are listed in Table 3.1. Figure 3.2
shows that Lewis and Suhr's results follow Hammett's relation (*914d, 1160*).

From the σ values and the equilibrium constants the constant ϱ is calculated to be $+6{\cdot}3$. This unusually high value is understood better if it is remembered that the constant determined, $(pK_1 + pK_2)/2$, is obtained from the product of two equilibria (3.9), namely equations (3.12) and (3.13). Their combination leads

$$\log K_1 + \log K_2 - (\log K_1^0 + \log K_2^0) = \sigma(\varrho_1 + \varrho_2) \qquad (3.15)$$

to equation (3.15) for Hammett's relation. The first equilibrium corresponds to the addition of a nucleophilic particle to the electrophilic diazonium ion and thus has similarities to azo coupling. For the latter reaction, Zollinger (*2231*) has found values of ϱ of about 4 (see § 10.6). The second equilibrium is analogous to the dissociation of substituted phenols, for which Hammett gives $\varrho = 2{\cdot}1$. The combination of the constants for these two processes used for comparison leads to a value of 6 for ϱ, which is in excellent agreement with Lewis and Suhr's experimental determination.

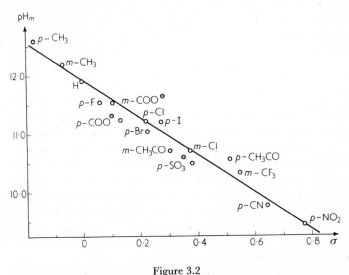

Figure 3.2

Diazonium–diazotate equilibrium of substituted diazobenzenes (*1334*)

p-Acetamidodiazobenzene behaves abnormally in that it acts as a *mono*basic acid. The qualitative experiments of Morgan (*1463, 2066*) and Dimroth (*605*) have shown that this is due to the fact that, on addition of alkali, such diazonium ions are not transformed into the diazohydroxide, but into compounds of the type of (XX), which are analogous to the diazo oxides and diazoalkanes (cf. § 3.3).

Table 3.1

Constants for the Diazonium–Diazotate Equilibria of Substituted Diazobenzenes[2]

Substituent	Temperature	Ionic strength	$\dfrac{pK_1 + pK_2}{2}$
p-NO$_2$	*ca.* 25°	1·0	9·44
p-CN	*ca.* 25°	1·0	9·77
p-SO$_3^\ominus$	*ca.* 25°	1·0	10·48
m-SO$_3^\ominus$	0°	0·73	10·84
m-Cl	*ca.* 25°	1·0	10·70
p-Cl $\left\{\begin{array}{c}\\ \\\end{array}\right.$	0°	0·73	11·61
	ca. 25°	1·0	11·21
H	*ca.* 25°	1·0	11·90
m-CH$_3$	*ca.* 25°	1·0	12·12
p-CH$_3$	*ca.* 25°	1·0	12·59

[2] Determinations at *ca.* 25° are by Lewis and Suhr (*1334*), those at 0° by Wittwer and Zollinger (*2178*).

The diazo equilibria have recently been investigated also by Passet and Porai-Koshits (*1590*), who arrived at the same conclusions as Wittwer and Zollinger (*2178*) and Lewis and Suhr (*1334*). The results obtained by the Russian workers for the conversion of the *anti*-diazotate into the diazonium ion will be discussed in § 4.2 dealing with the kinetics of the diazotate rearrangement.

The acidity constants determined by Hantzsch (*681*) and which he assigned to the equilibrium diazonium ion $\rightleftharpoons$ diazohydroxide are now to be equated to the constant for the rearrangement $(K_1 \cdot K_2)^{\frac{1}{2}}$.

All the considerations of this section hold for aqueous media. In less polar solvents K_2 is no longer so much greater than K_1 and it does not seem impossible that a medium should be found in which the ratio K_1/K_2 is such as to enable the presence of diazohydroxide to be proved directly.

3.6 Isolation of the Components of the Diazo Equilibria

(a) Diazonium salts

Diazonium salts are isolated only relatively rarely and the solutions or suspensions containing them are usually employed for further reaction as such. The ready solubility of most diazonium salts in water makes precipitation from this medium difficult and so to obtain solid diazonium salts diazotization is carried out in alcohol followed by precipitation with ether. As inorganic salts of nitrous acid are hardly soluble in alcohol, other means of nitrosation must be employed.

For this purpose Griess (*867*) originally used nitrous fumes, obtained by reduction of nitric acid with starch or arsenic trioxide, but Knoevenagel's method (*1238*) was a considerable improvement. He introduced diazotization with alkyl nitrites, which had previously been used only to prepare diazoamino compounds (*872*). In place of the very volatile ethyl nitrite (b.pt. 17°/760 mm), amyl nitrite is usually recommended, but in the form of a dilute standard solution in alcohol ethyl nitrite is convenient and can be kept easily.

The isolated diazonium salts must be carefully dried and handled and then only in small quantities. The nitrates especially tend to explode (cf. *156*), but *p*-nitrobenzenediazonium sulphate is relatively stable. The latter fact is technically important, because this diazo component coupled to β-naphthol on the fibre yields Para Red, much used since 1880. In order to relieve the dyer from carrying out the none too easy process of diazotization, the Farbwerke Meister, Lucius, und Brüning of Höchst marketed *p*-nitrobenzenediazonium sulphate as Azophor Red in the 'nineties. It was obtained by careful evaporation of the diazo solution in a vacuum at 40° to 45°, followed by removal of the residual water through anhydrous sodium and aluminium sulphates (*2528, 2555*). Cassella's corresponding product, Nitrazol C, was prepared by diazotization with nitrous fumes in concentrated sulphuric acid and solidification with sodium sulphate (*2532*). By now, these products have been superseded by the so-called stabilized diazonium salts, the diazotates, and, above all, the diazoamino compounds.

After 1945, the methods used by the I. G. Farbenindustrie in the manufacture of solid diazonium salts on the large scale at Offenbach became readily available (*2704, 2706*). In spite of a series of safety precautions, occasional explosions during drying or grinding could not be avoided. The stabilized diazonium salts commercially available usually contain only about 20 to 25% by weight of the actual diazo compound, the remainder consisting of stabilizers and diluents to bring the product to a standard strength.

The stabilizing action of arylsulphonic acids is important not only for the isolation of certain diazonium salts, but also for the retardation of the decomposition of diazo compounds in solution and hence is discussed in § 7.10.

Frequently it is advantageous to stabilize solid diazo compounds as complex salts. Griess (*874*) already described the complex salts from benzenediazonium chloride and auric or platinous chloride and Michaelis (*1441*) prepared the double salts with quadrivalent platinum, which have been much used in scientific work. On Werner's coordination theory, these would be described as bis-diazonium hexachloroplatinates (XXI) (*419*).

$$(Ar-N_2^\oplus)_2\ [PtCl_6]^{\ominus\ominus}$$

XXI

Double salts with mercury chlorides have significance in the preparation of organometallic compounds and they have been investigated by Nesmejanow's school (*1516–1519, 1522*) in particular.

In many cases, the zinc chloride double salts, the bisdiazonium tetrachloro-zincates, are readily prepared by the addition of zinc chloride to the diazo solution and they are of great technical importance (*699, 2530*). By quantity they are probably the biggest group of stabilized diazonium salts. Variamine Blue salts (4'-methoxydiphenylamine-4-diazonium salts) are obtained by diazotization of the appropriate amine in zinc chloride solution (*1740, 2703*).

Fluoroborates are used technically to some extent [Nitrazol CF extra (*2705*)], but they are especially important for the preparation of pure diazonium salts for research. The literature contains several recipes, which are generally applicable (*140, 1330, 1333, 1726, 1799*).

(b) *Diazohydroxides*

The determinations of Wittwer and Zollinger (*2178*) demonstrated that in aqueous solution the diazohydroxide can form only a very small fraction of the total diazo compounds present. It is therefore not surprising that so far they have not been isolated from this medium. Hantzsch (*935*) thought that he had prepared the diazohydroxide in solution by adding one equivalent of a strong base to a diazonium salt, but it is now known that his solutions contained diazonium and diazotate ions in equal amounts. Hantzsch came very near the truth, but such an abnormal equilibrium system would have seemed unacceptable in his day, as has already been mentioned. To interpret his conductometric and cryoscopic determinations (*681, 956, 962*), he supposed that there exists a strongly basic diazonium hydroxide, which quickly isomerizes to a pseudobase, the *syn*-diazohydrate. Hantzsch called the strong base the 'diazonium hydrate'. The assumption of its existence has been accepted by some authors (*1071, 1482c*), whereas others have disregarded it (*914, 2173*). According to Hantzsch, the diazonium hydrate is composed of ions. Apart from the then unknown concept of ion pairs, this implies that the compound is completely dissociated in water and, as already explained under 'diazonium hydroxide', Hantzsch's diazonium hydrate is equivalent to the diazonium ion in weakly alkaline solution. The ultra-violet spectrum of a very dilute, weakly alkaline solution of a diazonium salt, which Hantzsch (*971*) regarded as further evidence for the diazonium hydrate can also no longer be accepted as proof. The spectrum is identical with that of an acid diazo solution; in other words, under the conditions of the determination the diazonium ion has not yet been converted into the diazotate.

Curtius (*510*), as well as Battegay and Béha (*205, 206*), thought to have obtained 'diazonium hydroxides' by adding barium hydroxide to solutions of diazonium sulphates. It can now be hardly doubted that these weakly alkaline solutions contained an equimolar mixture of diazonium and diazotate ions. Hantzsch and Gerilowski (*965*) observed that a neutral solution of diazotized sulphanilic acid (benzenediazonium-4-sulphonate XXII), on addition of one equivalent of NaOH, becomes alkaline at first, but later reverts to neutrality. Hantzsch's explanation, that the diazonium hydroxide (XXIII) is formed first

$$
\begin{array}{ccc}
\underset{\substack{\text{XXIII}}}{\underset{\substack{\text{SO}_3\text{Na}}}{\overset{\substack{\text{N}\\ \|\|\\ \text{N—OH}}}{\bigcirc}}}
&\longrightarrow&
\underset{\substack{\text{XXIV}}}{\underset{\substack{\text{SO}_3\text{Na}}}{\overset{\text{N}=\text{N—OH}}{\bigcirc}}}
\end{array}
\qquad (3.16)^3
$$

$$
\underset{\substack{\text{XXII}}}{\underset{\substack{\text{SO}_3^{\ominus}}}{\overset{\substack{\text{N}\\ \|\|\\ \oplus\text{N}}}{\bigcirc}}}
\xrightleftharpoons[\text{fast}]{\substack{\textit{Hantzsch's}\\ \textit{hypothesis}}\ +\ \text{NaOH}}
$$

$$
\tfrac{1}{2}\ \underset{\substack{\text{XXII}}}{\underset{\substack{\text{SO}_3^{\ominus}}}{\overset{\substack{\text{N}\\ \|\|\\ \oplus\text{N}}}{\bigcirc}}}
+\ \tfrac{1}{2}\ \underset{\substack{\text{XXV}}}{\underset{\substack{\text{SO}_3^{\ominus}}}{\overset{\substack{\text{N}\diagdown\text{O}^{\ominus}\\ \text{N}}}{\bigcirc}}}
\xrightarrow{\text{relatively slow}}
\underset{\substack{\text{SO}_3^{\ominus}}}{\overset{\substack{\text{O}^{\ominus}\\ \diagup\text{N}\\ \text{N}}}{\bigcirc}}
\qquad (3.17)
$$

and reacts alkaline, but then rearranges into the diazohydroxide (XXIV), was doubted already by Bamberger (*161*). It is much more likely that half an equivalent of *syn*-diazotate (XXV) is formed rapidly (3.17). Since the reaction is reversible, hydroxyl ions are still present. They are the cause of the alkalinity, which disappears gradually, since the relatively slow isomerization of the *syn*- to the *anti*-diazotate is practically irreversible.

Of course, it has also been attempted to obtain diazohydroxides from the other side of the equilibrium, from the *syn*-diazotates. Again, current knowledge of the diazo system holds out little prospect of success in aqueous media. Morgan and Grist (*1466*) nitrosated *p*-aminomethylacylanilides with dinitrogen trioxide in acetone and isolated some rather unstable compounds, which were capable of coupling and which they regarded as diazohydroxides.

Under certain conditions, it is possible to obtain the ethers (XXVI) corresponding to the diazohydroxides, as shown particularly by Bamberger (*159*,

$$(\text{Ar—N}=\text{N})_2\text{O}$$
XXVI

169). The name 'diazoanhydrides' selected by Bamberger is to be preferred to Hantzsch's designation of 'diazo oxide', as with the latter term confusion with the diazonium derivatives of aminophenols could occur. In the light of the recent developments (*2437*), it seems probable that one of the azo groups in the diazoanhydrides is in the *cis*-configuration.

Since the researches of Hantzsch and Morgan, the problem of the existence of diazohydroxides has not been pursued in any detail experimentally. Usually their presence in aqueous solutions has been assumed as proved; many reactions were formulated without investigating the question of whether the mechanism

---

[3] Formulated according to Hantzsch (*965*).

really proceeded from the diazohydroxide. Recent textbooks of theoretical organic chemistry either do not discuss the problem or take the diazohydroxide to be a normal, that is stable, intermediate. Only Ingold (*1153g*) supposes that the loss of a proton from the diazohydroxide could occur with extraordinary ease. The polarographic investigations of Atkinson *et al.* (*81, 82*), from which certain conclusions about the velocity of interconversion between the various forms of the diazo compounds were drawn, have not been interpreted correctly according to Rüetschi and Trümpler (*1758*).

In Brönsted and Lewis's wider concept of acids and bases, the other covalent diazo compounds, such as the diazochloride $(Ar \cdot N : N \cdot Cl)$ and the diazoacetate $(Ar \cdot N : N \cdot O \cdot COCH_3)$, correspond not to the diazonium salts but to the diazohydroxide, the base $OH^\ominus$ having being replaced by the base $Cl^\ominus$ or $CH_3COO^\ominus$. From several researches carried out for other reasons it appears that these diazohalides (*75, 1330a*) and diazoacetates (*1111–1113, 1117, 1121, 1122, 1124*) are very unstable compounds. DeTar and Turetzky (*563*) estimate that the equilibrium constant of the formation of benzenediazoacetate from benzenediazonium and acetate ions in water is smaller than 10^{-5} l./mole. It is of interest that even in non-polar solvents (benzene) the concentration of the acetate does not seem to be increased. Huisgen's extensive investigations have shown unequivocally that, immediately nitrosoacetanilides have rearranged into diazoacetates, a hetero- or homo-lytic reaction follows and the diazoacetates cannot therefore be isolated (cf. § 7.5).

On the contrary, diazocyanides, diazosulphonates, and a few other covalent diazo derivatives are stable. At present, it is not possible to say anything about the cause of these differences in stability.

(c) syn-*Diazotates*

Griess (*875*) had long since obtained potassium benzene-*syn*-diazotate by treatment of a solution of the diazonium salt with cold, concentrated potassium hydroxide. The potassium salt is readily converted into less soluble salts, such as those of silver, zinc, mercury, and the alkaline earths, and Bamberger (*146, 159*) and Hantzsch (*937, 938, 940, 965*) have described a large number of *syn*-diazotates. Le Fèvre and Sousa (*1314, 1316*) developed better methods of preparation leading to very pure potassium salts. However, the preparation and isolation of the *syn*-diazotates from weakly basic amines, nitroanilines, for example, is difficult or, more usually, impossible, as these isomerize so quickly into the *anti*-diazotates. Investigation (*1316*) of the effect of light suggests that even in these cases *syn*-diazotates can exist.

During his researches on constitution, Bamberger was able to prepare *syn*-diazotates by some other routes, mentioned in § 1.5.

Recently Le Fèvre, Roper, and Reece (*2338*) doubted the existence of the *syn*-nitrodiazotates, but they must have overlooked the fact that Lewis and Suhr (*1334*) by means of their sensitive technique had actually determined the equilibrium between the diazonium ion and the *syn*-diazotate.

The most important property of *syn*-diazotates is their capacity to yield azo compounds *immediately* with coupling components in aqueous solution, but this is *not* due to their intrinsically greater reactivity, as will be shown in § 10.1. Rather is it caused by the diazonium ions, which are produced relatively rapidly from *syn*-diazotates. From the *anti*-diazotates they are formed only slowly and thus the apparent difference in coupling activity of the isomeric diazotates is readily explained.

According to Hantzsch (*970*), the aliphatic methyldiazotate can be obtained by the action of very concentrated potassium hydroxide on nitrosomethyl-urethan (see § 3.4).

4. Isomerism in Diazo Derivatives

4.1 Preparation of Isomeric Diazo Derivatives and the Determination of their Structure

In 1894, Schraube and Schmidt (*1842*) made a discovery in the field of diazotates which proved to be of great importance to the application of diazo compounds in textile technology. It constituted also a starting point for many scientific investigations and was the cause of probably the most notorious controversy in organic chemistry. Schraube and Schmidt found that the 'normal' potassium salt of diazobenzene rearranged under the influence of caustic alkali in aqueous solution at higher temperatures into a stable, less reactive potassium 'iso'-diazotate. As the latter gave N-methylphenylnitrosamine ($C_6H_5 \cdot NCH_3 \cdot NO$) with methyl iodide, it was regarded as the potassium salt $C_6H_5 \cdot NK \cdot NO$. Bamberger (*143*), who immediately began research into the isodiazotates, accepted their representation as derivatives of nitrosamines.

A few years previously, in one of his fundamental contributions to stereochemistry, Werner together with Hantzsch (*922, 980*) had recognized the two known forms of aromatic oximes ($Ar \cdot CH:NOH$) as stereoisomers. Since the diazotates can be considered to be derived from the oximes by substitution of nitrogen for the methine group, Hantzsch (*923*) put forward the hypothesis that here also stereoisomerism was occurring, just as in the oximes, hydrazones, and $\alpha:\beta$-substituted ethylenes. He therefore formulated the isomeric diazotates as (I) and (II), assigning the *syn*-structure (I) to the labile diazotate (or oxime), and the *anti* (II) to the stable one. If the more recent results of research into the

constitution and configuration of isomeric diazo and azo compounds are taken into account, it might be preferable to use in cases, such as those of the diazocyanides and the diazoacetates, the description *cis* instead of *syn* or Bamberger's 'normal' and *trans* instead of *anti* or iso. Fortunately, when in 1937 the isomerism of the azobenzenes was discovered (see below), the *cis*- and *trans*-nomenclature was adopted immediately. Even so, it still appears advisable not to discard the classic names altogether, as up to now for the most important pair of isomers, the *syn*- and *anti*-diazotates, the stereochemical interpretation is based only on analogy.

Hantzsch was unable to provide any direct chemical proof by experiment for his hypothesis. His grounds for assigning configurations were the analogies to oximes and ethylenes, such as the differences in stability already mentioned; however, some of his other reasoning is no longer convincing. For example, Hantzsch attributed the *cis*-structure to the normal diazotate obtained with alkali from *p*-diazobenzenesulphonic acid, because in the cyclic formula for the latter compound, current at the time, the atoms were already in the appropriate positions. But now it is known that diazotized sulphanilic acid is a zwitterion (formula XXII, § 3.6) and that alkali leads to the diazotate, not the diazohydroxide (see § 3.5).

All the same, lasting credit is due to Hantzsch for refuting the proposals, made so often since 1894, to interpret the isomerism of diazo derivatives otherwise than stereochemically. For his purpose, Hantzsch used the methods of physical chemistry, such as the determinations of conductivity and spectra, at a time when these were most unusual in the organic field.

Certain problems, for example, the differentiation between the *anti*-diazohydroxide (III) and the nitrosamine (IV), were quite insoluble in Hantzsch's day because of the lack of appropriate methods. The observation that the sodium

salt of the *anti*-diazotate reacts with methyl iodide to yield the *N*-derivative (*N*-methylnitrosamine), whereas the silver salt gives the *O*-ether (diazoether) was often taken to support the presence of structural isomerism, but Hantzsch, quite rightly, disagreed. It is now known that metal ions are not bound to specific atoms and that therefore the replacement of an ionic by a covalent link has no significance for the structure of a salt. Whether the acids, produced on acidification of *anti*-diazotates and, up to now, not obtained in a satisfactory state of purity, possess structure (III) or (IV) and whether *anti*-diazohydroxides and nitrosamines can be separated at all and identified chemically is doubtful, because the prototropic change between (III) and (IV) is certainly very rapid. The problem is analogous to that of the structure of diazoamino compounds (see § 8.2).

Bamberger's main achievements were the rediscovery of Blomstrand's diazonium formula and the development of a large number of methods for the preparation of diazotates and azo compounds. In the end, Bamberger abandoned his negative attitude towards the stereoisomerism of the diazotates by reason of his own experiments, which demonstrated the similarities in behaviour on oxidation of isomeric series of oximes and diazo compounds (*174*).

In spite of their historical importance, it is unnecessary to recapitulate here the arguments between Hantzsch and Bamberger from 1894 to 1912 or to enumerate the points made by Hantzsch. These have been covered adequately by Reddelien (*974*) and Saunders(*1776c*).

In the last twenty years, three workers in particular, Hartley, Le Fèvre, and Huisgen, have widened our knowledge of diazo isomerism. Their researches have provided proof for Hantzsch's conception in the case of many diazo compounds.

Through investigating solubility, Hartley (*982, 983*) discovered a second form of azobenzene in 1937. It is obtained from ordinary azobenzene on exposure to light and the stereoisomerism suspected between the two modifications was confirmed by their dipole moments. Normal (*trans-*) azobenzene (V) naturally has no dipole moment, i.e. $\mu = 0$ D, whilst the unstable *cis*-compound (VI) was found to have $\mu = 3$ D (*1307*). The isomers differ, for instance, in melting point, solubility, and chromatographic behaviour (*256, 460, 2208*). Their con-

V   VI

figurations were proved by complete crystal structure determinations (*920, 1719, 1720*). The data run parallel, as expected, to those of the stereoisomeric azoxybenzenes (VII, VIII) (*785, 1484*).

trans   VII   *cis*   VIII

The position of the photochemical equilibrium is determined largely by the absorbancies of the two forms at the wavelength of the light used. Irradiation with light of a wavelength at which *trans*-azobenzene has a greater extinction coefficient than the *cis*-compound will result in the formation of more of the *cis*-isomer and vice versa (*2321*).

The conversion of *cis*- into *trans*-azobenzene is catalysed by a great number of compounds, their variety suggesting that the rearrangement can occur by several mechanisms (see, for example, *1848, 1849*).

With some substituted azobenzenes and azonaphthalenes, *cis*-isomers have also been found (*461*). Frankel, Wolovsky, and Fischer (*753*) prepared the *cis*-compounds from the normal *trans*-1, 1'-, -1, 2'-, and -2, 2'-azonaphthalenes by irradiation followed by chromatographic separation. Their physicochemical properties (dipole moments and rate of *cis*→*trans* rearrangement) were analogous to those of azobenzene. Photochemical isomerization in related systems (triphenylformazans and phenylhydrazones) have been studied by R. Kuhn and co-workers (*2334, 2353, 2354*) (see also *2365*). Fischer (*2438*) investigated the temperature dependence of the azobenzene and azonaphthalene photo-isomerization equilibria.

In the actual acid and direct azo dyestuffs, the *cis–trans* equilibrium lies apparently so far over in favour of the stable *trans*-compound that the presence of the *cis*-form is not certain. The cause is most probably the fact that, almost without exception, these dyes are *o*-hydroxy- or *o*-aminoazo compounds. Such substituents are bound to the β-azonitrogen by a hydrogen bond as in (IX), thus stabilizing the *trans*-configuration. Azobenzene derivatives with substituents in all the *ortho* positions have unstable *cis*-forms because the apparently considerable steric strain prevents co-planarity. This effect is shown by 2,6,2′,6′-tetramethylazobenzene, studied by Brode (*325*).

IX

In *p*-hydroxyazo compounds no intramolecular hydrogen bond is possible and therefore here the *cis*-form should be more stable than in the case of *o*-hydroxy azo derivatives. Fischer and Frei (*2322*) showed recently that 4-phenylazo-1-naphthol equilibrates with its *cis*-isomer when its alcoholic solution at −140° is irradiated. The thermal conversion from *cis*- to *trans*-compound has been measured kinetically and found to proceed via the phenylhydrazone. Each step has an activation energy of about 11 kcal/mole, i.e. approximately half that of the *cis*⟶*trans* rearrangement of azobenzene and similar compounds without hydroxy groups.

The phototropy which occurs with azo dyes belonging to the class of disperse dyes is most likely due to a *trans*⟶*cis* rearrangement. *p*-Phenylazoaniline derivatives and some other types exhibit the phenomenon, that is, the dyeing on acetate rayon, in which the dye is present in the monodisperse state (i.e. in solution), becomes rapidly weaker or changes in hue on exposure to direct sunlight. In the dark, the original colour is regenerated. Von Mechel and Stauffer (*1390*), who first investigated this process thoroughly, realized that light of a wavelength corresponding to that of the main absorption band of the particular dye brought about a monomolecular photochemical reaction, which occurs for preference in non-polar solvents, acetylated cellulose being one of these. Comparison of spectra led them to suppose already that a *trans*⟶*cis* rearrangement could be involved, and this conclusion was substantiated by Brode and his co-workers and also by Atherton and R.H. Peters (*78, 79, 326, 327*). Brode was able to determine the absorption spectra of pairs of stereoisomers; for example, *trans*-N,N-dimethyl-*p*-phenylazoaniline has $\lambda_{max} = 410$ mμ, $\varepsilon = 28\,300$, whilst the *cis*-isomer exhibits two peaks $\lambda_{max} = 362$ and 460 mμ, $\varepsilon = 12\,000$ and $4\,300$, respectively. The spontaneous *cis*⟶*trans* back-reaction in the dark has a time of half-change of several minutes. In benzene solution it is catalysed by small amounts of water, alcohol and/or acid (*2198*). So far with hydroxyazo compounds the search for stereoisomers has been in vain. Apparently the *cis*-isomers are so unstable that they revert into the *trans*-form all too rapidly. On the contrary *cis*-methoxyazo derivatives have been isolated by Brode, Gould, and Inscoe (*328*), who have determined their rate of formation as well as that of the back-reaction. Atherton and Peters also observed *cis–trans* isomerism in aqueous solutions of Chrysophenine (X), that is, of an azo dye bearing sulphonic groups but no *o*-hydroxy or *o*-amino substituents. These authors found interesting connections between this isomerism and affinity for cellulose. Brode and co-workers (*2330*) showed that the spectra of Chrysophenine exhibit no fixed isosbestic points. This indicates that there must be conjugation between the two azo groups to give more than two types of interconvertible absorbing systems, namely, *trans-trans*, *trans-cis-*, and *cis-cis*-forms.

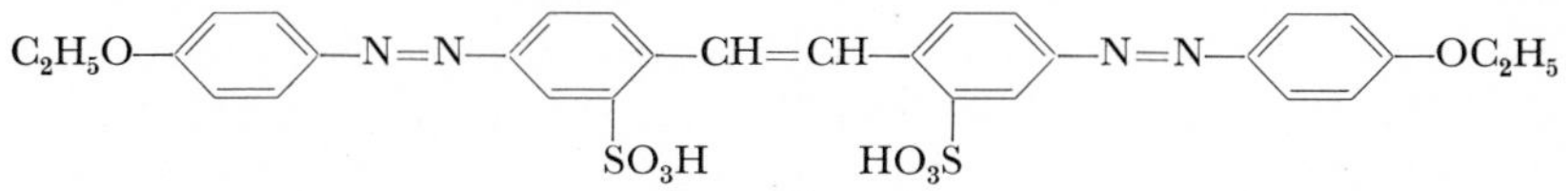

$$C_2H_5O\!-\!\langle\ \rangle\!-\!N\!=\!N\!-\!\langle\ \rangle\!-\!CH\!=\!CH\!-\!\langle\ \rangle\!-\!N\!=\!N\!-\!\langle\ \rangle\!-\!OC_2H_5$$

$$\overset{SO_3H}{}\qquad\overset{HO_3S}{}$$

X

The second important set of evidence for the stereoisomerism of diazo compounds is provided by Le Fèvre's studies (*760, 1309, 1310, 1318–1320*) in the physical chemistry of the diazocyanides discovered by Hantzsch (*929*). Table 4.1, in which the dipole moments of a series of isomeric pairs of aryldiazocyanides are listed, shows that the difference between the labile and the stable forms is not constant, as would have been expected only if they had been related to one another as nitrile to isonitrile. But, according to a detailed analysis, the results are in agreement with the occurrence of *cis–trans* isomerism. Structural isomerism was excluded also by determinations of diamagnetic susceptibility, the Faraday effect (optical rotation in a magnetic field), and infra-red spectra (*28, 29, 1884*).

Table 4.1

*Dipole Moments (*D*) of Diazocyanides (760, 1309, 1310, 1318–1320)*

	Labile form	Stable form
1-Naphthalenediazocyanide	3·2	5·6
2-Naphthalenediazocyanide	4·0	6·9
Diphenyl-4-diazocyanide	4·5	5·5
4-Chlorobenzenediazocyanide	2·9	3·7
4-Bromobenzenediazocyanide	2·9	3·8
4-Nitrobenzenediazocyanide	2·0	1·5
2, 4, 6-Tribromobenzenediazocyanide	2·5	4·0

Whether in the case of the other types of diazo compound, the diazosulphonates and the diazotates, where two isomers have been known for a long time, stereoisomerism is occurring also, at present depends for proof mainly on the analogy with the azobenzenes and the diazocyanides. The following qualitative comparisons are worth pointing out. The labile forms are more reactive and this is usually due to their much more rapid hydrolysis to the diazonium ion [cf. § 3.6 (c)]. On heating they rearrange, but the stable modifications isomerize on irradiation. These relationships have received confirmation through various determinations, particularly by Le Fèvre's school, who found characteristic differences in the finger print region of the infra-red spectra of pairs of isomeric diazotates and diazosulphonates and these corresponded to those between the two azobenzenes and the isomeric stilbenes (*1311*). The behaviour of both diazosulphonates on polarographic reduction can be interpreted on the basis of steric, but not structural isomerism (*759*).

Recently, Dijkstra and de Jonge (*590*) investigated the photochemistry of *p*-methoxybenzenediazosulphonate and found that irradiation did not cause the formation of the unstable isomer, but dissociation into diazonium and sulphite ions. From the equilibrium constant determined by Lewis and Suhr (*1340*) it follows that, in the concentrations used by Dijkstra and de Jonge, the primary product of irradiation, namely the *syn*-diazosulphonate, dissociates into diazonium and sulphite ions to an extent greater than 99·99%.

The ultra-violet spectra of the isomers, previously a field for many a dispute, differ mainly in the extinction, much less in the position of maximum absorption. As can be seen from the examples in Table 4.2, the *anti*-forms possess the greater molar extinction coefficients throughout.

Table 4.2

Differences in the Wavelength (mμ) and Extinction of the Band of Longest Wavelength in the Absorption Spectra of Isomeric Diazo and Azo Compounds

	$\lambda_{anti} - \lambda_{syn}$	$\varepsilon_{anti} - \varepsilon_{syn}$	References
o—Cl—C_6H_4—N=N—SO_3Na	− 8	900	*761*
C_6H_5—N=N—C_6H_5	− 5	4 500	*461*
p—Cl—C_6H_4—N=N—CN	+ 8	7 400	*1320*
p—NH_2—C_6H_4—N=N—C_6H_5	+45	16 600	*326*
O_2N—C_6H_4—N=N—ONa	+27	4 300	*1335*

Le Fèvre (*1315*) made use of the differences in the spectra of the isomeric diazotates in order to study the effect of light on this group of diazo compounds. In 0·15 N and 0·20 N caustic soda solution rearrangement to the unstable form occurred in a manner analogous to that found with azobenzenes, diazocyanides, and diazosulphonates, and hence it is very probable that the two diazotates are related to one another through *trans–cis* isomerism.

Among the *o*-, *m*-, and *p*-nitrobenzenediazotates Le Fèvre (*1315*) obtained evidence only for *one* isomer, the properties of which agreed with those of *anti*-diazotates. The conclusion that the *syn*-form is very unstable and so cannot be isolated is supported, in the case of the *o*- and *p*-derivatives, by the fact that mesomerism between the nitro and diazotate groups (XI a–XI b) requires co-planarity. In the *syn*-diazotate, however, the oxygen of that substituent would be prevented from coming into the plane of the benzene ring by the *o*-hydrogen atom.

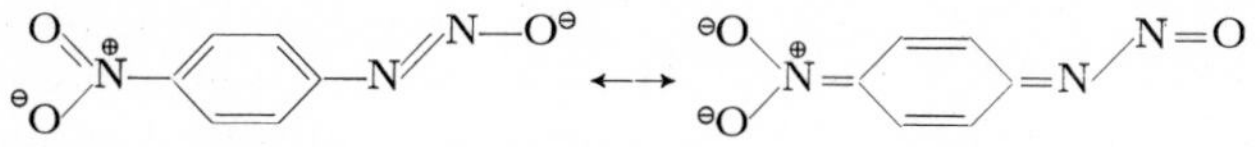

XI a   XI b

As this explanation for the instability of the *syn*-compound is valid only for the *o*- and *p*-, but not for the *m*-derivative, Le Fèvre (*1315*) investigated the latter in greater detail and discovered that irradiation actually does affect the ultra-violet spectrum. Since photochemical decomposition could be excluded, the change can be attributed to an alteration in the equilibrium between stereo-isomers.

Le Fèvre's suppositions have been confirmed for *p*-nitrobenzenediazotate by Lewis's kinetic investigations, discussed in the next section.

In further work, Le Fèvre tried to find isomerism in other compounds of the type ArN$_2$—X. With diazocarboxamides (X = CONH$_2$) (*762*) and diazosul-phones (X = SO$_2$Ar) (*764*) irradiation produced a reversible rearrangement, but the labile isomers could not be isolated. With diazoamino compounds (*763, 1308*) it is irreversible photochemical decomposition which is observed. The compounds thought by Hantzsch to be isomeric diazoamino derivatives were identified by Bamberger (*151*) as bisdiazoamino compounds.

The third, important set of evidence for the stereochemical nature of diazo-isomerism is due to Huisgen and concerns the formation of diazoesters from nitrosoacylanilides. As described in § 7.5, such a rearrangement necessarily must lead to *trans*-diazoesters. This can be demonstrated by the classic method of assigning configurations, and for his purpose Huisgen selected the rearrange-ment of cyclic *N*-nitrosocarboxamides. Further, it can be shown that only the *trans*-form of *o*-methylaryldiazoacetates is capable of ring closure to the inda-zole (4.1).

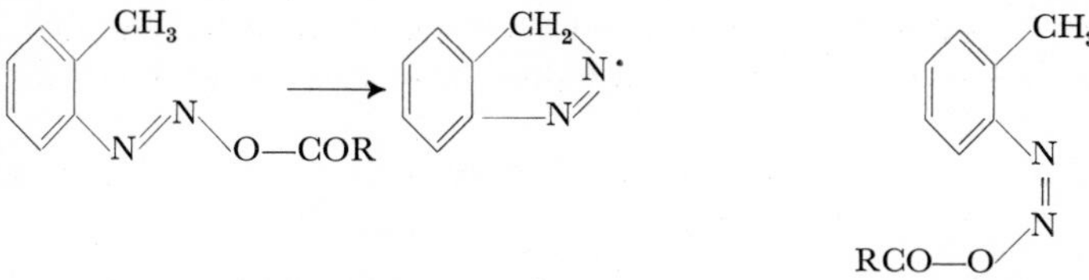

(4.1)

trans-form stable   *cis*-form unstable
                                            no ring closure

In spite of these researches, the stereochemical character of diazoisomerism has been repeatedly doubted even in recent years. Hodgson's objections (*1048*) were convincingly answered by Le Fèvre (*1314*). Angeli (*42–45*) had supposed that the diazotates represented a case of structural isomerism (XII–XIII), cor-

$$Ar-\overset{\oplus}{\underset{\underset{O^{\ominus}}{|}}{N}}=\overset{\ominus}{N} \qquad\qquad Ar-N=N-O^{\ominus}$$

$$\text{XII} \qquad\qquad\qquad\qquad\qquad \text{XIII}$$

responding to that of azoxy compounds, and E. Müller (*1482b, d*) has thoroughly discussed the recent work of Le Fèvre, Huisgen, and others in relation to Angeli's view. Rearrangement of an oxygen atom bound to nitrogen is an unusual process, but the formation of (XIII) from (XII) could occur by way of an α-β-phenyl rearrangement. However, experiments with N^{15} have excluded such a mechanism (*437, 1992*).

4.2 Kinetics and Mechanism of the Diazotate Rearrangement

Apart from Le Fèvre (*1314*), who dealt with the kinetics of the diazotate rearrangement in analogy to the isomerization of diazocyanides, azobenzenes, etc., Grachev (*850–852, 1651*) and, more recently, Lewis and Suhr (*1335*) have studied these acid–base and rearrangement equilibria. As described in § 3.5, the potentiometric titration of solutions of certain diazonium salts has shown that the *syn*-diazohydroxide is an unstable intermediate in the equilibrium (4.2). With negatively substituted diazo compounds, such as nitrodiazobenzenes, this reversible process is upset by rearrangement into the *anti*-diazotate. Lewis and

$$Ar-N_2^{\oplus} \underset{K_1}{\overset{+\ OH^{\ominus}}{\rightleftarrows}} (Ar-N=N-OH) \underset{K_2}{\overset{+\ OH^{\ominus}}{\rightleftarrows}} Ar-N=N-O^{\ominus} \qquad (4.2)$$

Suhr were able to investigate the equilibrium system (4.2) in the case of *p*-nitrodiazobenzene by determining the spectra of diazonium salt–buffer mixtures immediately after their preparation (about 6 seconds) and extrapolating the results to zero time. In this way, the spectra of the diazonium ion, of each of the isomeric diazotates and, in addition, that of the *anti*-diazohydroxide became available. In agreement with the work of Wittwer and Zollinger mentioned previously, no evidence for the *syn*-diazohydroxide could be obtained.

The spectra of the four forms in equilibrium exhibit the following bands:

diazonium ion	260 mμ, log ε = 4·14
	311 mμ, log ε = 3·24
anti-diazohydroxide	315 mμ, log ε = 3·70
syn-diazotate	305 mμ, log ε = 3·92
anti-diazotate	332 mμ, log ε = 4·10

That the spectrum of the *anti*-diazotate compared with that of the *syn*-compound has undergone a shift which is both batho- and hyperchromic is compatible with *trans–cis* isomerism.

Knowledge of the spectra makes possible the study of the kinetics of the various reactions. The rate of formation of the *anti*-diazotate from the diazonium ion is catalysed by hydroxyl ions in the range of pH 7·01 to 8·75, but above pH 10 it is independent of pH. In the intermediate region reaction (4.3a) is too fast to be measurable, though the equilibrium between the diazonium ion and the *syn*-diazotate can be determined. From the kinetic results it must be concluded that the total process comprises two slow steps, one of which is an addition of a hydroxyl ion. Bearing in mind the back-reaction (see below), this leads to the following mechanism:

$$\text{ArN}_2^{\oplus} + \text{OH}^{\ominus} \underset{}{\overset{\text{slow}}{\rightleftarrows}} \textit{syn-}\text{Ar}\!-\!\text{N}\!=\!\text{N}\!-\!\text{OH} \tag{4.3a}$$

$$\textit{syn-}\text{Ar}\!-\!\text{N}\!=\!\text{N}\!-\!\text{OH} + \text{OH}^{\ominus} \underset{}{\overset{\text{fast}}{\rightleftarrows}} \textit{syn-}\text{Ar}\!-\!\text{N}\!=\!\text{N}\!-\!\text{O}^{\ominus} + \text{H}_2\text{O} \tag{4.3b}$$

$$\textit{syn-}\text{Ar}\!-\!\text{N}\!=\!\text{N}\!-\!\text{O}^{\ominus} \underset{}{\overset{\text{slow}}{\rightleftarrows}} \textit{anti-}\text{Ar}\!-\!\text{N}\!=\!\text{N}\!-\!\text{O}^{\ominus} \tag{4.3c}$$

$$\textit{anti-}\text{Ar}\!-\!\text{N}\!=\!\text{N}\!-\!\text{OH} \rightleftharpoons \textit{anti-}\text{Ar}\!-\!\text{N}\!=\!\text{N}\!-\!\text{O}^{\ominus} + \text{H}^{\oplus} \tag{4.3d}$$

The reverse process consists of the rapid equilibration of the *anti*-diazotate with the corresponding diazohydroxide (4.3d), the constant K of which has been found to be $7·2 \times 10^{-7}$ mol./l. at 20° by Lewis and $24·5 \times 10^{-7}$ mol./l. at 12° by Grachev. On the basis of the kinetic results, the conversion of the *anti*-diazohydroxide into the diazonium ion must take place by two mechanisms, one probably consisting of an acid-catalysed splitting off of the OH group via the conjugate acid of the diazohydroxide, the other either having a rate-determining step of first order, such as the spontaneous dissociation of the diazohydroxide, or using isomerization to the unstable *syn*-diazohydroxide.

Passet and Porai-Koshits (*1590*) have recently studied the conversion of the *anti*-diazotate into the diazonium ion. The titration curve shows that a monobasic intermediate is formed rapidly; these authors consider it to be the nitrosamine which yields the diazonium ion in a slow second step.

4.3 Isolation and Technical Importance of Isomeric Diazo Compounds

The preparation and isolation of anti-*diazotates* is carried out exclusively by Schraube and Schmidt's original method: solutions of diazonium salts are added to moderately to highly concentrated solutions of alkali hydroxides. In the presence of negative substituents, the *anti*-diazotate is formed without difficulty, but positive groups, such as methoxy and alkyl, make necessary more drastic conditions (temperatures of up to 130°). If higher temperatures are being used, the cold diazonium solution must be added to the hot alkali; should the diazo solution be made alkaline and then heated, decomposition occurs preferentially. The *anti*-diazotates are isolated either by salting out, highly concentrated alkali being first partly neutralized or diluted, or precipitated with alcohol. Frequently, it is not at all easy to obtain diazotates pure, that is, free from salt and water of crystallization, but the disodium and dipotassium salts of 4-sulphobenzenediazotate are readily purified (*786, 965*).

On adding acid to solutions of *anti*-diazotates one would expect the *anti*-diazohydroxides (XIV) or the corresponding nitrosamines (XV) to be formed. So far all attempts at isolation have failed (*680, 948, 951, 973, 978, 1556, 1557*), but in one case the spectrum has been determined as described in the previous section (*1335*).

$$
\begin{array}{ccccc}
\underset{\text{N}}{\overset{\text{Ar}}{\diagdown}} & & \underset{\text{N}}{\overset{\text{Ar}}{\diagdown}} & & \underset{\text{N}}{\overset{\text{Ar}}{\diagdown}} \overset{\text{H}}{\diagup} \\
\| & \underset{-\text{H}^{\oplus}}{\overset{+\,\text{H}^{\oplus}}{\rightleftharpoons}} & \| & \underset{-\text{H}^{\ominus}}{\overset{+\,\text{H}^{\oplus}}{\rightleftharpoons}} & | \\
\underset{\text{OH}}{\overset{\text{N}}{\diagdown}} & & \underset{\text{O}^{\ominus}}{\overset{\text{N}}{\diagdown}} & & \underset{\text{O}}{\overset{\text{N}}{\diagdown}} \\
\text{XIV} & & & & \text{XV}
\end{array}
\tag{4.4}
$$

The preparation of the isomeric *diazocyanides* discovered by Hantzsch and his co-workers (*961, 963*) has been dealt with throughly by Le Fèvre (*1318*). Apart from their significance with regard to diazo isomerism, discussed earlier in this chapter, the cyanides are important as the only class of diazo compounds of which three isomers have been isolated, namely, the diazocyanide-HCN addition product, the *cis*- and the *trans*-diazocyanide. It depends on the experimental conditions as to which substance is the main product. If the reaction is performed in acid solution with an excess of cyanide, the diazocyanide-HCN addition compounds are obtained (*360, 776, 961, 976*). On the other hand if a solution of cyanide is added dropwise to one of the diazonium salt and it is ensured that an excess of diazonium salt and acid is present all the time, the diazocyanide results. If the process is carried out below —5° and in concentrated solution, the readily decomposed *syn*-cyanide crystallizes out and soon rearranges into the more stable *anti*-form (*936, 963*). Lastly, in the presence of alkali, products are obtained for which the structure Ar·N:N·C(NH)·O·NH·Ar has been established (*1008*).

The equilibria concerned in the formation of diazocyanides have been investigated spectroscopically by E.S.Lewis and Suhr (*1337*). The constants found for the equilibria (4.5a) of substituted diazobenzenes obey Hammett's equation, the remarkably high ϱ-value of 4·7 being obtained. The rate of isomerization, i.e. equation (4.5b), has been determined several times [(*1310, 1360, 1952*), see also § 4.1]. In addition Lewis and Suhr (*1337*) were able to follow the inter-

$$
\text{ArN}_2^{\oplus} + \text{CN}^{\ominus} \rightleftharpoons \textit{syn-}\text{Ar}\!-\!\text{N}\!=\!\text{N}\!-\!\text{CN}
\tag{4.5a}
$$

$$
\textit{syn-}\text{Ar}\!-\!\text{N}\!=\!\text{N}\!-\!\text{CN} \rightleftharpoons \textit{anti-}\text{Ar}\!-\!\text{N}\!=\!\text{N}\!-\!\text{CN}
\tag{4.5b}
$$

action of diazocyanide with excess of cyanide and to make it likely that the products are not diazonium cyanide double salts but compounds of the structure Ar·N:N·C(NH)·CN, as supposed by Hantzsch and verified by Bucherer by reduction to the diamino compound (*360*).

Griess already knew the *diazosulphonates* ($Ar \cdot N:N \cdot SO_3Na$), and Hantzsch discovered the existence of two isomers. They are readily obtained on addition of sulphite to weakly acid solutions of diazonium salts (*924, 1049*) (see § 7.4).

The *technical significance* of the *anti*-diazotates depends on the fact that on addition of acid they are slowly converted into diazonium ions. In the first place, the *anti*-form of 4-nitrobenzenediazotate became commercially available as Nitrosamin Red (BASF)[1], which is much more easily prepared than the corresponding diazonium salt. Nitrosamin Red was the forerunner of the Rapid Fast colours (GrE, IG)[1], which consist of mixtures of an *anti*-diazotate and a coupling component of the Naphtol AS type (GrE; 3-hydroxy-2-naphthanilide) (*2545–2547*). The constitutions of most Rapid Fast combinations are known and several firms manufacture them (*17761, 2704*). By now they have been replaced to a considerable extent by the Rapidogens (IG: diazoamino compounds + coupling components; see § 8.5).

Diazo compounds with hydroxy groups in *o*- or *p*-position cannot be converted into *anti*-diazotates. Diazo derivatives of 4-aminodiphenylamines behave analogously; as diazotates or diazoamino compounds they form explosive quinone imine diazides (XVI) (4.6) (*944, 945, 1467*). However, these amines are indispensable as diazo components for blues and blacks and so their *anti*-diazosulphonates are marketed in admixture with coupling components as Rapidazols (IG).

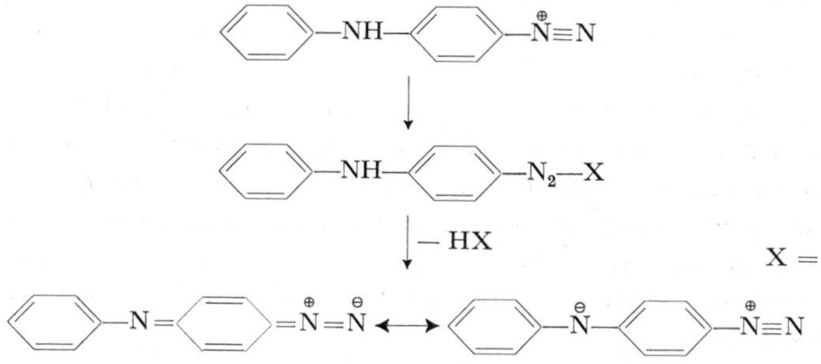

$$(4.6)$$

$$X = NHR, O^\ominus$$

XVI a   XVI b

---

[1] For abbreviations of dyestuff manufacturers' names see appendix, page 406.

5. Syntheses with Aliphatic Diazo Compounds

5.1 Introduction

The diazoalkanes are astonishingly versatile reagents, which have made themselves indispensable in preparative organic chemistry. Although as a class they have been known for well over half a century, new reactions of the diazoalkanes are constantly being discovered, as witnessed by the recent work of H. Meerwein, R. Huisgen, and W. von E. Doering. The versatility of the diazoalkanes can now be understood and classified on the basis of theoretical organic chemistry. In addition, their reactions serve as a good example of how the physical organic point of view, adopted particularly by F. Arndt in this field in the 'twenties and 'thirties, can lead to the discovery or extension of preparative methods.

The fundamentals of the mechanisms of the reactions of diazoalkanes will be dealt with in Chapter 6, but here are described the methods used to carry out these reactions and the significance of the more important of them is discussed. As shown in Chapter 6, most of the changes undergone by the diazoalkanes can be attributed to their basic nature. In the case of their interaction with Brönsted acids, the primary process (5.1) is the addition of a proton to the carbon atom of diazomethane or the α-carbon atom of its homologues (I), an alkyldiazonium ion (III) being formed. The same ion results also from the nitrosation of a primary aliphatic amine (II), and therefore the two paths should lead to identical products. This is indeed so, whenever the reaction conditions are strictly comparable, as various researches have demonstrated experimentally [for example,

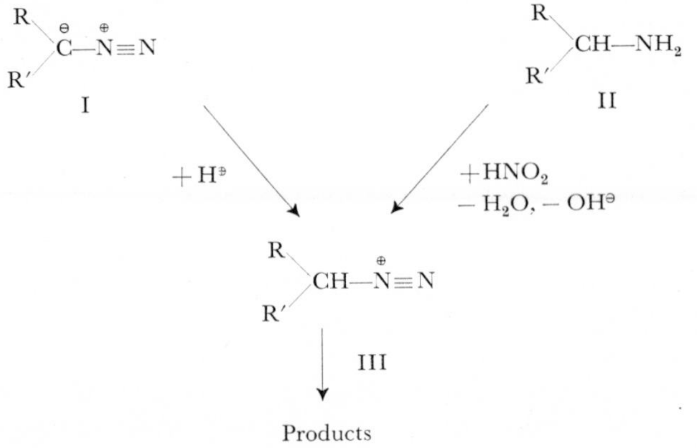

$$
\begin{array}{ccc}
\overset{R}{\underset{R'}{>}}\!\overset{\ominus}{C}\!-\!\overset{\oplus}{N}\!\equiv\!N & & \overset{R}{\underset{R'}{>}}\!CH\!-\!NH_2 \\
I & & II \\
\\
+H^{\oplus} & & +HNO_2 \\
& & -H_2O, -OH^{\ominus} \\
\\
& \overset{R}{\underset{R'}{>}}\!CH\!-\!\overset{\oplus}{N}\!\equiv\!N & \\
& III & \\
\\
& Products &
\end{array}
\tag{5.1}
$$

Huisgen and Rückardt (*1129*)]. It follows that it is relevant to discuss in this chapter not only the reactions of the diazoalkanes, but also the reaction which is the sequel to the diazotization of aliphatic amines, namely, deamination.

Some reactions of aliphatic diazo compounds, the preparative importance of which is less general, but which have theoretical implications, will be left to be discussed along with the mechanisms in Chapter 6.

5.2 Alkylations by Means of Diazoalkanes

The main application of diazoalkanes is in the alkylation of compounds bearing relatively strongly acid hydroxy groups, the preparation of methyl esters of carboxylic acids by means of diazomethane in ethereal solution being by far the best known. This type of reaction proceeds smoothly, quickly, and under mild conditions and in spite of the disadvantages of diazomethane (cost, poisonous nature), becomes the preferred method of esterification when the more vigorous conditions required by other alkylating agents may bring about decomposition or other side reactions of the starting material or the product. On the other hand, compounds, which carry substituents capable of interacting with diazoalkanes apart from the carboxy group, are suitable for this method only if esterification is greatly favoured kinetically.

Besides carboxylic acids, phenols and enols are alkylated by means of diazoalkanes. They give good yields, but react distinctly less rapidly, due to their lower acidity.

On the contrary, the acidity of alcoholic groups is, in general, insufficient to make conversion to the ethers possible as long as neighbouring substituents with —M or —I effects, such as COOR, are absent. For instance the alcoholic hydroxy groups of mesotartaric and tartronic acids and their esters can be methylated readily. For the same reason, 2-chloroethyl, allyl, and benzyl alcohols interact with diazomethane, but here the process is not clean.

In the case of compounds with weakly acid hydroxy groups, according to Meerwein (*1394, 1401*) it is better not to work in ether, but to use aliphatic hydrocarbons. Thus trichloroethyl alcohol, which does not react at all in ethereal solution, is readily converted into the methyl ether by diazomethane in heptane. The cause of this difference is probably connected with the fact that even ether possesses some basic character and the hydrogen bonds formed between the alcoholic hydroxy group as donor and the ether oxygen as acceptor lower the acidity of the former still further. On the other hand, Biltz and Paetzold (*252*) pointed out that the addition of catalytic amounts of amphoteric solvents can speed up the alkylation. Glycine does not interact with diazomethane in dry ether, but, on adding a little water or methanol, a vigorous process occurs leading to betaine (5.2).

$$\overset{\oplus}{H_3N}—CH_2—COO^{\ominus} \xrightarrow{+CH_2N_2} (H_3C)_3\overset{\oplus}{N}—CH_2—COO^{\ominus} \qquad (5.2)$$

Under certain conditions, the hydroxy groups of carbohydrates can also be methylated. R. Kuhn (*1283*, see also *994*) has prepared methyl glucosides by adding an ethereal solution of diazomethane to an aqueous methanolic solution of the sugar. Similar methods enable partial methylations of polysaccharides to be achieved (*998, 999, 1089*).

The ability of aliphatic hydroxy groups to react can be increased by complex formation. For this purpose Meerwein (*1401*) recommended the addition of a small amount of aluminium alcoholate and Newman (*1526*) and Eugen Müller (*1498*) found that fluoborate has an analogous effect. The reaction with such Lewis acids as catalysts proceeds via acidic oxonium compounds, illustrated in equation (5.3) for the aluminium complexes (see also *208, 415, 1506*). An indirect route for the alkylation of aliphatic alcohols by means of diazoalkanes involves the intermediate preparation of the neutral esters of selenious acid (*2390*).

$$ROH + Al(OR)_3 \rightleftarrows \underset{H}{\overset{R}{>}}O\overset{\oplus}{-}\overset{\ominus}{Al}(OR)_3 \xrightarrow{+ CH_2N_2} \underset{H_3C}{\overset{R}{>}}O\overset{\oplus}{-}\overset{\ominus}{Al}(OR)_3 \rightleftarrows \quad (5.3)$$
$$R{-}OCH_3 + Al(OR)_3$$

E. Müller and Rundel (*1487, 2580*) observed that ammonia, primary and secondary amines can be methylated with diazomethane if boron trifluoride is present as a catalyst. This reaction as well as the example of glycine (5.2) shows that not only hydrogen attached to oxygen is liable to substitution. In this connection the methylation of sulphones is particularly interesting: trimethylene trisulphone (IV) (*66*) and trisalkylsulphonylmethanes [(RSO$_2$)$_3$CH] (*281*) are readily *C*-methylated.

$$\begin{array}{ccc} & \overset{CH_2}{\diagup\;\diagdown} & \\ O_2S & & SO_2 \\ | & & | \\ CH_2 & & CH_2 \\ & \diagdown\;\diagup & \\ & SO_2 & \end{array}$$

IV

The methylation of sulphones is of significance as regards the question of whether a prototropic equilibrium of the keto-enol type is present in any particular compound. Arndt (*56*), especially, has employed this method for the *investigation of tautomeric systems*. It has already been mentioned that methylation with diazomethane is very much dependent on the acidity of the hydrogen atom to be substituted. When alkylating an enolizable ketone note must be taken of the fact that, because the electronegativity of oxygen is greater, hydrogen is always more acidic when bound to oxygen than when bound to carbon in the corresponding keto form. A *C*-methyl derivative can result only when the CH-acidity is sufficiently high.

The original supposition that the ratio of *C*- to *O*-methylation is a measure of the keto-enol equilibrium has proved not to be correct. This is because the proportion of *O*-methyl derivative formed is controlled not only by the relative acidities of enol and keto hydrogen, but also by the rate of addition of diazo-methane. Enol reacts comparatively quickly, but the equilibration between the tautomers is slow, so that the rate of the isomerization ketone→enol becomes one of the factors determining the ratio of products formed.

It is surprising that compounds are known which are readily O-methylated although no other method yields any evidence whatever of enolization. Examples of such compounds are ketones, carrying at one of the α-carbon atoms one or two sulphone groups [$RSO_2 \cdot CH_2COR'$ and $(RSO_2)_2CHCOR'$], and esters of nitroacetic acid ($O_2N \cdot CH_2COOR$). Arndt (58, 66) supposes that in these so-called 'indirect' methylations diazomethane attacks the carbonyl oxygen, but this is not convincing (1114) (cf. footnote 59 in ref. 1114).

Ketones, which neither enolize nor exhibit relatively high CH-acidity be-cause of appropriate neighbouring groups, react with diazoalkanes as described in § 5.3: apart from homologous ketones epoxy derivatives always result.

Bisdiazoalkanes are known and have been used for crosslinking reactions and similar purposes [for example (2206)].

Metal organic compounds can be prepared with the aid of diazomethane, as demonstrated by Wittig and K. Schwarzenbach (2364), who obtained $CH_2I \cdot ZnI$ and $Zn(CH_2I)_2$ by interaction of zinc iodide with one or two equi-valents of diazomethane, respectively, in ether solution.

5.3 Reactions of Diazoalkanes with Aldehydes and Ketones

It was Curtius (512) who first observed that aldehydes react with diazomethane, nitrogen being evolved. At the turn of the century, von Pechmann (1598), H. Meyer (1427), and Schlotterbeck (1803, 1804) were allowing some carbonyl compounds to interact with diazomethane and diazoacetic ester, but the syste-matic study of this field began almost 30 years later in the schools of F. Arndt, H. Meerwein, and E. Mosettig. The factual material has been collected to-gether recently and reviewed by Gutsche (895).

Normally diazomethane and its homologues react with aldehydes and keto-nes according to the scheme (5.4). Aldehydes ($R' = H$) give rise to the corres-

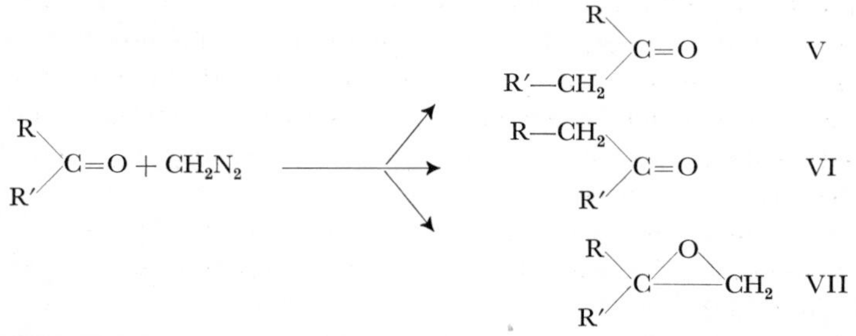

$$\begin{matrix} & & \underset{R'-CH_2}{\overset{R}{\diagdown}}C=O & V \\ \underset{R'}{\overset{R}{\diagdown}}C=O + CH_2N_2 \longrightarrow & & \underset{R'}{\overset{R-CH_2}{\diagdown}}C=O & VI & (5.4) \\ & & \underset{R'}{\overset{R}{\diagdown}}C\overset{O}{\diagup}CH_2 & VII \end{matrix}$$

ponding methyl ketone (V), the homologous aldehyde next up the series (VI), and the ethylene oxide derivative (VII). In the same way, from ketones are obtained two homologous ketones apart from an epoxy compound (VII), but, if the starting material is symmetrical (R = R'), the two products (V) and (VI) are, of course, identical. With α, β-unsaturated carbonyl compounds and quinones the reaction with diazomethane usually takes another course, which will be discussed later.

As explained in § 6.1, the reactions with carbonyl compounds consist of the addition of these electrophilic substances to the nucleophilic centre of the diazo-alkane, namely, its α-carbon atom. It follows that the reactivity increases with the electrophilic character of the aldehydes and ketones; therefore, the rate of addition of aliphatic is greater than that of aromatic carbonyl compounds and aldehydes react more rapidly than ketones. Another consequence is that when an aldehyde is treated with *excess* of diazomethane, only the methyl ketone is a stable product. In contrast to the methyl ketone, the homoaldehyde primarily formed hardly differs in reactivity from the starting material and so reacts with the diazomethane still present to yield the products one step higher up in the series.

On the other hand, the reactivity of the diazoalkanes increases with their basicity. Thus the more weakly nucleophilic diazoacetic ester interacts with aldehydes, but no longer with ketones.

For preparative work, the point of greatest interest is which of the three compounds, (V), (VI), or (VII), will be the main product in any particular case.

The epoxy compound is favoured by steric and electronic factors. For example, according to the conditions, acetone and diazomethane give 20 to 38% 2-buta-none and 33 to 40% 1, 2-epoxy-2-methylpropane, whilst 2-undecanone yields the corresponding epoxide solely and 1, 1, 1-trichloro-2-propanone to about 90% (*58, 1393, 1396, 1647*). The influence of the —M effect on the ratio of carbonyl to epoxy products can be seen very clearly from the behaviour of the aldehydes of the nitrobenzene series. *o*-Nitrobenzaldehyde predominantly (60 to 70%) forms the oxide (5.5), but its homologue, *o*-nitro-α-tolualdehyde, in which the nitro group no longer has a mesomeric effect on the carbonyl residue, and *m*-nitrobenzaldehyde can be converted into the corresponding methyl keto-nes (5.6 and 5.7).

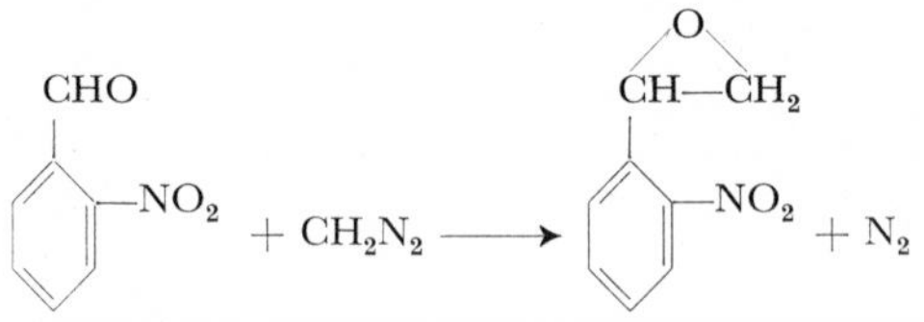

(5.5)

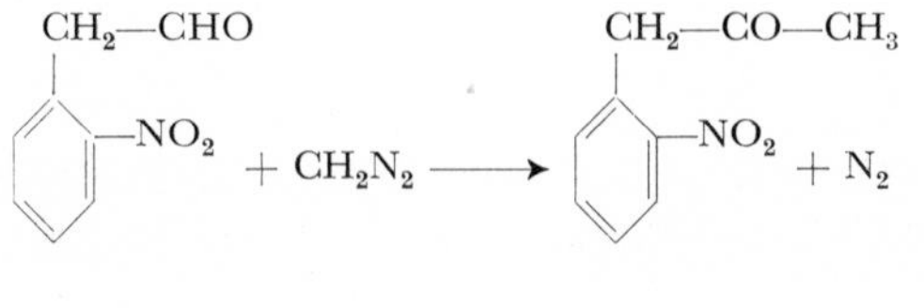

(5.6)

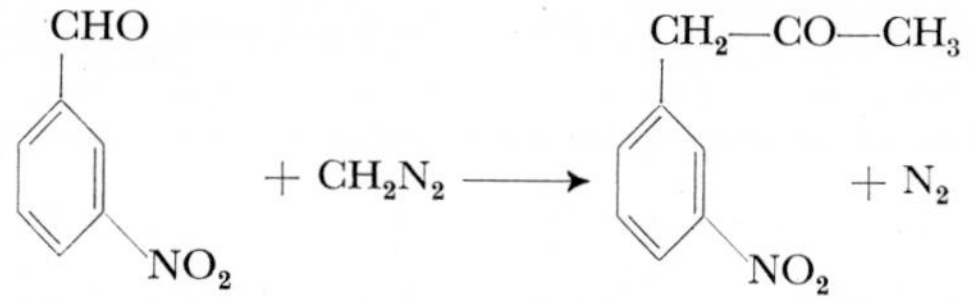

$$(5.7)$$

Methanol, which is capable of catalysing various reactions of diazoalkanes, affects the relationship between the products (V), (VI), and (VII) in several ways. In general it increases the proportion of the epoxide (*58, 61, 1472*), but with aldehydes, as the example of piperonal shows (5.8b), two methylene groups are frequently taken up and the homologous ethylene oxide becomes the main product.

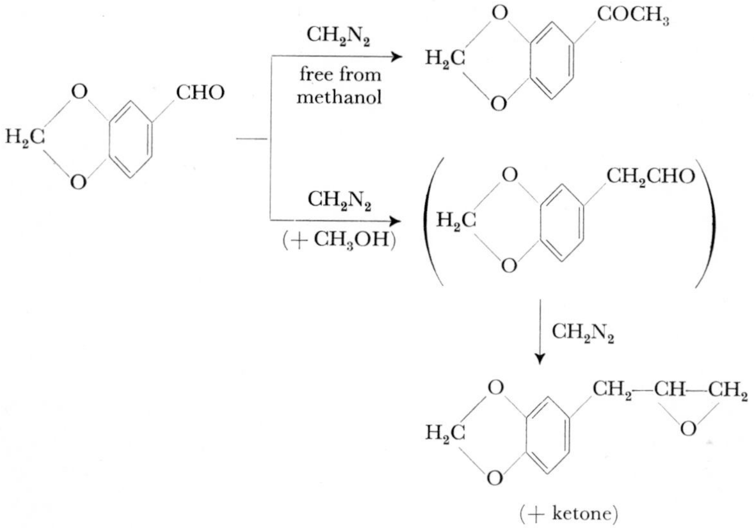

$$(5.8a)$$

$$(5.8b)$$

The reaction of diazomethane with quinaldaldehyde was recently studied by Capuano (*2311*).

Unsymmetrical ketones $(R \neq R')$ can give rise to two different homoketones and normally their relative electron affinity will be the determining factor. As the rearrangement is anionotropic, the movement of that group will be preferred which is better able to form a metastable anion. For example, CH_3 rearranges more readily than CH_2Cl and so from monochloro-2-propanone is obtained, apart from 1,2-epoxy-2-chloromethylpropane which is the main product (about 65%), 1-chloro-2-butanone (5.9) and not the 4-chloro isomer.

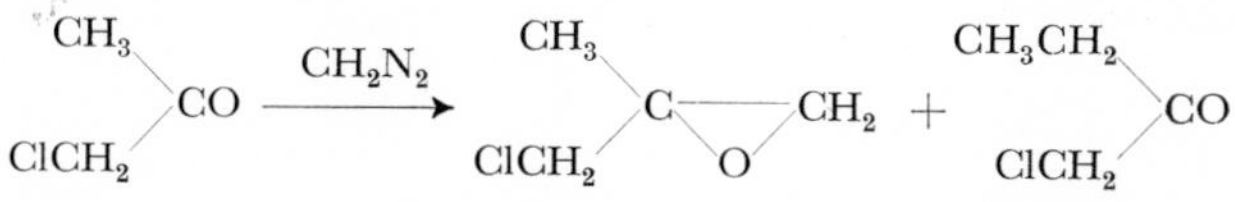

$$(5.9)$$

The case of aldehydes is one of competition between migration of hydride (methyl ketone synthesis) and of carbanion (homoaldehyde formation). The relationship between the two processes is influenced by methanol, as shown by the investigation of piperonal (5.8a).

With homologues of diazomethane the tendency to epoxide formation is present not at all or only to a very minor degree (*8, 1474*).

The configuration of the aldehyde group appears also to affect the ratio of the reaction products, as illustrated by the following example from the steroid field. 17-Formyl-4-androsten-17-ol-3-one (VIII) yields the 17-methyl ketone from the β-isomer, but the epoxide from the α-compound (5.10a, 5.10b) (*1661*).

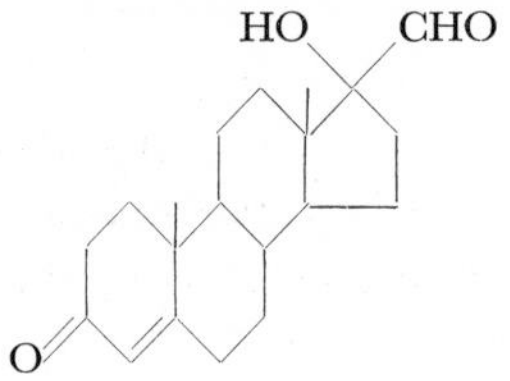

VIII

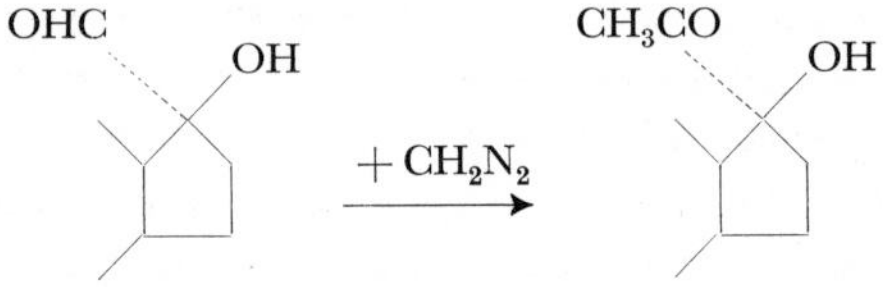

(5.10a)

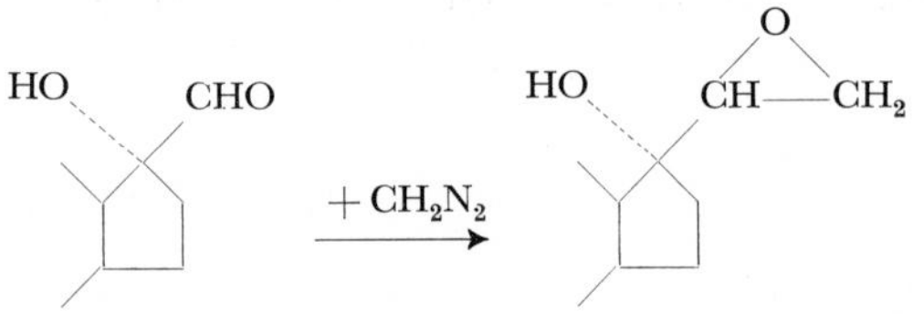

(5.10b)

As described in §5.2, enolizable ketones are *C*-methylated as well as converted into the enol ethers, but neither epoxide formation nor insertion of methylene groups has been observed. Substitution occurs also in ketones, of which the hydrogen attached to the α-carbon atom is made much more strongly acid through neighbouring groups.

Also out of line is the behaviour of α, β-unsaturated aldehydes and ketones and again that of quinones. As their reactions are comparable to those of olefins, they are to be treated along with them in § 5.4.

The addition of diazoalkanes to cyclic ketones (5.11) is of interest both preparatively and theoretically, and this ring enlargement was first carried out by Mosettig and Burger (*1473*), with cyclohexanone (IX, $n = 5$) as example. With

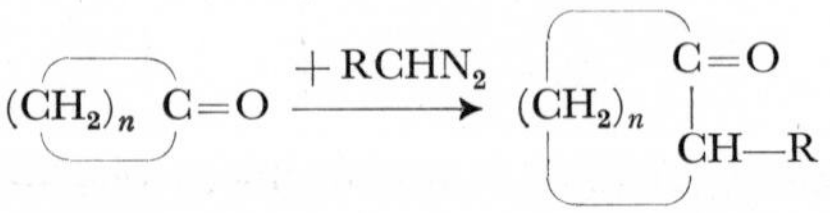

$$(CH_2)_n \; C{=}O \xrightarrow{\; + RCHN_2 \;} (CH_2)_n \begin{array}{l} C{=}O \\ | \\ CH{-}R \end{array}$$ (5.11)

IX

diazomethane in ethereal solution, the main product (63%) was the next higher homologue, cycloheptanone, but also obtained was 4% of the epoxide (X) and a mixture containing cyclo-octanone, the latter being formed through further reaction of cycloheptanone. If an excess of diazomethane is employed, the reaction can be made to yield cyclo-octanone mainly. Cyclopentanone is converted even with one equivalent of diazomethane not into cyclohexanone, but chiefly

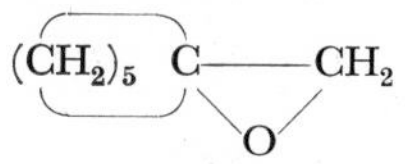

$$(CH_2)_5 \quad C\!\!-\!\!-\!\!-\!\!CH_2$$
$$O$$

X

into cycloheptanone (804). It appears that the seven-membered ring is formed particularly readily because in it the Pitzer strain is least (1213, 1214, 1244, 1657). In general the ease of ring expansion seems to be dependent on ring size; the yield is greatest for the conversion of cyclohexanone into cycloheptanone, then decreases up to cyclodecanone, and apparently increases again considerably only from the fifteen-membered ring onwards (1253, 1647). Substituted cyclic ketones usually lead to mixtures of the two possible positional isomers of increased ring size and some observations in the cyclohexanone series have been published (894, 1957, 2013).

Ring enlargement of ketones by means of diazomethane has been widely used in synthetic work and Nunn and Rapson's preparation of benz[a]azulene from 1, 4, 4a, 9a-tetrahydro-3(2H)-fluorenone (1542) will serve as an example (5.12).

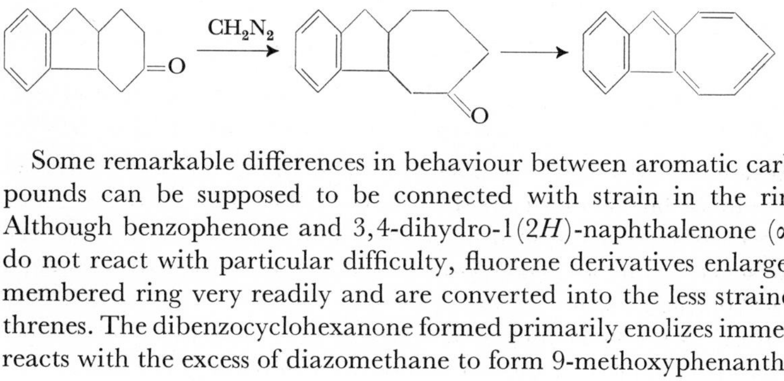

$$(5.12)$$

Some remarkable differences in behaviour between aromatic carbonyl compounds can be supposed to be connected with strain in the ring systems. Although benzophenone and 3,4-dihydro-1(2H)-naphthalenone (α-tetralone) do not react with particular difficulty, fluorene derivatives enlarge their five-membered ring very readily and are converted into the less strained phenanthrenes. The dibenzocyclohexanone formed primarily enolizes immediately and reacts with the excess of diazomethane to form 9-methoxyphenanthrene (5.13)

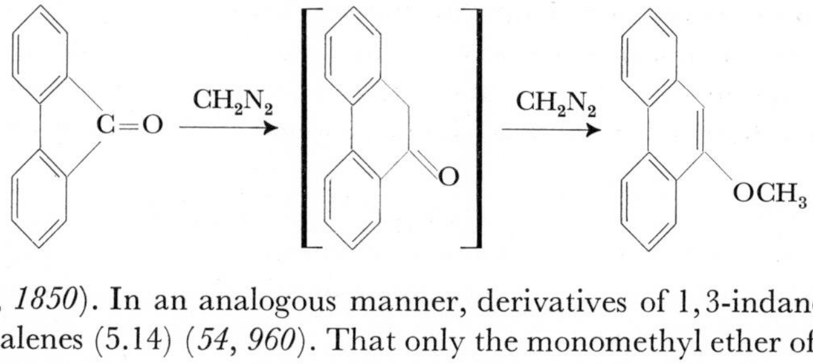

$$(5.13)$$

(201, 465, 1850). In an analogous manner, derivatives of 1,3-indandione lead to naphthalenes (5.14) (54, 960). That only the monomethyl ether of 1, 4-dihy-

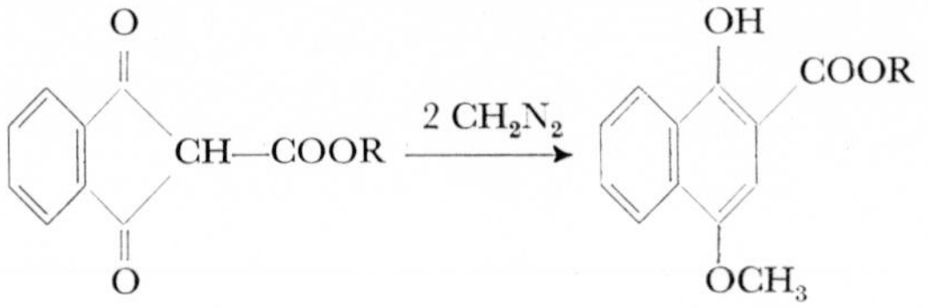

$$(5.14)$$

droxy-2-naphthoic acid is formed in the example quoted shows that the hydro-gen bond between the hydroxy group in position 1 and the oxygen of the car-boxy group inactivates the former towards diazomethane.

A similar reaction of a heterocyclic diketone has been described by Heller (*1006, 1007*), who found that isatin, in suffering ring enlargement followed by enolization, was converted into a quinoline derivative (5.15a), a side reaction of the β-keto group leading to the epoxide (5.15b).

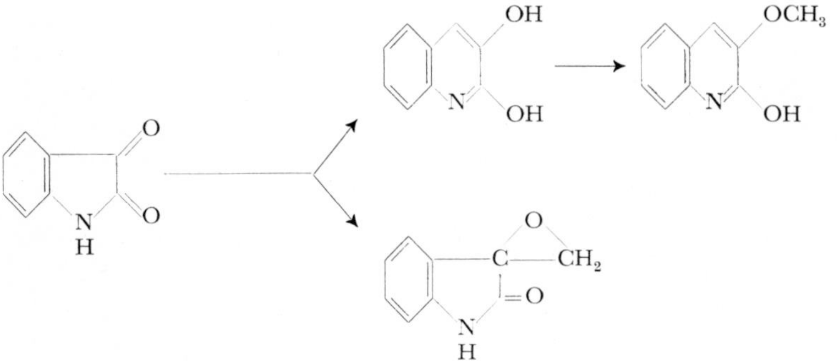

$$(5.15\,a)$$

$$(5.15\,b)$$

The corresponding heterocycles containing oxygen and sulphur, namely, 2,3-benzofurandione (XIa) and thianaphthenequinone (XIb), behave diffe-rently: they yield the cyclic methylene ethers (*1827*). However, this type of

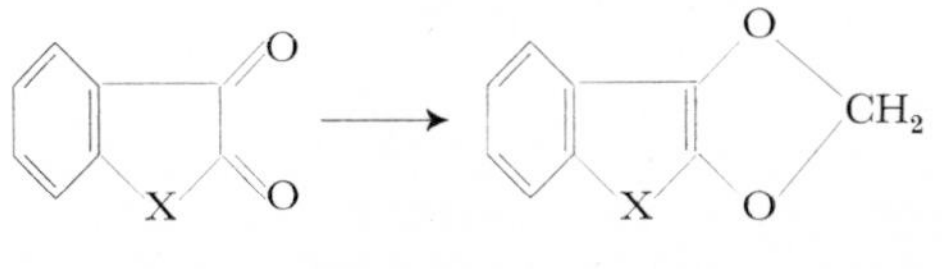

XIa: X = O
XIb: X = S

$$(5.16)$$

reaction does not occur universally with α-diketones, as evidenced by the pro-ducts obtained from isatin and mentioned above, for example. Contrary to the previous assumption that benzil (*253*) and phenanthrenequinone (*58, 715*) give cyclic methylene ethers, Eistert and his co-workers (*671*) recently postu-lated that epoxides analogous to (5.15b) are formed. In consequence the consti-tutions of the corresponding products from phenazinequinone (*1829*) and cyclo-pentane-1,2-dione (*751*) now seem uncertain. Of preparative interest is the possibility of converting a quinonemonoxime in this way into an oxazole (5.17) (*1823*).

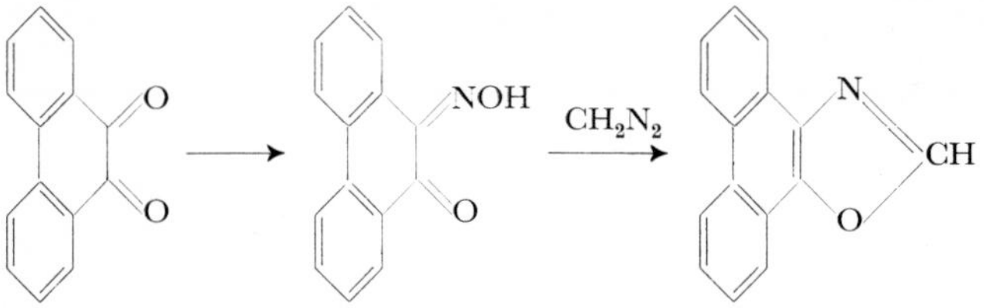

$$\text{(5.17)}$$

So far thioketones have not received much attention (*1824, 1826, 1830, 1833*), but xanthione and Michler's thioketone yield derivatives of ethylene sulphide (*1825*).

5.4 Reactions of Diazoalkanes with Systems Containing Double Bonds

In the reactions of the diazoalkanes which were discussed in the two preceding sections, the diazo group was always transformed into free nitrogen. In the case of a whole series of other reactions this is not so and the end product contains the *whole* of the diazoalkane molecule. For this reason, heterocyclic rings result, usually of the type of pyrazoline (*101, 103*). The mechanism of these reactions will be discussed in § 6.1.

Ethylene itself does not readily react with diazoalkanes, but ring strain or conjugation can facilitate reaction at the double bond.

Some instances of addition of diazoalkanes to strained double bonds present in ring systems have been described (*19, 20, 586, 2223*), the reaction between diazodiphenylmethane and the labile 1, 5-cyclo-octadiene being a case in point (5.18) (*2223*). Diazoacetic ester and diazomethane itself behave analogously.

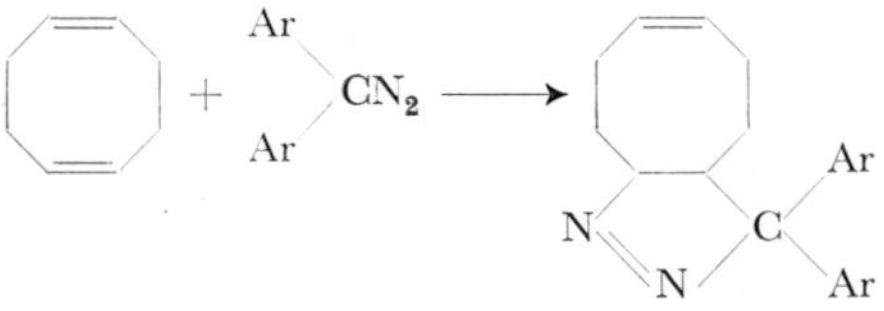

$$\text{(5.18)}$$

Butadiene yields vinylpyrazoline (5.19) (*1495*) and this reaction is typical of hydrocarbons containing conjugated double bonds. In this respect, acetylene can be regarded as an ethylene with an activated double bond, as with diazomethane it forms pyrazole (5.20) (*1096, 1219, 1600*). Recently, Troshchenko and Petrov (*2052*) found that vinylacetylene reacts not at the triple, but at the double bond, 3-ethynylpyrazoline being formed in very good yield. Kirmse and Horner (*1219*) investigated the reaction of ethynylbenzene with diazomethane and diazoacetic ester. Addition of the diazoalkane carbon atom takes place predominantly at the β-carbon atom of the ethynylbenzene. Diazomethane yields 3-phenylpyrazole together with minor amounts of the 4-isomer.

$$CH_2{=}CH{-}CH{=}CH_2 \xrightarrow{\ +CH_2N_2\ } \underset{\underset{\underset{N}{\diagdown\nearrow}}{\overset{|}{N}}}{CH_2}{-}\underset{\overset{|}{CH_2}}{CH}{-}CH{=}CH_2 \qquad (5.19)$$

$$HC{\equiv}CH \xrightarrow{\ +CH_2N_2\ } \underset{\underset{N}{\diagdown\nearrow}}{\underset{H_2C}{\overset{\|}{HC}}}{=}\underset{N}{\overset{|}{CH}} \rightleftarrows \underset{\underset{N}{\diagdown\nearrow}}{\underset{HC}{\overset{\|}{HC}}}{=}\underset{NH}{\overset{|}{CH}} \qquad (5.20)$$

The reactions with α, β-unsaturated carbonyl compounds are analogous and the formation of 5-acetyl-4-phenylpyrazoline from 4-phenyl-3-buten-2-one (benzylideneacetone) serves as an example (5.21) (*1908*). Apparently the benzy-

$$C_6H_5{-}CH{=}CH{-}COCH_3 \xrightarrow{\ CH_2N_2\ } \underset{\underset{NH}{\diagdown\nearrow}}{\underset{CH_2}{\overset{|}{C_6H_5{-}CH}}}{-}\underset{N}{\overset{\|}{C}}{-}COCH_3 \qquad (5.21)$$

lidene carbon atom is a more favourable electrophilic centre than the carbonyl carbon and the reactions characteristic of ketones (§ 5.3) are not in evidence. Vinylsulphamides and sulphonic esters behave similarly, yielding pyrazoline-5-sulphamides and sulphonic esters, respectively, according to Rondestvedt and Chang (*1729*).

The esters of α, β-unsaturated carboxylic acids undergo a parallel reaction, acrylic and fumaric esters giving pyrazoline-4-mono- and 4,5-dicarboxylic esters, respectively (*361, 362, 373–375, 377, 1601*). The latter are formed also from maleic esters (*26*) and this is of significance in the clarification of the mechanism of the formation of the pyrazoline rings (see § 6.1).

Enols of β-diketones are also α, β-unsaturated carbonyl compounds. Thus 2,4-pentanedione is able to interact with diazoacetic ester to yield a pyrazoline derivative (**XII**), which directly splits off water with the formation of the 3-acetyl-4-methylpyrazole-5-carboxylic ester (**XIII**) (*1227, 2384*). That pyra-

$$\underset{CH_3{-}\overset{|}{C}{=}CH{-}COCH_3}{\overset{\overset{OH}{|}}{}} \xrightarrow{\ +ROOC{-}CHN_2\ } \underset{\underset{ROOC}{\diagup}\underset{N}{\diagdown\nearrow}}{\underset{\overset{|}{CH}\ \ N}{CH_3{-}\overset{\overset{OH}{|}}{C}{-}CH{-}COCH_3}} \xrightarrow{\ -H_2O\ } \underset{\underset{ROOC}{\diagup}\underset{\underset{H}{N}}{\diagdown\nearrow}}{\underset{\overset{\|}{C}\ \ N}{CH_3{-}\overset{\|}{C}{-}C{-}COCH_3}} \qquad (5.22)$$

$$\text{XII} \qquad\qquad\qquad \text{XIII}$$

zole derivatives are obtained by the interaction of diazomethane and chloro-vinyl ketones is probably to be interpreted similarly: under the influence of the alkaline medium, hydrochloric acid is removed from the 4-chloropyrazolines produced as intermediates.

Quinones behave just like the α, β-unsaturated ketones discussed. 1,4-Benzo-quinone (*1598*) reacts with two equivalents of diazomethane to yield the derivative bearing two pyrazoline rings (XIV), but diazodiphenylmethane adds on only in the ratio 1:1, the product enolizing to (XV). 1,4-Naphthoquinone

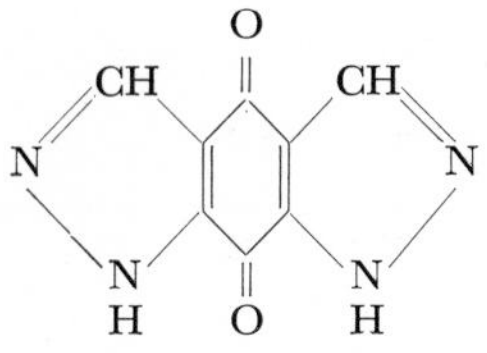

XIV 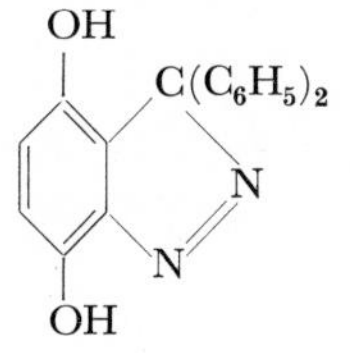   XV 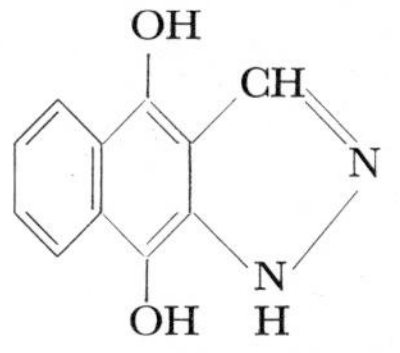   XVI

gives the pyrazole (XVI) with diazomethane (*717*). When *o*-alkyl groups are present, as in 2-methylnaphthoquinone (*229*) or 2,3,5,6-tetramethyl-1,4-benzoquinone (*1910*), the reaction takes another course either partly or wholly. The reactions of other tetrasubstituted 1,4-benzoquinones with diazomethane have been studied by Eistert and Bock (*668, 669*).

1,2-Quinones (*58, 715*) yield cyclic ethers (cf. 5.23) or epoxides (cf. § 5.3). Recently, Wessely and co-workers (*2138*) have investigated the interaction of diazoalkanes with acetylated quinols.

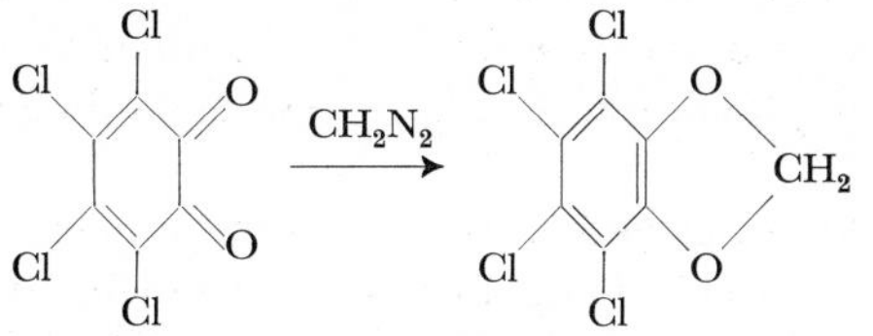

$$(5.23)$$

In general, pyrazolines possess only moderate stability to heat; they tend to lose nitrogen with the formation of olefins or to suffer ring contraction to cyclopropane derivatives (cf. 5.24). On several occasions cyclopropanes were ob-

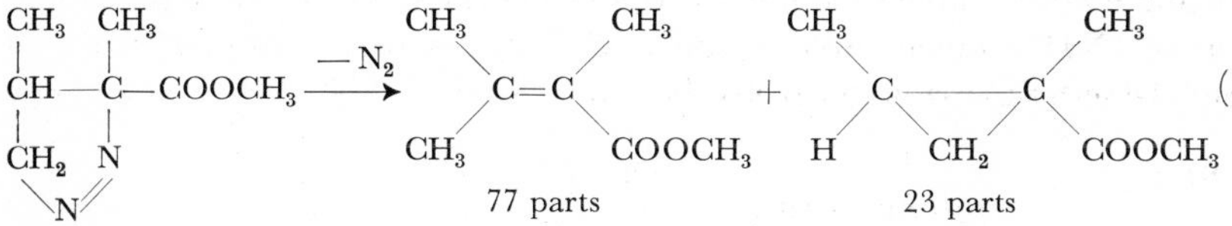

$$(5.24)$$

tained in reactions with diazomethane, yet the intermediate pyrazolines could not be isolated (*392, 1076, 2159*). Thus Burger and Yost (*392*) prepared two isomeric 2-phenylcyclopropanecarboxylic esters by condensing styrene with diazoacetic ester (5.25). The formation of cyclopropane derivatives by the interaction of allyl compounds with diazoacetic ester and diazodiphenylmethane has been studied by Dyakonow and his co-workers (*638–641, 643*). Schönberg,

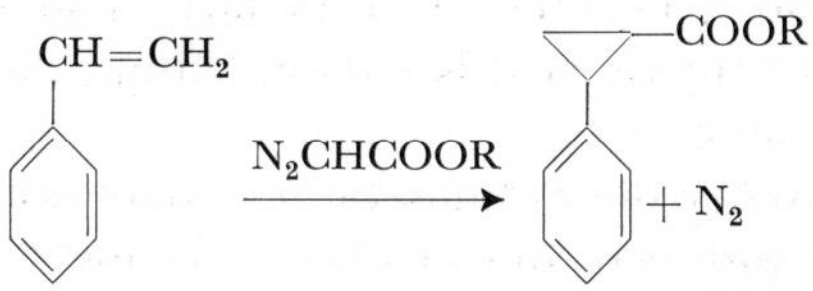

$$(5.25)$$

Mustafa, and Latif (*1828*) observed that diazofluorene and acenaphthylene react to form the spirocyclic compound (**XVII**), which rearranges into $\varDelta^{9,9'}$-bifluorene (**XVIII**) at 280°. Analogous spirocyclic compounds have been obtained by Horner and Lingnau (*1076*) from open chain ethylene derivatives.

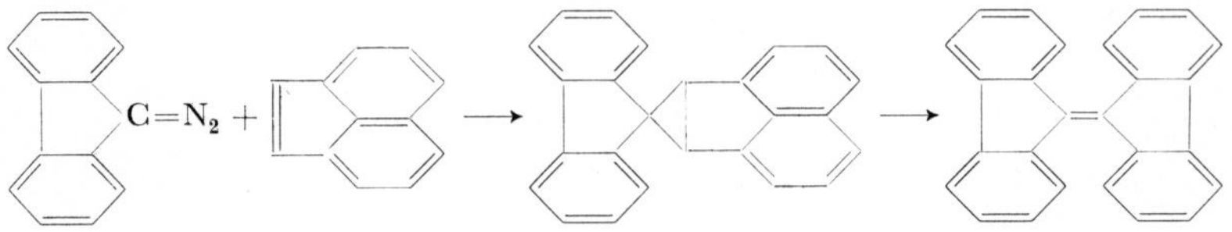

$$\text{(5.26)}$$

XVII   XVIII

Recently, Walborsky and his co-workers (*1150*) found that the addition of diazodiphenylmethane to (—)-menthyl acrylate and (—)-menthyl methacrylate, followed by saponification to 2,2-diphenyl- and 2,2-diphenyl-1-methylcyclopropanecarboxylic acid, respectively, proceeds asymmetrically, though only to a small extent.

The interesting products of the reaction between 1,3,5-trinitrobenzene and diazomethane, which leads to ring enlargement and addition to the double bonds, have been investigated by de Boer and van Velzen (*2379*).

Diazoalkanes are able to add not only to C:C, but also to N:N double bonds. Huisgen (*1118, 1119*) showed that the reactivity of azodiformic acid esters depends on the addition of all types of bases to the electrophilic azo bridge. The diazacyclopropane derivative (**XX**) obtained by E. Müller (*1479*) by means of diazoacetic ester can therefore be supposed to be produced via the addition product (**XIX**). The reaction corresponding to the pyrazoline formation discussed earlier in this section would lead to tetrazoles, but so far has not been encountered. However, the behaviour of cyano compounds indicates that, in principle,

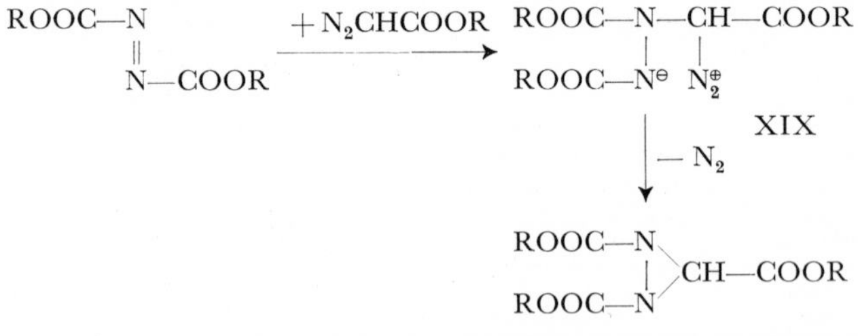

$$\text{(5.27)}$$

XIX

XX

ring formation, i. e. reaction with a nitrogen atom, is possible (5.28). A long time ago, 1,2,3-triazoles were obtained in this manner from cyanogen halides, cyanogen, and organic cyanides (*68, 1552, 1610, 2002*).

Similarly, the reaction of diazomethane with diarylcarbodi-imides (5.29) leads into the triazole series (*1738, 1739*) and in the corresponding way diazo-

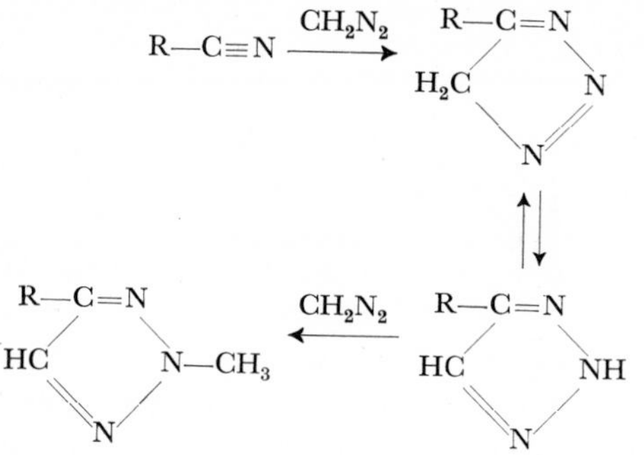

$$R-C\equiv N \xrightarrow{CH_2N_2} \begin{array}{c} R-C=N \\ H_2C \qquad N \\ N \end{array}$$

$$(5.28)$$

$$\begin{array}{c} R-C=N \\ HC \qquad N-CH_3 \\ N \end{array} \xleftarrow{CH_2N_2} \begin{array}{c} R-C=N \\ HC \qquad NH \\ N \end{array}$$

methane adds on to phenyl isothiocyanate at the CS-bond to give a thiadiazole (*1883*).

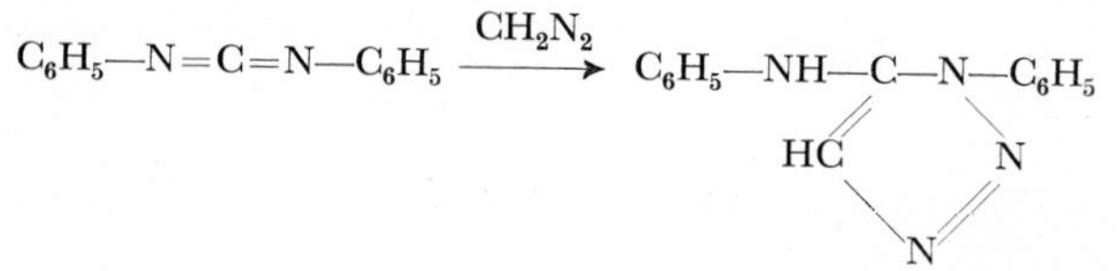

$$C_6H_5-N=C=N-C_6H_5 \xrightarrow{CH_2N_2} \begin{array}{c} C_6H_5-NH-C-N-C_6H_5 \\ HC \qquad N \\ N \end{array}$$

$$(5.29)$$

Especial interest attaches to the reactions of another type of system, that of ketenes. According to Staudinger (*1931, 1944*), the behaviour of diphenyl-ketene towards diazodiphenylmethane is analogous to that of carbodi-imides (5.30), but ketene itself is unable to retain the nitrogen within the molecule. Nitrogen is given off and ring closure of the carbonium ion formed leads to cyclopropanone, which cannot be isolated as such because it readily undergoes the ring enlargement usual for cyclic ketones (§ 5.3) to yield cyclobutanone (5.31) (*1350, 1351, 1877*).

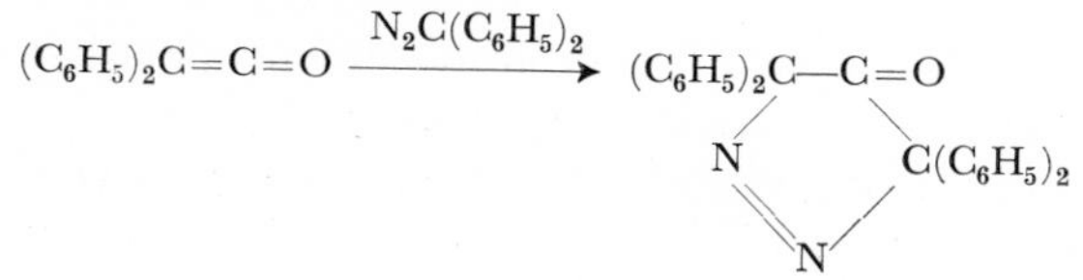

$$(C_6H_5)_2C=C=O \xrightarrow{N_2C(C_6H_5)_2} \begin{array}{c} (C_6H_5)_2C-C=O \\ N \qquad C(C_6H_5)_2 \\ N \end{array}$$

$$(5.30)$$

$$H_2C=C=O \xrightarrow{CH_2N_2} \left(\begin{array}{c} H_2C=C-O^\ominus \\ | \\ CH_2-N_2^\oplus \end{array} \right) \longrightarrow \begin{array}{c} H_2C \qquad C=O \\ CH_2 \end{array}$$

$$+ CH_2N_2$$

$$\begin{array}{c} H_2C-C=O \\ | \qquad | \\ H_2C-CH_2 \end{array} \qquad \begin{array}{c} \text{can be isolated} \\ \text{as hydrate} \end{array}$$

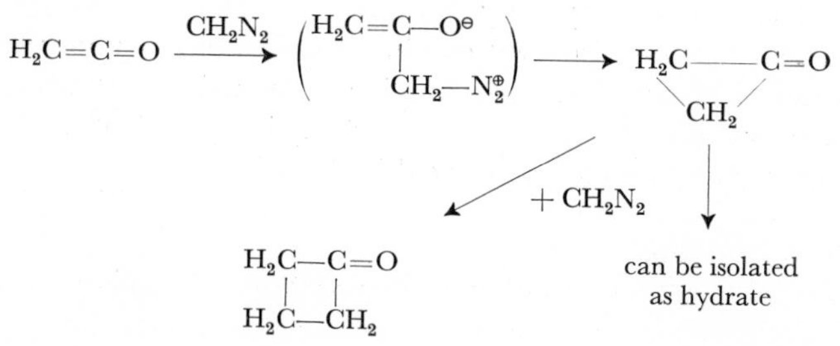

$$(5.31)$$

Benzoyl isocyanate represents a similar system, which also loses nitrogen, but stabilizes itself in another way (5.32) (*1883*).

6 Zollinger

$$C_6H_5-\overset{\underset{\|}{O}}{C}-N=C=O \xrightarrow{CH_2N_2} C_6H_5-\overset{\underset{|}{\underset{CH_2N_2^{\oplus}}{}}}{C}=N-\overset{\underset{\|}{O^{\ominus}}}{C}=O \longrightarrow C_6H_5-\overset{\underset{|}{O}}{C}\begin{array}{c} N \\ \\ CH_2 \end{array}C=O \qquad (5.32)$$

Reactions of diazomethane with amides have been studied recently by Gompper (*2387*).

All the reactions discussed so far in this and the previous section (§ 5.3) proceed under mild conditions, in particular as regards temperature. Only rarely is it necessary to exceed room temperature to any considerable extent and frequently the reactions are so vigorous as to require cooling. The diazoalkane is either prepared previously and its solution in ether, ligroine, methanol-ether, etc. added to the solution of the starting material or it is made *in situ* from the usual reagents, such as the nitrosoalkyl derivatives of urea or urethan.

5.5 Thermolysis and Photolysis of Diazoalkanes

The reactions now to be considered require fundamentally different conditions to those described in the previous sections; they necessarily involve either high temperatures or irradiation. This suggests underlying differences in mechanism. Whereas in each case dealt with so far, the primary process was addition of the whole diazoalkane molecule, with subsequent liberation of nitrogen, if appropriate, in the following preparative applications of diazoalkanes, preliminary fission occurs into molecular nitrogen and the electrically neutral particles :CHR, called methylene or carbene radicals. These particles then react with double bond systems if available or in other ways. The structure of methylene radicals and the investigations into their appearance as intermediates will be discussed in § 6.3, but here their reactions with olefinic and aromatic compounds will be considered from the preparative point of view.

These processes are of great interest as regards the conversion of benzene derivatives into substances with seven-membered rings. As long ago as 1885, Buchner and Curtius (*366*) studied the thermal decomposition of diazoacetic ester in benzene and, subsequently, Buchner (*305, 306, 363, 364, 367, 368, 372, 376*) continued this work in great detail. At temperatures above about 120°, there is obtained the so-called norcaradienecarboxylic ester, which, in turn, readily rearranges into cycloheptatrienecarboxylic ester (5.33). The constitution of these products will be considered in § 6.3 (c).

$$\begin{array}{ccccc} & \xrightarrow{N_2CHCOOR} & & \\ \end{array} \quad \text{CH—COOR} \longrightarrow \quad \text{CH—COOR} \qquad (5.33)$$

As the high temperatures used are a disadvantage in the more general application of this method of ring enlargement, the optimum conditions for the reaction have been investigated thoroughly. Traces of heavy metals have been shown by Grundmann (*890*) to be very objectionable and by their careful exclusion the yield could be increased fourfold.

A more gentle method of preparing derivatives of norcaradienecarboxylic ester was found by G. O. Schenck and H. Ziegler (*1793*) in the photolysis of diazoacetic esters in aromatic hydrocarbons. Comparisons between the thermal and photochemical processes showed unequivocally that photolytically decomposed diazoacetic ester at lower temperatures (60 to 65°) leads to considerably improved yields of pure products.

The photolysis of diazomethane in a variety of solvents subject to attack (alcohols, ethers, carbonyl compounds, and aromatic hydrocarbons) had already been investigated previously by Meerwein and his co-workers (*1397, 1402*) with great success.

Their first paper (*1402*) deals with ethers and alcohols. Diazomethane irradiated in ethyl ether yields ethyl n-propyl and ethyl isopropyl ether, and in tetrahydrofuran the α- and β-methyl derivatives are obtained. Isopropyl alcohol is converted not only into its ether, but also into s- and t-butanol (5.34).

$$
\begin{array}{c}
CH_3 \\
\diagdown \\
CHOH \\
\diagup \\
CH_3
\end{array}
\xrightarrow[\text{light}]{CH_2N_2}
\begin{array}{c}
CH_3 \\
\diagdown \\
CHOCH_3 \; + \\
\diagup \\
CH_3
\end{array}
\begin{array}{c}
CH_3 \\
\diagdown \\
CHOH \; + \\
\diagup \\
CH_3CH_2
\end{array}
\begin{array}{c}
CH_3 \\
| \\
CH_3\!-\!C\!-\!OH \\
| \\
CH_3
\end{array}
\qquad (5.34)
$$

Under these conditions, aldehydes and ketones give the same products as those described in § 5.3.

On the contrary, it is interesting that carboxylic esters could only be made to react by irradiation (*1397*), the homologous esters being formed, for example, ethyl acetate and methyl propionate from methyl acetate. The hydrogen atom attached to carbon in esters of formic acid apparently cannot be exchanged and no esters of acetic acid result.

Apart from the homologous esters, the same products are obtained as from ketones (5.35) and thus an ester carbonyl group when irradiated in the presence of diazomethane behaves analogously to an aldehyde or keto group.

$$
\begin{array}{c}
HC\!=\!O \\
| \\
OCH_3
\end{array}
\xrightarrow[\text{light}]{CH_2N_2}
\begin{array}{c}
HC\!=\!O \\
| \\
OCH_2CH_3
\end{array}
\; + \;
\begin{array}{c}
\overset{\displaystyle O}{\diagup\diagdown} \\
HC\!-\!\!-\!CH_2 \\
| \\
OCH_3
\end{array}
\; + \;
\begin{array}{c}
HC\!=\!O \\
| \\
CH_2\!-\!OCH_3
\end{array}
\qquad (5.35)
$$

Recently, Doering and his co-workers (*608, 612*) have shown that not only those CH-, CH_2-, and CH_3-groups which are attached to ether oxygen can be methylated. In fact, any alkyl group can be attacked and there is hardly any discrimination between primary, secondary, tertiary, vinylic, and allylic CH-bonds. For instance, the interaction of n-pentane with diazoacetic ester leads to substitution in positions 1, 2 and 3 (5.36), with only slight preference for the β- and γ-carbon atoms.

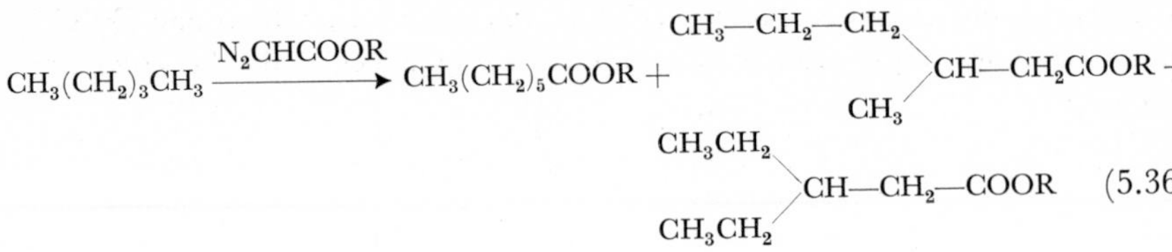

$$CH_3(CH_2)_3CH_3 \xrightarrow{\;N_2CHCOOR\;} CH_3(CH_2)_5COOR +$$

$$\begin{array}{c} CH_3-CH_2-CH_2 \\ \diagdown \\ CH-CH_2COOR + \\ \diagup \\ CH_3 \end{array}$$

$$\begin{array}{c} CH_3CH_2 \\ \diagdown \\ CH-CH_2-COOR \quad (5.36) \\ \diagup \\ CH_3CH_2 \end{array}$$

Not only CH-, but also CCl-residues are liable to photolytic attack by diazo-alkanes, Urry and his co-workers (*2069, 2071*) having shown that the scheme (5.37) applies. In this way, carbon tetrachloride takes up four equivalents of

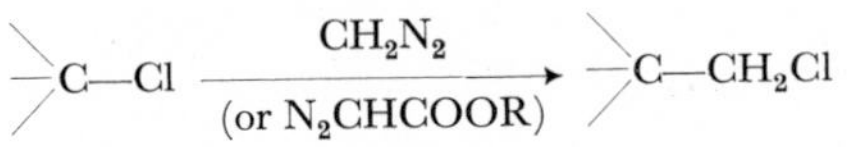

$$\begin{array}{c} \diagdown \\ C-Cl \xrightarrow[\text{(or } N_2CHCOOR)]{\;CH_2N_2\;} \diagdown C-CH_2Cl \qquad (5.37) \\ \diagup \end{array}$$

diazomethane to give 1,3-dichloro-2,2-bis(chloromethyl) propane $[C(CH_2Cl)_4]$ in 60% yield.

The researches of Meerwein's school (*1397, 2082*) into the photolysis of diazomethane in aromatic hydrocarbons confirmed and extended the work of Schenck and Ziegler (*1793*). In benzene there was obtained a 72% yield of a mixture of two compounds of the molecular formula C_7H_8, designated as nor-caradiene and cycloheptatriene. In sunlight the main product was the first hydrocarbon (59 to 74%), but, with a mercury vapour lamp behind a water filter, the second preponderated. Doering and Knox (*611*) were unable to observe the former compound in similar experiments, probably because it rearranges relatively easily under the influence of heat or light of short wave-length (*1793*). In chlorobenzene and anisole, Meerwein *et al.* were also only able to isolate one derivative C_7H_7X (X = Cl or OCH_3, the orientation not being established), apart from benzyl chloride and a mixture of chlorotoluenes or the three cresol ethers, respectively.

The physical characterization of compounds of the type of the addition pro-ducts of diazomethane or diazoacetic ester and benzene (*466, 614*) has made it doubtful whether the products are indeed norcaradiene (XXI) and cyclo-heptatriene (XXII). The problem will be discussed in § 6.3 (c), but in this chapter the classic descriptions will be retained without implying that these definitely correspond to the actual constitutions.

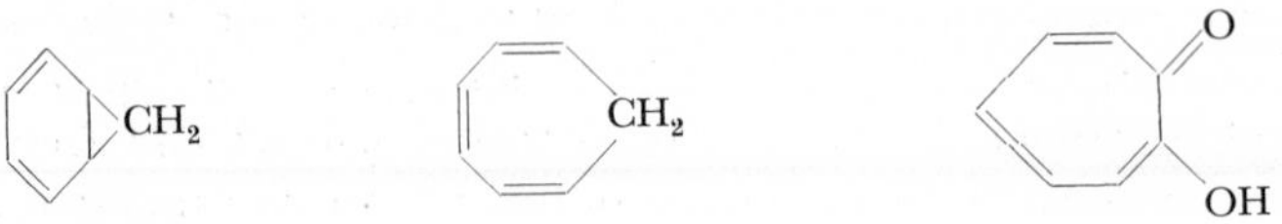

XXI   XXII   XXIII

Potassium permanganate converts norcaradiene and cycloheptatriene into tropolone (XXIII).

An interesting intramolecular photolytic reaction was discovered by Gutsche and Johnson (*896, 897*) in the case of 2-(β-phenylethyl)phenyldiazomethane

(XXIV), which yields compound (XXVI) apart from 2-phenylindan (XXV). Equation (5.38) represents a new route to substances with the colchicine skeleton.

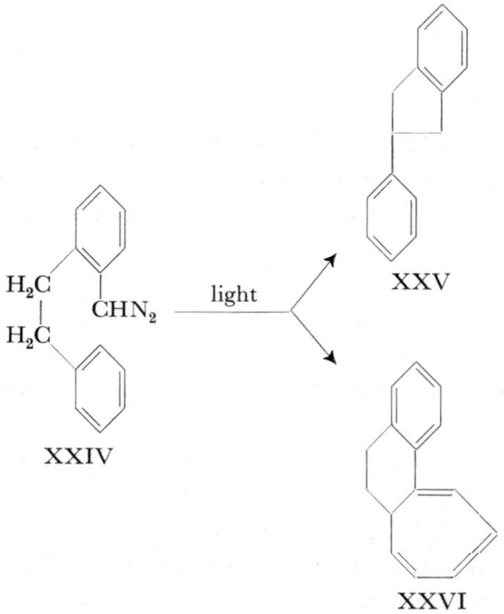

$$(5.38)$$

When it comes to substituted and polycyclic ring systems, Buchner's method of ring enlargement occasionally gives rise to uncertainty, since that, because of the different modes of addition possible, mixtures of isomers may be formed.

This problem has attained great importance in the determination of the constitution of azulenes and in their synthesis, although for the first azulene synthesis in 1936 Pfau and Plattner (1614) employed another method and the best route to this ring system, that of Hafner and Ziegler (901–903, 2222, see also 1257), depends on other reactions. Even so, Buchner's method of ring enlargement of indans is still the method which has yielded the greatest number of azulene derivatives. Plattner (1645) in 1940 was the first to use diazoacetic ester for this purpose. The photochemical ring enlargement of indan with diazomethane was studied in 1953, more or less simultaneously, by Doering et al. (616), by S. Dev (566), and by Alder and Schmitz (18).

The known ring enlargements which lead to azulene and its derivatives have been reviewed by Gordon (843) and by Treibs and his colleagues (2047).

The work of Arnold (72, 73), as well as that of Schenck and Ziegler (1793), provides an example of the difficulties of the indan ring expansion as regards orientation. According to Arnold (72), under the influence of heat diazoacetic ester, that is, the carboxymethylene formed from it, adds on to indan in the 4,5-position, because from the norcaradiene derivative produced 5-methylazulene can be prepared (5.39a). However, photolysis enabled Schenck and Ziegler to obtain the 5,6-addition product (5.39b), but 1-isopropylindan yields 1-isopropyl-6-methylazulene (5.40) on thermolysis (73). All the same, some

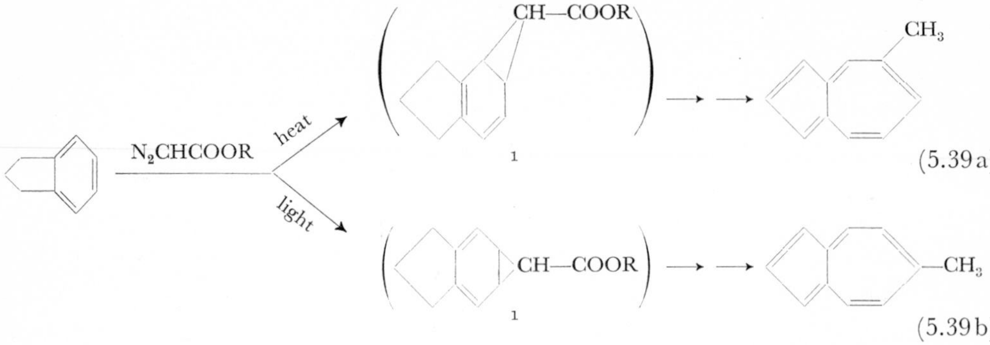

$$(5.39\,a)$$

$$(5.39\,b)$$

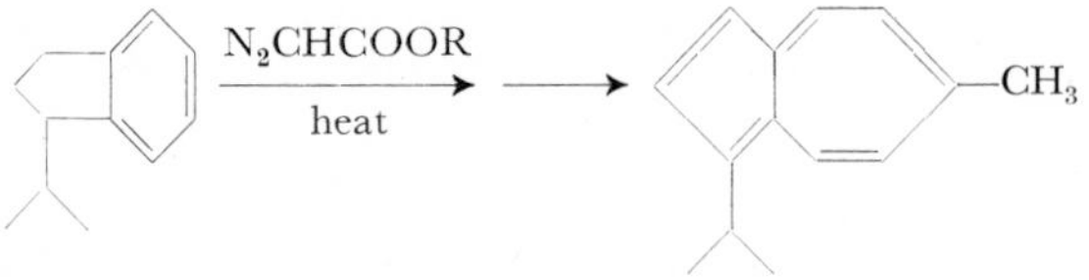

$$(5.40)$$

plausible rules can be deduced. In particular, it seems that, if possible, carboxy-methylene adds on to unsubstituted double bonds, as for instance, Plattner's (*1644*) experiment with 4,7-dimethylindan shows (5.41).

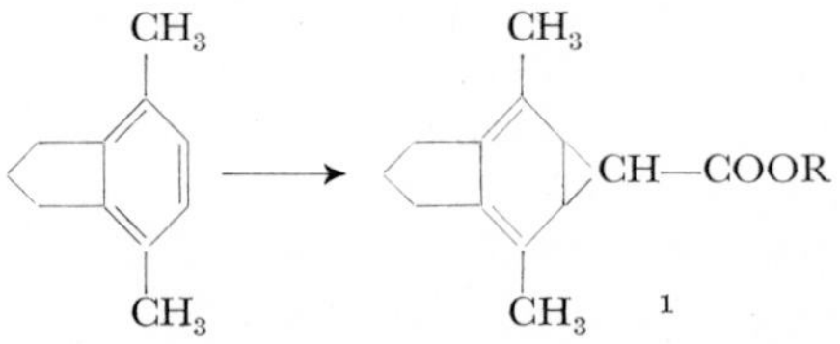

$$(5.41)$$

Some of these azulene syntheses are complicated even more by the fact that in the dehydrogenation which follows the ring expansion, rearrangement may occur. Thus, in the attempt to make 1-isopropyl-4,8-dimethylazulene from 1-isopropyl-4,7-dimethylindan, Herz (*1014*) obtained 2-isopropyl-4,7-dime-thylazulene because of the mobility of the isopropyl group. Recently, in the systematic investigations of the Zurich school apparatuses have been developed for the dehydrogenation, which permit a reduction in the time spent in the high temperature chamber at 320° to 350° with consequent increases in yield (*1269, 1640, 1658*).

Schenck and Steinmetz (*1792*) have studied the photolysis of diazoacetic ester in the presence of such aromatic heterocycles as thiophene and furane.

The thermolysis of diazoalkanes in the presence of tertiary amines has been re-investigated. Staudinger and J. Meyer (*1940*) had found that the decomposition of diazodiphenylmethane which produces the azine of benzophenone is

---

[1] For the constitution of these compounds see § 6.3 (c).

unaffected by triethylamine, but Bamford and Stevens (*188*) have observed interaction with amines in other cases. Thus from 9-diazofluorene and *N*,*N*-dimethyl-9-fluorenamine, 9-dimethylamino-9,9'-bifluorene is obtained (5.42).

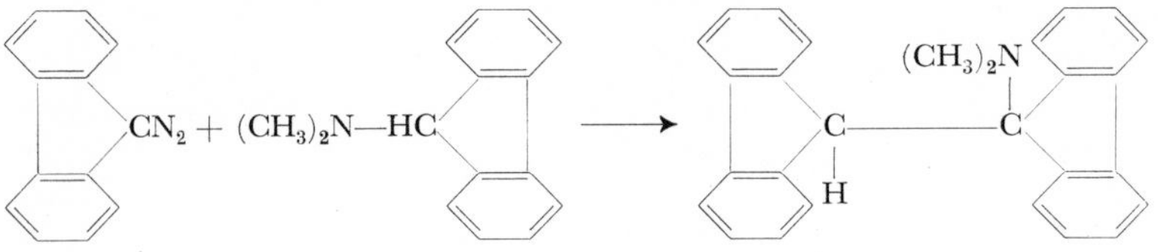

$$(5.42)$$

5.6 The Preparation and Reactions of Diazoketones

Diazoketones, $R \cdot CO \cdot CHN_2$, were discovered at the beginning of this century by Wolff (*2188–2190*), who obtained them by a laborious process. He observed that these compounds are transformed into carboxylic acids in water, especially in the presence of silver ions (5.43). The reaction, now known as the Wolff

$$R—CO—CHN_2 + H_2O \longrightarrow R—CH_2—COOH + N_2 \qquad (5.43)$$

rearrangement, only became of preparative significance when more ready methods of preparation were developed. Arndt and Eistert (*57, 59, 60, 62*) found that carboxylic acid chlorides or bromides can be converted into diazo-ketones almost without exception and in good yield, when they are added to a cold solution of an excess of diazomethane. The same method was described only a little later by Bradley and Robinson (*298*). Surprising is the fact that neither Staudinger (*1932*) nor Nierenstein (*431, 1341, 1368, 1528*) hit on this reaction in their investigations of the interaction of acyl halides with diazo-methane. They obtained substantially only halogenomethylketones.

Research into the mechanism of the reaction by Arndt's school and by Bradley and Schwarzenbach (*300*) has clarified the relationship between the various products. First, the diazomethane is acylated by the acid chloride (5.44a). Under Nierenstein's conditions the diazo group is replaced by the chloride liberated in the first step to give the halogenomethylketone (5.44b), but according to Arndt, Eistert, and Bradley's method an excess of diazomethane is used, thus intercepting hydrogen chloride by conversion into methyl chloride (5.44c).

$$RCOCl + CH_2N_2 \longrightarrow RCOCHN_2 + HCl \qquad (5.44a)$$

$$RCOCHN_2 + HCl \longrightarrow RCOCH_2Cl + N_2 \qquad (5.44b)$$

$$HCl + CH_2N_2 \longrightarrow CH_3Cl + N_2 \qquad (5.44c)$$

By combining this reaction sequence with Wolff's diazoketone rearrangement an elegant and much used method for the preparation of homologous carbo-xylic acids results, the so-called Arndt–Eistert synthesis (5.45) (*62, 63, 117*).

$$RCOCl + 2\ CH_2N_2 \longrightarrow RCOCHN_2 + CH_3Cl + N_2$$

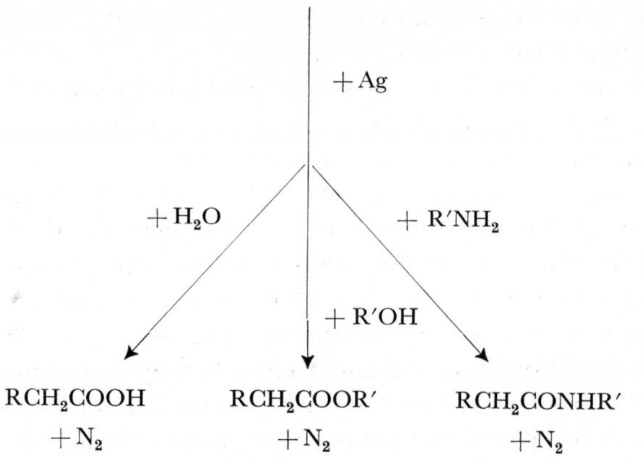

$$+ Ag$$

$$+ H_2O \qquad\qquad + R'NH_2$$

$$+ R'OH$$

$$\begin{array}{ccc} RCH_2COOH & RCH_2COOR' & RCH_2CONHR' \\ + N_2 & + N_2 & + N_2 \end{array}$$

(5.45)

Bradley and Robinson (*299*) have found that acid anhydrides behave similarly, the methyl ester being formed as well as the diazoketone (5.46).

$$(RCO)_2O + 2\ CH_2N_2 \longrightarrow RCOCHN_2 + RCOOCH_3 + N_2 \qquad (5.46)$$

The Arndt–Eistert synthesis has been very widely employed. Bachmann and Struve (*117*) and Eistert (*662–665*) have reviewed the literature up to the early 'forties. Only few cases are known in which the reaction fails; for example, mesitoyl chloride (**XXVII**) would not react with diazomethane (*115*). Sulpho-

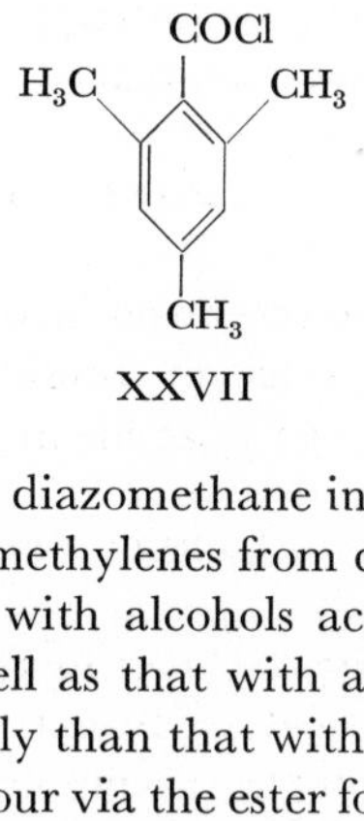

COCl
H₃C   CH₃

CH₃

XXVII

nyl chlorides do not react with diazomethane in this sense (*67*), rather do they catalyse the formation of polymethylenes from diazomethane.

In general, the interaction with alcohols according to equation (5.45) to yield homologous esters, as well as that with amines or ammonia to amides, occurs somewhat more smoothly than that with water. At times, Eistert (*662–665*) even recommends the detour via the ester for the preparation of the homologous acid. This is so, for example, in the simultaneous elongation of aliphatic, α,ω-dicarboxylic acids at both ends (*2099, 2197*). On the other hand, some instances have been described in which two methylene groups have been introduced by two successive Arndt–Eistert syntheses (*113, 1646*).

Sometimes it has been found possible to carry out an Arndt–Eistert synthesis in spite of the presence in the molecule of other groups capable of reaction with diazomethane. Thus, 3-hydroxy-2-naphthoic acid can be converted into its homologue without attack on the hydroxy group (*1277*) and 9-oxo-4-fluorene-carboxylic acid gives 9-oxo-4-fluoreneacetic acid in good yield, no interaction with the keto group being observed (*116*).

In practice it is essential in Arndt–Eistert syntheses to add the acid chloride (1 equivalent) slowly in solution or suspension to an excess of diazomethane (at least $2\frac{1}{2}$ equivalents) dissolved in ether and cooled (0° to 5°). Usually the evolution of nitrogen is very vigorous. If the diazoketone is not precipitated, it is isolated by evaporation. Purification is hardly ever required. If the acid chloride is not too reactive, the diazoketone synthesis can be carried out in a medium containing alcohol (*667*), but ethanol must be absent when reactive acid chlorides or certain other compounds are being used (*672, 1883*) (cf. § 5.4).

As catalyst for the Wolff rearrangement a freshly prepared suspension of silver oxide is generally employed. To obtain the homologous acid, a solution of the diazoketone in dioxane is slowly added to a warm solution of sodium thiosulphate, containing some silver oxide and perhaps still some sodium carbonate. The reaction is always accompanied by reduction of silver oxide and occasionally must be revived by the addition of a further portion of it.

To prepare the ester, silver oxide is added to a hot solution or suspension of the diazoketone in water-free alcohol, and an analogous process is used for anilides. For unsubstituted amides, ammonia can be led into an alcoholic solution of the diazoketone or aqueous ammonia added to a solution in dioxane.

It is possible to apply the Arndt–Eistert synthesis to higher diazoalkanes.

Apart from making available homologous carboxylic acids, the diazoketones have gained preparative significance in other directions also.

Bromine or iodine in acetic acid yields dibromo- or di-iodo-ketones, respectively (5.47) (*1660*). Whilst, as mentioned above, hydrogen halides lead to halo-

$$RCOCHN_2 + Br_2 \longrightarrow RCOCHBr_2 + N_2 \qquad (5.47)$$

genomethylketones (5.44b), dilute sulphuric acid hydrolyses diazoketones to ketols (5.48). This reaction has achieved considerable importance through Reichstein's synthesis of 11-deoxycorticosterone from stigmasterol (*1948, 1949*).

$$RCOCHN_2 + H_2O \longrightarrow RCO-CH_2OH + N_2 \qquad (5.48)$$

Aromatic diazoketones with appropriate *o*-substituents undergo cyclization in presence of acids; for example, α-diazo-*o*-nitroacetophenone yields 1-hydroxy-isatin (5.49a) (*59*), and α-diazo-*o*-methoxyacetophenone is converted into 3(2)-benzofuranone (5.49b) (*292*).

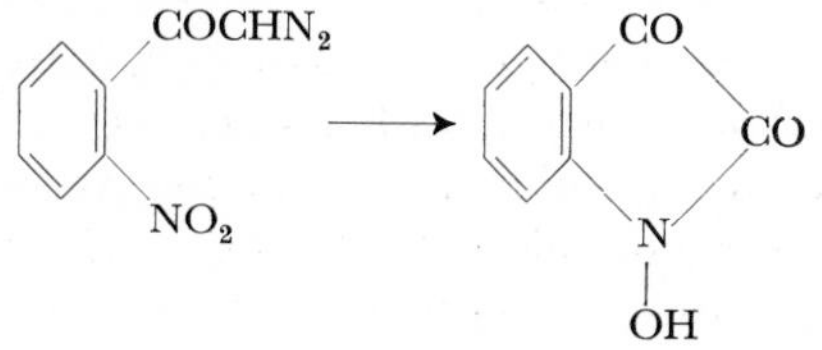

(5.49a)

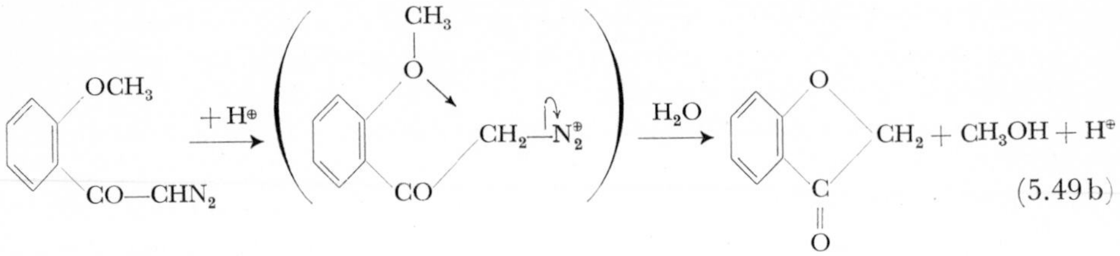

$$\text{(5.49 b)}$$

The decomposition of diazoketones in aqueous solution is catalysed by copper ions. Such reactions have been studied by several chemists, for example, by Haupter and Pucek (*2389*).

α-Diazo-β,β'-dicarbonyl compounds are much more resistant to acid than the α-diazoketones (*65*). However, under energetic conditions, especially in the presence of copper powder, unsaturated diols can be obtained from them, as illustrated by the conversion of 2-diazo- into 2-hydroxy-5,5-dimethyl-1,3-cyclo-hexanedione (5.50), taken from the work of Eistert *et al.* (*670*).

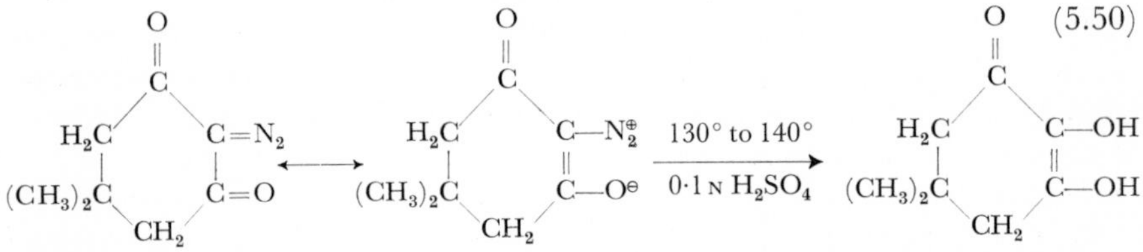

$$\text{(5.50)}$$

Purely thermal decomposition in general gives cyclopropane derivatives or 1,2-diacylethylenes, formation of the latter occurring particularly in presence of copper compounds (*889*). Yates (*2199*) has found that no Wolff rearrangement takes place in the presence of copper. A ketocarbene is formed which reacts with the solvent as described in §6.3. According to Ernest and co-workers (*683, 684, 2319*) unsymmetrical 1,2-diacylethylenes can also be obtained in this way (5.51).

$$R\text{—CO—CHN}_2 + N_2CH\text{—CO—}(CH_2)_n\text{—COOCH}_3$$

$$\Big\downarrow \text{ in boiling benzene} + CuO \qquad\qquad \text{(5.51)}$$

$$R\text{—CO—CH=CH—CO—}(CH_2)_n\text{—COOCH}_3 + 2\,N_2$$

Mostly the diazoketones behave similarly to the diazoalkanes in thermolysis, the reactions proceeding, as described in § 6.3, via the very reactive carbene radicals. Under favourable steric conditions, these do not give the product of dimerization as in (5.51), but undergo an intramolecular reaction with alkyl groups. Thus, for instance, Jeger and his colleagues (*866*) found that the action of heat and copper converted 21-diazo-20-allopregnanone (**XXVIII**) into the cyclic ketone (**XXIX**) through interaction with the C-18-methyl group. Similar ring closures of diazoketones have been employed by Meerwein (*1400*), Alder

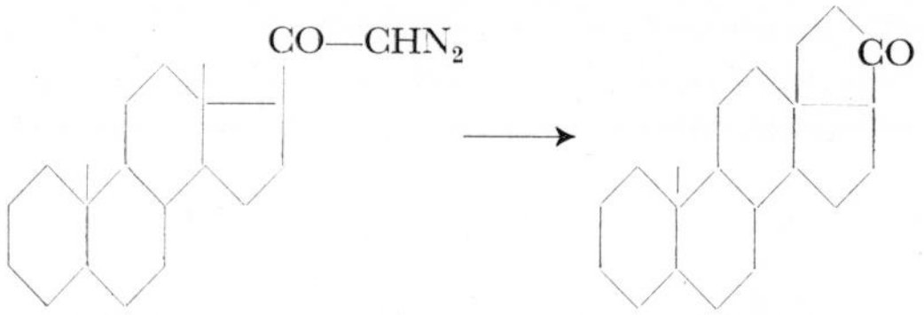

$$(5.52)$$

XXVIII   XXIX

(*17*), and others (*315, 1800*) to build up tricyclic systems. This is illustrated by the ready preparation of tricyclene (**XXX**) from diazocamphane (5.53), itself easily obtained by oxidation of camphor hydrazone.

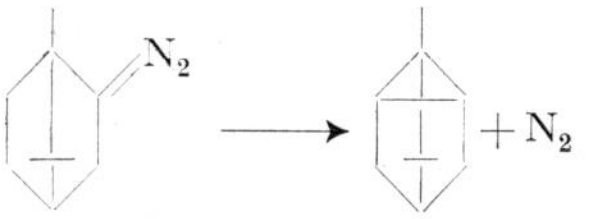

$$(5.53)$$

XXX

Generally the photochemical reactions of diazoketones, recently investigated particularly by L. Horner, proceed analogously to the thermal ones. Some interest for preparative purposes attaches to this work, as it has made available the ketenes which appear as intermediates in the Wolff rearrangement. Since photolysis has also provided information valuable from the point of view of the mechanism of the reactions of diazoketones, its treatment is held over into the next chapter. According to Horner (*1081*) many Arndt–Eistert syntheses give better yields when carried out photolytically than if the conventional silver oxide catalysis is employed. Some Wolff rearrangements, such as that of the diazo-ketone from pentachloropropionyl chloride (**XXXI**), are supposed to occur solely on irradiation (5.54) (*1727*). In the example cited, there could be isolated only the product of splitting off hydrogen chloride, namely, $\beta,\gamma,\gamma,\gamma$-tetrachloro-crotonic acid (**XXXII**).

$$Cl_3C\!-\!CCl_2\!-\!CO\!-\!CHN_2 \longrightarrow (Cl_3C\!-\!CCl_2\!-\!CH_2\!-\!COOH) \longrightarrow Cl_3C\!-\!CCl\!=\!CH\!-\!COOH$$

XXXI   XXXII   (5.54)

3-Diazocamphor (**XXXII a**) is an example of a compound which behaves differently in photolysis than in thermolysis. Thermolytically the tricyclohep-tanone (**XXXII b**) is formed, whereas light initiates a ring contraction. Horner and Spietschka (*1083a*) showed that in water 1,6,6-trimethylbicyclo[2,1,1]-hexane-5-carboxylic acid (**XXXII c**) is produced.

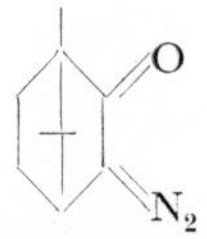

XXXII a 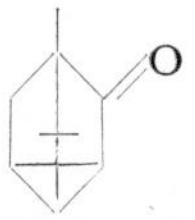   XXXII b 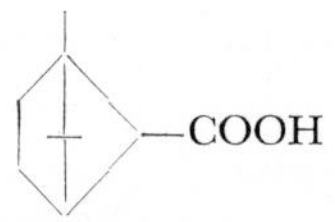   XXXII c

An important field for the preparative application of diazoketones lies in carbohydrate chemistry. Thus chain lengthening can be carried out on carboxylic acids via the corresponding diazoketones. An instance is provided by the preparation of 1,8-dihydroxymucyldimethane hexa-acetate (XXXIV) from tetra-acetylmucyl dichloride (XXXIII) (*298, 2196*). The reduction of diazo-

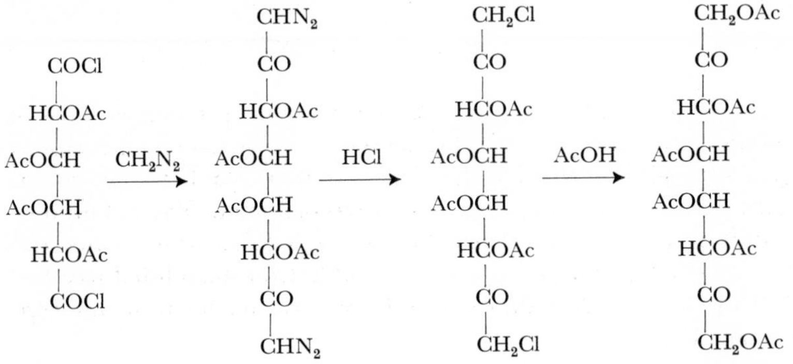

$$
\begin{array}{ccccccc}
& & \mathrm{CHN_2} & & \mathrm{CH_2Cl} & & \mathrm{CH_2OAc} \\
& & | & & | & & | \\
\mathrm{COCl} & & \mathrm{CO} & & \mathrm{CO} & & \mathrm{CO} \\
| & & | & & | & & | \\
\mathrm{HCOAc} & & \mathrm{HCOAc} & & \mathrm{HCOAc} & & \mathrm{HCOAc} \\
| & & | & & | & & | \\
\mathrm{AcOCH} & \xrightarrow{\mathrm{CH_2N_2}} & \mathrm{AcOCH} & \xrightarrow{\mathrm{HCl}} & \mathrm{AcOCH} & \xrightarrow{\mathrm{AcOH}} & \mathrm{AcOCH} \\
| & & | & & | & & | \\
\mathrm{AcOCH} & & \mathrm{AcOCH} & & \mathrm{AcOCH} & & \mathrm{AcOCH} \\
| & & | & & | & & | \\
\mathrm{HCOAc} & & \mathrm{HCOAc} & & \mathrm{HCOAc} & & \mathrm{HCOAc} \\
| & & | & & | & & | \\
\mathrm{COCl} & & \mathrm{CO} & & \mathrm{CO} & & \mathrm{CO} \\
& & | & & | & & | \\
& & \mathrm{CHN_2} & & \mathrm{CH_2Cl} & & \mathrm{CH_2OAc} \\
\end{array}
$$

(5.55)

XXXIII   XXXIV

ketones of sugars to the corresponding hydrazones with ammonium sulphide is also notable; this has been investigated by Wolfrom (*2194, 2195*) and others (*746*). The method has been used, for example, to convert the tetra-acetate of 1-deoxy-1-diazo-*keto*-D-fructose (XXXV) into the 1-hydrazone of 3,4,5,6-tetra-

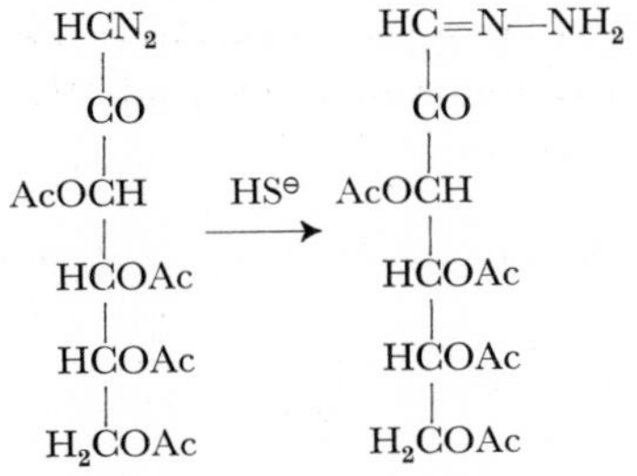

$$
\begin{array}{ccc}
\mathrm{HCN_2} & & \mathrm{HC{=}N{-}NH_2} \\
| & & | \\
\mathrm{CO} & & \mathrm{CO} \\
| & & | \\
\mathrm{AcOCH} & \xrightarrow{\mathrm{HS^{\ominus}}} & \mathrm{AcOCH} \\
| & & | \\
\mathrm{HCOAc} & & \mathrm{HCOAc} \\
| & & | \\
\mathrm{HCOAc} & & \mathrm{HCOAc} \\
| & & | \\
\mathrm{H_2COAc} & & \mathrm{H_2COAc} \\
\end{array}
$$

(5.56)

XXXV   XXXVI

O-acetyl-D-*arabino*-hexosone (XXXVI). The $\mathrm{CHN_2}$-group of such diazoketones can be reduced to $\mathrm{CH_3}$ by means of aluminium amalgam (*2194*) or hydriodic acid (*2192*). The interaction of aldehyde groups in sugars and diazomethane has also been studied by Wolfrom (*2193*).

Little work has been done on the action of bases on α-diazoketones, but recently Yates and Shapiro (*2204*) reported the products obtained with sodium hydroxide. α-Diazoacetophenone yields benzoic acid, acetophenone, 3-benzoyl-4-phenylpyrazole and its 5-hydroxy derivative, hydrocyanic acid, hydroxyl-amine, and ammonia.

Few other syntheses of α-diazoketones are used today. Lately, Newman (*1524*) has shown that the α-diazoketone (XXXVIII) can be made from the hydra-zone (XXXVII) by oxidation with mercuric trifluoroacetate in the presence of triethylamine in acetonitrile.

$$\text{(CH}_3\text{)}_3\text{C}-\overset{\overset{\displaystyle NNH_2}{\|}}{\text{C}}-\text{C}-\text{C(CH}_3\text{)}_3 \quad\xrightarrow{\text{(CF}_3\text{COO)}_2\text{Hg}}\quad \text{(CH}_3\text{)}_3\text{C}-\overset{\overset{\displaystyle N_2}{\|}}{\text{C}}-\text{C}-\text{C(CH}_3\text{)}_3 \qquad (5.57)$$

           XXXVII   XXXVIII

Kirmse and Horner (*1220, 2332*) have studied the synthesis and reactions of diazothioketones. In contrast to the α-diazoketones the thio compounds possess the cyclic structure of 1,2,3-thiadiazoles. They are more stable to thermolysis than the diazoketones. Irradiation yields derivatives of 2-methylene-1,3-dithiole (1,4-dithiafulvene), i.e. the dithio analogues of the product which Yates and Robb (*2201*) obtained by thermolysis of 1,2- and 2,1-diazonaphthol (see formula XXXXVI, § 7.8). Diazothioketones have little tendency to undergo Wolff rearrangement.

Bisdiazoketones were described for the first time only ten years ago (*1327*) and since then their behaviour towards acidic hydrogen, carbonyl compounds, and acetylene has been investigated (*1027, 1342, 1690, 1772*).

Recently Miller and White (*2343*) observed an isosbestic point in the ultraviolet spectra of 1,8-bisdiazo-2,7-octanedione in acetonitrile–water mixtures. They explained this phenomenon by assuming phototropic equilibria involving the hydrogen atoms from the 1- or 3-position. However, Fahr (*2320*) found similar isosbestic points in the spectra of compounds such as (**XXXIX**) which are not able to undergo tautomerism. Hence addition of water to the carbonyl group is probably the cause.

$$\text{ROOC}-\underset{\underset{\displaystyle N_2}{\|}}{\text{C}}-\text{CO}-\text{CO}-\underset{\underset{\displaystyle N_2}{\|}}{\text{C}}-\text{COOR}$$

                         XXXIX

5.7 The Deamination of Aliphatic Amines

As already mentioned in §§ 1.1 and 1.6, the interaction of nitrous acid with aliphatic primary amines differs characteristically from that with arylamines.

The parent compound, methylamine, is typical in that it combines with nitrous acid to give a moderately stable salt, methylamine nitrite $CH_3\overset{\oplus}{N}H_3\overset{\ominus}{N}O_2$, as reported by Euler (*691*) and confirmed later (*1515, 1681, 2010*). Whitmore and Thorpe (*2147*) indeed stated that they were unable to obtain methanol or any other product from methylamine, but this was refuted by Austin, Hughes, and Ingold (*96*). Austin (*93*) demonstrated clearly that when conditions are chosen correctly on the basis of Taylor's work (*2010*), that is, when mineral acid is added slowly to a solution of methylamine hydrochloride and sodium nitrite, ready reaction occurs. The buffering action of the nitrite ions suffices to convert some of the methylammonium ions into the reactive free amine and the slow addition of acid serves to minimize the losses of nitrous acid as nitric oxide. Under such conditions, Austin was able to isolate

> 6 to 25% methyl alcohol
> 45 to 35% methyl nitrite
> 13% methyl chloride
> 6% nitromethane
> 10 to 12% methylnitrolic acid
> 103% evolved gas (nitrogen plus carbon dioxide),

accounting for about 80 to 90% of the amine reacted. It can be seen that much of the methyl alcohol formed is esterified by nitrous acid and is swept out of the reaction medium as the very volatile methyl nitrite (b. pt. $-18.5°$). The process is sensitive to anion intervention and methyl chloride, methyl bromide, and nitromethane result in the presence of chloride, bromide, and nitrite ions, respectively. Part of the nitromethane formed is converted into methylnitrolic acid according to equation (5.58).

$$CH_3NO_2 + HNO_2 \longrightarrow O_2N—CH=N—OH + H_2O \qquad (5.58)$$

Austin's study is the most extensive one of a reaction the first example of which is due to Piria (*1633*). Piria observed that both asparagine and aspartic acid are converted into malic acid when treated with hydrochloric acid and nitric acid containing dissolved oxides of nitrogen. Strecker (*1967*) examined the action of nitrous acid on hippuric acid, glycine, and leucine, and found that nitrogen was evolved in all cases, 'nitrogen-free' products being obtained. Eventually this work led to the Van Slyke gasometric determination of α-amino-acids (*2072*). However, many α-aminoacids liberate more gas than expected and Austin (*94*) demonstrated that with glycine the extra volume is due to nitrous oxide and carbon dioxide as well as to nitrogen. Austin was able to show that intervention by nitrite ions, as in the case of methylamine, here gives α-nitroacetic acid, which either decomposes into nitromethane and carbon dioxide or reacts with nitrous acid to form methylnitrolic acid and carbon dioxide. At pH 4 to 5 methylnitrolic acid is converted into a polymer of fulminic acid, which decomposes into cyanic acid or into formic acid and hydroxylamine. The latter with nitrous acid yields nitrous oxide. In extending this work, Austin and Howard (*95, 1090*) similarly obtained nitrous oxide and carbon dioxide from alanine, but glutamine, from which 98% nitrogen is evolved under Van Slyke conditions instead of the expected 50%, gives nitrogen only. The explanation turned out to lie in the intramolecular cyclization of the carbonium ion first formed, the resulting cyclic carbonium ion reacting with water to yield a hydroxyamino compound which is able to react with nitrous acid under mild conditions (5.59).

The action of nitrous acid on the homologues of methylamine was first investigated by Linnemann (*1345–1347*) and Siersch (*1891*) almost a century ago. Here too the process is nearly always complicated by side reactions or rearran-

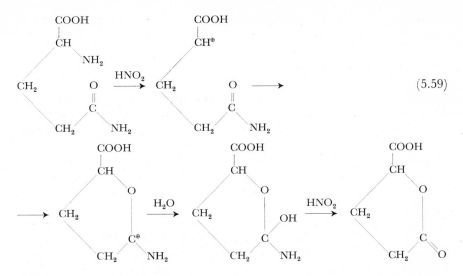

$$(5.59)$$

gements. Since it can be taken as certain that in all these reactions aliphatic diazonium ions are formed in the first place, the consideration of the preparative aspects of deamination properly belongs to this chapter, that is, to the other reactions of aliphatic diazo compounds. However, the mechanism of the decomposition of aliphatic diazonium ions will be discussed in detail in §§ 6.5 and 6.6, but it may be anticipated that the rate-determining formation of the diazonium ion will normally be followed by S_N1 reactions. The carbonium ion resulting from the dissociation (5.60b) interacts either with bases (5.60c–d) or loses a proton to yield an olefin (5.60f). These secondary reactions may be accompanied by rearrangements. Recently, Streitwieser (*1971, 1974*) has raised the

$$HR—CH_2—NH_2$$

$$\downarrow +HNO_2 \qquad\qquad (5.60\,a)\,^2$$

$$(HR—CH_2—\overset{\oplus}{N}\equiv N)$$

$$\downarrow \qquad\qquad\qquad (5.60\,b)$$

$$(HR—CH_2^{\oplus}) + N_2$$

$+H_2O$	$-H^{\oplus}$	$+X^{\ominus}$	$-H^{\oplus}$	$+R'OH$

HR—CH$_2$OH	HR—CH$_2$X	HR—CH$_2$—OR'	R=CH$_2$ + H$^{\oplus}$
+ HOR—CH$_3$	+ XR—CH$_3$	+ R'O—R—CH$_3$	
(5.60 c)	(5.60 d)	(5.60 e)	(5.60 f)

---

^{2} Metastable intermediates are placed in parentheses.

question of whether the rearrangements are able to occur already at the diazo-nium stage (cf. § 6.6). The formation of esters (5.60d, $X^\ominus$ = anion of a Brönsted acid) becomes dominant particularly when the deamination is carried out in the presence of large amounts of acid (*701, 1912*) or with nitrosyl chloride (NOCl, $X^\ominus = Cl^\ominus$) (*196, 318, 1913*).

For deamination a region of higher pH is employed than for the diazotiza-tion of aromatic amines, the solution usually containing either acetic acid or a little mineral acid. Too high a hydrogen ion concentration is to be avoided, because, as aliphatic amines are stronger bases than the arylamines, the amine–ammonium equilibrium is displaced in favour of the conjugate acid which cannot be nitrosated (cf. § 2.5). On this difference is based the diazotization of aromatic amines bearing in addition an aliphatic amino group which is to be left unaffected.

The composition of the products of deamination reactions is very dependent on the constitution of amine. In Houben-Weyl's treatise, H. Söll (*1919*) has reviewed comprehensively the deaminations studied up to 1957, and, therefore, here only the most important types will be considered. To date, only very little systematic work has been done on the dependence of the composition of the products on the conditions of the reaction, such as pH, medium, acid, and nitrosating agent [see for example (*1098*)].

Apart from the primary alcohols, the deamination of n-alkylamines results in secondary alcohols and olefins, n-propylamine yielding, for instance, only about 7% n-propanol, but 32 to 40% isopropanol and 28% propylene (*1891, 2147*). In the case of n-butylamine, the proportion of non-primary alcohols formed is greater: according to Whitmore (*2146*) 25% n-butanol, 13% 2-butanol, and 36% 1-butylene are obtained. With the higher normal alkylamines Adamson and Kenner (*5*) always found about 50% alcohols and 25 to 30% of the α-unsa-turated hydrocarbons. When the carbon chain of alkylamines branches at the α-atom, the rearrangement into isomeric alcohols becomes quite insignificant; particularly striking is the reaction of isopropylamine, which V. Meyer (*1437*) showed to give, apart from propylene, only isopropanol, but no propanol. It is possible, however, that in 1876, the methods of analysis not being so highly developed, small quantities of by-products would remain undetected. At any rate, the essential result has been confirmed by the recent work of Cannell and Taft (*411*) on isobutylamine (**XXXX**), which furnishes as the main product the alcohol derived from the most stable carbonium ion. As stability increases from primary to secondary and finally to tertiary carbonium ions (*1153b, 1969*), iso-butylamine yields preponderantly t-butanol (**XXXXI**), though small amounts of isomeric butanols and butenes are also formed. This explanation makes it

$$\begin{array}{ccc}
& CH_3 & \\
& | & \\
H_3C\!-\!\overset{\displaystyle}{\underset{\displaystyle |}{C}}\!-\!CH_2\!-\!NH_2 & & \\
& H & \\
\end{array} \qquad\qquad
\begin{array}{ccc}
& CH_3 & \\
& | & \\
H_3C\!-\!\overset{\displaystyle}{\underset{\displaystyle |}{C}}\!-\!CH_3 & \\
& OH & \\
\end{array}$$

XXXX   XXXXI

readily comprehensible why, as mentioned above, the rearranged alcohol was not obtained from isopropylamine, yet produced in large amount from n-propyl-amine.

Rearrangements in this sense are rarely observed in the deamination of *cyclo-alkylamines*, which normally result in the corresponding secondary alcohols and in cyclo-olefins. Exceptional behaviour is exhibited by the amino derivatives of small ring systems and of those cycloalkylamines which bear an aryl residue in α-position to the amino group. Ring contraction occurs in these cases either partially or wholly. Thus, 2-phenylcyclohexylamine (XXXXII) yields α-cyclo-pentylbenzyl alcohol (XXXXIII) (*1531, 1532*) and cyclobutylamine gives equal parts of cyclopropanemethanol (XXXXIV) and cyclobutanol (XXXXV) as well as a little 1-buten-4-ol (XXXXVI) (*1710, 1711*). In a way, the forma-tion of 1-propen-3-ol (XXXXVII) from cyclopropylamine (*1350*) can be

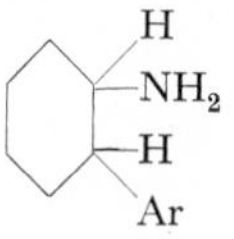

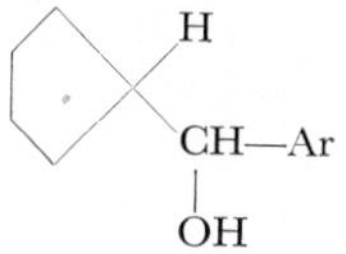

$$CH_2=CH-CH_2-CH_2OH$$
XXXXVI

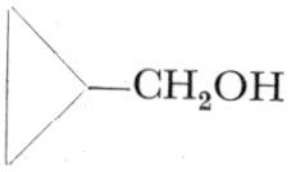

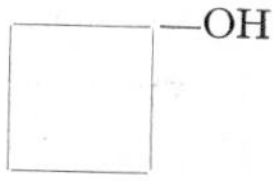

$$H_2C=CH-CH_2OH$$
XXXXVII

regarded as a ring contraction. As shown in §§ 6.5 and 6.6, these ring contrac-tions are dependent on the stability and structure of the intermediate carbo-nium ions. The rule that the alcohol corresponding to the tertiary carbonium ion is favoured is encountered also among the cycloalkylamines; for example, the deamination of *cis*-2-methylcyclohexylamine (XXXXVIIIa) leads to a mix-ture of which *trans*-2-methylcyclohexanol (XXXXIXa) is the main consti-tuent, but 1-methylcyclohexanol can also be isolated (*51, 428*).

The problems of conformation and configuration which arise in the deami-nation of cyclohexylamine derivatives are of particular interest. With 2-alkyl-cyclohexylamines it appears that in general the stereo-isomer in which the amino group is equatorial yields the alcohol with the same configuration, whilst an axial amino group leads to the alcohol of inverted configuration together with cyclo-olefin (*291, 528, 1448, 1532*). For example, *trans*-2-methylcyclohexyl-amine, which exists almost exclusively in the conformation having both the methyl group and the amino group equatorial (XXXXIXb), yields *trans*-2-methylcyclohexanol (XXXXIXa) (*51*). The isomeric *cis*-amine probably con-stitutes a mixture of comparable amounts of axial-amino, equatorial-methyl and equatorial-amino, axial-methyl conformations (XXXXVIIIa and XXXXVIIIb, respectively); the deamination gives mostly *trans*-2-methyl-cyclohexanol with some 1-methylcyclohexanol and olefin, but only a trace of *cis*-2-methyxalcyclohenol (*428*). Analogous results have been obtained by Streitwieser (*1972*) with cyclohexylamine-2-*d*. The deamination (5.61 and

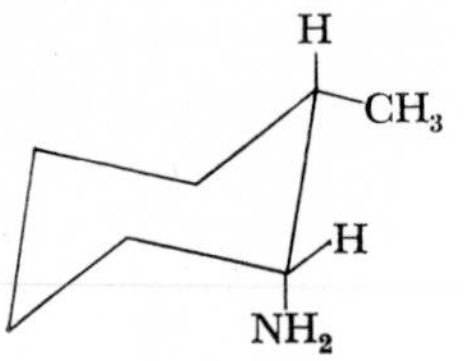

Azo and Diazo Compounds

XXXXVIIIa

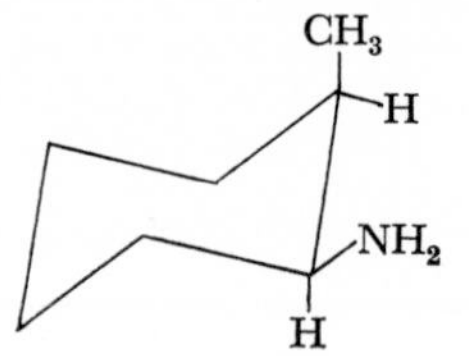

XXXXVIIIb

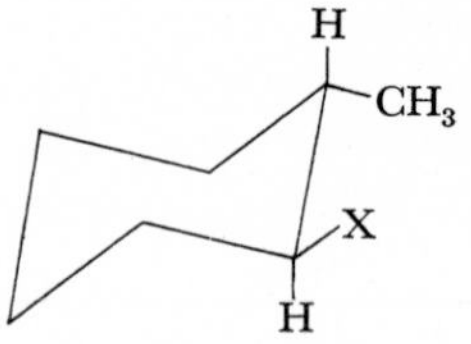

XXXXIXa: X=OH
XXXXIXb: X=NH$_2$

5.62) of isomenthylamine (L) and neoisomenthylamine (LI), investigated by J. Read and co-workers (*1685, 1686*), will serve as a further illustration.

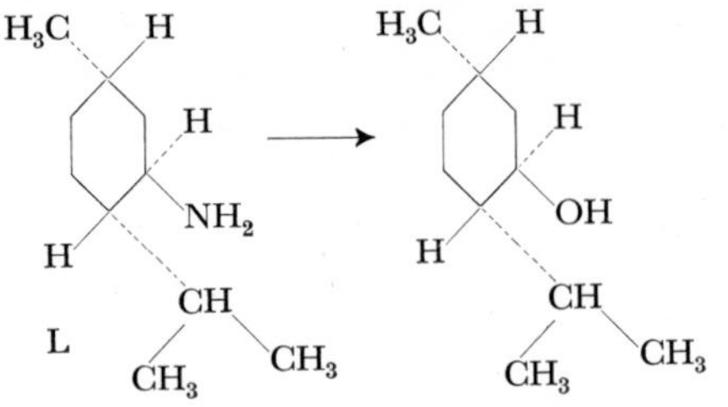

$$(5.61)$$

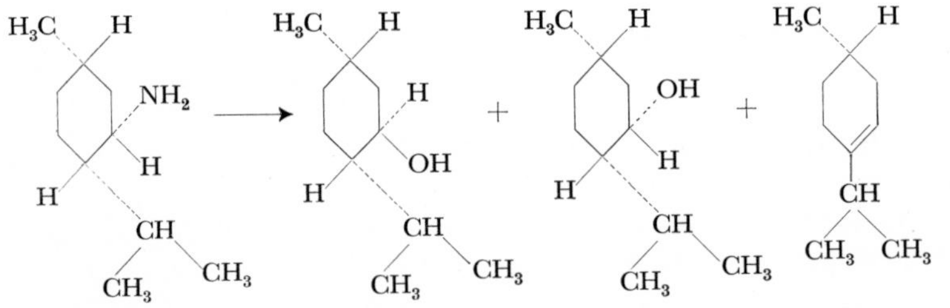

$$(5.62)$$

These results are in agreement with the general principles developed for the reactivity of conformational isomers [see, for example (*198–200, 527*)]. The behaviour of decahydronaphthylamines is similar (*525, 528, 529*). Prelog (*1659*) has studied the deamination of cycloalkylamines with larger rings, in particular, that of cyclodecylamine, and, because of the occurrence of transannular reactions (*1656*), these have thrown light on the mechanism.

Considerable preparative importance attaches to the deamination of *cyclo-alkanemethylamines*, described as the Demjanow ring expansion (*542–546*). The reaction yields predominantly the cycloalkanol with a ring containing an additional carbon atom. Again, this expansion is due to the rearrangement of the first formed primary into the more stable secondary carbonium ion. The by-products here also are the unrearranged alcohol, olefins, and other compounds. Thus, cyclohexanemethylamine (LII) yields cycloheptanol (LIII) and cyclohexanemethanol (LIV) in the ratio 2:1, together with olefins and some 1-methylcyclohexanol (LV) (*1912*). Because of the relative stabilities of carbonium ions, one would have expected that the formation of the tertiary alcohol

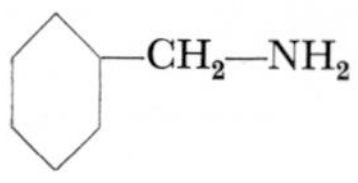

LII 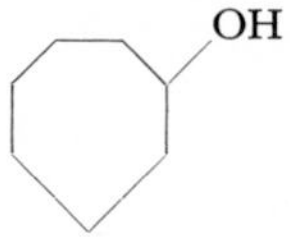   LIII 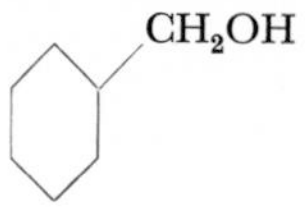   LIV 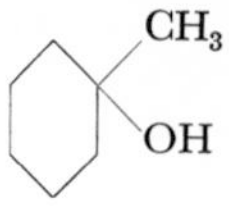   LV

(LV) would have been favoured. Apparently yet other factors must be responsible for the proportions of the products obtained. If the α-carbon bears an alkyl or aryl residue as well as the amino group, Demjanow ring expansion occurs only to a minor extent or not at all. This also applies to cycloalkane-ethylamines and to benzylamine. Analogously the deamination of 2,2,3,3-tetrafluorocyclobutylmethylamine gives 2,2,3,3-tetrafluorocyclobutylmethanol and not the corresponding cyclopentanol derivative (*130*).

Demjanow ring expansion has played a noteworthy role in the synthesis of azulenes; thus, decahydro-5-cyclopentacycloheptenol (LVII) is obtained in good yield from hexahydro-5-indanmethylamine (LVI).

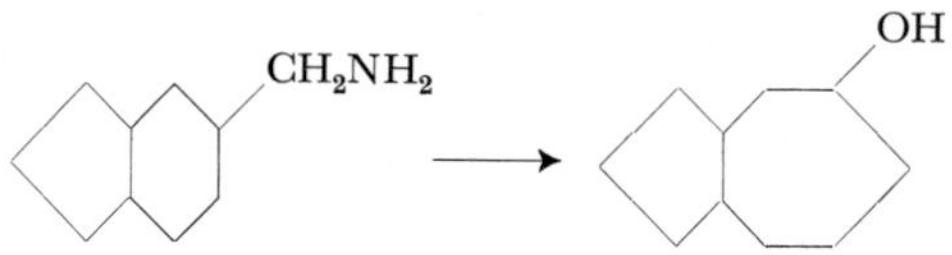

$$(5.63)$$

LVI   LVII

The reactions of *1,2-aminoalcohols and 1,2-diamines* with nitrous acid are many-sided. Most probably the reason for the resemblance between the deamination of each of these two groups of compounds is the formation of 1,2-aminoalcohols from the 1,2-diamines in the first stage. The action of nitrite on 1,2-amino-alcohols (LVIII) is usually accompanied by rearrangement leading to ketones or aldehydes, but occasionally it also yields glycols or epoxides.

Aldehydes and ketones are obtained when the carbonium ion (LIX) formed in the deamination is able to rearrange into a more stable one (LX) by migration of an alkyl, aryl, or hydrogen substituent. Splitting off a proton then converts (LX) into the aldehyde or ketone (LXI). If, however, the original carbonium ion (LIX) is relatively stable, it may add a base before rearranging. This may occur either intramolecularly with formation of the epoxide (LXII) or solvolytically to yield the glycol (LXIII). Other nucleophilic particles may take the place of water in a given case, thus leading, for instance, to glycol monoesters. The nature of the substituents R, R′, R″, and R‴ determines the course of the reaction. Söll (*1919*) has listed systematically the examples known to date and his detailed discussion should be consulted. Here only the most important types are summarized in Table 5.1.

The deamination of *1,3- and 1,4-aminoalcohols* gives diols or compounds that can be regarded as their derivatives.

The decomposition of alkyldiazo esters, which also proceeds via carbonium ions and yields products similar to those obtained in the deamination of amines, will be considered in § 6.5.

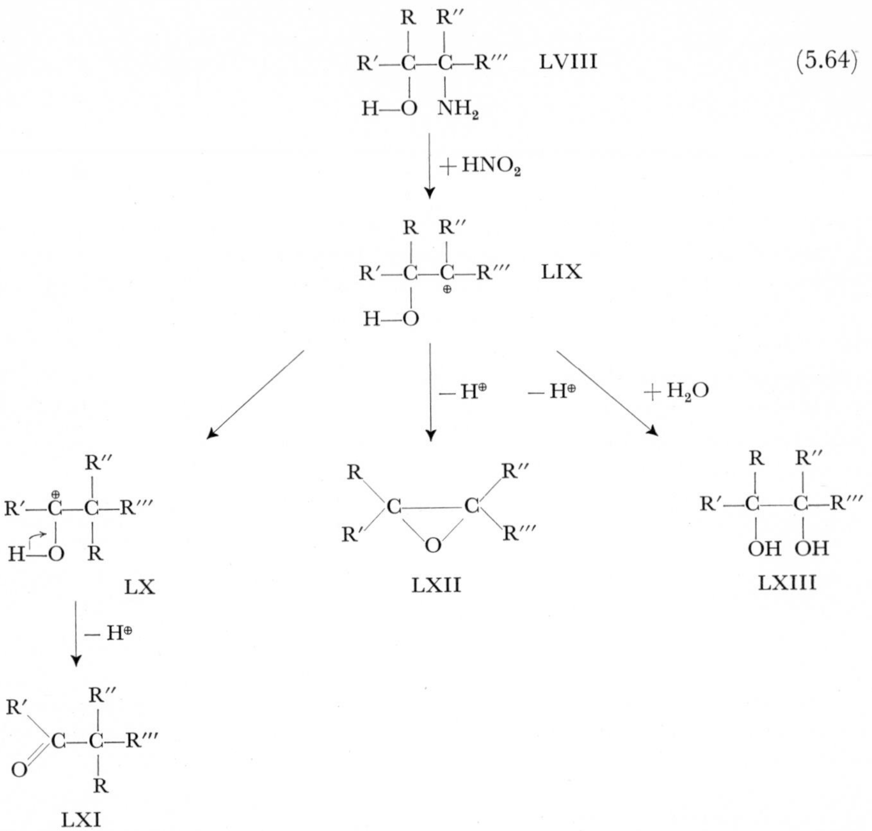

$$\begin{array}{c} R \quad R'' \\ | \quad | \\ R'-\overset{|}{C}-\overset{|}{C}-R''' \quad \text{LVIII} \\ | \quad | \\ H-O \quad NH_2 \end{array} \qquad (5.64)$$

$$\Big\downarrow +HNO_2$$

$$\begin{array}{c} R \quad R'' \\ | \quad | \\ R'-\overset{|}{C}-\overset{|}{\underset{\oplus}{C}}-R''' \quad \text{LIX} \\ | \\ H-O \end{array}$$

$$-H^\oplus \qquad -H^\oplus \qquad +H_2O$$

$$\begin{array}{c} R'' \\ | \\ R'-\overset{\oplus}{C}-\overset{|}{C}-R''' \\ | \quad | \\ H-O \quad R \\ \text{LX} \end{array} \qquad \begin{array}{c} R \qquad\qquad R'' \\ \diagdown\quad\quad\diagup \\ C-\!\!-\!\!-C \\ \diagup\quad\diagdown\quad\diagdown \\ R' \quad O \quad R''' \\ \text{LXII} \end{array} \qquad \begin{array}{c} R \quad R'' \\ | \quad | \\ R'-\overset{|}{C}-\overset{|}{C}-R''' \\ | \quad | \\ OH \quad OH \\ \text{LXIII} \end{array}$$

$$\Big\downarrow -H^\oplus$$

$$\begin{array}{c} R' \quad\quad R'' \\ \diagdown\quad\quad | \\ C-\overset{|}{C}-R''' \\ \diagup\quad\quad | \\ O \quad\quad R \\ \text{LXI} \end{array}$$

Rearrangements of alkyl and aryl groups in substituted ethylamines during deamination reactions are well known. They are important in the discussion of the mechanism of deamination and therefore will be dealt with in that context (§ 6.6).

Table 5.1

The Deamination of 1, 2-Aminoalcohols

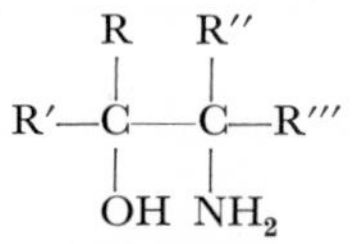

$$R'—\underset{\underset{OH}{|}}{\overset{\overset{R}{|}}{C}}—\underset{\underset{NH_2}{|}}{\overset{\overset{R''}{|}}{C}}—R'''$$

Type	R	R'	R''	R'''	Products	Remarks	Selected references
1	H	H	H	alkyl	aldehyde	Followed by reaction with aminoalcohol	1503
2	aryl	H	H	alkyl	ketone	Migration of R'	2038
3	aryl	H	H	aryl	glycol epoxide		700, 1687 1684
4	aryl	alkyl	H	H	ketone	Migration of R	2037
5	aryl	aryl'	H	H	ketone	Migration of R or R' with steric and constitutional effects	223, 482 499, 500 1669
6	aryl	alkyl	H	alkyl	ketone	Migration of R	1445
7	aryl	aryl'	H	alkyl	ketone	As type 5	499, 500 2039
8	alkyl	alkyl	H	aryl	glycol		700
9	aryl	aryl	alkyl	aryl	ketone		1386
10	cycloalkyl		H	H	ketone	Ring expansion (Tiffeneau rearrangement) glycol	1018 1653
11	cycloalkyl		H	alkyl	ketone	Ring expansion	677
12	cycloalkyl		H	aryl	glycol + ketone		678
13	alkyl	cycloalkyl		H	ketone glycol epoxide	Ring contraction	488, 502 1477 1477 1769
14	H	cyclopentyl		H	glycol epoxide		809, 1476 809
15	H	cyclohexyl		H	aldehyde ketone	Ring contraction	1475 1653

6. Mechanisms of the Reactions of Aliphatic Diazo Compounds

6.1 Diazoalkanes as Nucleophilic Reagents

In discussing the acid–base equilibria of aliphatic diazo compounds [§ 3.4, scheme (3.4)], it was pointed out that diazoalkanes are amphoteric. Some years ago, R. Huisgen (*1114*) systematically summarized their reactions, nearly all of which he was able to classify as belonging to one of three large groups. In the first group, diazoalkanes appear as the nucleophilic, in the second, as the electrophilic component of heterolytic processes. The third group comprises those reactions in which a nitrogen molecule is split off primarily. So far little is known of the interaction of diazoalkanes with radicals.

In essence, Huisgen's classification will be followed in this chapter. In the present and the following sections will be discussed the nucleophilic and electrophilic reactions of diazoalkanes, respectively, and the consideration of the third group is left to § 6.3. The polymerization of diazoalkanes is dealt with separately in § 6.4.

From the limiting structures of diazomethane it becomes apparent immediately that the mesomeric forms (Ia) and (Ib) give rise to the basic character of the molecule. Reaction with an acid $\overset{\cdot}{A}$ converts (Ia) into $A \cdot CH_2 \cdot \overset{\oplus}{N}_2$; thus a

$$H_2\overset{\ominus}{C}-\overset{\oplus}{N}\equiv N \longleftrightarrow H_2C=\overset{\oplus}{N}=\overset{\ominus}{\underline{N}}| \longleftrightarrow H_2\overset{\ominus}{\underline{C}}-\overset{\oplus}{N}=\underline{N} \longleftrightarrow H_2C=\overset{}{N}-\overset{}{\underline{N}} \longleftrightarrow H_2\overset{\oplus}{C}-\overset{}{N}=\overset{\ominus}{\underline{N}}|$$

| Ia | Ib | Ic | Id | Ie |

proton yields the alkyldiazonium ion. In (Ib), the β-nitrogen is the basic centre and $\overset{\cdot}{A}$ therefore leads to the ion $H_2C : \overset{\ominus}{N} : N \cdot A$.

In the limiting structure (Ic), the β-nitrogen carries only a sextet of electrons and so (Ic) symbolizes the electrophilic character of diazoalkanes. By reaction with a nucleophilic reagent $B^{\ominus}$, $H_2C : N \cdot \overset{\ominus}{N} \cdot B$ is formed. In addition, diazoalkanes with at least one hydrogen atom at the α-carbon can behave as Brönsted acids: loss of a proton yields the anion $[H\overset{\ominus}{C} : \overset{\oplus}{N} : \overset{\ominus}{N} \longleftrightarrow HC \cdot N : \overset{\ominus}{N}]$, from which isodiazoalkanes, such as $H\overset{\ominus}{C} : \overset{\oplus}{N} : NH$, may result. These equilibria between tautomers were already dealt with in § 3.4.

The mesomeric forms (Id) and (Ie) are only of secondary importance for an understanding of the ways in which diazoalkanes react. The part played by the various limiting structures has been discussed by many authors on the basis of a variety of experimental results. Infra-red spectra, particularly the position of the NN-vibration band, proved very helpful, the work in this field having been reviewed by Fahr (*694*).

In the reactions considered in §§ 5.2, 5.3, and 5.4 from the preparative standpoint, the diazoalkane invariably appears as the nucleophilic component. On interaction with compounds bearing an acid hydrogen atom (carboxylic acids, enols, ammonium derivatives, certain alcohols), it is most probable that primarily a proton is transferred to the diazoalkane. With evolution of nitrogen, the highly reactive alkyldiazonium ion formed then yields a carbonium ion, which, as the final step, attacks a base, namely the anion of the acid HB used in the first step (6.1 a) or another particle HB′ available in the system (6.1 b).

$$\begin{array}{c} R \\ \diagdown \\ \diagup C=N_2 \\ R' \end{array} \xrightarrow{+H^{\oplus}} \begin{array}{c} R \\ | \\ R'-C-N_2^{\oplus} \\ | \\ H \end{array} \longrightarrow \begin{array}{c} R \\ | \\ R'-C^{\oplus}+N_2 \\ | \\ H \end{array} \underset{+HB'}{\overset{+B^{\ominus}}{\diagup\diagdown}} \begin{array}{l} RR'CH-B \qquad (6.1\,a) \\ \\ \\ RR'CH-B' + H^{\oplus} \qquad (6.1\,b) \end{array}$$

A series of observations supports the concept of the intermediate formation of a diazonium ion. It has been known for a long time (*1933*), that the reactivity of diazoalkanes is dependent in a characteristic manner on the nature of the substituents R and R′. Starting from diazomethane (R = R′ = H), the rate of the reaction decreases as one or two of the hydrogen atoms are replaced by aryl groups, the basic character of the α-carbon of the mesomeric form (I a) being progressively reduced. The inductive and mesomeric effects of carbonyl and alkoxycarbonyl groups similarly lower the basicity and thus the nucleophilic reactivity of diazoalkanes, the differences in behaviour, usually large, between diazomethane and diazoacetic ester being the best known example for this.

The classic investigations of the character of the acid catalysis of the reaction of diazoacetic ester with phenol in a non-polar medium (benzene) by Brönsted and Bell (*334*) provide convincing evidence. Formation of phenoxyacetic ester (6.2) occurs only on addition of a relatively strong acid, such as chloroacetic acid, and the rate of reaction is proportional to the concentration of the latter. Phenol itself is too weak an acid to be able to catalyse the reaction. Obviously, acid catalysis is taking place, but whether it is in Brönsted's sense specific (i.e. by protons) or general (equation 6.2a or 6.2b, respectively) could be decided only recently, when the difficulties caused by the use of an aprotic medium were surmounted. The observation that the rates of reactions catalysed by carboxylic

$$ROOC-\overset{\ominus}{C}H-\overset{\oplus}{N_2} + H^{\oplus} \longrightarrow ROOC-\overset{\oplus}{C}H_2 + N_2 \qquad (6.2\,a)$$

or

$$ROOC-\overset{\ominus}{C}H-\overset{\oplus}{N_2} + ClCH_2COOH \longrightarrow ROOC-\overset{\oplus}{C}H_2 + N_2 + ClCH_2COO^{\ominus} \qquad (6.2\,b)$$

$$ROOC-\overset{\oplus}{C}H_2 + R'-OH \longrightarrow R'-\underset{\underset{H}{|}}{\overset{\oplus}{O}}-CH_2-COOR \qquad (6.2\,c)$$

$$\overset{\oplus}{\underset{H}{R'-O}}-CH_2-COOR + ClCH_2COO^{\ominus} \longrightarrow R'-O-CH_2-COOR + ClCH_2COOH \quad (6.2\,d)$$

acids are linearly related to the dissociation constants of the acids (determined in water), but that the catalytic effect of picric acid is out of line, was originally taken to support the occurrence of general acid catalysis. Such reasoning is no longer tenable. When the solvent is benzene, dimerization equilibria of carboxylic acids are superimposed upon the protolysis and their position for a series of carboxylic acids is probably subject to the same free energy relations as the acid–base equilibria, but in the case of the substituted phenol, picric acid, other factors, such as steric ones, play a part.

The reaction of diazoacetic ester with a carboxylic acid in benzene is of first order with respect to the diazo compound, but the carboxylic acid appears kinetically as the square of its concentration (334). This fact also can be reconciled with the mechanism (6.2a)–(6.2c)–(6.2d) or (6.2b)–(6.2c)–(6.2d), if the first step occurs more rapidly than the second (cf. § 6.5).

In contrast, the rate of the corresponding reactions of aliphatic diazo compounds free from carbonyl groups is *directly* proportional to the concentration of the carboxylic acid, as has been demonstrated by Norris and Strain (1540) for diazodi-p-tolylmethane as well as by Roberts (1712, 1713) and Taft (1997) for analogous compounds. That the mechanism is the same, but that the kinetic relations differ, becomes apparent from Roberts's experiments (1714) with deuterated acids, the isotope effect found implying a rate-determining proton transfer.

On the basis of these investigations it can be assumed that in aprotic solvents general acid catalysis is indeed taking place.

On the contrary, the reactions of the diazoalkanes in aqueous medium exhibit all the signs of specific proton catalysis. It is well known that before the present day methods for the convenient potentiometric determination of pH were generally available, the kinetics of the evolution of nitrogen from solutions of diazoacetic ester served as an important way of measuring the hydrogen ion concentration (313, 314, 748).

In the general equation (6.1) for this reaction, it is indicated that the alkyldiazonium ion $RR'CH \cdot N_2^{\oplus}$ can interact not only with the anion of the acid HB used, but also with that of other acids HB'. As source of HB' the proton-containing solvents come particularly into consideration. In contrast to (6.1a), where the acid HB is consumed in the overall reaction, (6.1b) is a true catalysis, as the proton required for the first step is subsequently regenerated.

The mechanisms for the decomposition of the alkyldiazonium ion in reaction (6.1) will be discussed in § 6.5. Here will be considered briefly only the relation between (6.1a) and (6.1b), that is, between stoichiometric and catalytic interaction with acid. In aqueous medium and in presence of strong mineral acids (perchloric, sulphuric), diazoalkanes uniformly follow the catalytic scheme (6.1b), but already the nitrate ion is able to compete successfully as a base with the water. Whilst diazoacetic ester yields glycolic ester, $HOCH_2 \cdot$

COOR, with dilute sulphuric acid in a clean reaction according to (6.1 b), the same concentration of acid in the presence of a large amount of potassium nitrate leads to the formation of the corresponding nitrate, $O_2NOCH_2 \cdot COOR$ (*748*). As this reaction consumes acid, the rate decreases with time and, finally, the process stops completely. In an analogous manner, the decomposition of diazoacetic ester catalysed by perchloric acid can be brought to a halt by halides, their effectiveness increasing as expected with nucleophilic character in the order $Cl^{\ominus} < Br^{\ominus} < I^{\ominus}$ (*314*).

In the catalysis by very strong acids in a polar, but aprotic, medium even diazoalkane still present can compete successfully as a base, as is shown by the formation of tetraphenylethylene from diazodiphenylmethane. Roberts (*1716*) has demonstrated that the reaction in acetonitrile with toluenesulphonic acid proceeds according to equation (6.3). The interaction of diazoalkanes with sulphur dioxide, which has some importance for the preparation of stilbene derivatives (*1015, 1943*), possibly takes a similar course (cf. *1016, 1232*).

$$(C_6H_5)_2\overset{\ominus}{C}\text{—}\overset{\oplus}{N}_2 + H^{\oplus} \longrightarrow \longrightarrow (C_6H_5)_2\overset{\oplus}{C}H + N_2 \qquad (6.3\,a)$$

$$(C_6H_5)_2\overset{\oplus}{C}H + \overset{\oplus}{N}_2\text{—}\overset{\ominus}{C}(C_6H_5)_2 \longrightarrow (C_6H_5)_2CH\text{—}\overset{\oplus}{C}(C_6H_5)_2 + N_2 \qquad (6.3\,b)$$

$$(C_6H_5)_2C\text{=}C(C_6H_5)_2 + H^{\oplus} \qquad (6.3\,c)$$

From the point of view of mechanism, the reactions of diazoalkanes with carbonyl compounds correspond to those with Brönsted acids. The basic carbanion of the diazoalkane (limiting structure I a) adds on to the electrophilic carbon atom of the carbonyl group (6.4). The carbonium-alcoholate zwitterion (III), formed via the diazonium compound (II), stabilizes itself either by ring closure to the epoxy derivative (IV) or by migration of one of the two substituents (V, VI).

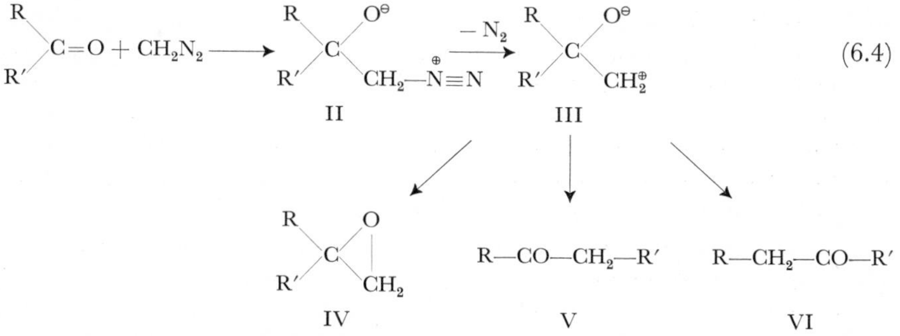

$$(6.4)$$

As mentioned in § 5.3, these reactions are especially important for the ring enlargement of cycloalkanones. Gutsche and his co-workers (*898, 899*) have investigated the factors which affect the ratio of products (IV):(V):(VI) by means of model compounds. Using infra-red analysis, they obtained the results summarized in Table 6.1 with *p*-substituted 2-arylcyclohexanones.

Table 6.1

Products of the Reaction of Diazomethane with p-substituted 2-Arylcyclohexanones according to Gutsche et al. (898, 899)

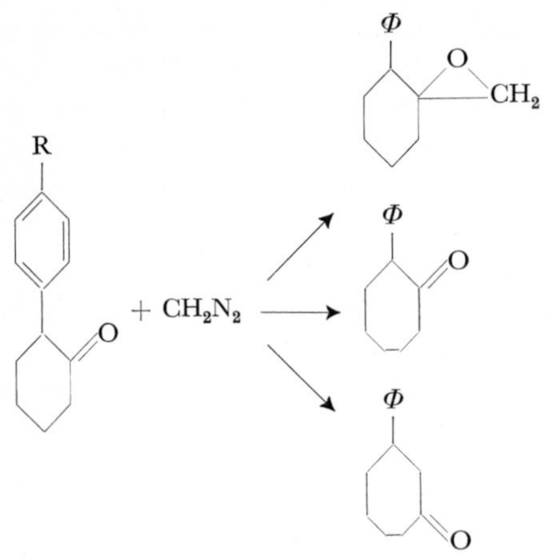

	R =	H	CH$_3$O	CH$_3$	Cl
	Φ epoxide CH$_2$	22 %	14 %	21 %	26 %
R—C$_6$H$_4$— 2-arylcyclohexanone + CH$_2$N$_2$ →	Φ (2-arylcycloheptanone)	59 %	57 %	55 %	45 %
	Φ (3-arylcycloheptanone)	14 %	21 %	20 %	20 %

In every case examined considerably more 2- than 3-arylcycloheptanone is obtained, which shows the importance of steric factors. Electronic effects, however, are secondary, as can be seen from the relatively small variations in the composition of the product brought about by changing the substituent in the aromatic nucleus.

The fundamental mechanism represented by equation (6.4) is valid also for the interaction of aldehydes with diazoalkanes (R′ = H), but if a more strongly basic group is substituted for R′, such as NH$_2$, OR″, or O$^\ominus$ (i.e. in the case of acid amides, esters, or carboxylates, respectively), the electrophilic character of the carbon atom of the carbonyl group is depressed so strongly as to prevent reaction with diazoalkanes. On the other hand, diazoalkanes do attack acid chlorides (R′ = Cl). However, the intermediate diazonium compound (VII) does not lose nitrogen as demanded by equation (6.4), but, under the influence of a base, hydrogen chloride is split off, leaving the diazoketone (6.5). As pointed out in § 5.6, formation of diazoketone occurs only when *excess* of diazo-

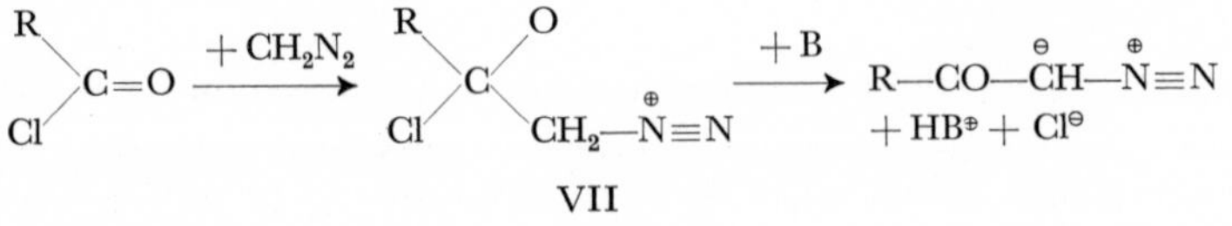

$$\begin{array}{c} R \\ \diagdown \\ \diagup \\ Cl \end{array} C{=}O \xrightarrow{+ CH_2N_2} \begin{array}{c} R \\ \diagdown \\ \diagup \\ Cl \end{array} C \begin{array}{c} O \\ \diagdown \\ CH_2{-}N{\equiv}N \\ \oplus \end{array} \xrightarrow{+B} R{-}CO{-}\overset{\ominus}{CH}{-}\overset{\oplus}{N}{\equiv}N \quad (6.5)$$
$$+ HB^{\oplus} + Cl^{\ominus}$$

VII

methane is employed. The additional diazomethane enters (6.5) as the base B
which serves to bind the liberated hydrogen chloride, proton transfer yielding
the methyldiazonium ion. This reacts with the chloride ion to give methyl
chloride and nitrogen. Newman and Beal (*1525*) showed that, instead of an
excess of diazomethane, triethylamine may be used to neutralize the hydrogen
chloride.

The analogous reaction is possible with diazoacetic ester, especially when the
acid chloride carries strongly negative substituents. The interaction with phosgene, already investigated by Staudinger and his co-workers (*1932*) in 1916,
provides an example. As the diazodicarbonyl compounds formed are stable to
acid, an excess of diazoacetic ester is unnecessary.

The diazonium-alcoholate zwitterions (II) and (VII) possess both an electrophilic and a nucleophilic centre (N_2 and $O^\ominus$, respectively) and, in principle, an
intramolecular reaction would be feasible. The result would be a 1, 2, 3-oxa-
diazolidine (VIII), but, in contrast to the thiadiazoles [cf. § 5.4 and equation
(6.7) below], these cyclic alkyldiazo ethers are not stable. Such intramolecular

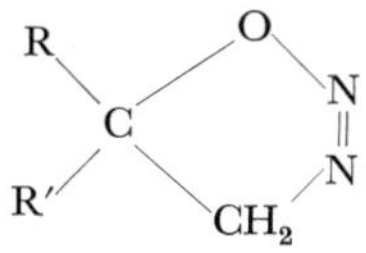

VIII

reactions of the addition products from diazoalkanes and electrophilic compounds are of significance in the case of unsaturated systems. The lone pair of
electrons on the carbon atom of the diazoalkane attacks that carbon atom of the
double bond which possesses electrophilic character either because of appropriate substituents or through conjugation with further unsaturation (for
examples see § 5.4). On the one hand, this primary process increases the electrophilic nature of the diazo group by converting it into a diazonium residue, but,
on the other hand, it produces an excess of electrons at the double bond. In
consequence, the second step does not consist of the splitting off of nitrogen, but
of intramolecular azo coupling (6.6). In this manner those examples cited in
§ 5.4 can be interpreted, which involved the formation of pyrazole and pyrazo-

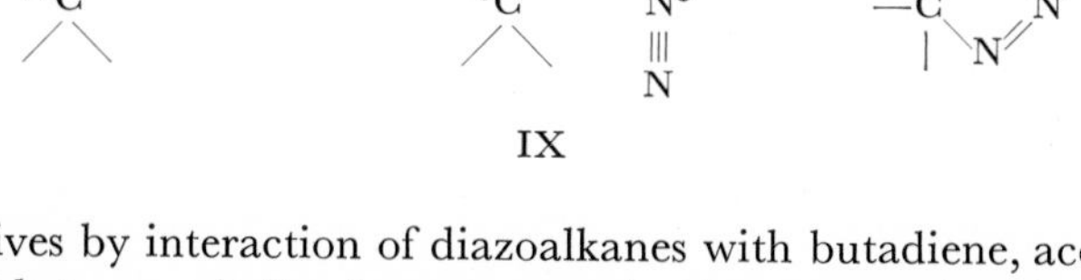

$$(6.6)$$

IX

line derivatives by interaction of diazoalkanes with butadiene, acetylene, α,β-
unsaturated ketones, nitriles, ketenes, etc. Analogous reactions have also been
discovered in the case of unsaturated nitro compounds (*1583–1585, 1587*) and
strained double-bond systems (*19, 20, 2223*). The observation (*26, 1601*) that

maleic and fumaric esters yield the *same* addition product is important. In the intermediate diazonium compound (IX), the olefinic double bond has become single and so free to rotate. However, very recently doubt has been thrown on mechanism (6.6) by Huisgen (*2440*), whose kinetic determinations do not indicate a two-step process, but a concerted 1,3-addition of the double bond system to the diazoalkane.

The reactions of α-diazo-β, β′-dicarbonyl compounds with hydrogen sulphide (*1945*) and amines (*2191*) exhibit a certain similarity in mechanism with these cyclizations to pyrazolines as the second step also consists of an intramolecular azo coupling (6.7 and 6.8).

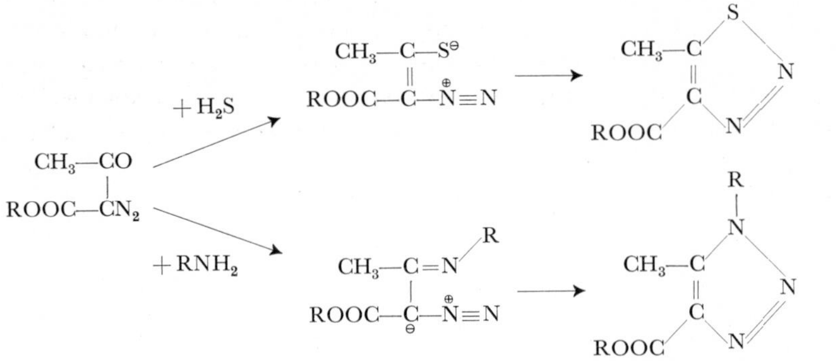

$$
\begin{array}{ccc}
& CH_3-C-S^{\ominus} \\
& \underset{ROOC-\overset{\oplus}{C}-N\equiv N}{\|} & \longrightarrow
\end{array}
\qquad (6.7)
$$

$$
CH_3-CO \\
ROOC-\overset{|}{C}N_2
$$

$$
+ H_2S
$$

$$
+ RNH_2
$$

$$
\begin{array}{ccc}
& CH_3-C=N^{R} \\
& \underset{ROOC-\underset{\ominus}{C}-N\equiv N}{\|} & \longrightarrow
\end{array}
\qquad (6.8)
$$

In a series of further reactions in which the diazoalkanes take part as the nucleophilic component, the electrophilic one is provided by Lewis acids, such as aromatic diazonium ions (*1120*) (cf. § 9.3), dinitrogen tetroxide, $O_2\overset{\delta\oplus}{N}\cdot\overset{\delta\ominus}{N}O_2$ (*2160*), mercuric chloride (*1882*), and other salts of heavy metals able to enlarge their electron shells [cf. Huisgen (*1114*)]. The acid-catalysed formation of polymethylene from diazomethane also belongs to this group of reactions (cf. § 6.4).

Nucleophilic reactions of diazoalkanes at the β-nitrogen, as expected on the basis of the limiting structure (Ib), are relatively less important. Addition of *p*-nitrodiazobenzene to an excess of diazomethane gives the tetrazole derivative (X) as a by-product. It is probably formed by electrophilic attack of the aryldiazonium ion on the nitrogen of the diazoalkane according to equation (6.9).

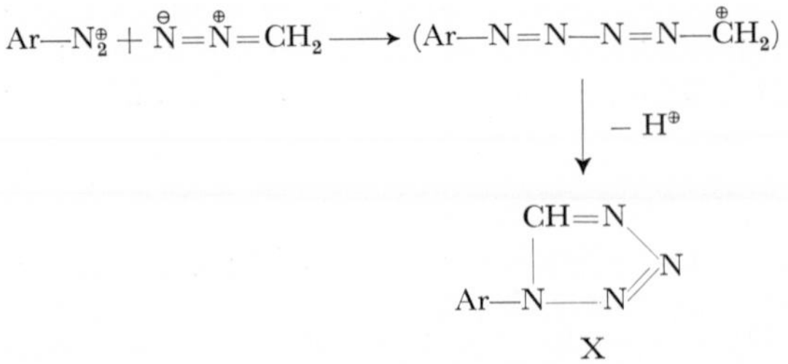

$$
Ar-N_2^{\oplus} + \overset{\ominus}{N}=\overset{\oplus}{N}=CH_2 \longrightarrow (Ar-N=N-N=N-\overset{\oplus}{C}H_2)
$$

$$
\Big\downarrow -H^{\oplus}
\qquad (6.9)
$$

$$
\begin{array}{c}
CH=N \\
| \qquad\ \ \diagdown N \\
Ar-N-N
\end{array}
$$

X

A further example is the formation of ketazine from azibenzil, mentioned in § 6.3 (equation 6.14).

6.2 Diazoalkanes as Electrophilic and Radical Reagents

Compared with all these nucleophilic reactions, those in which the diazoalkanes appear as electrophilic reagents because of the mesomeric form (Ic) are of minor significance. The addition of a base to a diazoalkane is an incomparably more difficult process than the analogous reaction with an aryldiazonium ion.

However, the reaction of diazoalkanes with Grignard reagents to be noted in § 9.2 does represent a case of electrophilic addition of a diazoalkane. The anions of organometallic compounds are so strongly nucleophilic as to be able to force reaction with the β-nitrogen of the diazoalkane. The recently discovered azo coupling of 2-diazo-5,5-dimethyl-1,3-cyclohexanedione (diazodimedon, XI) with coupling components such as resorcinol and phloroglucinol (*1879*) provides a further example of electrophilic attack by a diazoalkane. The electrophilic character of (XI) is caused by the two acidifying carbonyl groups in the β, β'-positions, possibly supported by effects due to ring strain. Diazophenols could be regarded as vinylogues of diazodimedon.

XIa XIb

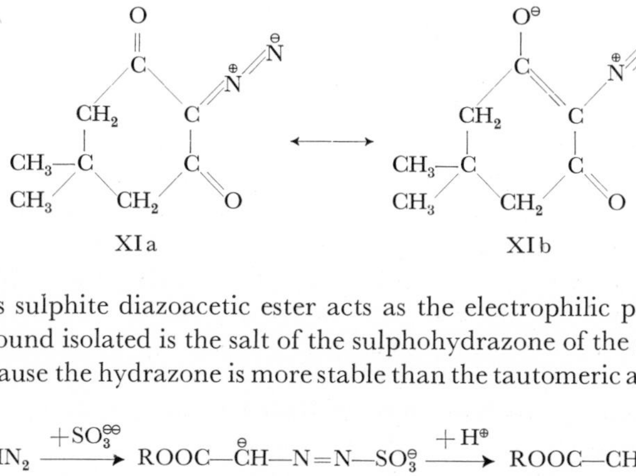

Towards sulphite diazoacetic ester acts as the electrophilic partner (*1599*). The compound isolated is the salt of the sulphohydrazone of the glyoxylic ester (XII), because the hydrazone is more stable than the tautomeric azo compound.

$$\text{ROOC—CHN}_2 \xrightarrow{+\text{SO}_3^{\ominus\ominus}} \text{ROOC—}\overset{\ominus}{\text{C}}\text{H—N=N—SO}_3^{\ominus} \xrightarrow{+\text{H}^{\oplus}} \underset{\text{XII}}{\text{ROOC—CH=N—NH—SO}_3^{\ominus}} \qquad (6.10)$$

Diazoalkanes are electrophilic reagents in their reactions with tertiary phosphines. The phosphazines formed are hydrolysed to hydrazones and phosphine oxides (6.11a). If only a small amount of water is available, a tetrazine results (6.11b) (*1073*, *1941*, *1942*).

$$\text{R}_3\text{P} + \text{N}_2\text{CR'R''} \longrightarrow \text{R}_3\text{P=N—N=C}\begin{smallmatrix}\text{R'}\\ \text{R''}\end{smallmatrix} \xrightarrow{+\text{H}_2\text{O}} \text{R}_3\text{P=O} + \text{H}_2\text{N—N=C}\begin{smallmatrix}\text{R'}\\ \text{R''}\end{smallmatrix} \qquad (6.11\,\text{a})$$

(6.11 b)

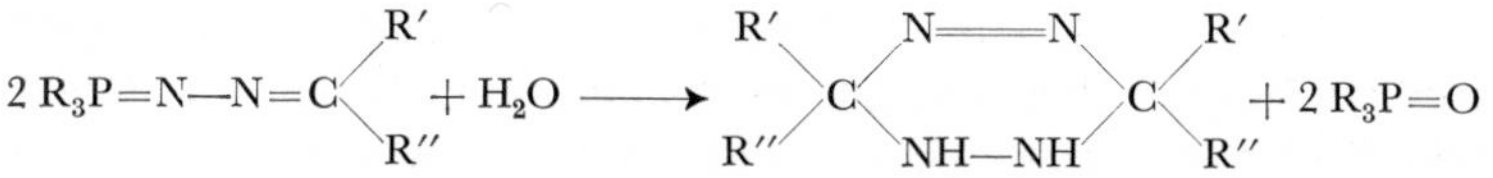

Urry, Eiszner, and Wilt (*2068–2071*) suppose that the photolysis of diazo-methane and diazoacetic ester in carbon tetrachloride, tetrabromide, and simi-lar substances is based on a chain mechanism, in which the methylene ($\overline{C}H_2$) formed primarily takes part as a di-radical ($\dot{C}H_2$). The possibility of radical intermediates in the Wolff rearrangement of diazoketones has been discussed by Leffler (*1321c*).

It is very probable that the reaction between diazodiphenylmethane and nitric oxide in the dark, studied by Kirmse (*1218*), has a radical mechanism. According to equation (6.12), it yields apart from benzophenone and nitrous oxide another compound, to which structure (XIII) may be assigned (*2333*).

$$Ar_2C{=}N_2 + NO$$

$$\downarrow -N_2$$

$$(Ar_2\dot{C}{-}N{=}O \longleftrightarrow Ar_2C{=}N{-}O^{\bullet} \longleftrightarrow Ar_2C{=}\dot{N} \rightarrow O)$$

$$\downarrow +NO$$

$$\left(Ar_2C{=}N{\diagdown}^{NO}_{\diagdown O}\right)$$

$$\diagup \qquad\qquad \diagdown$$

$$Ar_2C{=}O + N_2O \qquad\qquad\qquad Ar_2C{=}N{-}NO_2$$

(6.12)

$$\text{XIII}$$

$$Ar = C_6H_5$$

6.3 Methylene Radicals as Intermediates in Reactions of Diazoalkanes

In the reactions of §§ 6.1 and 6.2 which proceeded with evolution of nitrogen, the first step was always the addition of an electrophilic particle to the diazo-alkane before nitrogen was liberated. In contrast, the reactions of this section occur by splitting off nitrogen primarily. The residual fragment of the diazo-alkane is the so-called carbene (XIV), $\overline{C}H_2$ being termed methylene. As these compounds carry only a sextet of electrons on the carbon atom, they must neces-

$$\text{XIV}$$

sarily be extremely reactive in their search for electrons and Doering and Knox (*612*) have described the carbenes as 'the most indiscriminate reagents known in organic chemistry'. The lack of selectivity exhibited by them, as in the examples cited in § 5.5, is a sure sign of high reactivity. Apart from the splitting off of hydrogen halide from halogenoalkanes and the decomposition of ketenes, the pyrolysis and photolysis of diazoalkanes constitute the most important source of carbenes.

At the end of the last century Nef (*1507–1510*) supposed that particles of the methylene type could be intermediates in reactions and experimentally the existence of methylene can be proved particularly by the pyrolysis of diazomethane in the presence of a tellurium mirror (*1594, 1699*), polymeric tellural-dehyde $(TeCH_2)_n$ being formed. According to Staudinger (*1938*), pyrolysis of diazomethane in an atmosphere of carbon monoxide yields ketene (6.13) and, presumably, this reaction also proceeds via methylene. The supposition is

$$CH_2N_2 \xrightarrow{\text{light or heat}} :CH_2 \underset{-CO}{\overset{+CO}{\rightleftarrows}} H_2C{=}C{=}O \qquad (6.13)$$

strengthened by the work of M. Bergmann (*1815*), of Kistiakowsky (*1735, 2167*), and of Norrish and Porter (*1541*), who were able to detect methylene by means of tellurium mirrors in the pyrolysis of ketene (6.13). The photolysis of diazomethane is quite analogous (*1217*). The remarkably high quantum yields ($\sim$4) are in agreement with the great reactivity of methylene and the formation of higher hydrocarbons (*182*) (cf. § 6.4)[1].

The structure of the carbenes has not yet been settled unequivocally. Whether the two lone electrons on the methylene carbon atom pair off (RR'C:) or whether they remain independent (di-radical, $RR'\overset{\cdot}{C}$) has been discussed both from the point of view of quantum theory (*1289, 1325, 1541*) and of experiment. The compound RR'C: can be regarded as the conjugate base of the carbonium ion $RR'\overset{\oplus}{C}H$. The schools of Kistiakowsky, W.A.Noyes, and others (*766, 768, 1222–1226, 1541, 1735, 1965*) have usually prepared carbenes from ketenes and have studied them mainly in the gas phase, whilst Doering, Skell, Hine, and their co-workers [cf. (*610, 1033–1035, 1901, 1902*) and other papers] have investigated solutions of carbenes obtained from halogenomethanes. It appears that according to Kistiakowsky photolysis of ketenes gives rise to an especially reactive, 'hot' methylene, whilst according to Skell the reactions of the carbenes in solution can be explained by means of the structure with paired electrons. However, the reactions of diazodiphenylmethane, discussed in subsection 6.3 (c), show that in certain cases carbenes can behave even in solution as di-radicals, experiments of Skell and his co-workers (*687*) demonstrating that diphenylmethylene differs from other carbenes. Herzberg and Shoesmith (*2328*) recently compared the flash photolysis of CH_2N_2 and CD_2N_2 in order to obtain further insight into the structure of methylene.

The detailed consideration of this problem is beyond the scope of this book as it would involve the behaviour of carbenes formed from ketenes and halogenomethanes [cf. (*609, 767*)].

---

[1] Quantum yields of photolyses in solution are lower (0·1 to 1) as was shown by Kirmse and Horner (*1220*) for a range of 36 diazo compounds irradiated monochromatically in methanol.

There are considerable differences in behaviour between carbenes obtained from diazoalkanes photolytically and those derived by thermal decomposition. Probably because of their greater energy content, carbenes resulting from the action of light exhibit rather less selectivity than the corresponding products of thermolysis. In this respect usually only secondary importance attaches to whether the carbenes were formed in solution or in the gas phase.

The tendency to yield carbenes runs parallel with the basicity of diazoalkanes only to a limited extent, the stabilization of the carbene formed apparently also having an effect on the rate of reaction. The ease of decomposition of diazo groups bound to secondary carbon atoms, such as that in 2-diazopropane, is surprising.

Carbenes can undergo a whole series of subsequent reactions, which can be divided into six groups:

(a) *Addition of excess of diazoalkane*, as shown by the formation of ketazine from azibenzil (6.14) (*1074*). Unsymmetric reactions of this type are also known (*2200*).

$$\underset{\underset{Ar}{|}}{Ar-CO-\overline{C}} + \underset{\underset{Ar}{|}}{N_2=C-CO-Ar} \longrightarrow \underset{\underset{Ar}{|}}{Ar-CO-C}=N-N=\underset{\underset{Ar}{|}}{C-CO-Ar} \qquad (6.14)$$

(b) *Dimerization to ethylenes*, as found in 1892 by Curtius (*518*) in the thermolysis of diazodiphenylmethane. The simultaneous appearance of the corresponding ethane is due to the ability of carbenes to abstract hydrogen from the solvent (*1074, 1586*).

(c) *Attack on a multiple bond*, a type of reaction for which several examples were included in § 5.5. Experiments with dibromomethylene carried out by Skell and his co-workers (*1899–1902*) are significant for the mechanism of this addition. As the reaction proceeds stereospecifically, Skell concludes that mechanism (6.15) applies, and that intermediates of the type (XVa) or (XVb) are improbable for the same reason.

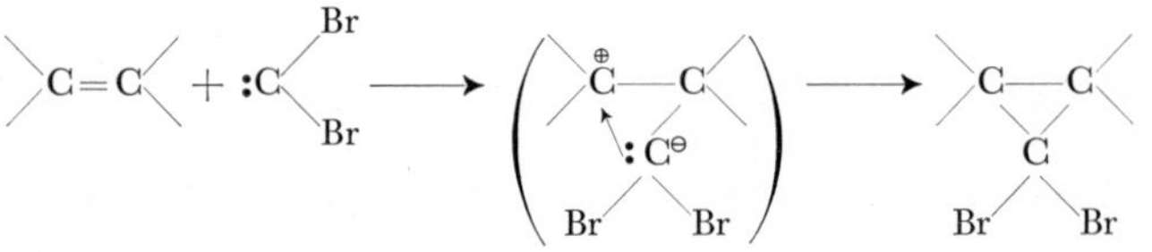

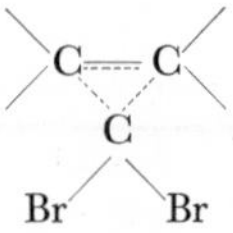

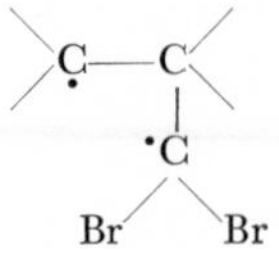

Surprisingly, Skell (*687*) has found that the carbene obtained from diazodiphenylmethane by photolysis possesses the nature of a di-radical. Unlike with the other carbenes, addition to olefins is not stereospecific. Further, the rates of reaction with 1,3-butadiene and 1,1-diphenylethylene are much greater than those with isobutylene, 1-hexene, and cyclohexene, in accord with the relative reactivities of these compounds towards radicals. A structure for diphenyl-methylene with two unpaired electrons of parallel spin (triplet state) is sup-ported also by some work due to Horner *et al.* (*1221*) in which reaction with oxygen gave benzophenone and with tetraethyl-*p*-phenylenediamine a Wur-ster salt.

Of special interest are the products of the interaction of diazoalkanes and aromatic hydrocarbons. In 1885 Buchner and Curtius (*366*) investigated the thermolysis of diazoacetic ester in toluene and discovered a compound, $C_8H_9CO_2C_2H_5$, i.e. an isomer of tolylacetic ester, which they described as *pseudo*-tolylacetic ester. Subsequently, Buchner studied this product and its derivatives in detail and his realization that in the reaction six-membered rings are converted into seven-membered ones of the type of cycloheptatrienecarbo-xylic acid is important and most remarkable at that time (*363, 370*). Thorough examination of the mother liquors of the corresponding acid amides, particu-larly that of *pseudo*-phenylacetamide, led to the isolation of several isomers. Starting with benzene and diazoacetic ester and proceeding via the amides, Buchner (*364*) obtained three isomeric acids of constitution C_7H_7COOH. He was also aware of the connection with the degradation products of the tropane alkaloids, among which Einhorn, Willstätter, and Tahara (*656–658, 2163*) found two compounds identical with two of Buchner's as well as yet another compound believed to be a fourth isomer.

Buchner (*365*) supposed that in the thermolysis of diazoacetic ester in ben-zene the primary process consisted of the addition of a methylene group to a benzene double bond, in other words, that the *pseudo*-phenylacetic ester was based on the bicyclic system of norcaradiene with condensed six- and three-membered rings. Secondary reactions were thought to convert this compound into the four isomeric cycloheptatrienecarboxylic acids ($\alpha, \beta, \gamma, \delta$). By means of various reactions Buchner (*365*) and Willstätter (*2164*) were able to deter-mine the positions of the double bonds in the isomers, but the structures origi-nally assigned have been revised twice (*535, 890*). In recognition of his exten-sive investigations, the compounds have come to be known as 'Buchner acids'. According to G.O.Schenck and H.Ziegler (*1793*) photolysis of diazoacetic ester in benzene, followed by hydrolysis, also leads to norcaradienecarboxylic acid and the isomeric cycloheptatrienecarboxylic acids.

Recently, the school of Doering (*614*) established some surprising facts about the constitution and reactions of these compounds. Doering showed that the spectra not only of the seven-membered ring compounds, but also of the norca-radiene derivatives have great similarity to those of tropylidenes. Compounds containing a carane skeleton possess quite a different spectrum, however, and these results were confirmed chemically by means of the Diels–Alder adducts. Einhorn and Tahara's δ-cycloheptatrienecarboxylic acid (*656*) proved to be a mixture of the α- and β-isomers. Doering thus ascribed the following structures to the Buchner acids:

α-acid, m. pt. 71°

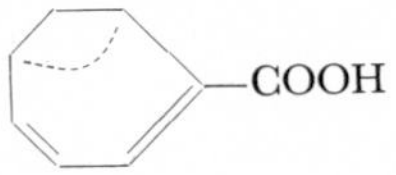

—COOH

β-acid, m. pt. 56°

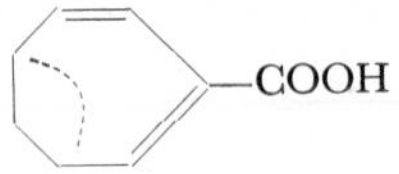

—COOH

γ-acid, liquid

—COOH

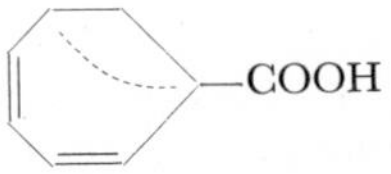

δ-acid, m. pt. 31°   mixture of α- and β-isomers
                             in the ratio 47:53

norcaradienecarboxylic
acid, liquid

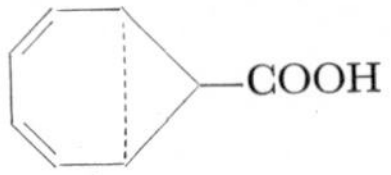

—COOH

E. J. Corey (466) came to analogous conclusions in the case of other compounds of the type of norcaradiene. Alder, Jungen, and Rust (12) studied the Diels–Alder addition reactions of the Buchner acids independently but at the same time as Doering and their assignations for the α-, β-, and γ-acids agree with his.

Badger (120) supposes that the Buchner addition of diazoalkanes indicates the position of double bonds, that is, the double bond character of particular links in a conjugated system. Badger's postulate is confirmed by the results obtained so far with aromatic hydrocarbons. Naphthalene (369) and anthracene (126) add at the 1,2-, pyrene (126) at the 4,5-, benz[a]anthracene (126) at the 5,6-, and phenanthrene (624) at the 9,10-position, but, on the other hand, ring enlargement of indan with diazoacetic ester gives two isomeric cyclopenta-cycloheptenecarboxylic esters (1641, 2050) and substituted indans mostly yield mixtures also. According to the more recent views (1356) on the Mills–Nixon effect (cf. § 11.3) it would be expected that just in the case of indan the links of the benzene nucleus should be able to be clearly differentiated. Presumably the Mills–Nixon effect is simply too weak to influence the point of entry of the carbene.

A very short while ago, Denney and Klemchuk (547) observed a kinetic isotope effect in an intramolecular ring closure of a carbene. Irradiation converts 2-(2'-deuterophenyl)-phenyldiazomethane into fluorene, in which the deuterium is distributed between the five- and the six-membered rings (6.16). Determination of deuterium in the fluorenone obtained on oxidation showed that

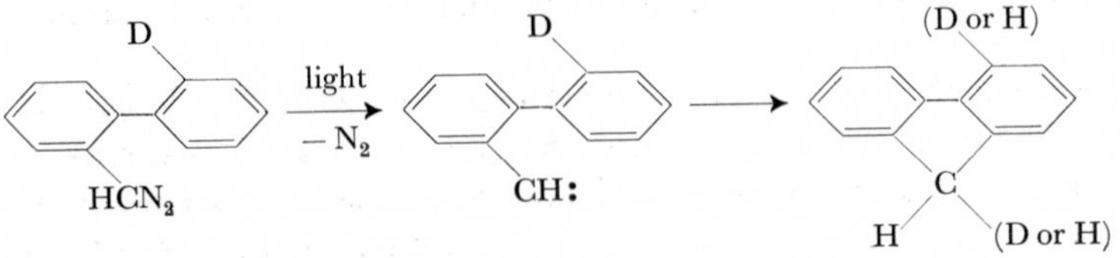

(6.16)

more than half the heavy hydrogen is present on benzenoid carbon atoms, giving an isotope effect k_H/k_D of 1·12.

Volpin and co-workers (*2409*) have prepared cycloheptatriene from benzene and C^{14}-diazomethane.

(d) *Interaction with a lone pair of electrons borne by an atom held by a single bond.* This group includes the long known reaction of diazomethane and diazoacetic ester with amines leading to *N*-alkyl compounds (*504, 506*) as well as the formation of mercaptoles from disulphides (6.17) (*1831, 1832*). Of interest from the point of view of mechanism is the alkylation of allyl halides (*639, 642–644, 1628*). Huisgen (*1114*) proposes that the reaction of 3-chloro-1-butene, for example, which was investigated by D. D. Phillips (*1628*), proceeds via a chloronium intermediate capable of a subsequent Claisen-like rearrangement (6.18).

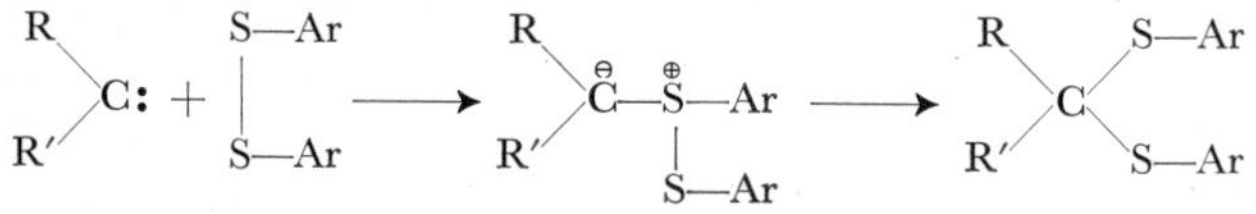

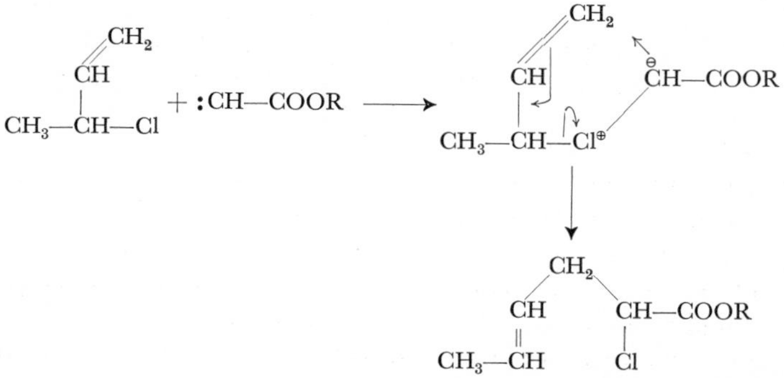

The reactions of diazoalkanes with carbon tetrachloride, chloroform, and similar compounds, to which Urry et al. (*2068–2071*) assigned a radical mechanism, can be interpreted equally well, according to Huisgen (*1114*), as taking place by similar rearrangements of chloronium intermediates.

(e) *Attack on a CH-bond.* A parallel mechanism, but with an oxonium intermediate, can be formulated for the reaction of carbenes with ethers (6.19). However, the classic work of Meerwein (*1402*) and especially Doering's researches (*608, 612*) made this doubtful, as reaction with methylene occurred equally readily at the ω- as at the α-positions of the ether molecule. Some support for mechanism (6.19) is provided by the observations of the Meerwein school (*1397*) on formic and acetic esters which indicate increased reactivity in alkyl groups held by ether links.

Decision between the applicability of mechanism (6.19) or (6.20) was obtained by Franzen and Fikentscher (*758*) by means of C^{14}-diazomethane. According to the oxonium mechanism (6.19), all the radioactive carbon should be found at the α-position of the product and a direct, completely random

$$C_2H_5O-CH_2-CH_3 + :C^{14}H_2 \longrightarrow C_2H_5\overset{\oplus}{O}-CH_2-CH_3 \longrightarrow C_2H_5O-C^{14}H_2-CH_2-CH_3 \quad (6.19)$$
$$\underset{\ominus C^{14}H_2}{|} \qquad\qquad\qquad\qquad \alpha \qquad \beta \qquad \gamma$$

$$C_2H_5O-CH_2-CH_3 + :C^{14}H_2 \longrightarrow C_2H_5O-CH_2-CH_2-C^{14}H_3 \qquad\qquad (6.20)$$
$$\alpha \qquad \beta \qquad \gamma$$

attack on the carbon atoms of the ether should result in uniform distribution of radioactivity over all three positions. Experimentally the whole of the C^{14} was proved to go to the γ-position, thus demonstrating not only direct attack on a CH-bond, but also that methylene reacts distinctly more readily with a primary than a secondary carbon atom. This is in agreement with investigations of the interaction of hydrocarbons with methylene (*608, 613, 617, 1243*). Diphenyl-carbene formed photolytically alkylated CH-groups in some cases only (*1221*).

(f) *Rearrangement of α-ketocarbenes.* This type of reaction possesses considerable preparative importance since the Wolff rearrangement of diazoketones forms part of the Arndt-Eistert synthesis of homologous carboxylic acids and presents a possible route to ketenes. The method of rearranging α-diazoketones was described in § 5.6, silver ions being the usual catalyst, but in some cases the same products are obtained by means of copper or cuprous salts (*1357*). In § 5.6 it was also pointed out that thermolysis and photolysis give analogous results. All these observations indicate that an unstable intermediate is formed primarily and that the subsequent reactions are independent of the nature of the catalyst, the function of which consists in facilitating the formation of the intermediate. Thus, for example, the silver ion acts as a Lewis acid towards the diazoketone; the intermediate diazonium compound (XVI) splits off nitrogen as usual, but also the silver ion, to yield the ketocarbene (XVII) as intermediate. Migration of the substituent R as a carbanion converts the sextet at the carbene carbon atom into an octet of electrons and produces a ketene. Under the conditions of the Arndt–Eistert synthesis, the ketene reacts further with water,

$$O=C-\overset{\ominus}{C}H-\overset{\oplus}{N}\equiv N + Ag^{\oplus} \longrightarrow O=C-CH-\overset{\oplus}{N}\equiv N \longrightarrow O=C-\overset{\cdot\cdot}{C}H + N_2 + Ag^{\oplus}$$
$$\underset{R}{|} \qquad\qquad\qquad\qquad \underset{R}{|}\ \underset{Ag}{|} \qquad\qquad\qquad \underset{R^{\nearrow}}{|}$$
$$\text{XVI} \qquad\qquad\qquad \text{XVII} \qquad\qquad (6.21)$$

$$\downarrow$$

$$O=C=CH-R$$

alcohols, or amines to form carboxylic acid, esters, or amides, respectively (cf. equation 5.45). In compounds of the type $RCO \cdot CN_2 \cdot CH_2R'$, migration of hydride in place of group R has been noted, α, β-unsaturated ketones $RCO \cdot CH:CHR'$ being formed (*756*).

From mechanism (6.21) it can be seen that the carbonyl group stays unaltered, the oxygen remaining attached to the same carbon atom (*757, 1099*). If the carbonyl carbon atom is marked with C^{14}, all the radioactive carbon reappears in the carbonyl group of the product, that is, in the carboxyl group if an Arndt–Eistert reaction is carried out. This fact excludes the possibility that the decomposition of the diazoketone takes place via an acetylene oxide of the type (XVIII).

$$R—C{=\!\!=\!\!=}C—R$$
$$\underset{O}{\diagdown\!\diagup}$$

XVIII

By mechanism, the Wolff rearrangement corresponds to the Hofmann degradation of amides and the Curtius degradation of azides, though in these reactions the intermediate does not carry a sextet of electrons on a carbon, but on a nitrogen atom. The octet is made up again by the migration of a substituent from a neighbouring atom together with the electrons of the link by which it is attached. Recently, the Curtius degradation has been carried out not only by means of heat, but also photolytically (1081).

All these rearrangements occur with retention of configuration, neither racemization nor inversion taking place (893, 1291, 1292). Earlier reports (1293) to the contrary could not be confirmed (2149) and in the conversion of 2-methylbutyric into 3-methylvaleric acid via the diazoketone 78% of the possible optical activity is observed in the product (1786). Wiberg and Hutton (2149) showed that the optical yield in the rearrangement of optically active diazoketones depends to some extent on the nature of the catalyst employed, but this could also be due to differences in the stability of the diazonium-like intermediate (XVI). Hence almost all the evidence points to the intramolecular nature of the rearrangement, the residue R remaining attached to the ketocarbene group throughout.

In some instances it is possible to intercept the intermediate ketocarbene; thus, in the decomposition of azibenzil (6.22) in methanol, benzoin methyl ether (XIX) is formed apart from the diphenylacetic ester (XX) expected to be produced via diphenylketene (1846). The intramolecular ring closures and dimerizations discussed in § 5.6 can equally be regarded as reactions in which the ketocarbenes are intercepted.

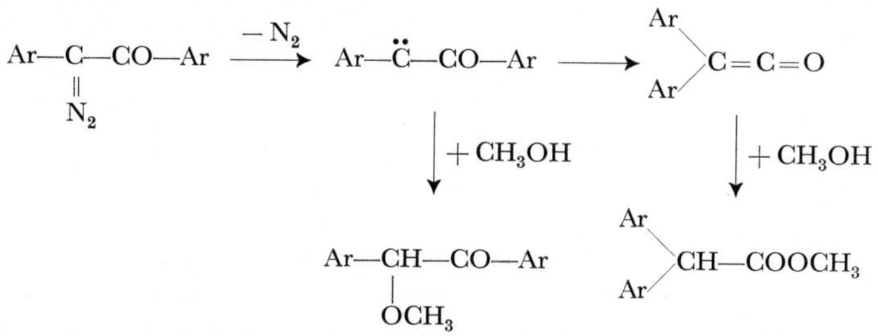

$$
\begin{array}{ccccc}
\text{Ar—C—CO—Ar} & \xrightarrow{-N_2} & \text{Ar—}\ddot{\text{C}}\text{—CO—Ar} & \longrightarrow & \underset{\text{Ar}}{\overset{\text{Ar}}{\diagup}}C=C=O \\
\underset{\underset{N_2}{\|}}{} & & & & \\
& & \downarrow +CH_3OH & & \downarrow +CH_3OH \qquad (6.22) \\
& & \text{Ar—CH—CO—Ar} & & \underset{\text{Ar}}{\overset{\text{Ar}}{\diagup}}CH—COOCH_3 \\
& & \underset{\text{OCH}_3}{|} & & \\
& & \text{XIX} & & \text{XX}
\end{array}
$$

Whilst the transitory appearance of the ketocarbenes can only be demonstrated by capture with suitable reagents, the ketenes can be isolated readily if the reactions are carried out in inert media. Schroeter (1845, 1847) and

Staudinger (*1936*) had already prepared ketenes by this method. Recently a series of modified preparations have been described by Horner's school (*1075, 1081, 1083*) and others (*756, 1907*). It is interesting from the point of view of mechanism that in the photolysis of the unsymmetrical α-diazo-β, β'-diketone diazobenzoylacetone only the methyl, but not the phenyl, group migrates (6.23) (*1083*).

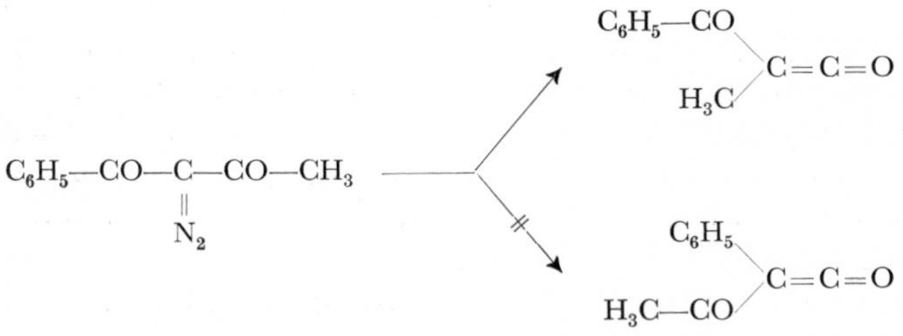

$$
C_6H_5-CO-\underset{\underset{N_2}{\|}}{C}-CO-CH_3 \quad
\begin{cases}
\nearrow \quad \underset{H_3C}{\overset{C_6H_5-CO}{}}{>}C=C=O \\[2em]
\searrow \quad \underset{H_3C-CO}{\overset{C_6H_5}{}}{>}C=C=O
\end{cases}
\tag{6.23}
$$

The ring contraction undergone by *o*-diazophenols, which corresponds to the Wolff rearrangement, will be discussed in § 7.8.

A different type of rearrangement occurs with the diazoketone (XXI), as found by Newman (*1524*). Since apparently a Wolff rearrangement is sterically impossible with t-butyl residues, it is a methyl group which migrates, leading to the isolation of 2,2,4,5-tetramethyl-4-hexen-3-one (XXII).

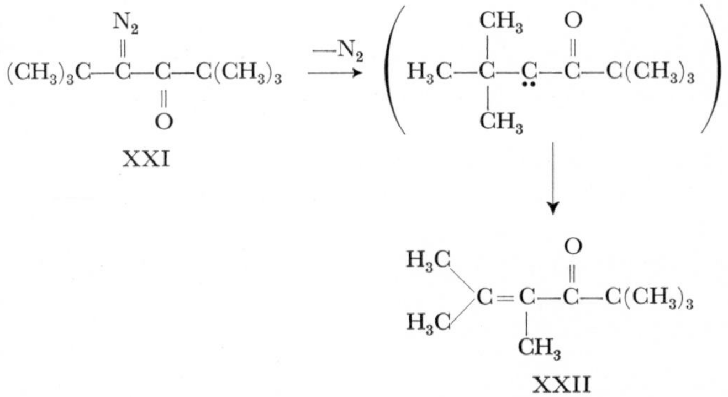

$$
(CH_3)_3C-\underset{\underset{O}{\|}}{\overset{\overset{N_2}{\|}}{C}}-C-C(CH_3)_3 \quad \overset{-N_2}{\longrightarrow} \quad
\left(H_3C-\underset{\underset{CH_3}{|}}{\overset{\overset{CH_3}{|}}{C}}-\overset{..}{C}-\underset{}{\overset{\overset{O}{\|}}{C}}-C(CH_3)_3 \right)
\tag{6.24}
$$

$$
\underset{H_3C}{\overset{H_3C}{}}{>}C=\underset{\underset{CH_3}{|}}{C}-\overset{\overset{O}{\|}}{C}-C(CH_3)_3
$$

XXI   XXII

6.4 Polymerization of Diazoalkanes

At the turn of the century already Bamberger and Tschirner (*182*) observed that in experiments with diazomethane compounds of higher molecular weight are formed. In 1928, Meerwein and Burneleit (*1396*) remarked in a footnote that the action of aluminium alcoholates or boric esters on diazomethane produces polymethylene, and this work was followd up by Werle (*2128*) in Meerwein's laboratories (*1391*). The decomposition of diazomethane in the presence of metallic copper, halogenoborates, and boroalkyls also leads to polymethylene (*378, 379, 662, 1195*). Similarly, polyethylidene can be obtained from diazoethane (*1770*). The physicochemical and physical properties of the products leave no doubt but that they consist of largely unbranched paraffins (*1038, 1266*) and they correspond therefore to Ziegler's polyethylene and not to that obtained by the high pressure process [cf. (*9*)]. Molecular weights of up to 3 000 000 can be reached.

Feltzin, Restaino, and Mesrobian (*702*) have investigated the kinetics of polymerization of six different diazoalkanes in ethereal solution with copper stearate or fluoborate as catalyst. The reactivity of the straight-chain diazoalkanes decreases from diazoethane to diazodecane and diazodiphenylmethane is still more stable. The rate is proportional to the concentration of the diazo compound and that of the catalyst. As neither hydroquinone nor 2,2-diphenyl-1-picrylhydrazyl decreases the velocity of the reaction, a radical mechanism can hardly be operative.

However, the polymerization can be attributed to an alkylation catalysed by Lewis acids, such as that discussed in § 6.1. The first step (6.25a) is the formation of a diazonium-like addition product leading to a carbonium ion, which itself now acts as a Lewis acid in attacking another molecule of diazoalkane and thus starts chain growth (6.25b). As termination reactions, Feltzin *et al.* (*702*) considered disproportionation (6.25c) as well as interaction of the carbonium ion with the β-nitrogen atom of the diazoalkane, the latter serving as base

$$BF_3 + CH_2N_2 \longrightarrow F_3\overset{\ominus}{B}{-}CH_2{-}\overset{\oplus}{N}{\equiv}N \longrightarrow F_3\overset{\ominus}{B}{-}\overset{\oplus}{C}H_2 + N_2 \qquad (6.25\,a)$$

$$F_3\overset{\ominus}{B}{-}\overset{\oplus}{C}H_2 + n\,CH_2N_2 \longrightarrow F_3\overset{\ominus}{B}{-}CH_2{-}(CH_2)_{n-1}{-}\overset{\oplus}{C}H_2 + nN_2 \qquad (6.25\,b)$$

$$F_3\overset{\ominus}{B}{-}CH_2{-}(CH_2)_{n-1}{-}\overset{\oplus}{C}H_2 \longrightarrow F_3\overset{\ominus}{B}{-}CH_2{-}(CH_2)_{n-2}{-}CH{=}CH_2 + H^{\oplus}$$
$$\qquad (6.25\,c)$$
$$\downarrow$$
$$CH_3{-}(CH_2)_{n-2}{-}CH{=}CH_2 + BF_3$$

$$F_3\overset{\ominus}{B}{-}CH_2{-}(CH_2)_{n-1}{-}\overset{\oplus}{C}H_2 + \overset{\ominus}{N}{=}\overset{\oplus}{N}{=}CH_2 \longrightarrow F_3\overset{\ominus}{B}{-}CH_2{-}(CH_2)_{n-1}{-}CH_2{-}N{=}\overset{\oplus}{N}{=}CH_2$$
$$\qquad (6.25\,d)$$
$$\downarrow$$
$$CH_3{-}(CH_2)_{n-1}{-}CH{=}N{-}N{=}CH_2 + BF_3$$

(6.25d). The disproportionation can be regarded as attack of the carbonium ion on the basic centre at the carbon atom of the diazoalkane molecule with evolution of nitrogen and subsequent loss of a proton. The steps (6.25b) and (6.25c) correspond to the formation of tetraphenylethylene from diazodiphenylmethane mentioned in § 6.1 (equations 6.3b and 6.3c).

It is improbable that carbene-like states serve as intermediates in the formation of polymethylene. Meerwein (*1402*) found that in the photolysis of diazomethane only small amounts of ethylene were produced, which implies that the highly reactive methylene immediately interacts with the solvent, the chances of collision with a diazomethane molecule being very low. However, in the absence of other molecules, that is, when gaseous and undiluted, higher hydrocarbons do appear, as pointed out in § 6.3 (*182*). The first step may consist of interaction of methylene with diazomethane or dimerization of methylene.

If the reactivity of the carbene is lowered by suitable substituents, such as phenyl or ethoxycarbonyl groups, dimerization also in solution becomes feasible [cf. subsection 6.3 (b)].

6.5 Comparison of Deamination with Diazoalkane Decomposition

It has been pointed out in § 5.7 that the deamination of aliphatic amines with nitrous acid yields in the first place diazonium compounds, but that these have little stability and decompose rapidly in different ways. In consequence, kinetic investigations of deamination can only yield directly information about the mechanism of formation of aliphatic diazonium ions, but not about their mode of decomposition. It is for this reason that in this book the kinetics of deamination were discussed in Chapter 2 alongside the mechanism of aromatic diazotization. The work of Taylor (*2010–2012*), Austin (*93, 97*), Powell (630), and others leaves no doubt but that the formation of alkyldiazonium ions is rate-determining. However, for the deamination of 9-amino-9,10-dihydro-9,10-diethanoanthracene with nitrosyl chloride at —70°, Wilhelm and Curtin (*2363*) give 10^{-2} sec^{-1} as the minimum rate constant for the decomposition of the intermediate diazonium ion.

Thus the study of the mechanism of deamination is made considerably more difficult. In general, it has been assumed that the process consists of an $S_N 1$ substitution and support comes particularly from the fact that the nitrogen molecule is the group most readily replaced in nucleophilic substitution. In the diazonium ion the nitrogen molecule is already preformed to a large extent and, since in the alkyldiazonium ion, in contrast to its aromatic analogue, the CN-bond is not stabilized mesomerically, fission occurs more easily. There is left a carbonium ion, which, after rearrangement where appropriate, is converted into stable particles in subsequent reactions.

On the basis of such a simple picture a complete parallel would be expected between deamination and other reactions which correspond closely to the limiting case of Ingold's $S_N 1$ mechanism, such as the solvolyses of alkyl halides or *p*-toluenesulphonates. However, usually this is not so (*318*). From the examples cited in the next section it can be seen that frequently deamination yields the various products in quite different ratios. Even more striking are the results of nucleophilic substitution at bridgehead carbon atoms, studied particularly by Bartlett and his co-workers (*53, 192, 195–197*). Thus, for instance, the deamination of 1-amino-7,7-dimethylnorcamphane (XXIII a) proceeds smoothly, whilst the 1-chloro compound (XXIII c) is completely inert towards basic reagents. These differences lead to the conclusion that, if the primary product of the decomposition of alkyldiazonium ions is indeed a carbonium ion, it is not identical in every respect with the cationic intermediates appearing in other $S_N 1$ reactions. A final and generally acceptable interpretation of

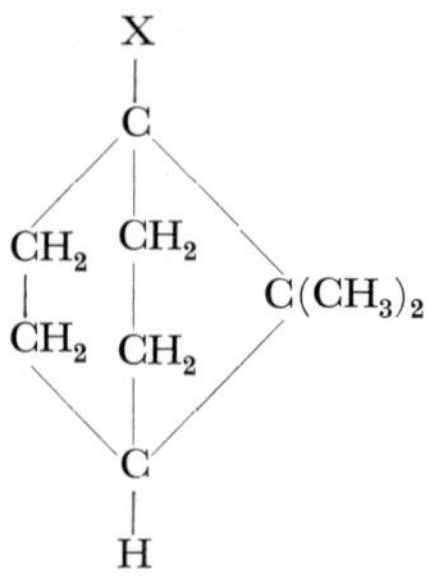

$$
\begin{array}{c}
X \\
| \\
C
\end{array}
$$

CH$_2$ CH$_2$
| | C(CH$_3$)$_2$
CH$_2$ CH$_2$

C
|
H

XXIIIa: X = NH$_2$

XXIIIb: X = N$_2^\oplus$

XXIIIc: X = Cl

the mechanism of deamination remains still to be given, but just recently discussion has intensified and it is to be hoped that in the near future decisive experiments will be forthcoming. In this book, for example in §§ 2.1, 5.7, and 6.1, deamination is generally formulated as an S_N1 reaction, but it must be stressed that this should not be taken to imply that unequivocal proof has been provided in the particular cases.

Before considering the problem further, it is appropriate to compare deamination with the decomposition of diazoalkanes. It was stated in § 6.1 that the reactions of diazoalkanes catalysed by acid proceed via alkyldiazonium intermediates. Convincing support for assuming a common intermediate for both reactions has been adduced by Huisgen and Rüchardt (*1129, 1130*). As shown in Table 6.2, the propanol mixtures contain a remarkably constant proportion of the iso-form whether obtained by deamination of n-propylamine, by decomposition of n-diazopropane with strong or weak Brönsted acids, or by degradation of an *N*-nitroso-*N*-n-propylarylamide (*1125*), which isomerizes in the first place to an alkyldiazoester. The somewhat greater proportion of isopropanol formed in the last instance is presumably due to the higher temperature.

Table 6.2

Decomposition of n-Propyldiazonium Ions in Aqueous Dimethylformamide (40:60 by volume)
(1129, 1130)

System	Temperature °	Proportion of iso-form in propanol mixture (%)
n-Propylamine + HClO$_4$ + NaNO$_2$ . . .	0	30·8
n-Diazopropane + HClO$_4$	0	28·1
n-Diazopropane + C$_6$H$_5$COOH	0	27·2
N-Nitroso-*N*-n-propylbenzamide	80	32·7

Correspondingly, Curtin and Gerber (*501*) had demonstrated that 1-diazo-2-butene (XXIV) as well as 3-diazo-1-butene (XXV) in aqueous perchloric acid yields approximately the same mixture of 3-buten-1-ol (XXVI) and 2-buten-1-ol (crotyl alcohol; XXVII) as obtained by Roberts and Mazur (*1710*)

by deaminating 1-amino-2-butene or 2-amino-1-butene (6.26). The similarity
of the behaviour of 1- and 2-butene derivatives as regards the composition of
the products can be attributed to the predominance of the mechanism involving
allylic rearrangement at the carbonium ion stage.

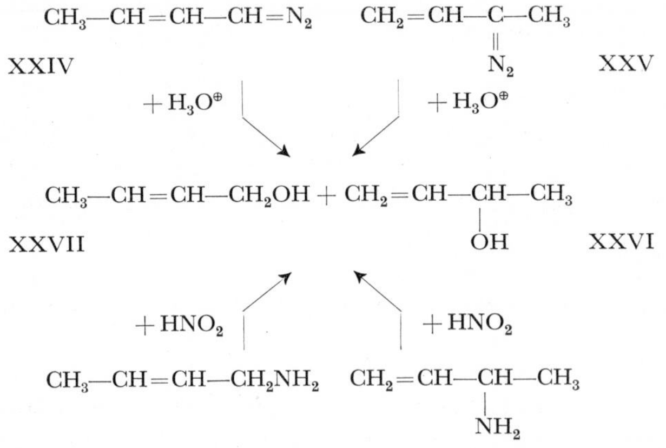

$$CH_3\!-\!CH\!=\!CH\!-\!CH\!=\!N_2 \qquad CH_2\!=\!CH\!-\!\overset{\|}{\underset{N_2}{C}}\!-\!CH_3$$

XXIV   XXV

$$+H_3O^{\oplus} \qquad\qquad +H_3O^{\oplus}$$

$$CH_3\!-\!CH\!=\!CH\!-\!CH_2OH + CH_2\!=\!CH\!-\!\underset{OH}{\overset{|}{CH}}\!-\!CH_3$$

XXVII   XXVI   (6.26)

$$+HNO_2 \qquad\qquad +HNO_2$$

$$CH_3\!-\!CH\!=\!CH\!-\!CH_2NH_2 \quad CH_2\!=\!CH\!-\!\underset{NH_2}{\overset{|}{CH}}\!-\!CH_3$$

The isomerizations found to occur in these investigations are characteristic
for the reaction of primary alkylamines with nitrous acid. Already in the classic
work of Victor Meyer (*1437*), Siersch (*1891*), and Linnemann (*1346, 1347*) it
was shown that in aqueous medium n-propylamine gives, apart from propylene,
an alcoholic fraction consisting of 42% n- and 58% iso-propanol, but that deamination converts isopropylamine exclusively into isopropanol. Normally the
isomerizations lead from primary to secondary and from secondary to tertiary
alkyl products, that is, in the direction of the more stable carbonium ion. The
fact that the isomerization does not go to completion implies that, assuming an
S_N1 mechanism, the rearrangement of the carbonium ion (XXVIII) by hydrogen migration occurs in competition with the direct addition of the nucleophilic solvent $S^\ominus$ to (XXVIII). The reversible rearrangement into the isomeric
carbonium ion $R'^\oplus$ (XXIX) is then followed by an analogous addition. The
ratio of the rate constant k_s to a quantity which contains both k' and k'_s, deter-

$$R\!-\!NH_2 \xrightarrow{HNO_2} R\!-\!\overset{\oplus}{N}\!\equiv\!N \longrightarrow R^\oplus \xrightarrow[k_s]{+S^\ominus} R\!-\!S$$

XXVIII

$$k' \updownarrow \qquad\qquad\qquad (6.27)$$

$$R'^\oplus \xrightarrow[k'_s]{+S^\ominus} R'\!-\!S$$

XXIX

mines the ratio between the products [R—S]/[R'—S]. (It may be hazarded
that k'_s, the rate of addition to the more stable carbonium ion, is smaller than k_s.

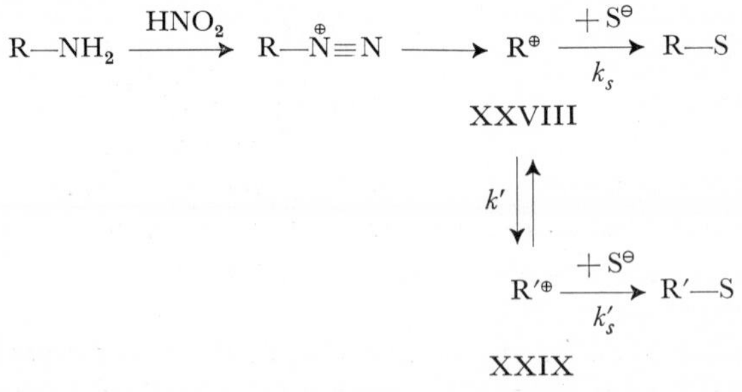

Should k' be of the same order of magnitude, the overall rate constant of the formation of R'—S from $R^\oplus$ via $R'^\oplus$ is a complicated function. If, however, k' is very large, $[R—S]/[R'—S] = k_s/k'_s$.) Since k_s and k'_s are greatly dependent on the nature of the medium, the composition of the solvent exercises an important effect on the ratio of the products. For an example it is appropriate to revert to the deamination of n-propylamine. According to V. Meyer (1437), in water 58% isopropanol, that is, R'—S, is obtained, but under Huisgen's conditions (1129, 1130), namely, in aqueous dimethylformamide (40:60 by volume), only about 31% of isomerization is observed. All the same, the data available are insufficient to permit far-reaching conclusions to be drawn about the dependence on the solvent of the addition reactions of carbonium ions.

6.6 Mechanism of Nucleophilic Substitution of Alkyldiazonium Ions

In this section will be discussed researches concerned with the problem of determining the type of reaction to which the replacement of the diazonium group belongs. After considering some results which clearly favour an S_N1 mechanism, attention will be paid particularly to the frequent observation that the products of deamination do not correspond to those obtained in S_N1 reactions of analogous compounds, such as alkyl halides and p-toluenesulphonates, which are known to proceed via carbonium ions.

A very compelling experiment supporting the S_N1 character of deamination was performed by Curtin and Gerber (501), who found that in the reaction of 1-diazo-2,2-dimethylpropane (diazoneopentane) with 3,5-dinitrobenzoic acid in ether the main product consists of trimethylethylene (6.28). A methyl group has therefore migrated. According to Dostrovsky, Hughes, and Ingold (621,

$$(CH_3)_3C—CH=N_2 \xrightarrow[\text{ether}]{ArCOOH} (CH_3)_2C=CHCH_3 \qquad (41\%)$$
$$+ \underset{\underset{OCOAr}{|}}{(CH_3)_2C—CH_2—CH_3} \qquad (1·2\%)$$
$$+ (CH_3)_3C—CH_2—OCOAr \quad (0·28\%)$$

(6.28)

(The yields are based on the nitroso compound used in the synthesis of the diazoneopentane.)

622), bimolecular substitutions of neopentyl derivatives occur without, but monomolecular ones with, rearrangement. The migration of the methyl group is all the more significant as evidence for the S_N1 nature of this reaction, because, as shown below through the work of Huisgen and Rüchardt (1129, 1130), in ether rearrangement would be expected to take place at most only to a small extent.

Thus it has been noted on several occasions that in relatively non-polar media the reactions of alkyldiazo compounds do not lead to the same products as those of the corresponding alkyl halides or other substances able to give rise to carbonium ions, in spite of being carried out under identical conditions.

Characteristic is, for example, Roberts's comparison (*1716, 1717*) of the ethanolysis of diphenylmethyl chloride in the presence of benzoic acid with the
analogous reaction of diazodiphenylmethane. In the ethanolysis the competing
reaction of the weakly nucleophilic benzoate hardly plays a part, but in the
decomposition of diazodiphenylmethane there is formed apart from 40% diphe-
nylethoxymethane no less than 60% diphenylmethyl benzoate. It is clear that
the mechanism must accommodate special factors which favour reaction with
the benzoate ion in this case. Even more remarkable is the result obtained by
Adamson and Kenner (*6*) in the decomposition of diazo-n-propane with benzoic acid in ether, only n-propyl and not isopropyl benzoate being found. From
the experiments of V. Meyer and others mentioned previously, considerable
amounts of the iso-compound would have been expected.

Huisgen and Rüchardt (*1129, 1130*) have re-examined the reaction and have
confirmed Adamson and Kenner's surprising result in its essentials, though they
were able to demonstrate the presence of a small quantity (1·5%) of the iso-
ester. The proportion of the iso-ester increases with the polarity of the solvent.
In aqueous media the iso-compound constituted about 4·3%, but this should be
compared with its much greater importance (27·2%) in the conversion into
alcohols (see Table 6.2).

Huisgen and Rüchardt (*1129, 1130*) interpret these facts as making probable
the appearance of an oriented ion pair (**XXX**). Decomposition *within* the ion

$$CH_3-CH_2-CH_2-\overset{\oplus}{N}\equiv N$$

$$O \diagdown \underset{\ominus}{\overset{}{}} \diagup O$$

$$C$$

$$|$$

$$C_6H_5$$

XXX

pair leads to n-propyl benzoate, but if (**XXX**) is first separated by means of
water to give a free diazonium ion (**XXXI**), then loss of nitrogen yields a solvated carbonium ion (**XXXII**), which can react either directly or after isomerization (**XXXIII**), just as in scheme (6.27). Huisgen and Rüchardt represent the decomposition of diazo-n-propane, of *N*-nitroso-*N*-n-propylbenzamide,
and the deamination of n-propylamine by means of scheme (6.29), which again
brings out the relationships between the reactions of these three compounds,
alkyldiazonium ions being the keypoint throughout.

The investigation of Curtin and Gerber (*501*) already referred to also contains results suggesting oriented ion pairs. Whilst in aqueous medium 1-diazo-
2-butene as well as 3-diazo-1-butene gives the mixture of alcohols shown in
scheme (6.26), 3,5-dinitrobenzoic acid in ether leads only to the ester of corresponding structure and no isomerization is observed.

It can thus be said that valuable experimental evidence exists for the S_N1
character of the decomposition of alkyldiazonium ions, but the fact that the
solvolysis of alkyl halides and *p*-toluenesulphonates normally leads to less rearrangement than that of alkyldiazonium ions provides an important problem,

$$\text{n-C}_3\text{H}_7-\text{N} \overset{\text{NO}}{\underset{\text{CO}-\text{R}}{\big\langle}} \quad \longrightarrow \quad \text{n-C}_3\text{H}_7-\text{N}=\text{N}-\text{O}-\text{COR}$$

$$\text{CH}_3-\text{CH}_2-\text{CH}_2-\overset{\oplus}{\text{N}}\equiv\text{N}$$

$$+\,\text{RCOOH} \qquad \text{XXX} \qquad \underset{\underset{\text{R}}{\overset{|}{\text{C}}}}{\overset{\text{O}\diagdown\ \diagup\text{O}}{}}\overset{\ominus}{} \quad \xrightarrow{\ -\text{N}_2\ } \quad \begin{array}{l}\text{CH}_3\text{CH}_2\text{CH}_2-\text{O}-\text{COR} \\ (+\text{a little iso-ester})\end{array}$$

$$\text{CH}_3-\text{CH}_2-\overset{\ominus}{\text{CH}}-\overset{\oplus}{\text{N}}\equiv\text{N}$$

$$+ \text{ aq.}$$

$$\xrightarrow{\ +\,\text{HClO}_4 \text{ in } \text{H}_2\text{O}\ } \quad \text{CH}_3-\text{CH}_2-\text{CH}_2-\overset{\oplus}{\text{N}}\equiv\text{N}\cdot\text{aq.} \qquad\qquad (6.29)$$

$$\text{XXXI}$$

$$+ \text{HNO}_2 \qquad\qquad \Big| -\text{N}_2$$

$$\text{CH}_3-\text{CH}_2-\text{CH}_2-\text{NH}_2$$

$$\text{CH}_3-\text{CH}_2-\overset{\oplus}{\text{CH}}_2\cdot\text{aq.} \xrightarrow{\ +\text{H}_2\text{O}\ } \text{CH}_3\text{CH}_2\text{CH}_2\text{OH} + \text{H}^\oplus$$

$$\text{XXXII}$$

$$\text{CH}_3-\text{CH}=\text{CH}_2 + \text{H}^\oplus$$

$$\text{CH}_3-\overset{\oplus}{\text{CH}}-\text{CH}_3\cdot\text{aq.} \xrightarrow{\ +\text{H}_2\text{O}\ } \text{CH}_3-\underset{\overset{|}{\text{OH}}}{\text{CH}}-\text{CH}_3 + \text{H}^\oplus$$

$$\text{XXXIII}$$

still under discussion. The formation of secondary or tertiary products from n-alkyl halides occurs in general when only very weakly nucleophilic reagents are available, that is, when $k_s \ll k'$ in scheme (6.27). Since about 1950 the fundamental difference between these solvolyses and the deamination has attracted considerable attention.

The problem is intimately connected with that of the structure of carbonium ions. Based on facts such as those presented above, it has been postulated that the carbonium ions formed from diazo compounds are characterized by either being very rich in energy or by lacking solvation or by being otherwise particularly reactive (see, for example, *135, 423, 424, 485, 499, 747, 1708, 1709, 1718, 1878*).

However, the experimental data have also been interpreted in other ways. Thus Darzens (*524*), Burr (*135*), and others (*1387*) have proposed a concerted mechanism in which deamination proceeds via a diazohydroxide. Because of their experiences with alkyldiazonium carboxylate ion pairs in non-polar solvents, Huisgen and Rüchardt (*1129, 1130*) have considered an S_N2 mechanism with frontal attack. Streitwieser (*1971, 1972, 1974*) proposed an S_N2-like process with an extreme degree of neighbouring group participation. The same author (*1971*) has also provided a comprehensive review of a great number of facts gleaned from the literature which can only be interpreted with difficulty using classical or non-classical carbonium ions as intermediates.

At present the discussion of this problem has not yet found its conclusion and considerable advances remain to be made. For this reason, the views expressed are here treated less fully than either the work carried out to support them or their significance in the field of nucleophilic aliphatic substitution justifies.

Huisgen and Reimlinger (*1126*) have pointed out that the splitting off of nitrogen from an alkyldiazonium ion probably represents the only known instance of an exothermic ionization at a carbon atom sp^3-hybridized in the normal manner. The consequences flowing from the recognition of this fact were first evaluated in the case of the decomposition reactions of the nitroso-acylalkylamines (*1126, 1127, 1129, 1130*) and then applied by Huisgen and Rüchardt (*1129, 1130*) to deamination proper.

Figure 6.1 contains the essentials of the energy profile diagram of the solvolysis of alkyl halides or alkyldiazonium ions. In the usual way (see, for example, *193*), the potential energy of the individual stages is plotted against the reaction coordinate to show the progress of the reaction. In order to compare the two processes, the potential energy of the starting materials has been set to the same value, although the actual energy content of the diazonium ion is considerably greater than that of the alkyl halide. It can be seen that the alkyl halide must overcome an activation energy barrier (18 to 25 kcal/mole) to form a carbonium ion, which possesses more potential energy than the original system. Hence the formation of carbonium ions here is an endothermic process. On the contrary, the very rapid decomposition of alkyldiazonium ions is exothermic and the activation energy barrier corresponds to only 5 to 10 kcal/mole. This estimate, due to Huisgen, is based on an activation energy of 23 kcal/mole determined by Waring and Abrams (*2108*) for the decomposition of aromatic diazonium ions. The absence of the resonance stabilization between aryl and diazonium groups would be expected to lower the activation energy for alkyldiazonium ions to the value quoted above. The changes in the entropy of solvation act in the same direction: the solvated nitrogen atoms of the alkyldiazonium ion cease to be so, whilst in the solvolysis of alkyl halides the halide ion of the intermediate is more strongly solvated than the halogen atom of the starting material.

Recently, Hammond (*915*) has propounded a rule according to which the structure of the transition state of a highly endothermic reaction largely corresponds to that of the products, whereas that of a highly exothermic process continues to resemble more nearly those of the reactants. In the transition state T of the solvolysis of alkyl halides the covalent carbon–halogen bond is therefore already essentially broken and the carbon is almost a carbonium ion. However, the decomposition of alkyldiazonium ions is totally different: here the transition state T' is passed at a time when the positive charge is still mainly on the nitrogen. The configuration and type of bonding of the carbon atom of the transition state T', which determine the course of the reaction, are largely equivalent to those of the sp^3-hybridized atom present initially (see also *485*).

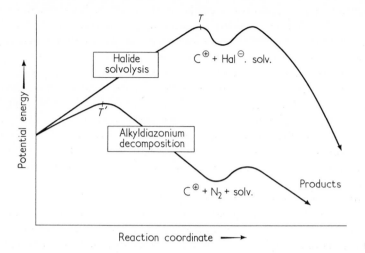

Figure 6.1

Energy profile diagram for the solvolysis of alkyl halides and alkyldiazonium ions (*1125*)

Streitwieser (*1974*) has accepted Huisgen's energy profile diagram and pointed out an important consequence of it, when other particles such as solvent or gegenions, take part in the transition state of the decomposition of diazonium ions. If the energy of activation of the process is only 5 to 10 kcal/mole, it is to be expected that the range of activation energies of competing reactions would be similarly limited. For example, if in the solvolysis of an alkyl halide ($E_a = 25$ kcal/mole) a side reaction possesses an energy of activation 20% greater ($E_a' = 30$ kcal/mole) it may be assumed that the ratio of the activation energies of the corresponding reactions of an alkyldiazonium ion would also be 100:120, say, 5 and 6 kcal/mole, respectively. Provided the entropies of activation are equal, it follows that the side reaction will give rise to 0·02% of the total products in the case of the alkyl halide, but to 16% in that of the alkyldiazonium ion. It can be seen from this example that even when the analyses of the reaction products suggest great differences, these are still founded on largely equivalent mechanisms and energetics.

The energy profile diagram provides an explanation of the great difference in reactivity between a halogeno and a diazonium group bound to a bridgehead carbon atom, a difference already mentioned at the beginning of this section. The inertness of 1-chloro-7,7-dimethylnorcamphane (XXIIIc) towards nucleophilic reagents is due to the fact that the rigid, bicyclic ring system does not permit the bridgehead atom to achieve the planar carbonium form. 1-Diazonium-7,7-dimethylnorcamphane (XXIIIb) on the contrary requires only little activation in order to lose the molecule of nitrogen and in the transition state the configuration of a planar carbonium ion has by no means had to be achieved. In addition it may be concluded from Bartlett's experiments (*192, 195–197*) that the participation of solvent molecules or neighbouring groups in deamination is unnecessary.

There arises now the question of whether a classical 7, 7-dimethylnorcamphane carbonium ion will not have to be formed as the reaction proceeds further. This would be expected from Figure 6.1. At present a definite answer is not available. One could imagine that its formation is forced to occur because the back-reaction (carbonium ion $+ N_2 \rightarrow$ alkyldiazonium ion) is against all experience; in spite of the high energy content of the carbonium ion, the energy level of the system of intermediate products (carbonium ion $+ N_2$) is so much lower than T' because of the strongly exothermic character of the conversion of $-N_2$ into N_2 that the back-reaction is impossible in practice.

As an alternative in the case of 1-diazo-7-7-dimethylnorcamphane has been discussed an S_N1 reaction of the corresponding diazohydroxide. Reaction (6.30), studied by Asahina and Yamaguti (*76*), proceeds most readily and so makes such a mechanism very improbable [see also Bartlett and Lewis (*197*)].

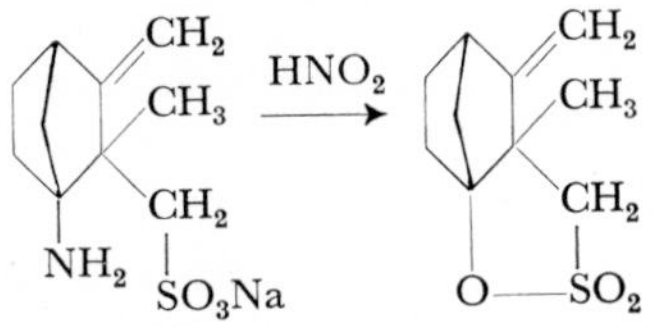

$$(6.30)$$

Mills (*1448*) and Huisgen (*1125*) considered an S_N2 *process with frontal attack* for the reactions of the oriented diazonium carboxylate ion pair (*vide supra*). Of course, frontal attack is forbidden in normal bimolecular nucleophilic substitutions [see for example (*615*)], but, since the activation energy required for the splitting off of the nitrogen molecule is only very small, the help of the base in stretching the C—N bond is not necessary to the same extent as it is, say, with a C—Cl link. In the transition state belonging to this mechanism (XXXIV) therefore, one hybridized sp^3 orbital would hold *both* the incoming and the outgoing substituent. Along the reaction coordinate of Figure 6.1 the character of the orbital alters progressively. According to Huisgen, the more help is required from the base the more the hybridization partakes of the sp^3 than of the p character.

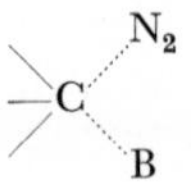

$$\begin{array}{c} \diagdown \quad\quad N_2 \\ -C \cdots \\ \diagup \quad\quad B \end{array}$$

XXXIV

The kinetics of the reactions of diazoacetic ester with acids, described by Hammett (*914e*) and by Roberts (*1714*), agree with such a mechanism. In the decomposition of the ester in benzene the acid concentration does not enter the kinetic equation directly, as would have been expected if the formation of the alkyldiazonium ion had been rate-determining, but as the square. The rate of the analogous reaction in aqueous hydrochloric acid is not only proportional to the hydrogen but also to the chloride ion concentration. This can be interpreted as being due to a preliminary equilibrium between diazoalkane and alkyldiazonium ion, followed by a slow reaction of second order between the alkyldiazonium ion and water or chloride.

Presumably the reactions with thiocyanate performed by Taft and Cannell (*412, 1998*) are similar. The deamination of isobutylamine in water gives a very different ratio of iso- to s- to t-product when sodium thiocyanate is added (without NaSCN: 10:19:71, with 7·7 M NaSCN: 23:21:56). Even more marked is the effect of thiocyanate on the deamination of n-alkylamines. Since the thiocyanate ion possesses two nucleophilic centres (N and S), the ratio between the products of the reaction of (XXXV):(XXXVI), i.e. thiocyanate to isothiocyanate, is informative: in fact it is independent of the constitution of the starting material and of the nature of the reaction. For example, the ratio (XXXV): (XXXVI) in the t-butyl fraction [R = $(CH_3)_3C$] remains practically the same whether t-butyl chloride undergoes solvolysis in the presence of thiocyanate or whether isobutylamine or t-butylamine is deaminated (XXXV:XXXVI = 1·9

$$R—SCN \qquad\qquad R—NCS$$
$$XXXV \qquad\qquad\quad XXXVI$$

to 2·5). All these results point to the possibility that the thiocyanate ion participates at least to some extent in the breaking of the C—N bond.

As regards the S_N2 mechanism with frontal attack the work on the deamination of cycloalkylamines (*233, 291, 526, 528, 529, 1097, 1448, 1972*) (see § 5.7) is of interest. In general equatorial alcohols are obtained in good yield from equatorial cyclohexylamines, the formation of olefins being very much suppressed. However, solvolysis of equatorial cycloalkyl *p*-toluenesulphonates gives axial cycloalkanols (*2171*). On the other hand, deamination of axial amines produces large amounts of olefins and only little of the alcohols, which possess predominantly the equatorial conformations [in contrast to Shoppee's experience with steroids (*1890*)]. That steric factors are not responsible for stabilizing particular conformations has been shown by Streitwieser and Coverdale (*1972*): *cis*-cyclohexylamine-2-*d* yields 94% *cis*- and only about 6% *trans*-cyclohexanol-2-*d*. Since presumably both the reactant and the product will have carried the largest group in the more stable equatorial position, this shows that the conformation is maintained also in a cyclohexylamine in which the 2-substituent (deuterium) is practically indistinguishable sterically from protium.

Shoppee and co-workers (*1890, 2335*) found that steroids with an equatorial amino group in the 2-, 3-, 4-, 6-, or 7-position show the same characteristics as equatorial cyclohexylamines, whilst the axial amines react, also with retention of configuration, uniquely to furnish the corresponding axial alcohols, much elimination occurring concomitantly. This contrast with the behaviour of axial

9 Zollinger

cyclohexylamine cannot be explained unambiguously. Shoppee *et al.* think that steric hindrance is important in bi- and poly-cyclic systems (e.g. in axial 4 β-cholestanamine) and found a connection to exist between the degree of steric hindrance to the approach of the basic reagent in deaminations of axial aminosteroids and the substitution/elimination ratio, increased steric hindrance leading to less of the hydroxy products.

In recent years, as already mentioned briefly, Streitwieser (*1971, 1972,1974*) has developed another mechanism for deamination, starting with Huisgen's energy profile diagram. He has propounded the hypothesis that the different competing reactions branch out not from the carbonium but from the diazonium ion. For Streitwieser's mechanism the observation (*1974*) is important that optically active butylamine-1-*d* (*1973*) yields 35% s-butyl and 65% n-butyl acetate on reaction with sodium nitrite in glacial acetic acid. The latter compound proved to be 69% inverted and 31% racemized. A pure S_N1 reaction would be expected to give complete racemization, a pure S_N2 one with frontal attack should have led to retention of configuration. Streitwieser has postulated that the positive charge which develops on the carbon atom as the exothermic ionization process takes place produces the inversion of configuration. In other words, Streitwieser assumes that the alkyldiazonium decomposition takes place by a concerted mechanism: the dissociation of the C—N bond has a most pronounced effect on the changes occurring simultaneously within the molecule or on the addition of the nucleophilic reagent.

On this basis can be interpreted, for example, the difference between the deamination of s-butylamine in water (*1974*) and the acetolysis of s-butyl *p*-toluenesulphonate (*343*). The olefin fraction from the deamination consists of 25% 1-butene, 19% *cis*-, and 56% *trans*-2-butene, whilst that from the *p*-toluenesulphonate contains 10% 1-butene, 43% *cis*-, and 47% *trans*-2-butene. The relative amounts of *cis*- and *trans*-isomer obtained in the second process is in agreement with the formation of a carbonium ion intermediate. On Streitwieser's mechanism the deamination should yield predominantly the *trans*-compound, because in 2 of the 3 conformations of the 2-butanediazonium ion of importance here a *trans*-elimination of $H^{\oplus}$ and N_2 is possible. In general concerted eliminations prefer to take place with the ejection of a hydrogen in *trans*-position to the leaving group.

In a review, Streitwieser (*1971*) has interpreted a great number of instances cited in the literature on the basis of his mechanism. However, since such very pronounced participation by neighbouring groups is most unusual, the final decision on the acceptability of the mechanism cannot yet be made.

Very important for the discussion of mechanism are the migrations undergone by alkyl and especially aryl groups, observed particularly in the deamination of substituted ethylamines. The concept of *bridged or non-classical carbonium ion pair intermediates*, originally postulated by Lane and Wallis (*1291*) for the Wolff rearrangement of optically active diazoketones, has been developed particularly by Cram (*477–481, 483, 484*) by means of the solvolysis of 3-phenyl-2-butyl *p*-toluenesulphonates. Thus, whilst acetolysis of the L-*threo* diastereomers gives complete racemization, in the case of the L-*erythro* isomer the sign and size of the optical rotation remain unaltered by the substitution. This can be understood if phenonium ions such as (XXXVII) and (XXXVIII) appear as intermediates capable of holding the configuration at 2-C and 3-C. The phe-

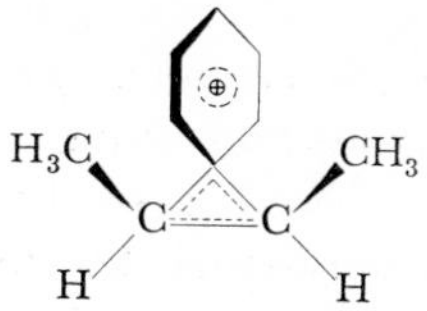

XXXVII 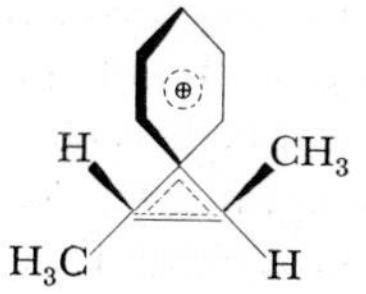   XXXVIII

nonium ion (XXXVII) is symmetrical, whilst the isomeric ion (XXXVIII) has no plane of symmetry. Ring opening occurs at 2-C and 3-C with equal probability. Since the ion (XXXVII) is internally compensated, it leads only to the racemic product, but ring opening at either carbon atom of the optically active ion (XXXVIII) gives the same optically active compound. The latter has the configuration of the starting material.

Rearrangements during deamination have been proved to occur by Roberts and his co-workers (*1708, 1715, 1718*) as well as by Lee and Spinks (*1304*) by means of 1-C^{14}-ethylamine and its derivatives. Thus 1-C^{14}-2-phenethylamine is converted into not only 1-C^{14}- but also 27% 2-C^{14}-2-phenethanol in the form

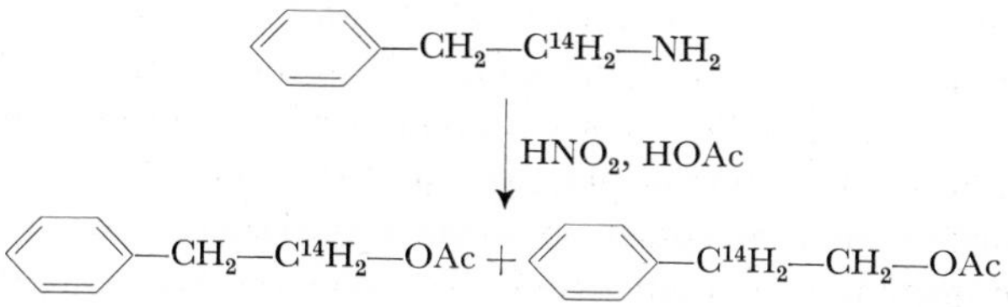

$$\text{HNO}_2, \text{HOAc} \qquad\qquad (6.31)$$

of their acetates (6.31) (*1304, 1715*). This permits the conclusion that 54% of the reaction proceeds via a symmetrical phenonium ion (XXXIX). With

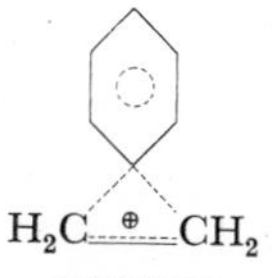

XXXIX

1-C^{14}-2-*p*-methoxyphenethylamine the corresponding quantity is as high as 90%, which is in accord with limiting structures of the type of (XXXVII). However, analogous experiments with 1-C^{14}-propylamine (*1708*) gave apart from 2-propanol a 1-propanol fraction which contained only 8·5% of the rearranged product. 1-C^{14}-Ethylamine produces only very little 2-C^{14}-ethanol (1·5% on the yield of alcohol) (*1718*). It follows that intermediates equivalent to the phenonium ion (**XXXIX**) but with a hydrogen or methyl as bridge are formed with considerably more difficulty than the ethyl or propyl cation has in reacting with the solvent.

The parallel investigation of the deamination of 1-C^{14}-cyclopropanemethyl-amine by Roberts *et al.* (*1381, 1711*) led to a mixture of cyclobutanol and cyclopropanemethanol, the C^{14}-distribution showing that the reactivity of the three methylene groups originally present is very much but not exactly the same. To explain this result, Roberts and his co-workers assume that the intermediate is not the symmetrical tricyclobutonium ion (**XXXX**), but consists of three *dl*-pairs of distinct, isomeric, unsymmetrical, pyramidal, and non-classical bicyclobutonium ions (**XXXXI**a–c), which are able to rearrange into one another rapidly but not instantaneously.

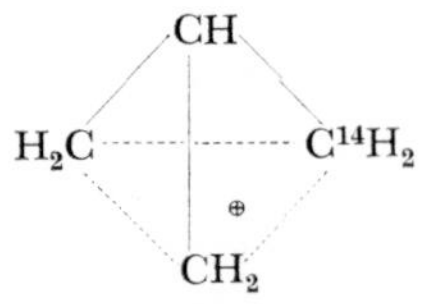

$$\text{XXXX}$$

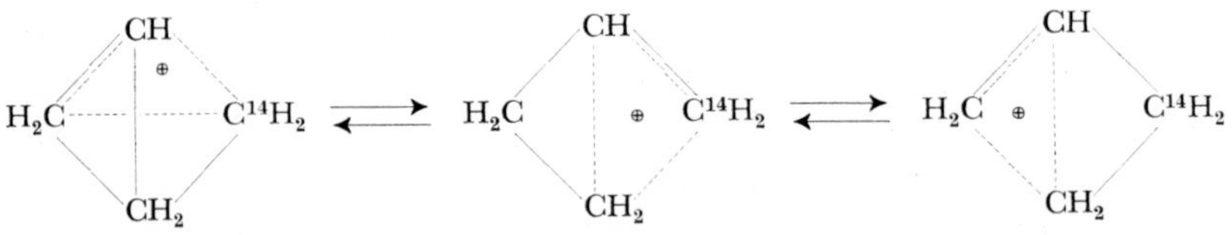

$$\text{XXXXI a} \qquad \text{XXXXI b} \qquad \text{XXXXI c}$$

The behaviour of 3-phenyl-2-butylamine is of interest because of its relation to the solvolyses of the corresponding *p*-toluenesulphonates mentioned above. Bonner and Tanner (*287*) deaminated the compound marked in the 1-position (**XXXXII**) and proved 3-phenyl-2-butanol (**XXXXIII**) as well as the products of hydrogen and methyl migration (**XXXXIV, XXXXV**) to have been formed. The 1-carbon atom of (**XXXXIII**) turned out to contain exactly 50% of the radioactivity of the starting material and so it was concluded that the open carbonium ion has only an extremely short life being converted almost immediately into a bridged ion.

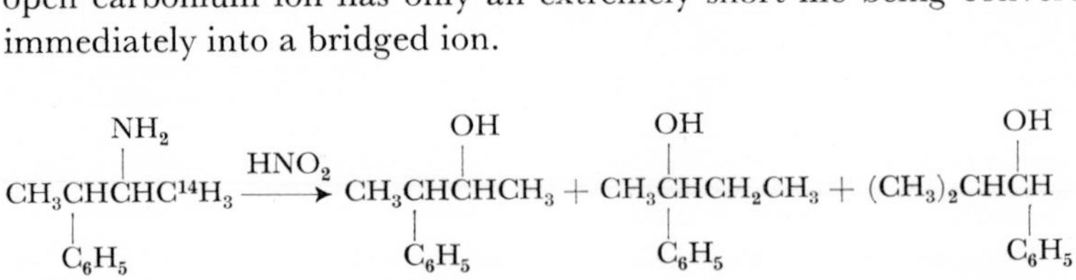

$$\underset{\substack{| \\ C_6H_5 \\ \text{XXXXII}}}{\overset{\substack{NH_2 \\ |}}{CH_3CHCHC^{14}H_3}} \xrightarrow{HNO_2} \underset{\substack{| \\ C_6H_5 \\ \text{XXXXIII}}}{\overset{\substack{OH \\ |}}{CH_3CHCHCH_3}} + \underset{\substack{| \\ C_6H_5 \\ \text{XXXXIV}}}{\overset{\substack{OH \\ |}}{CH_3CHCH_2CH_3}} + \underset{\substack{| \\ C_6H_5 \\ \text{XXXXV}}}{\overset{\substack{OH \\ |}}{(CH_3)_2CHCH}} \qquad (6.32)$$

Cram and McCarty (*485*) have analysed the mixtures obtained on deaminating each of the diastereomers of 3-phenyl-2-butylamine and were able to confirm that not only does the phenyl group migrate but so also do hydrogen and methyl. There are important differences in the composition of the reaction products from the two isomers. In the case of the *threo*-amine 32% can be attributed to methyl, 24% to phenyl, and 24% to hydrogen migration, whilst the products from the *erythro*-amine are in agreement with the assumption that 68% of the intermediates was formed by migration of phenyl, 20% by that of hydrogen, and only 6% by that of methyl. These proportions are clearly in accord with the conformational populations of the starting materials (Figure 6.2), provided it is postulated that a *trans*-conformation between the diazonium

Conformations of the L(+)-*threo*-diazonium ion

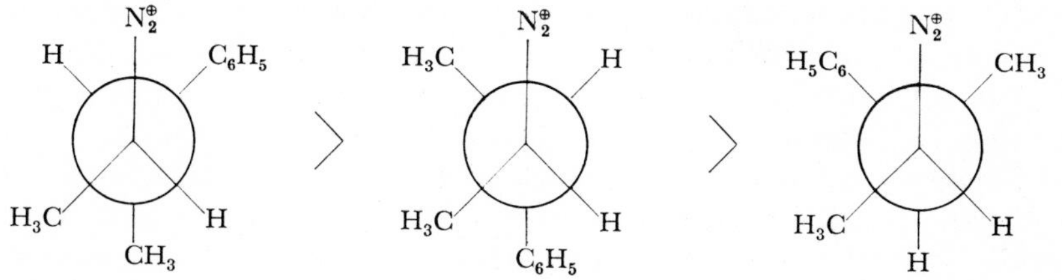

Conformations of the L(+)-*erythro*-diazonium ion

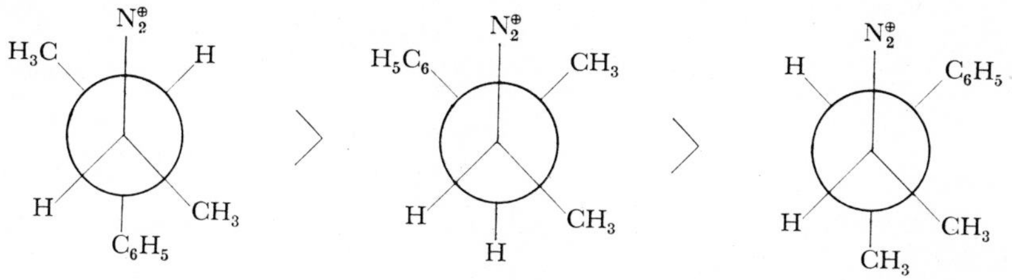

Figure 6.2

Conformational populations in the diastereomers of the 3-phenylbutane-2-diazonium ion

and the migrating group is a condition of reaction. Cram and McCarty concluded from their experiments that symmetrical, bridged ions of the type of (**XXXVII**) and (**XXXIX**) are most probably concerned in phenyl migration and possibly also in methyl migration.

However, deaminations of 1,1-diaryl-2-aminoethanols and 1,2,2-triphenylethylamine, labelled at the 1-position and/or in the 1-phenyl residue, give results which can be interpreted according to Curtin and Crew (*499*) and Bonner and Collins (*283–286, 455–457*), respectively, without assuming the formation of bridged ions and simply by means of open carbonium ions in equilibrium with one another [e.g. (**XXXXVI**) and (**XXXXVII**)]. It is not

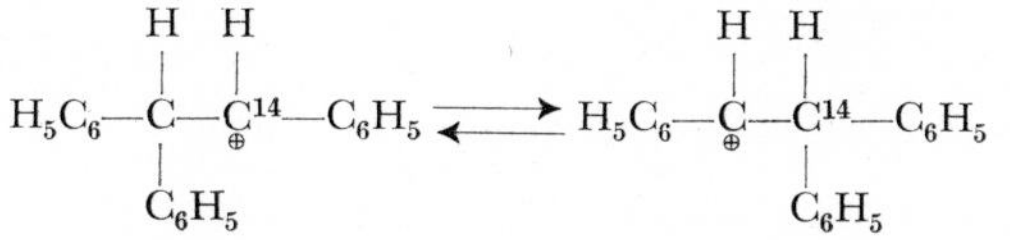

XXXXVI   XXXXVII

decided at present whether a symmetrical phenonium ion is here a relatively stable intermediate or only a transition state nor whether the process is based on a concerted mechanism of nitrogen evolution with phenyl migration (neighbouring group participation according to Streitwieser) or whether it is the result of the high energy content of carbonium ions formed primarily and described as 'hot' (Cram, Curtin, Roberts, and others). The discussion of this topic has by no means been concluded yet.

Bonner and Collins considered with the help of scheme (6.33) the results of the deamination of labelled $1, 2, 2$-triphenylethylamine (**XXXXVIII**) (*286*) and those of stereochemical experiments (*457*). They explain the data on the basis of equilibrating classical carbonium ions (**XXXXIX–LII**) which tend essentially to retain their configurations because of (*a*) steric shielding from attack in the rear by the entering group and (*b*) the similarity in rate of phenyl migration (k_Φ) and that of rotation about the central C—C bond (k_r). Bonner and Collins's arguments may be compared with Roberts's explanation of the deamination of 1-C^{14}-cyclopropanemethylamine (see above). In both cases the distribution of C^{14} in the products excludes a mechanism with one symmetrical cationic intermediate and therefore suggests that four classical and three non-classical ions, respectively, are in rapid, but not instantaneous equilibrium.

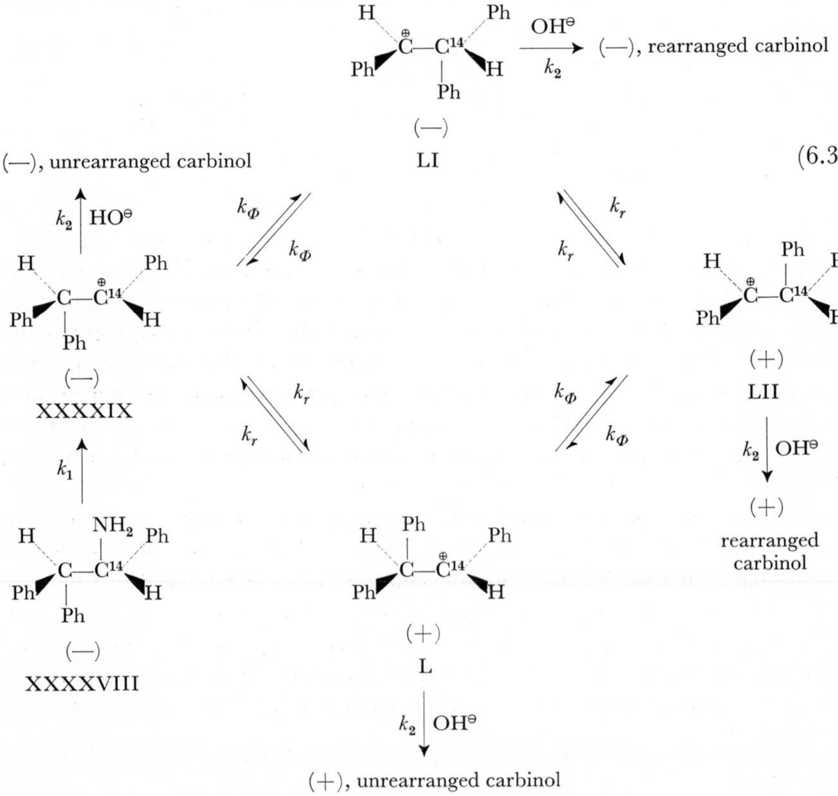

(6.33)

Of interest also are investigations into the migration of differently substituted 2,2-diarylethylamines. Here the selectivity in deaminations is always less than in other nucleophilic substitutions. Whilst in the acetolysis of 2-phenyl-2-*p*-tolylethyl *p*-toluenesulphonate the tolyl group migrates three times as rapidly as the phenyl group (*396*), in deamination the ratio is only 1·18:1 (*135, 222*)[2]. Even more marked is the contrast between pinacolone rearrangements and semipinacolic deaminations: the ratio between methoxyphenyl and phenyl residues in the rearrangement of a glycol is 500:1 (*111, 114, 2209*) and is to be compared with one of 1·56:1 for the deamination of the corresponding 2-aminoethanol (*499*). Interpretations differ. The low selectivity in migration can be explained by the high energy content of the 'hot' carbonium ions. On the other hand, Streitwieser (*1971*) postulates that the low energy of activation of the splitting off of nitrogen from the diazonium ion is of the same order of magnitude as the activation energy of rotation about the C—C bond. Thus the ratio between the populations of conformations (LIII) and (LIV) should approximate to 1 and this factor would have more influence on the nature of the products here than with reactions of higher activation energies. Whilst

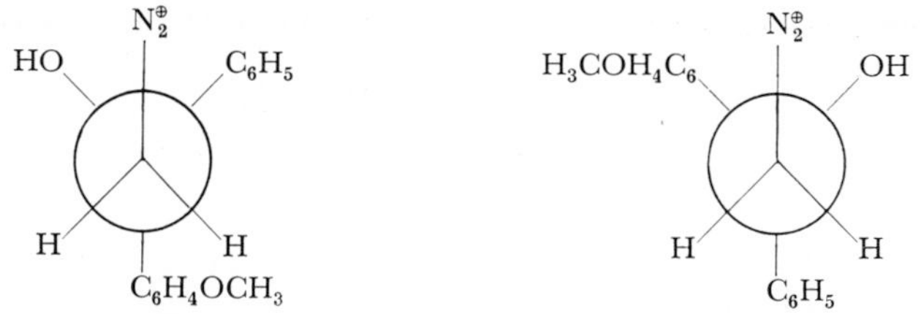

LIII   LIV

Streitwieser goes on to deduce a large degree of participation by the aryl groups in the splitting off of nitrogen, Huisgen (*1129, 1130*) points out that according to the energy profile diagram (Figure 6.1) the positive charge on the carbon atom in the transition state is so small that help from neighbouring groups is neither necessary nor possible. Presumably therefore the primary intermediate is an open carbonium ion. The ratio between the migration of methoxyphenyl and phenyl residues in the decomposition of nitrosoacylamines is practically the same as that in deamination, in agreement with mechanism (6.29).

A further informative experiment was reported recently by Raaen and Collins (*1669*) who studied the deamination of $1\text{-}C^{14}\text{-}2,2$-diphenyl-2-*o*-tolylethylamine. They found the ratio between migration of tolyl and phenyl to be 0·75, whereas in the corresponding pinacolone rearrangement it attains 3·0. In itself preponderating phenyl migration is surprising, but it can be explained as follows. In the first place the diazonium ion yields an open carbonium ion, but this is so short-lived that it cannot reach equilibrium with its rotational

---

[2] Presumably Ciereszko and Burr's observation of more rapid migration of phenyl than tolyl groups is erroneous (*424*).

isomers. Phenyl migration predominates because two of the three conformations (LV) to (LVII) produced on evolution of nitrogen favour it and the carbonium ion 'has no time' to rotate into the energetically preferred conformation (LVII) *before* the neighbouring aryl group is drawn into the reaction.

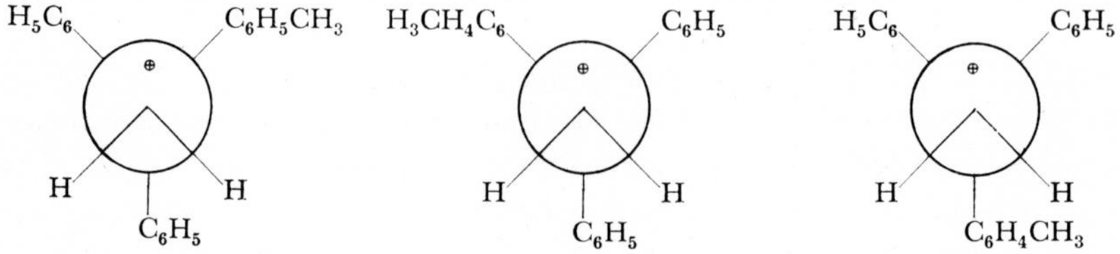

H_5C_6 — $C_6H_5CH_3$ $H_3CH_4C_6$ — C_6H_5 H_5C_6 — C_6H_5

H — H H — H H — H

C_6H_5 C_6H_5 $C_6H_4CH_3$

LV   LVI   LVII

Summarizing the discussion presented in this section, it must be admitted
that the present situation in this field is unsatisfactory in that it is not yet possible to integrate all the observations into one universal mechanism. In spite
of the expenditure of much effort, a great deal of work remains to be done in
order to advance beyond the current, rather rudimentary understanding of
these reactions.

7. Reactions of Aromatic Diazo Compounds

7.1 Introduction

In contrast to their aliphatic analogues, the aromatic diazonium ions are particles of considerable stability. As already mentioned briefly in § 3.3, the tendency to split off nitrogen is lessened even further when the aromatic nucleus carries electron-releasing substituents, that is, those with $+M$ and $+I$ effects. The mesomerism (I a–I b) stabilizes the CN-bond.

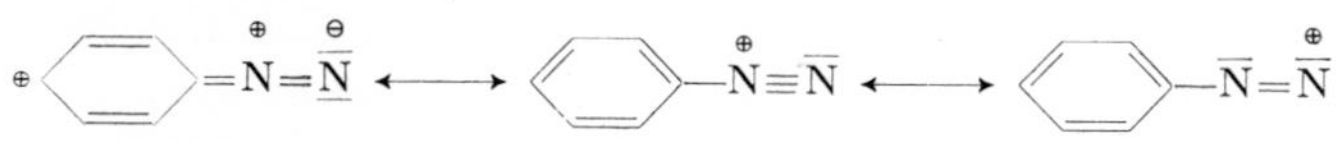

(as well as o-quinonoid structures)

$\qquad$ I b $\qquad$ I a $\qquad$ I c

The limiting structures (I b) and (I c) show that aryldiazonium ions possess electrophilic character and (I c) provides a basis for understanding reaction with a nucleophilic partner at the nitrogen atom. Processes of this type will be dealt with in § 7.4, but those of the greatest preparative and technological importance, namely, azo coupling and the formation of diazoamino compounds, are discussed in detail in Chapters 9 to 11 and 8, respectively.

Structure (I b) is the starting point for the attack by nucleophilic reagents on the nucleus. The diazonium group exhibits the greatest $-M$ effect of any substituent known to date and hence surprising reactions are frequently observed to occur at the aromatic ring when an arylamine is converted into the diazonium salt. This is simply a consequence of changing an electron-releasing substituent (NH_2) into a strongly electron-attracting one ($N_2^{\oplus}$). Reactions of this type are considered in § 7.3.

In analogy to the deamination of aliphatic amines, aromatic diazo groups can also undergo nucleophilic substitution. This process, which is dealt with in § 7.2, at the moment represents the only example of an aromatic S_N1 reaction.

Unlike the aliphatic diazo compounds, the aromatic ones take part in many important radical reactions (§ 7.5) as well as in processes catalysed by metals or metal ions, the mechanisms of which are by no means clear in all cases (§ 7.6).

Waters (2111) has grouped the reactions of aromatic diazo compounds according to mechanism and Saunders (1776i), in reviewing them from the preparative point of view, developed a system which enables all the known reactions to be classified.

From the standpoint of the technology of azo dyestuffs, all these various reactions are frequently described as diazo decompositions. On the one hand, this is due to the fact that these processes compete with the actual azo coupling (or formation of the diazoamino compound) by removing the diazonium ions which alone are capable of coupling. On the other, aromatic diazo compounds on standing in substance or in solution as well as during coupling often yield the so-called diazo resins, the composition of which will be considered in § 7.9.

How a reaction of an aromatic diazo compound is proceeding is best followed experimentally using azo coupling as a test. Suitable components, such as resorcinol, 2-naphthol-3,6-disulphonic acid, or 8-amino-1-naphthol-3,6-disulphonic acid, on tiles or filter paper, can provide proof of the presence of unreacted diazo compound almost without exception.

The methods for the kinetic investigation of such reactions, in which nitrogen is liberated quantitatively, were developed by Hausser and Muller (*990–992*), who chose to measure the rate by the amount of gas formed. Most of the subsequent workers in the field of kinetics of the diazo decomposition followed suit. Directions for the manometric determination of nitrogen with the highest accuracy have been given recently by DeTar (*552*). These methods are limited to decompositions in which the whole of the diazo nitrogen is liberated as N_2 and so cannot be applied when diazo resins or azo compounds are produced.

Euler (*688*) used the mineral acid formed in the normal decomposition as a means of determining the kinetics, but this method is less exact as shown by Hantzsch (*942*) and by Cain (*401*).

Often, particularly when the conditions are such that not all the diazo nitrogen is liberated as N_2, it is advantageous to follow the decrease with time of the concentration of the diazonium ions. At predetermined periods, portions of the decomposing solution are added to an appropriate component which couples quickly and quantitatively and the azo dye formed is estimated colorimetrically (*1332, 1370*).

Elofson's polarographic determination of the concentration of diazonium ions (*676*) is probably also suitable for the investigation of diazo decompositions (see § 10.1).

7.2 Nucleophilic Substitution of the Diazonium Group

A great many of the reactions which occur during diazo decomposition in aqueous acid solution belong to the S_N1 type of nucleophilic aromatic substitution. The diazonium ion dissociates in a rate-determining first step (7.1), giving an aryl cation and a molecule of nitrogen. Subsequently, the carbonium ion quickly interacts with nucleophilic agents (7.2 a–d).

That this mechanism obtains can be shown in several ways. Back in the early kinetic investigations it had been found that the diazo decomposition is a reaction of first order. If solvent molecules are involved (7.2 a and 7.2 d), this result would also be compatible with an S_N2 mechanism, but the fact, frequently confirmed (*401, 979, 1654, 1655, 1855, 1856*), that the reaction (7.2c) is not proportional to the concentration of and is practically independent of the nature of the halogen ions present speaks unequivocally in favour of an S_N1 process. In several investigations (*979, 1654, 1655*), it has been found that a high salt

$$Ar-\overset{\oplus}{N}\equiv N \longrightarrow Ar^{\oplus} + N\equiv N \tag{7.1}$$

$$Ar^{\oplus} + H_2O \longrightarrow Ar-\overset{\oplus}{O}H_2 \underset{\longleftarrow}{\longrightarrow} Ar-OH + H^{\oplus} \tag{7.2a}$$

$$Ar^{\oplus} + OH^{\ominus} \longrightarrow Ar-OH \tag{7.2b}$$

$$Ar^{\oplus} + X^{\ominus} \longrightarrow ArX \qquad X^{\ominus} = \text{halide ion} \tag{7.2c}$$

$$Ar^{\oplus} + ROH \longrightarrow Ar-\underset{H}{\overset{\oplus}{O}}-R \underset{\longleftarrow}{\longrightarrow} Ar-O-R + H^{\oplus} \tag{7.2d}$$

content of the reaction medium retards the decomposition, but only to a small extent, and this can be interpreted to be due to ionic strength, be it either a general or specific salt effect according to Brönsted. The slight decrease in the rate of decomposition observed by Cain (*401*) and by Blumberger (*270*) on increasing the excess of sulphuric acid is probably another example of the same phenomenon.

Recently, DeTar *et al.* (*554, 558*) have determined the diazo decomposition of the benzenediazonium ion and that of some simple monosubstituted derivatives in acid solution between 15° and 44° with extremely high precision. They were able to show unequivocally that simple ions (Cl$^{\ominus}$, HSO$_4^{\ominus}$, and BF$_4^{\ominus}$), the hydrogen ion concentration (0·01 M HCl, 0·05 M and 0·005 M H$_2$SO$_4$), and cupric ions have no influence on the decomposition.

The isolation of a series of interesting products, such as diphenylchloronium salts, is readily understood as resulting from reactions following (7.1) and (7.2), that is, as a consequence of the interaction of aryl cations with chlorobenzene already formed (*1520*).

The influence of substituents on the rate of the decomposition of diazonium ions is that expected on the basis of the S_N1 mechanism (*1333*): reaction is favoured by electron-releasing groups in *m*-position, but those with a —M and —I effect (for example, NO$_2$ or COOH) in *m*- or *p*-orientation hinder the splitting off of nitrogen.

That diazobenzenes with hydroxy, alkoxy, alkyl, or aryl residues in the *p*-position are more stable than the parent compound is apparently incomprehensible. Hughes (*1100*) supposes that this surprising stabilization is caused by an increase of the double bond character of the CN-link brought about by the +M effect of the substituent (II a–II b). The hindrance to decomposition is particularly marked in the case of *o*- and *p*-diazophenols.

CH$_3$—O—⟨ ⟩—$\overset{\oplus}{N}$≡N ⟷ CH$_3$—O=⟨ ⟩=$\overset{\oplus}{N}$=$\overset{\ominus}{N}$|

II a   II b

E. S. Lewis *et al.* (*1332*) found that *p*-toluene-α, α, α-*d₃*-diazonium ions decompose a little more rapidly than the undeuterated compound. This 'inverted' kinetic isotope effect is attributed by Lewis to the lower hyperconjugation of a CD- compared with a CH-bond, the hyperconjugation being more important in stabilizing the diazonium salt than the cation formed from it. The extremely small difference in reactivity between the two substances ($k_H/k_D = 0.99$) is probably due to the fact that hyperconjugation is only weak, as is being increasingly realized, in spite of the earlier frequent overvaluation of the effect (*136, 216, 1888*).

A dimethylamino group increases the stability of the diazonium ion in strongly acid solution, when it is converted into an ammonium residue [$\overset{\oplus}{N}H(CH_3)_2$] (*107, 847*). In weakly acid media it still retards decomposition through the mesomerism analogous to (IIa–IIb) (*538, 1449*). Various observations (*1333, 2161*) show, however, that factors other than electronic ones must be taken into account in explaining the effect of substituents on the diazo decomposition.

Several reviews of the influence of substituents on the rate of decomposition of diazobenzene are available, that by Crossley, Kienle, and Benbrook (*496*) probably being the most comprehensive. In addition the publications by Snow (*1918*) and by Kothe (*1268*) record semiquantitative determinations of the decompositions of a great number of diazo compounds at 22° and 100°, respectively.

Recently, E. S. Lewis (*1329*) was able to reach some conclusions about the stability of the aromatic carbonium ion, which appears as an intermediate in these reactions. He determined the ratio between the chlorobenzene and the phenol formed, that is, between the products of reactions (7.2a) and (7.2c), in relation to the concentrations of salt and hydrochloric acid present. According to equation (7.3), this ratio is connected with the ratio between the corresponding rate constants k_W and k_{Cl} of the reactions (7.2a) and (7.2c), respectively. From the equation k_W/k_{Cl} can be calculated and is found to have a value of 2.5 ± 0.5 at 100°. It can be compared with the competition factors between chloride ion and water determined for reactions of other carbonium ions. Thus Swain *et al.* (*1989*) quote values of k_W/k_{Cl} of 3000, 600, and 180 for the triphenylmethyl, diphenylmethyl, and t-butyl cations and so the aromatic carbonium ion is considerably less selective in its behaviour. It follows from the laws deduced by Nelson and Brown (*1511, 1512*) as well as by Hammond (*915*) that it is less stable than the aliphatic carbonium ions mentioned, but it is more stable than the carbenes, which exhibit even lower selectivity (*608*) (see § 5.5).

$$\frac{[ArCl]}{[ArOH]} = \frac{k_{Cl}\,[Cl^{\ominus}]}{k_W\,[H_2O]}$$ (7.3)

Although in general, apart from the salt effect, the concentration of acid has no influence on the rate of reaction, as already pointed out, in solutions containing hydrobromic acid decomposition is accelerated (*496, 1454*). The problem has been investigated in detail by E. S. Lewis and Hinds (*1330*), who determined the ratio between the products (p-bromonitrobenzene and p-nitro-phenol) and the dependence of the rate on the concentration of the various ions present in solution for the diazo decomposition of p-nitrodiazobenzene in dilute sulphuric or hydrobromic acids in the presence of bromides. The reaction proved to be independent of the concentrations of hydrogen and sulphate ions, but is strongly affected by bromide. In the absence of bromide, the apparent first-order rate constant $k_{app.} = 1.6 \times 10^{-4}$ sec^{-1}; it increases in the presence of 2·12, 4·00, and 6·00 mol./l. bromide to $k_{app.} = 1.98, 2.50$, and 2.89×10^{-4} sec^{-1}, respectively, the ratio of products altering in parallel in favour of p-bromonitrobenzene. The change in the apparent rate constant is proportional to the bromide concentration.

These results can be explained by means of a system of three simultaneous reactions. Apart from the S_N1 processes (7.1) + (7.2a) and (7.1) + (7.2c), which lead to nitrophenol and bromonitrobenzene via the aryl cation, there occurs also a bimolecular reaction, namely, the rate-determining attack of the diazonium ion by bromide (7.4).

$$Ar-N_2^{\oplus} + Br^{\ominus} \longrightarrow Ar-Br + N_2 \qquad (7.4)$$

p-Phenylenebisdiazonium salts are especially interesting in nucleophilic substitutions because one diazonium group is activated by the other which represents the most powerful electron-attracting substituent known. E. S. Lewis and M. D. Johnson (*2411, 2412*) investigated the rates of reaction with various nucleophiles (water, hydroxyl, chloride, bromide, thiocyanate, and azide ions). In these reactions a bimolecular rate-determining step is involved also; however, in this instance Lewis and Johnson postulate an S_Ni mechanism (bonding of the attacking nucleophile both to carbon and to the terminal nitrogen of the diazonium group to be replaced) instead of the S_N2-type substitution (7.4).

Ward and co-workers (*2410*) recently described an improved method for replacing a diazonium residue by a nitro group.

Following the consideration of the decomposition of diazo compounds in aqueous media, it is worth while to glance at the behaviour of diazo compounds in other hydroxylic solvents, such as alcohols and carboxylic acids.

Kornblum (*1260, 1265*) pointed out some years ago that the reaction of diazonium salts with alcohols had been frequently misinterpreted. Griess (*871*) reported in 1864 that benzenediazonium sulphate and nitrate yield benzene and acetaldehyde with ethyl alcohol. Although it was shown repeatedly, not least by Hantzsch (*968*), that this reaction consists first of all of a nucleophilic substitution resulting in phenetole, $C_6H_5OC_2H_5$, and that benzene is obtained only in 5% yield, it continues to be quoted in textbooks as a method for replacing amino groups by hydrogen. Even Hantzsch's work is cited in the sense that diazo decomposition in methanol leads to the corresponding methoxy compound, whilst in ethanol reduction takes place.

The confusion is probably due in part to the fact that boiling in alcohol is not usually carried out in the total absence of water. Phenols are therefore expected as undesirable by-products, which are tested for by means of the coupling reaction. If the result is negative, it has mostly been assumed that the replacement of the diazo group by hydrogen has been completed successfully, but this assumption is unjustified, as, under the normal conditions of the coupling test, phenol ethers are also unable to couple with diazo compounds of average reactivity (cf. § 9.4). However, in weakly acid to neutral media the appearance of the reduction product and of acetaldehyde is possible, but this process employs a radical mechanism, which probably corresponds to that in methanol (563–565, 1406). As shown in § 7.5, it depends on the conditions of the reaction whether in alcohol a phenol ether is formed by an S_N1 mechanism or an aromatic hydrocarbon by a radical one. Kornblum's criticism is certainly valid, but there is known a series of reductive diazo fissions by means of alcohol, for which it can be shown unequivocally that the diazo group has been replaced by hydrogen and not by an alkoxy residue.

According to Pray's determinations (1654, 1655), the rate of decomposition of diazo compounds in various alcohols is 1·7 to 2·8 times more rapid, that in simple fatty acids 1·1 to 1·3 times slower than in water. These small differences from the aqueous decomposition indicate that also in alcohols and acids the reaction begins with a rate-determining unimolecular formation of aryl cations.

$$ArN_2^{\oplus} + \quad \text{COOR} \longrightarrow \text{COOR} \left(+ \text{COOAr} \right) \tag{7.5}$$

In investigating the action of heat on phenyldiazonium fluoborate in methyl benzoate at 76° and 100°, Makarova and Gribcenko (1367) recently obtained methyl m-phenylbenzoate apart from a little of the p-isomer. The analogous reaction in the n-propyl or n-butyl ester also follows scheme (7.5), but in addition some phenyl benzoate is formed. The fact that the phenyl group enters mainly in the m-position suggests that the process consists of a heterolytic arylation with phenyl cations as electrophilic components and not of a homolysis.

7.3 Reactions at the Aryl Nucleus Consequent on Diazotization

The preceding section dealt with those reactions in which the diazonium group was replaced. Splitting off of $-\overset{\oplus}{N}_2$ is bound to give products which no longer are diazo compounds. Here will be considered several reactions in which the diazo group is retained as a diazonium residue or in a slightly modified form and which are therefore not really reactions at the diazo group. However, they are characterized by chemical changes to *other* substituents of the same aryl nucleus induced by the formation of the diazonium group.

It has already been mentioned in the introduction (§ 7.1) that these reactions are a consequence of the limiting structure (Ib) and the strong —M character of the diazonium group. They are nucleophilic aromatic substitutions of the S_N2 type [see (382)].

In the first place must be considered the replacement of substituents by solvent particles under the influence of the diazonium group. The conversion of an amino into a diazo residue makes that substituent readily exchangeable which is easily eliminated as a nucleophilic moiety. The classic example of the effect of the diazonium group is the behaviour of 2,4-dinitrodiazobenzene (IV): whilst in 2,4-dinitroaniline (III) the nitro groups practically cannot be replaced by OH, the 2,4-dinitrodiazobenzene formed from it readily exchanges a nitro for a hydroxy group (7.6). Contrary to early claims (2533), this reaction occurs not only in alkaline, but also in acid solution and affects not only the o-, but also the p-nitro substituent, though to a lesser extent. As mentioned by

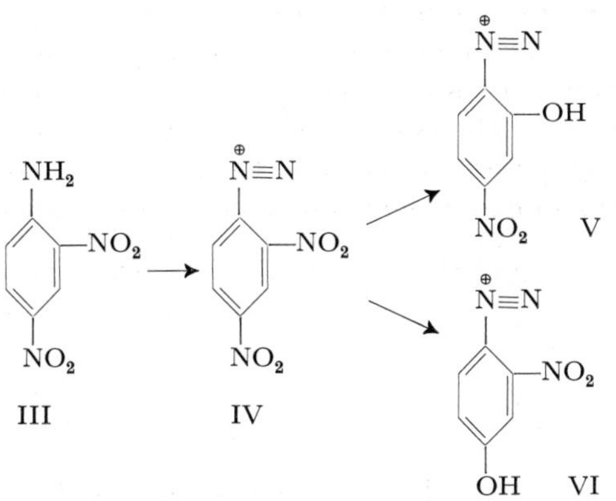

$$(7.6)$$

Fierz-David and Blangey (709e), when special precautions are taken it becomes possible to protect freshly prepared dinitrodiazobenzene against nucleophilic substitution according to equation (7.6). Normally replacement of NO_2 by OH constitutes an unwanted side reaction, but, for example, the formation of nitro-diazophenols by this process is not an undesirable consequence of the diazotization of dinitroaniline and it is utilized on the large scale for the manufacture of 5-nitro-2-diazophenol (V), important for the preparation of metal–complex dyes. Separation from the isomer (VI) produced simultaneously depends on solubility differences.

Apart from hydroxy groups, other substituents, particularly halogens, can also be introduced into diazobenzene derivatives in this way. The groups to be replaced are those easily eliminated as nucleophilic particles: besides NO_2 (as nitrite ion), they comprise halogens (as the corresponding anions) and alkoxy groups (as alcoholate ions). Sulphonic acid residues are also readily exchanged, but, as the sulphite ion liberated can give rise to unwanted reductions, it is advantageous in these cases to add the appropriate amount of an oxidizing agent (sodium hypochlorite or hydrogen peroxide).

At about the turn of the century, a series of papers appeared from Meldola's school concerned with the exchange of substituents.

As an example of Meldola's work on the replacement of nitro groups by chlorine atoms the diazotization of 2,3-dinitro-*p*-anisidine (VII) in dilute

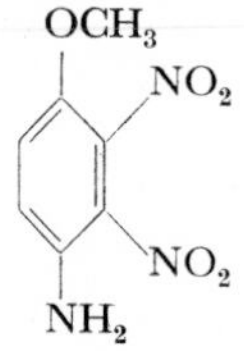

aqueous hydrochloric acid which yields 2-chloro-4-methoxy-3-nitrodiazobenzene may be mentioned (*1410*). If such diazotizations of certain dinitroanisidines are carried out using glacial acetic acid as solvent, the methoxy and not a nitro residue may be exchanged (*1414, 1421*). This happens with 3,5- and 2,5-dinitro-*p*-anisidine (VIII, IX). In the case of 4,6-dinitro-*m*-anisidine (X) neither a nitro nor the methoxy group could be replaced. If the amine to be diazotized bears a hydroxy instead of the methoxy residue, exchange of substituents is no longer possible at all, as is evident, for instance from the behaviour of 2,3-dinitro-4-aminophenol (*1412*).

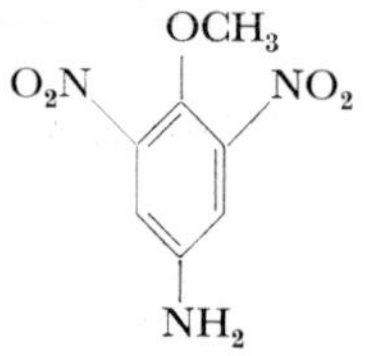

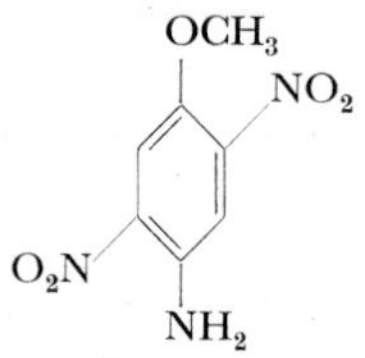

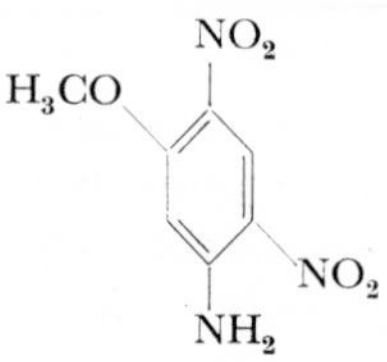

From these observations it can be seen that the nucleophilic substitution occurs only when the diazonium group is in the *o*- or *p*-position and when in addition a nitro residue is present in an *o*-position (*1411*). Under comparable conditions, the nitrite ion appears to be a better nucleophilic leaving group than the methoxide ion (*1413*).

If during diazotization a nitro group is being replaced, the nitrite ion liberated acts as diazotizing agent, as was found already by Meldola and Eyre (*1409*). It is possible therefore to carry out such a diazotization with less than the theoretical amount of sodium nitrite. In principle this is the same reaction as that described in § 1.5 as self-diazotization.

Orton (*1556*) and Meldola (*1420*) showed that bromine and chlorine are approximately equally readily exchanged in diazotizing naphthylamine and aniline derivatives, but exact determinations have not yet been made.

Far in advance of others, Orton (*1557*) tackled the question of whether the reaction involves the diazonium or the diazotate ion. Unfortunately, at that time the necessary spadework as regards pH measurement, buffer solutions, etc., had not yet been done, and the experimental clarification of the problem by means of modern techniques still needs to be carried out. It can be hazarded that the reactivity of the diazonium ion is considerably greater than that of the diazotate. Recently, Bolto, Liveris, and Miller (*282*) have compared the influence on the rate of nucleophilic aromatic substitutions of diazonium with that of nitro and trimethylammonium groups. As expected the activation caused by the diazonium residue exceeds that of a nitro substituent, which in turn is more effective than $-\overset{\oplus}{N}(CH_3)_3$.

Lewis and Suhr (*2413*) studied the rates of substitution of halogen by thiocyanate in halogenated benzenediazonium ions. They reported the order of reactivity to be *p*-I > *p*-Br > *p*-Cl > *p*-F and observed that the rate was inversely proportional to the dielectric constant of the solvent.

7.4 Aromatic Diazo Compounds as Electrophilic Reagents

As already pointed out in the introduction (§ 7.1), one of the limiting structures (Ic) shows that aryldiazonium ions are Lewis acids in which the β-nitrogen forms the centre of electrophilic character. The addition of bases is described as diazo or azo coupling and, according to the nature of the atom of the base which provides the lone pair of electrons, *C*-, *N*-, or *O*-coupling can occur. In these reactions are formed azo compounds, diazoamino bodies, or diazoethers. The first two groups of substances are accorded special treatment as befits their great importance in pure and applied chemistry (Chapters 8 to 11).

In Chapter 8, dealing with the reaction between diazo compounds and amines, only those are discussed which lead to diazoamino derivatives. Here will be considered those processes involving aryldiazonium salts and bases containing the group $\diagdown$NH in which no diazoamino compounds are produced.

Griess (*876*) already found that benzenediazonium perbromide in the presence of ammonia is converted into azidobenzene (phenyl azide) (7.7). Probably the diazoamino compound is formed first. As mentioned in § 8.1, diazonium salts and ammonia normally yield bisdiazoamino derivatives, but there is no doubt that also in this double reaction the diazoamino compound is the primary product. In the presence of the perbromide anion this is quickly dehydrogenated to the azide, the competing reaction with a second diazonium ion being probably so much slower that it is of no practical consequence. Azido

$$\text{Ar—N}_2^\oplus \text{ Br}_3^\ominus + \text{NH}_3 \longrightarrow (\text{Ar—N=N—NH}_2) \longrightarrow \text{Ar—N}_3 + 3\,\text{H}^\oplus + 3\,\text{Br}^\ominus \qquad (7.7)$$

compounds can be prepared analogously from diazonium iodochlorides and from double salts with heavy metal salts in which the metal is in a high state of oxidation, as, for example, in diazonium chloroplumbates (*419*).

The intermediate appearance of diazoamino compounds has been confirmed by the experiments of Clusius and Hürzeler (*435*) with diazobenzene marked with N^{15} at the α- or β-position. Ammonia is added exclusively at the β-nitrogen and no rearrangements whatever occur.

By means of N^{15} it has also proved possible to settle the long discussed question of whether azides possess a ring (XI) or linear (XII) structure. In the former

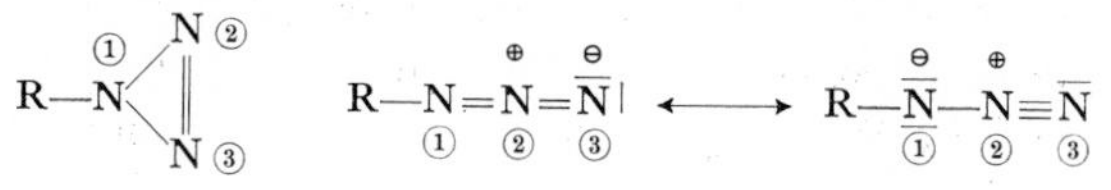

XI   XIIa   XIIb

the nitrogen atoms 2 and 3 are equivalent, but this is not so in the latter. If azidobenzene, prepared from unmarked phenylhydrazine and $HN^{15}O_2$ (1344), is converted into appropriate decomposition products, the distribution of isotopes among these should distinguish between the two possible formulas. For this purpose, Clusius and Weisser (442) selected the reaction with phenylmagnesium bromide, which gives diazoaminobenzene, and followed it by reductive fission. The results obtained by spectroscopic analysis were in accord with the linear arrangement (XII). Clusius and Weisser's paper gives a summary of the arguments advanced, on the one hand, in favour of Curtius's ring structure (XI) (509) and, on the other, for the linear one, first propounded by Thiele (2032).

Substances, such as chloramide and hydroxylamine, which can be regarded as oxidized derivatives of ammonia, react with diazo compounds to give azides (722, 742, 744, 745, 1365, 2549), although in good yield only in some cases, for example, with Chloramine T (N-chloro-p-toluenesulphonamide). Depending on conditions, hydroxylamine produces the amine and N_2O or the azide (7.8) (1365). If the diazo compound is added to an alkaline solution of hydroxylamine, mainly the amine is formed, but when mixed in neutral or acid solution and only then made alkaline, the azide results.

$$ArN_2^{\oplus} + NH_2OH \Big\langle \begin{array}{l} ArNH_2 + N_2O + H^{\oplus} \\ \\ ArN_3 + H_3^{\oplus}O \end{array} \qquad (7.8)$$

With hydrazines, the intermediates probably have the structure indicated in equation (7.9). They have not been isolated and would be subject to prototropy. The products are amines and azides and, in general, when $Ar \neq Ar'$, all four species can be shown to be formed (511, 722, 882, 884). However, the products from the interaction of diazo compounds with acid hydrazides can be isolated and they are important for the synthesis of tetrazoles (7.10) (606).

$$Ar-N_2^{\oplus} + H_2N-NH-Ar' \xrightarrow{-H^{\oplus}} (Ar-N=N-NH-NH-Ar') \Big\langle \begin{array}{l} ArN_3 + H_2NAr' \\ \\ ArNH_2 + N_3Ar' \end{array} \qquad (7.9)$$

$$ArN_2^{\oplus} + H_2N-NH-COR \longrightarrow \begin{array}{c} NH-N \\ | \quad\quad \diagdown N-Ar \\ NH-CO \\ | \\ R \end{array} \longrightarrow \begin{array}{c} N=N \\ | \quad\quad \diagdown N-Ar \\ N=C \\ | \\ R \end{array} \qquad (7.10)$$

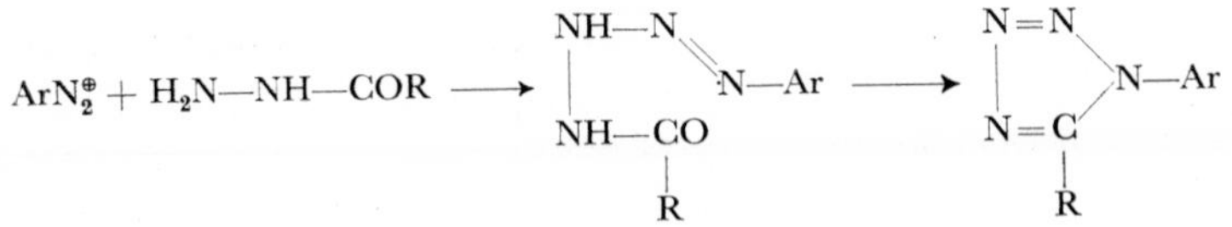

The simplest and most certain synthesis of aromatic azido derivatives consists of the reaction between diazonium salts and hydrazoic acid (7.11), a reaction discovered by Noelting (1539) and of general validity. Because of the

$$ArN_2^{\oplus} + N^{\ominus} \longrightarrow ArN_3 + N_2 \qquad (7.11)$$

similarity between the azide and halide ions, one could suppose that a reaction of S_N1 type was occurring, as discussed in § 7.2, but recent work by Clusius, Huisgen, and Ugi has shown that, surprisingly, quite another mechanism operates.

Using N^{15}, Clusius, Hürzeler, and Vecchi (436, 440) found that azidobenzene formation did not follow the classic S_N1 course (7.12c), but that a mixture of two differently labelled products was formed (7.12a and 7.12b). By the

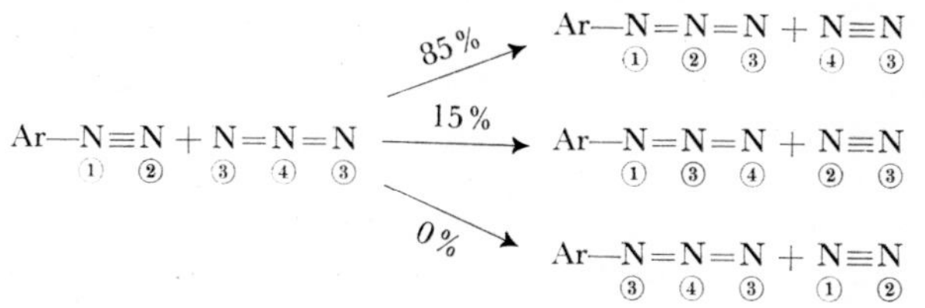

$$Ar\text{—}N\text{=}N\text{=}N + N\text{≡}N \qquad (7.12a)[1]$$
$$\text{(1) (2) (3) \quad (4) (3)}$$

$$\xrightarrow{85\%}$$

$$Ar\text{—}N\text{≡}N + N\text{=}N\text{=}N \xrightarrow{15\%} Ar\text{—}N\text{=}N\text{=}N + N\text{≡}N \qquad (7.12b)$$
$$\text{(1) (2) \quad (3) (4) (3)} \qquad\qquad \text{(1) (3) (4) \quad (2) (3)}$$

$$\xrightarrow{0\%}$$

$$Ar\text{—}N\text{=}N\text{=}N + N\text{≡}N \qquad (7.12c)$$
$$\text{(3) (4) (3) \quad (1) (2)}$$

introduction of substituents into the phenyl ring, it was shown that the main route (7.12a) is favoured by increasing the electrophilic character of the diazonium ion. Simultaneously and partly in collaboration with Clusius's school, Huisgen and Ugi (1131, 2060–2062) have investigated the reaction kinetically and preparatively. That it proceeds almost quantitatively is a remarkable observation, but the nitrogen is liberated kinetically in two steps. For example, in the interaction between benzenediazonium chloride and lithium azide in methanol at —39·5°, 76% of the theoretical amount of nitrogen is obtained in a reaction of first order with a half-life of 4·6 minutes, whereas the remaining 24% can afterwards be driven off at —0·8° also in a reaction of first order (half-life 13·7 minutes).

Combination of the results of the kinetic experiments and those employing tracers proves both the course of the reaction and the constitution of the inter-

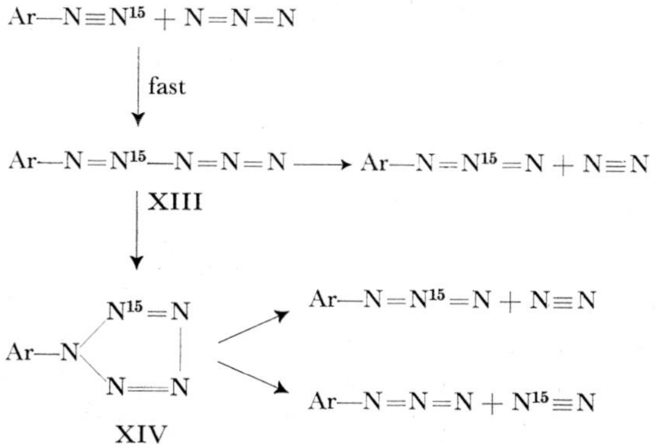

$$Ar\text{—}N\text{≡}N^{15} + N\text{=}N\text{=}N$$

$$\Big\downarrow \text{fast}$$

$$Ar\text{—}N\text{=}N^{15}\text{—}N\text{=}N\text{=}N \longrightarrow Ar\text{—}N\text{=}N^{15}\text{=}N + N\text{≡}N$$

$$\Big| \text{XIII}$$

$$\qquad\qquad\qquad\qquad (7.13)$$

$$\begin{matrix} & N^{15}\text{=}N & \nearrow & Ar\text{—}N\text{=}N^{15}\text{=}N + N\text{≡}N \\ Ar\text{—}N\big< & | & \big< & \\ & N\text{=}N & \searrow & Ar\text{—}N\text{=}N\text{=}N + N^{15}\text{≡}N \end{matrix}$$

$$\text{XIV}$$

mediates (7.13). In a rapid first step, analogous to N-coupling, is formed benzenediazoazide (XIII), which can give azidobenzene directly, the nitrogen

---

[1] For clarity the charges are omitted. The percentages correspond to the composition of the products obtained by Clusius et al. (436).

liberated in the process corresponding to that given off in the experiment at
$-39 \cdot 5°$ mentioned above. But benzenediazoazide can also isomerize into
phenylpentazole (XIV), which in turn decomposes into azidobenzene and
nitrogen.

These investigations provide the first evidence for the existence of the pentazole system, a five-membered ring with aromatic character consisting exclusively of nitrogen atoms. Subsequently, Ugi (2062) succeeded in isolating
under very mild conditions a substance containing the pentazole nucleus. At
$-30°$ the starting materials proved to be soluble, whereas the arylpentazoles
formed were insoluble in a mixture of ligroine and aqueous methanol, so that
they could be separated and obtained in crystalline form in yields of 27 to
52%. Pentazoles are colourless, highly unstable compounds, without basic
properties. + M Substituents in the p-position greatly increase the stability,
the main ultra-violet absorption band undergoing a large batho- and hyper-
chromic displacement at the same time (see Table 7.1). This suggests the participation of limiting structures of the type of (XV), which possess some similarity to the corresponding limiting structures of nitrobenzene derivatives with
+ M substituents in the p-position. By decomposition of labelled p-ethoxy-
phenylpentazole Ugi and co-workers (2361) were able to give a proof for the

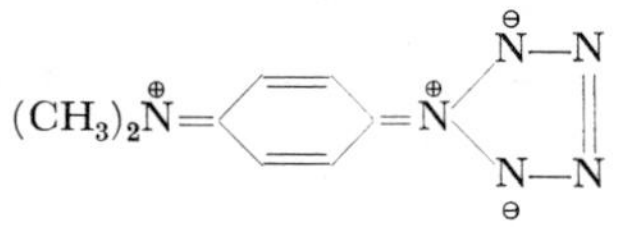

XV

Table 7.1

Properties of Arylpentazoles (2062)

Aryl group	Decomposition point	$\lambda_{max.}$	ε
Phenyl	$- 5°$ to $- 3°$	250 mμ	7 200
p-Ethoxyphenyl	$+26°$ to $+29°$	272 mμ	12 000
p-Dimethylaminophenyl . .	$+50°$ to $+54°$	333 mμ	15 000

constitution of this ring system. It is worth noting, that even in 1903 Hantzsch
(947) intuitively felt that in the azidobenzene synthesis lay the possibility of
building up the pentazole ring.

The exceptionally great rate of N-coupling to the azide ion (7.13) compared
with that to amines is also remarkable. It is far in excess of the reactivity of
the azide ion in aliphatic nucleophilic substitutions [cf. the appropriate constants determined by Swain and Scott (1990)].

In this connection may be mentioned also the heterocyclic azidinium salts
(XVI) investigated by H. Balli (138). They can be regarded as N-diazonium
compounds and, accordingly, they behave as electrophilic reagents capable of

adding bases, such as sulphinate anions (7.14a), at the γ-nitrogen. With an azide ion two azidinium ions yield a triazacyanine, for example, (XVII).

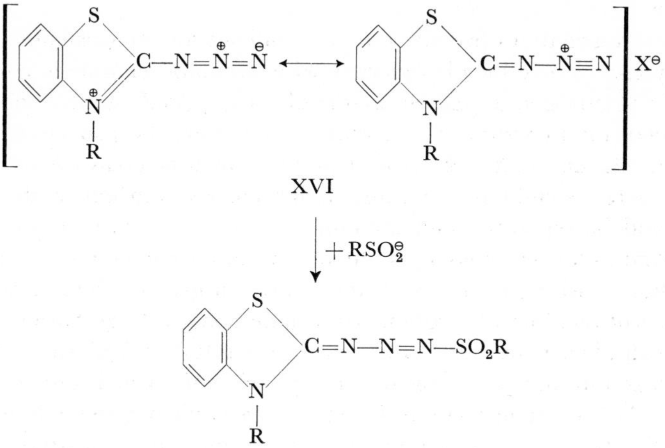

XVI

$$\Big\downarrow + RSO_2^\ominus \qquad\qquad (7.14\,a)$$

$$XVI + N_3^\ominus \longrightarrow$$

$$\Big\downarrow + XVI \qquad\qquad (7.14\,b)$$

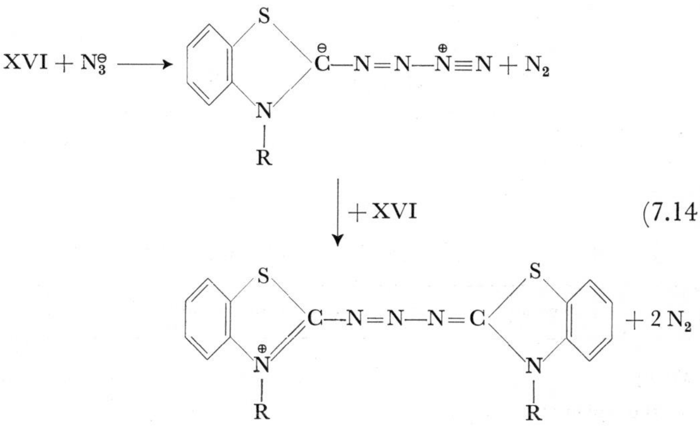

XVIII

The *diazoethers* played a considerable part in the classic controversy over diazo isomerism between Hantzsch and Bamberger. Their preparation by O-coupling can be achieved only in certain cases, as the basic character of an alcoholic or phenolic oxygen atom is relatively weak and so a covalent bond between it and the β-nitrogen of the diazo group has little stability. Dimroth *et al.* (*605*), in their investigations connected with the mechanism of azo coupling (see § 10.4), were able to show by conductivity determinations that 4-benzamido-1-diazonaphthalene forms diazoethers to a considerable extent with acetyldibenzoylmethane, *p*-nitrophenol, or pentamethylphenol in aqueous solution. With the weaker conjugate bases of 2,4-dinitrophenol and of picric acid no evidence of the formation of diazoethers was obtained. In the case of phenols with substituents in the *o*- and *p*-positions which readily undergo electrophilic substitution (H, COOH, CH$_2$OH, etc.; cf. § 10.5), diazoethers cannot normally be isolated even when the phenolate is relatively strongly basic. However, from 2-naphthol-6,8-disulphonic acid and *p*-chlorodiazobenzene in strongly alkaline solution (pH > 13) is obtained a compound, the properties of which suggest it to be a diazonaphthol ether (*356, 2238*).

For the preparation of diazoethers nucleophilic substitution of alkyl halides by diazotates is in general to be preferred to *O*-coupling. In contrast to *O*-coupling, the diazo compound appears in the alternative method not as the electrophilic, but as the nucleophilic, component. Von Pechmann and Frobenius (*1603*) as well as Bamberger (*147*) showed that here it makes no difference whether *syn*- or *anti*-diazotates are used. The causes of this fact have not been investigated. Probably the diazoethers obtained are in the *trans*-form. The *cis*-ethers, the primary products from *syn*-diazotates are presumably very unstable and isomerize rapidly. The nature of the cation of the diazotate salt, however, exerts a considerable effect: silver *p*-nitrobenzenediazotate and methyl iodide give the diazoether, whilst the sodium salt leads to *N*-methyl-*N*-nitroso-*p*-nitroaniline. In the latter instance the diazotate therefore reacts as the nitrosamine.

Diazobenzene methyl ether is a very unstable, yellow oil, rapidly hydrolysed in water. In consequence it interacts readily with coupling components (*1605*) and gives the radical reactions typical of diazo compounds (*154*). Hantzsch (*949*) observed an interesting decomposition of diazoethers in water, which yields the amine and nitrous acid (7.15). It involves, in a way, the reversal

$$\text{Ar—N=N—OR} + 2\,\text{H}_2\text{O} \longrightarrow \text{ArNH}_2 + \text{ROH} + \text{HNO}_2 \qquad (7.15)$$

both of *O*-coupling and of diazotization. Presumably the diazoethers belong to the *trans*-series (*925, 927, 930*); the *cis*-isomer has been looked for, but not found. The fact that alkaline hydrolysis of diazoethers leads to *syn*-diazotates (*689, 690*) agrees with this, as it is easy to picture the hydrolysis proceeding via the intermediate (XVIII).

$$\begin{array}{c} \text{Ar—N} \\ \qquad \diagdown \\ \qquad\qquad \text{N---OR} \\ \qquad\qquad \vdots \\ \qquad\qquad \text{OH}^{\ominus} \end{array}$$

XVIII

Sulphur-containing compounds, such as thiophenols (*964*), mercaptans (*770, 1760*), and thiocarboxylic acids (*770*), yield *diazothioethers* (*S*-azo compounds) by an *S*-coupling reaction. As expected from the more strongly nucleophilic character of thioalcohol anions as compared with alcoholates [cf. Streitwieser (*1970*)], the diazothioethers are more stable than the diazoethers. The inability of thiophenols to couple in the nucleus (*770*) is noteworthy. Downes and Sykes (*2381*) recently found that at high alkalinities quaternary thiazolium salts do not couple in the 2-position, but at the sulphur atom after opening of the heterocyclic ring.

The formation of diazosulphones and diazosulphonates can also be described as *S*-coupling. The sulphur atom of sulphinic acids and sulphite ions, respectively, appears here as the basic centre of the nucleophilic component. Isomerism between diazosulphones and diazonium sulphinates, assumed by Claasz (*426*), does not take place according to Meerwein (*1399*), who was able to isolate true solid diazonium sulphinates only in special cases.

The formation of diazosulphonates was described by Schmidt and Lutz (*1822*) as long ago as 1869 and has been much studied because of the technical importance of the products (see § 4.3). Particularly Hantzsch (*924, 926, 928, 933, 958*), Bamberger (*150, 153, 176*), and Hodgson (*1043, 1049, 1057*) have been interested in the preparation of the isomers. It can now be assumed with a high degree of probability that the two diazosulphonates are stereoisomers in view of the work of Hantzsch, Freeman, and Le Fèvre in particular (see §4.1).

Apart from a fundamental paper by Hantzsch and Schmiedel (*975*), the course of the formation and isomerization of the diazosulphonates has received adequate study only recently. Dijkstra and de Jonge (*590*) as well as E. S. Lewis and Suhr (*1336*) have determined the equilibria involved and the rates of the separate steps shown in scheme (7.16). By kinetic investigation in the pH range 4.62 to 8.95, Dijkstra and de Jonge were able to show that only the sulphite and not the bisulphite ion can take part in the reaction and Lewis and Suhr demonstrated that the equilibrium constant K of substituted benzenediazonium ions obeys Hammett's equation ($\varrho = 5{\cdot}5$).

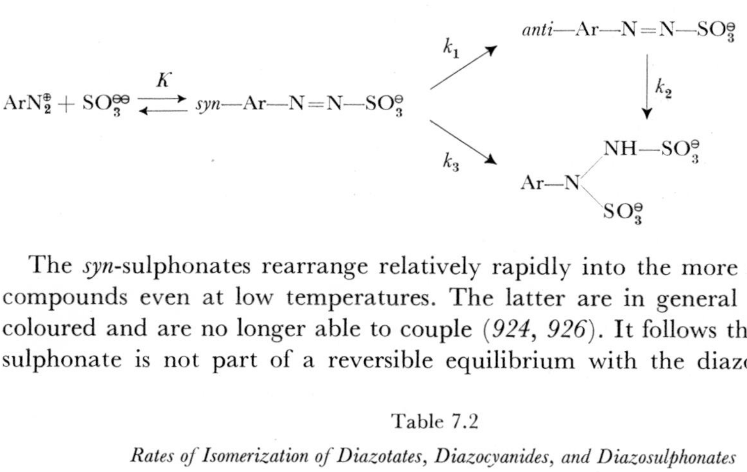

$$\text{ArN}_2^{\oplus} + \text{SO}_3^{\ominus\ominus} \underset{K}{\overset{}{\rightleftarrows}} syn\text{---Ar---N}{=}\text{N---SO}_3^{\ominus} \overset{k_1}{\nearrow} \quad anti\text{---Ar---N}{=}\text{N---SO}_3^{\ominus}$$

$$\underset{k_3}{\searrow} \quad \text{Ar---N} \Big\langle {\text{NH---SO}_3^{\ominus} \atop \text{SO}_3^{\ominus}} \Big\downarrow k_2 \qquad (7.16)$$

The *syn*-sulphonates rearrange relatively rapidly into the more stable *anti*-compounds even at low temperatures. The latter are in general less deeply coloured and are no longer able to couple (*924, 926*). It follows that the *anti*-sulphonate is not part of a reversible equilibrium with the diazonium ion.

Table 7.2

Rates of Isomerization of Diazotates, Diazocyanides, and Diazosulphonates

Aryl residue	Diazotates at 25° in water (*1334*)	Diazocyanides at 25° in benzene (*1310*)	Diazosulphonates at 0° in water (*1336*)
Phenyl	2×10^{-6} sec^{-1}	$1\,540 \times 10^{-6}$ sec^{-1}	$1{\cdot}9 \times 10^{-3}$ sec^{-1}
p-Chlorophenyl . . .	5×10^{-6} sec^{-1}	$18{\cdot}1 \times 10^{-6}$ sec^{-1}	$0{\cdot}5 \times 10^{-3}$ sec^{-1}
p-Nitrophenyl . . .	$54\,000 \times 10^{-6}$ sec^{-1}	$7{\cdot}22 \times 10^{-6}$ sec^{-1}	$1{\cdot}8 \times 10^{-3}$ sec^{-1}

Lewis and Suhr (*1336*) have determined the rate of isomerization [constant k_1 of scheme (7.16)]. The values found for three diazosulphonates are included in Table 7.2 together with the corresponding rates for diazotates (*1334*) and diazocyanides (*1310*). It is striking that the diazosulphonates unlike the other two groups are hardly affected by substituents. The more rapid isomerization of diazotates in the presence of a —M substituent (NO_2) suggests that the greater participation of mesomeric structures of the type of (XIX) weakens the —N=N—double bond and so facilitates isomerization. In the case of the diazo-cyanides such substituents oppose the electron-attracting effect of the cyano group (XX). However, the sulpho residue has been shown to attract electrons less than the cyano group by Büchler, Wittwer, and Zollinger (*2241*) and so the negligible effect of a nitro substituent on the isomerization of the diazosulpho-nates becomes comprehensible.

$$\ominus \langle\!=\!\rangle =N-N=O \qquad \text{XIX}$$

$$\oplus \langle\!=\!\rangle =N-N=C=N^\ominus \qquad \text{XX}$$

In the presence of an excess of sulphite *syn*- as well as *anti*-diazosulphonates are reduced. The reaction leads via hydrazinedi- and mono-sulphonic acids to the hydrazines. Lewis and Suhr (*1336*) have determined the appropriate rate constants k_2 and k_3 and their results will be mentioned in § 7.7.

P-Coupling can be said to occur in the formation of azophosphonic esters [$ArN_2PO(OCH_3)_2$] from diazonium salts and dimethyl phosphite [HPO $(OCH_3)_2$] (*1977*). *P*-Coupled intermediates (7.17 a) are formed in the reaction between diazonium salts and tertiary phosphines, studied by Horner et al. (*1073*, *1086*). The *P*-azo compound hydrolyses to triphenylphosphine oxide (7.17 b), but if a second equivalent of the tertiary phosphine is available, phenylhydrazine is finally obtained along with the phosphine oxide (7.17 c–d) (*2329*).

$$ArN_2^\oplus + (C_6H_5)_3P \longrightarrow Ar-N=N-\overset{\oplus}{P}(C_6H_5)_3 \qquad (7.17\,a)$$

$$Ar-N=N-\overset{\oplus}{P}(C_6H_5)_3 + H_2O \longrightarrow (C_6H_5)_3PO + ArH + N_2 + H^\oplus \qquad (7.17\,b)$$

$$Ar-N=N-\overset{\oplus}{P}(C_6H_5)_3 + (C_6H_5)_3P + H_2O \longrightarrow$$

$$Ar-NH-NH-\overset{\oplus}{P}(C_6H_5)_3 + C_6H_5)_3PO \qquad (7.17\,c)$$

$$Ar-NH-NH-\overset{\oplus}{P}(C_6H_5)_3 + H_2O \longrightarrow Ar-NH-NH_2 + (C_6H_5)_3PO + H^\oplus \qquad (7.17\,d)$$

To the same type of reaction, as has been discussed in this section so far, belong those processes which follow diazotization and which can be described as intramolecular coupling. In these cases, the diazonium group formed inter-acts with an *o*-substituent. This is the cause of the difficulties in the di- or tetr-azotization of *o*-phenylenediamine, where the *o*-aminobenzenediazonium ion (XXI) first produced immediately reacts with the amino group to yield a tri-

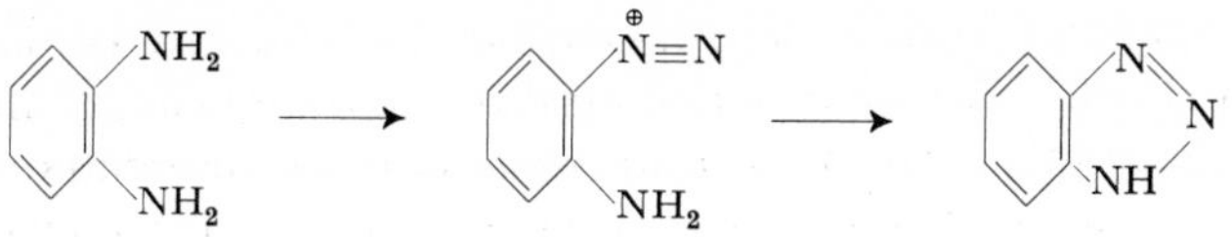

(7.18)

XXI   XXII

azole (**XXII**), which can be regarded as an intramolecular diazoamino compound (7.18). The heterocycle here cannot be opened by means of acid.

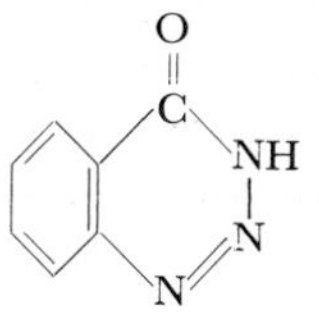

XXIII

In the analogous manner, arylamines bearing an *o*-carbamoyl group give rise to benzotriazines (**XXIII**), *o*-aminothiophenols to benzothiadiazoles (**XXIV**), *o*-aminostyrenes to cinnolines (**XXV**), and *o*-alkylanilines under certain circumstances to indazoles (**XXVI**). Contrary to the products from

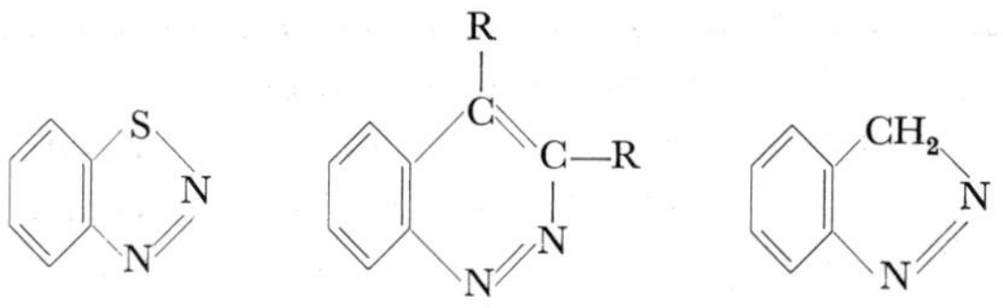

XXIV   XXV   XXVI

o-aminothiophenols, those from *o*-aminophenols do not possess a heterocyclic ring (*1313*) (see § 3.2).

The literature concerned with these heterocyclic compounds is very extensive and has been reviewed by Saunders (*1776a*), parts of the field being covered also by Jacobs (*1159*), Leonard (*1326*), and Simpson (*1897*).

Because the term intramolecular coupling was used above, reference must be made to Huisgen (*1124*), as he recently studied the indazole formation. It is probable that this does not start from the *o*-alkylbenzenediazonium ion, which would correspond to a 'normal mechanism' for coupling, and Huisgen supposes that it originates from a covalent diazo compound, such as the *anti*-diazoacetate.

7.5 Homolytic Reactions of Diazo Compounds

In order to understand the partly very complex radical decompositions of diazo compounds, it is best to begin by considering those of the *nitrosoacylarylamines* (**XXVII**). As Bamberger (*145, 163, 168*) already showed, the behaviour of these substances is similar to that of the diazo compounds: they react with aromatic hydrocarbons rather like alkaline diazo solutions with the formation of diaryls and they couple with phenols (*946*), though surprisingly in the *o*-position. It is therefore not far-fetched to think of tautomerism with diazoacylates (**XXVIII**). Nitrosoacylarylamines can be prepared by acylation of *syn*- and

$$\text{Ar—N}\begin{array}{c}\diagup\text{N=O}\\ \diagdown\text{CO—R}\end{array} \qquad\qquad \text{Ar—N=N—O—CO—R}$$

$$\text{XXVII} \qquad\qquad\qquad \text{XXVIII}$$

anti-diazotates (*162, 1596, 1602, 2186*) or by nitrosation of acylarylamines (*728, 749, 993*). The kinetics of decomposition in non-polar solvents have been investigated by Hey and co-workers (*886, 1025, 1026*) and they found the reaction to be of first order. They postulated the mechanism to consist of a rapidly equilibrating tautomerism, nitrosoacetylarylamine $\rightleftarrows$ diazoacetate, followed by homolytic fission of the latter into nitrogen, a phenyl, and an acetyl radical (*7.19*).

$$\text{Ar} \diagdown \text{N} = \text{N} \diagup \text{O—CO—CH}_3 \longrightarrow \text{Ar}^{\cdot} + \text{N}_2 + \dot{\text{O}}\text{—COCH}_3$$

$$+ \text{Ar}'\text{—H}$$

$$\text{Ar}'\text{—Ar} + \text{CH}_3\text{—COOH}$$

$$(7.19)$$

Recently, DeTar (*551*) and Huisgen (*1111, 1112, 1117, 1121*) have concerned themselves particularly with the conversion of the nitrosoacylarylamine into the diazoacylate and their results led them to modify Hey's hypothesis. They maintain that the homolysis is a rapid reaction following the rate-determining rearrangement of the nitrosoacetylarylamine into the metastable diazoacetate and Hey (*1023, 1024*) has now accepted the 'rolling off' mechanism propounded by Huisgen.

As the rearrangement proceeds also in inert media, it does not require the intervention of other substances. A favourable effect from polar solvents is hardly perceptible and therefore a mechanism involving the separation of a free acyl cation is not likely. The appearance of free ions could be avoided by a simultaneous exchange of acyl residues between two molecules of nitroso compound, but, as the acyl migration rigidly adheres to the first order, it must consist of an intra- and uni-molecular isomerization. Huisgen and Krause (*1121*) describe the rearrangement as a rolling off through a state (**XXIX**) in which a four-membered ring stabilized by mesomerism is present.

$$\text{Ar—N}\begin{array}{c}\diagup\text{N}\diagdown\\ \diagdown\text{C}\diagdown\text{O}\\ \text{O}\diagup \quad \text{R}\end{array} \longrightarrow \left(\text{Ar—N}\begin{array}{c}\diagup\text{N}\diagdown\\ \overset{\oplus}{\diagdown}\text{C}\diagdown\text{O}\\ \ominus\text{O}\diagup \quad \text{R}\end{array}\right) \longrightarrow \text{Ar—N}\begin{array}{c}\diagup\text{N}\diagdown\\ \diagdown\text{O}\\ \text{C}\\ \text{O}\diagup \text{R}\end{array}$$

$$(7.20)$$

$$\text{XXIX}$$

One of the consequences is that acyl migration is easiest when the four-membered ring of the transition state is planar. This was confirmed by varying the nature of the groups R and Ar: *o*-substituted aryl compounds rearrange more slowly, because in them the aromatic nucleus is forced out of the common plane, thus reducing the considerable resonance between it and the rest of the molecule. On the other hand, voluminous acyl residues turn the COR group in such a way that the nucleophilic attack on the carbonyl carbon atom is facilitated, the transition state (XXIX) attaining a conformation illustrated by Figure 7.1. The effect of the acyl residue on the rearrangement of aliphatic

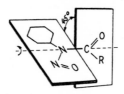

Figure 7.1

Transition state of the nitrosoacylarylamine rearrangement
from R. Huisgen and L. Krause (*1121*), Figure 1

nitrosoacylamines has been clarified in detail by Huisgen and Reimlinger (*1125*). The various conformations possible differ considerably in their energy content depending on the relative directions of the dipoles of the nitroso and carbonyl groups. Large acyl groups enforce an energetically unfavourable conformation, which, through a type of steric acceleration, facilitates arrival at the transition state (XXIX).

According to equation (7.20), acyl migration should result in the *trans*-diazotate. Huisgen (*1112*) was able to confirm this by studying the conversion of *N*-nitrosobenzolactams (XXX) into cyclic diazoesters (XXXI). The fact that

$$\text{XXX} \longrightarrow \text{XXXI} \tag{7.21}$$

XXX   XXXI

the five-membered ring compound (XXX, $n = 1$) did not rearrange, whereas the corresponding homologues with seven- and eight-membered rings ($n = 3$ or 4, respectively) did so smoothly shows that the *trans*- and not the *cis*-form must be present in the products. However, diazonium and carboxylate ions interact to give the *cis*-diazoester, which can isomerize subsequently into the *trans*-compound (7.22) (*1124*).

$$\tag{7.22}$$

Contrary to the hypotheses advanced previously, the experimental results on the homolytic part of the nitrosoacylarylamine decomposition are against the appearance of *free* radicals, because the acetoxy radicals, $RCOO\cdot$, formed according to equation (7.19), should have given evidence of their presence, as they do in the Kolbe electrolysis, through their typical reaction of decarboxylation followed by the combination of two methyl radicals with production of ethane.

From Huisgen's investigation of the dependence of the products of acyl migration in *o*-methylated nitrosoacylarylamines on the nature of the solvent (*1122*) become apparent those factors which determine the two ways of reaction (coupling and homolytic fission) open to the *trans*-diazoester. The formal role of radicals as reaction carriers in homolysis is not questioned, but the experiments discount the spontaneous dissociation into *free* radicals. Homolysis is triggered off only by offering appropriate solvent molecules, for example, alcohol. For the radical intermediates the acceptor is already fixed before they are released from their original molecule and so they never become free in the sense of triphenylmethyl radicals. This view is supported by DeTar's observation (*556*) that with optically active 2-methyl-6-nitrobiphenyl-2'-diazonium salts only little racemization occurs. Taken together with the more recent results from studying the rearrangements of the radical intermediates (*560*), it must be concluded that the succeeding steps occur relatively rapidly.

These experiments also throw light on the alcohol diazo interaction dealt with in § 7.2. The replacement of diazo groups by hydrogen, doubted *in general* by Kornblum (*1260, 1265*), is probably possible under certain circumstances. The formation of phenol ethers and the reductive diazo decomposition are *not* competitive reactions of the diazonium ion. The polar exchange with alkoxy corresponds with the reactions of the free cation, whilst the redox process represents the method of decomposition favoured by the covalent diazo compounds. Translated into the terms of preparative chemistry, this implies that phenetole formation is to be carried out in acid solution in the presence of the anions of strong mineral acids, whilst for the reduction it is advantageous to use a neutral or weakly alkaline medium as well as high concentrations of those conjugate bases which give covalent diazo intermediates relatively readily (acetate etc.). DeTar's work (*563–565*) shows clearly that under such conditions homolytic reactions occur even with diazonium salts: molecular oxygen considerably affects the decomposition of diazonium fluoborates in methanolic acetate buffers. As expected for a homolysis, oxygen lowers the rate of decomposition of the diazoacetate formed as a metastable intermediate, but gives rise to other products (diazo resins).

Currently, DeTar and Kosuge (*557*) as well as W. Lee, J. G. Calvert, and E. Malmberg (*1305*) have concerned themselves with the interaction between diazonium salts and alcohols in acid solution. They have come to the conclusion that present data do not permit a definite decision to be taken as to whether hydride transfer plays a significant role in some of these reactions or whether an electron transfer step is the universal criterion of the mechanism of these processes.

Even if these more recent investigations make it probable that in the decomposition of covalent diazo compounds no *free* radicals appear, there is no doubt at all that the process is homolytic and not heterolytic. This follows from the orientation observed in the products of the substitution of aromatic bodies by the particles obtained in diazo fission. The orientation corresponds to that found in reactions which are known to involve free radicals, especially those from phenylazotriphenylmethane and benzoyl peroxide (*839, 840, 2152, 2158*) : benzene derivatives are substituted in all three positions, *ortho*, *meta*, and *para*, *o*- and *p*-reaction preponderating even when the nucleus carries *m*-directing residues. Hey (*86, 87, 1019*) has used the phenylation of nitro- and chloro-benzene by a variety of reagents as an example. The small and remarkably constant percentage of *m*-diphenyl derivative formed (Table 7.3) shows that the nitrobenzene molecule is always substituted by similar reagents, namely, radicals.

Table 7.3

Reaction of Nitrobenzene with Aryl Radicals

Source of radical	Per cent *m*-substitution in the nitrobenzene nucleus
$CH_3-\!\!\langle\bigcirc\rangle\!\!-N=N-ONa$	9·4; 8·3; 9·1
$CH_3-\!\!\langle\bigcirc\rangle\!\!-N(NO)COCH_3$	8·7; 8 0
$CH_3-\!\!\langle\bigcirc\rangle\!\!-N=N-N(CH_3)_2$	7·0; 8·5
$(CH_3-\!\!\langle\bigcirc\rangle\!\!-CO-O)_2$	9·5; 9·2

Analogous results have been obtained with an aromatic heterocycle (pyridine) (*1022*). Naphthalene is substituted predominantly in α-position by radicals generated by the decomposition of aryldiazonium salts. Marshall and Waters (*2342*) obtained the following isomer percentages in the arylation of naphthalene by p-$R\cdot C_6H_4{}^{\bullet}$ radicals:

R = NO_2	α: 83%	β: 17%
H	80	20
$NHCOCH_3$	77	23
OCH_3	74	26

The most convincing evidence for the radical or cryptoradical mechanism of these CN-dissociations is provided by the quantitative investigations of Hey (*85, 86, 1021*) and DeTar (*551, 562*) into the activating and *o/p*-directing effects of the nitro group, as well as by the parallelism between the reactions of nitrobenzene with basified diazonium salt solutions, on the one hand, and with benzoyl peroxide, on the other. Hypotheses to the contrary, in which the radical character of the decomposition of covalent diazo compounds is disputed (*1041, 1042*), remain unproved through lack of experimental data (*1026*), but it is certain that the decomposition of alkyldiazoesters proceeds not homolytically, but heterolytically (*1125, 1126, 1129, 1130*) (see § 6.5).

The studies concerned with the nitrosoacylarylamines are very valuable for an understanding of the structure and reactivity of diazoesters. Their detailed discussion was made necessary above, because considerably less knowledge, firmly founded on experiment, is available in the case of the mechanism of the homolytic fission of other diazo compounds. This is particularly so for aqueous diazo solutions. It is known from many-sided practical experience, that the stability of diazo compounds in weakly alkaline medium exhibits a minimum (*1776h*). In the absence of exact determinations, it can only be said that this minimum roughly corresponds with the maximum of the diazohydroxide concentration, which implies that the decomposition is greatest at the pH equivalent to the constant $(pK_1 + pK_2)/2$ for the diazo equilibrium. As according to the arguments advanced in § 3.5, even in this region of pH the diazohydroxide is present only in traces, experimental investigation is difficult. That this step in the diazo equilibrium is more suitable for homolytic reactions can be expected, because it is less stabilized by mesomerism than either the diazonium or the diazotate ion and the OH-radical is a moiety relatively readily eliminated. Similar factors are probably responsible for the fact that diazocyanides do not undergo homolytic decomposition in the absence of catalysts (*1952*).

The most important preparative application of the homolytic dissociation of covalent diazo compounds lies in the Gomberg reaction (*112, 841, 842*). This consists of the immediate arylation which occurs when aqueous sodium hydroxide is added slowly to an intimate mixture of an aqueous solution of a diazonium salt and an aromatic hydrocarbon. Hey *et al.* (*675*) showed that the yield can be improved considerably by substituting sodium acetate for the hydroxide. As expected, substitution proceeds in the *o*- and *p*-positions even in the presence of *m*-directing groups. Azobenzenes and triphenyls have been found as by-products.

Horner and Stöhr (*1086*) demonstrated that the decomposition of diazonium ions in the presence of a tertiary amine (triethylamine) is similar to that initiated by water and hydroxyl ions. Probably the diazohydroxide is formed first and breaks down as discussed above. Products of the interaction of the diazo compound with the tertiary amine could not be found.

The arylation of quinones (*1287, 2307, 2391, 2502*) with diazo solutions presumably takes place via the diazoacetate, followed by homolytic fission, as the reaction is greatly favoured by acetate ions. Support comes, for example, from the fact that 2-hydroxy-1,4-naphthoquinone is arylated in alkaline solution, but in acid azo coupling occurs (7.23) (*308, 1200, 1523*). The arylation of quinones is probably closely related by mechanism to the Meerwein reaction between diazonium salts and α, β-unsaturated carbonyl compounds (see § 7.6).

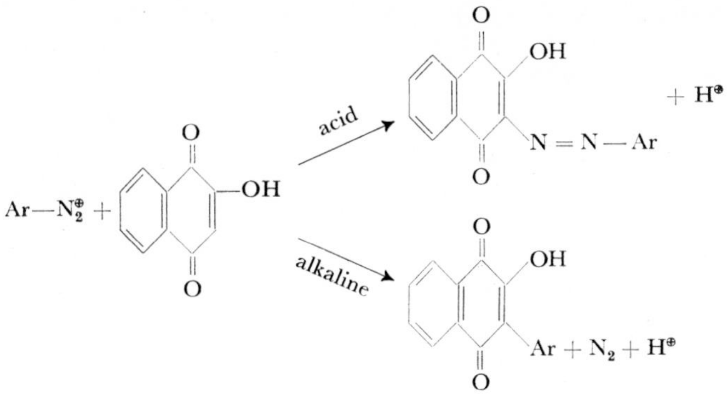

$$Ar-N_2^\oplus + \quad\xrightarrow{acid}\quad \text{(structure)} \quad + H^\oplus$$

$$\xrightarrow{alkaline} \quad \text{(structure)} \quad Ar + N_2 + H^\oplus$$

(7.23)

7.6 Catalysed Reactions of Diazo Compounds

Aromatic diazo compounds are of great importance for a series of syntheses which lead to products no longer containing the diazo nitrogen. These comprise the Pschorr phenanthrene synthesis and related ring closures, the Meerwein reaction between diazo compounds and α, β-unsaturated carbonyl compounds and the related arylation of quinones, and, finally, the Sandmeyer reaction. These processes cannot be classified unequivocally, because their mechanism is either not yet known with complete certainty (Sandmeyer reaction) or obviously can occur heterolytically as well as homolytically or via a cryptoradical. For this reason they are here considered together under the title of catalysed reactions and this appears appropriate in spite of the fact that in some cases, such as those of certain Sandmeyer reactions, a catalyst is not essential.

In 1896 Pschorr (*1663*) described a five-stage phenanthrene synthesis, starting with a Perkin condensation between phenylacetic acid and o-nitrobenzaldehyde to α-phenylcinnamic acid. After reduction of the nitro group, comes the step (7.24) associated with Pschorr's name: o-amino-α-phenylcinnamic acid is first diazotized and, on addition of copper powder, nitrogen is given off with ring closure to phenanthrene-9-carboxylic acid, which in the final stage is decarboxylated.

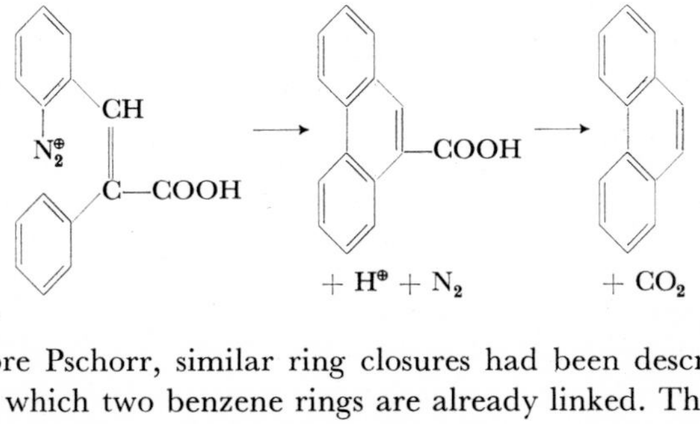

$$\text{(structure)} \xrightarrow{\quad} \text{(structure)} -COOH \xrightarrow{\quad} \text{(structure)}$$

$$+ H^\oplus + N_2 \qquad\qquad + CO_2$$

(7.24)

Shortly before Pschorr, similar ring closures had been described for other compounds in which two benzene rings are already linked. Thus Graebe and Ullmann (*854*) found that 2-diazobenzophenone can be converted into fluo-

renone in the analogous manner (7.25), whilst, when Staedel (*1924*) added
nitrous acid to 2,2'-diaminobenzophenone, he obtained some 1-hydroxyfluo-

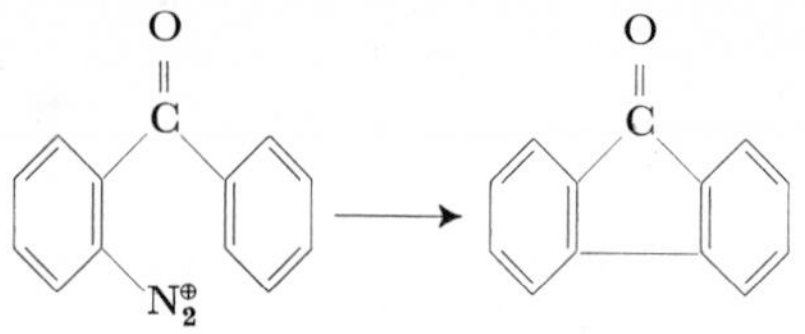

(7.25)

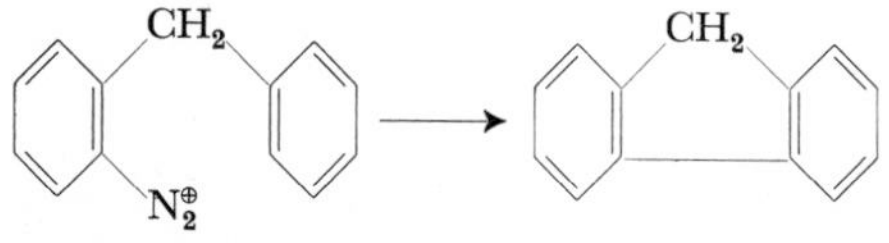

(7.26)

renone. The ring closure of 2-benzyldiazobenzene to fluorene (7.26) was described by O. Fischer and Schmidt (*732*).

Lately the field of application for ring-closures of this type has been greatly
widened. Apart from derivatives of such carbocyclic systems as those of fluo-
ranthene, pyrene, and chrysene (*741, 1771, 1896*), Pschorr's method has been
called on particularly for the synthesis of heterocycles, of which may be mentioned carbazole (*405, 855*) and its derivatives, dibenzofuran (XXXIIa) (*856*),
dibenzothiophene (XXXIIb) (*497, 561*), dibenzothiophene dioxide (XXXIIc)
(*561*), sultones (e. g. XXXIII) (*1794*), and sultams (XXXIV) (*2065*). The
heterocyclic nitrogen compounds phenanthridone (XXXV) and aporphin
(XXXVI) have been the subject of many investigations. The formation of
phenanthridone derivatives has been studied especially by Hey (*995–997,
1020*), whilst compounds containing the aporphin skeleton are of significance
because of their relation to alkaloids [e. g. (*190, 1725, 1801, 1802*)].

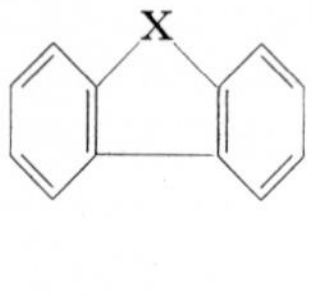

XXXIIa: X = O
XXXIIb: X = S
XXXIIc: X = SO$_2$

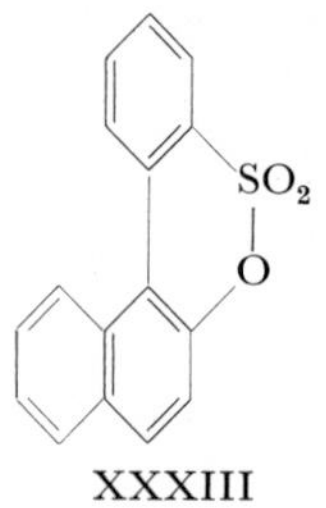

XXXIII

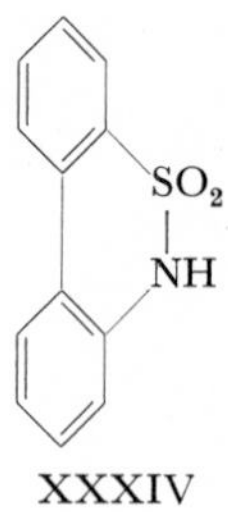

XXXIV

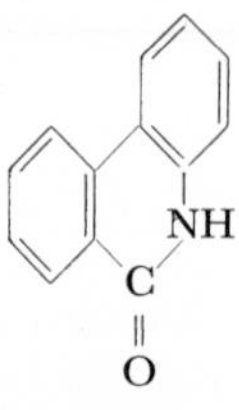

XXXV

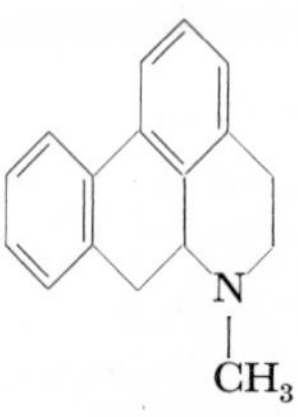

XXXVI

An interesting ring closure which may have some relation to the reactions of the Pschorr type has been discovered by Stiles and Libbey (2360). 9-o-Diazophenyl-9-fluorenol decomposes in warm dilute sulphuric acid to produce, in addition to the expected phenolic product, tribenzo-2,4,6-cycloheptatrien-1-one in 24% yield (7.27). No metallic catalyst is used for this reaction.

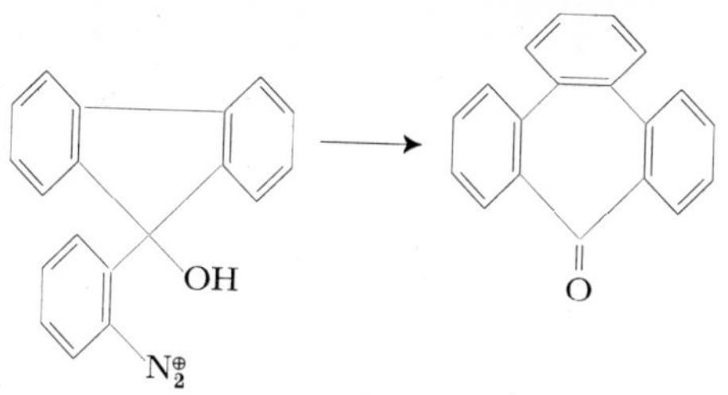

$$(7.27)$$

DeTar (553) has given a comprehensive list of the known phenanthrene syntheses together with a discussion of the fundamentals of the mechanism, a less extensive review by Leake (1302) being available also.

The mechanism of such cyclizations of diazo compounds has not yet been proved unequivocally. From DeTar's investigations (555) it seems that the Pschorr reaction occurs homolytically in the case of o-diazostilbene. On heating in acid, the cis-derivative (XXXVII) yields primarily indazole and benzaldehyde (7.28b), phenanthrene appearing only as a by-product (7.28a). In the presence of copper powder, however, the reaction becomes considerably more rapid and mainly phenanthrene is obtained. This suggests that the formation of phenanthrene takes place by a homolytic, perhaps cryptoradical, mechanism, whereas the indazole arises heterolytically. As expected, trans-2-diazostilbene gives no phenanthrene.

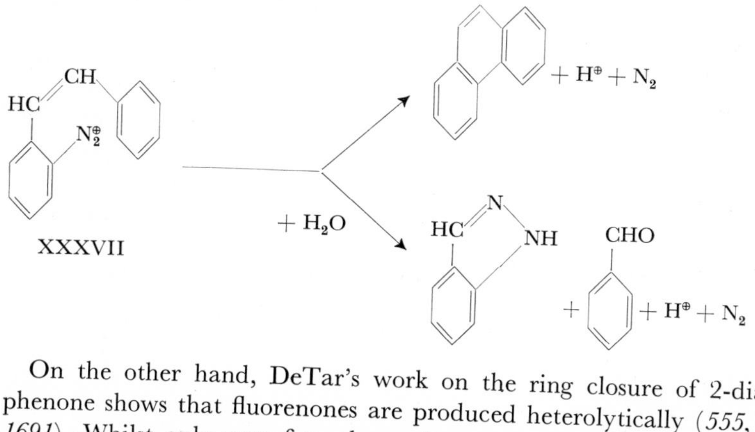

$$+ H^{\oplus} + N_2 \qquad (7.28a)$$

$$(7.28b)$$

On the other hand, DeTar's work on the ring closure of 2-diazobenzophenone shows that fluorenones are produced heterolytically (555, 559, 560, 1691). Whilst only very few phenanthrene syntheses are known which will succeed without copper, most preparations of dibenzofuran and fluorenone derivatives are carried out in the absence of metal catalysts. However, a strongly acid medium seems essential and concentrated sulphuric acid is frequently used. As described in § 7.5, high acidity in general favours heterolysis of aryl-diazonium ions; on the contrary, for typical radical processes, such as the Gomberg reaction, the presence of bases is important.

DeTar's experiments with substituted 2-diazobenzophenones (559, 560) confirm the heterolytic nature of the fluorenone synthesis. The ionic mechanism (7.29) involves the carbonium ion (XXXVIII), which may react with the other aromatic nucleus or with water. If the starting material bears a methyl

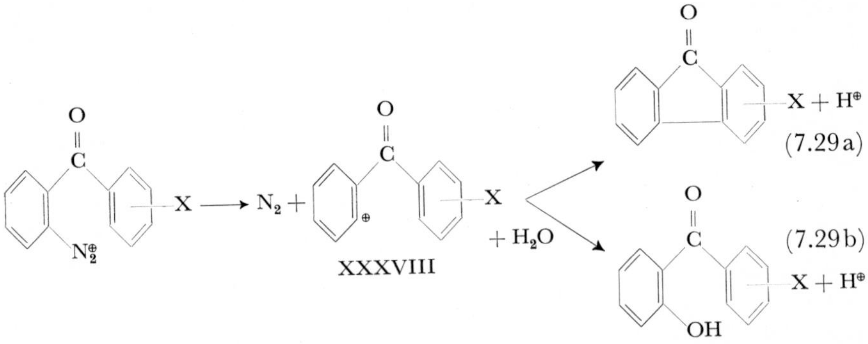

group in the 4′-position ($X = 4'\text{-}CH_3$), 61% 3-methylfluorenone and 34% 2-hydroxy-4′-methylbenzophenone are obtained, but with 2-diazo-3′-nitroben-zophenone ($X = 3'\text{-}NO_2$) only 33% of cyclized products (2- and 4-nitrofluo-renone) and 67% 2-hydroxy-3′-nitrobenzophenone result. The lower yield of nitro compounds in the fluorenone synthesis follows from mechanism (7.29a), as the nitro group is expected to reduce the efficacy of the second benzene ring as nucleophilic partner in the reaction, but for a homolytic mechanism it would have been anticipated from Hey's work (84, 87) that the nitro substituent would facilitate the ring closure (see § 7.5).

The reaction between aromatic diazo and α, β-unsaturated carbonyl compounds in aqueous acetone in the presence of cupric chloride is described as the *Meerwein reaction*, having been first observed by Meerwein and his collaborators (1395) in the case of coumarin and cinnamic acid derivatives (7.30 to 7.32).

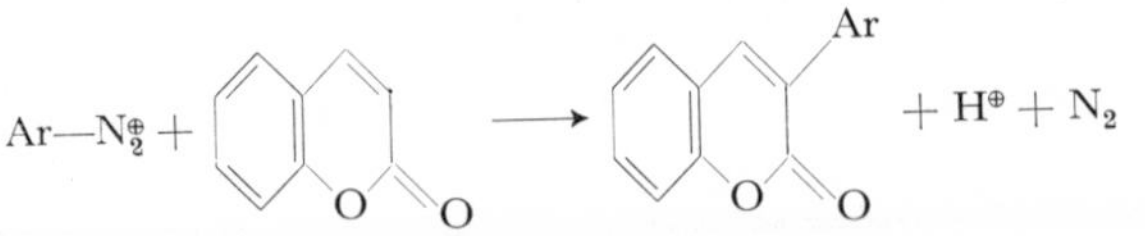

$$Ar\text{-}N_2^{\oplus} + C_6H_5\text{-}CH=CH\text{-}CHO \longrightarrow C_6H_5\text{-}CH=\underset{\underset{Ar}{|}}{C}\text{-}CHO + H^{\oplus} + N_2 \qquad (7.31)$$

$$Ar\text{-}N_2^{\oplus} + Cl^{\ominus} + C_6H_5\text{-}CH=CH\text{-}COOCH_3 \longrightarrow C_6H_5\text{-}\underset{\underset{Cl}{|}}{CH}\text{-}\underset{\underset{Ar}{|}}{CH}\text{-}COOCH_3 + N_2 \quad (7.32)$$

It seems, however, that the reaction is not restricted to α,β-unsaturated carbonyl compounds, as Bergmann and Shapiro (*231*) found that 3-butenoic (vinylacetic) acid, a β,γ-unsaturated acid, reacts with 4-chlorodiazobenzene to give 4-(4-chlorophenyl)-3-butenoic acid (7.33), though in very poor yield.

$$\text{Ar–N}_2^\oplus + \text{CH}_2\text{=CH–CH}_2\text{–COOH} \longrightarrow \text{Ar–CH=CH–CH}_2\text{–COOH} + \text{H}^\oplus + \text{N}_2 \qquad (7.33)$$

Recently it has even been shown that benzene, styrene, anthracene, and their simple substitution products can be arylated with diazo compounds under the conditions of the Meerwein reaction (*573–575*). The arylation of acrylic acid (*2383*) seems to be related to reaction (7.32).

Meerwein (*1395*) and Bergmann (*231*) originally supposed that these arylations proceed through aryl cations, in other words, that they are consequent on the S_N1 decomposition of the diazonium ion. According to Bergmann, the fact that vinylacetic acid is arylated in the γ-position supports the heterolytic nature of the reaction because this position is that to which the hydrogen goes in the ionic addition of hydrogen bromide to the same compound. In the presence of peroxides, that is, under homolytic conditions, hydrogen bromide adds the other way round, the hydrogen ending up at the β-position. As the Meerwein reaction (7.33) occurs only to an extent of 5%, this argument is not convincing.

A radical mechanism has been proposed by Koelsch and Boekelheide (*1250, 1251*), Eugen Müller (*1481*), and Waters (*2112*), and such a process is corroborated especially by the comparative investigations of the Meerwein arylation carried out by Rondestvedt and Vogl (*1730, 1731, 2083, 2084*) as well as by Dickerman et al. (*574, 575*). Particularly clear are the results in the reaction between chlorobenzene and diazobenzene under Meerwein conditions (*575*): the mixture of 2-, 3-, and 4-chlorodiphenyls obtained gives an infra-red spectrum agreeing very well with that of the product from the corresponding Gomberg reaction. In a like manner, the nitrophenylations of nitrobenzene, on the one hand, with 4-nitrodiazobenzene by the Meerwein reaction and, on the other, with 4-nitrobenzoyl peroxide result in mixtures of dinitrodiphenyls of great similarity, containing only a little of the *m*-product which would have been expected to predominate on the basis of a heterolytic mechanism. The observation that iodine interrupts the course of the reaction (*1247*) is also evidence for homolysis, as iodine is able to intercept the aryl radicals formed.

The doubts originally entertained as regards the appearance of radical intermediates were due particularly to the fact that in Meerwein arylations of ethylene derivatives no polymerization had been observed. This side reaction should have occurred if free radicals had appeared in the system. To avoid this difficulty, Rondestvedt (*2083, 2084*) suggested that the radicals are formed, but are not free to escape from the reaction zone, implying that a cryptoradical mechanism is operating similar to that proved to take place by Huisgen (*1122*) in the decomposition of nitrosoacylarylamines (see § 7.5). Some support for this concept comes from the differences between Meerwein arylations and analogous reactions which do proceed via free radicals (from aroyl peroxides or 1-aryl-3,3-dimethyltriazenes): the former always give the better yields and a few compounds, such as acrylonitrile and acrylic acid, are arylated *only* under Meerwein conditions and not with the other sources of aryl radicals cited.

Recently, Dickerman, Weiss, and Ingberman (*576*) have studied the kinetics of the Meerwein reaction. The rate is proportional to the concentration of the diazo compound and that of the ion $Cu^I Cl_2^{\ominus}$, but is little affected by the nature and concentration of the unsaturated component. The following mechanism was deduced:

$$ArN_2^{\oplus} + CuCl_2^{\ominus} \longrightarrow Ar^{\cdot} + N_2 + CuCl_2 \qquad (7.34\,a)$$

$$Ar^{\cdot} + \; \overset{H}{\underset{}{}} C = C \overset{}{\underset{}{}} \; \longrightarrow Ar-\overset{H}{\underset{|}{\overset{|}{C}}}-\overset{|}{\underset{|}{C}}{\cdot} \qquad (7.34\,b)$$

$$Ar-\overset{H}{\underset{|}{\overset{|}{C}}}-\overset{|}{\underset{|}{C}}{\cdot} + CuCl_2 \longrightarrow \overset{Ar}{\underset{}{}} C = C \overset{}{\underset{}{}} + CuCl + H^{\oplus} + Cl^{\ominus} \qquad (7.34\,c)$$

$$Ar^{\cdot} + \; C = C \overset{}{\underset{}{}} \; \longrightarrow Ar-\overset{|}{\underset{|}{C}}-\overset{|}{\underset{|}{C}}{\cdot} \qquad (7.34\,d)$$

$$Ar-\overset{|}{\underset{|}{C}}-\overset{|}{\underset{|}{C}}{\cdot} + CuCl_2 \longrightarrow Ar-\overset{|}{\underset{|}{C}}-\overset{|}{\underset{|}{C}}-Cl + CuCl \qquad (7.34\,e)$$

$$Ar^{\cdot} + CuCl_2 \longrightarrow ArCl + CuCl \qquad (7.34\,f)$$

$$Ar^{\cdot} + CH_3COCH_3 \longrightarrow ArH + CH_3COCH_2{\cdot} \qquad (7.34\,g)$$

$$CH_3COCH_2{\cdot} + CuCl_2 \longrightarrow CH_3COCH_2Cl + CuCl \qquad (7.34\,h)$$

The scheme shows that the primary process (7.34a) consists of the formation of an aryl radical from the diazonium ion by means of a complex between cuprous chloride and a chloride ion. The aryl radical then undergoes one of two sets of reactions, (7.34b–c) or (7.34d–e), the latter with and the former without saturating the reactive double bond, but both leading to arylated products and regenerated cuprous chloride. The reactions (7.34b–c), which are supposed to take place preferentially with compounds bearing a hydrogen at one of the carbon atoms, have not been proved unequivocally. The processes (7.34f–h) yield significant by-products as far as the mechanism of the Meerwein reaction is concerned. The formation of chloroacetone had already been noted and investigated by Meerwein (*1395*). The three reactions (7.34f–h) are important in answering the question raised by the absence of polymerization in the arylation of olefins, as they prevent the build-up of the concentration of free aryl radicals. The olefin radicals formed in the steps (7.34b) and (7.34d) would also be able to initiate polymerization, but their interaction with cupric chloride, (7.34c) and (7.34e) respectively, is more rapid. The scheme also explains why Meerwein arylation, unlike the Sandmeyer reaction, is carried out with the help of cupric and not cuprous salts, the cupric compound being required for the interception of aryl, aralkyl, and acetonyl radicals. For the original radical-forming step (7.34a), the merest traces of cuprous ions suffice and they are produced by side reactions of the cupric chloride. For example, Dickerman (576) records experiments using concentrations of cuprous ions of $3 \cdot 2 \times 10^{-4}$ mol./l. in solutions containing $2 \cdot 8 \times 10^{-2}$ to $5 \cdot 6 \times 10^{-2}$ mol./l. cupric chloride. The dispute over whether mono- or di-valent copper is the actual catalyst is thereby settled, at least in part, as both states of oxidation are necessary. This is in agreement with Kochi's studies (1245, 1246), which stressed the significance of cuprous ions in particular.

The observation that the kinetics of the Meerwein reaction are of second order, but that the rate does vary somewhat in a series of unsaturated compounds, cannot yet be explained with certainty by means of the experimental data available. It is possible that the reason lies in differing stabilities of the various aralkyl radicals or in that the radicals of equations (7.34) do not actually become free, but appear only as cryptoradicals in complexes.

A mechanism of this type has been advanced by Vogl and Rondestvedt (2083, 2084), who noted that the Meerwein arylation of maleic and fumaric esters always yielded roughly the same proportion of cis- and trans-derivatives, the latter preponderating. They therefore proposed a concerted reaction, which explains the favoured addition of the aryl residue in cis-relation to the ester group on the other ethylenic carbon atom.

Clearly, the problem is not yet solved, although the literature contains several papers describing complexes of cuprous salts with unsaturated compounds [e.g. (33, 34, 988, 1198, 2107)].

Finally, the most important of the diazo substitutions considered in this section is the *Sandmeyer reaction*. Back in 1866, Griess (878) showed that the diazo group can be replaced by halogen, particularly by iodine, but the reaction only became of great preparative importance when in 1884 Sandmeyer (1773) discovered the catalytic effect of cuprous salts. It is usual to add a cold, aqueous solution of the diazonium salt to a solution of the cuprous halide and the corresponding halogen acid at an elevated temperature. Subsequently, it was found that the diazo group can be exchanged not only for halogen, but also for a series of other residues. Sandmeyer (1774) already observed the reaction with cyanides, which later proved valuable particularly in the synthesis of thioindigoid dyes. In some cases, nitrite ions lead to the substitution of nitro for diazo groups (959, 1047, 1775, 2078), but frequently the yields are unsatisfactory. Hodgson (1051, 1061) reported that better results are obtained in the copper-catalysed exchange reaction of aryldiazonium cobalt nitrites. The interaction with azide ions has already been dealt with in § 7.4, as by mechanism the process is not of the Sandmeyer type.

Gattermann (779) discovered that cuprous salts may be replaced by finely divided copper and a series of groups can in fact be introduced better by means of this variant, frequently called the Gattermann reaction. Examples are provided by isocyanates (781), although they give poor yields, and by metal or metalloid containing groups, such as Bart's reaction with arsenites to form arsenic acids $[Ar \cdot AsO(OH)_2]$ (*191*) and Nesmejanow's introduction of chloro-mercuri groups (7.35) (*1516, 1518, 1519*).

$$Ar—N_2^{\oplus} + Cl^{\ominus} + HgCl_2 \longrightarrow [ArN_2]^{\oplus} [HgCl_3]^{\ominus}$$

$$\downarrow acetone + Cu \qquad (7.35)$$

$$Ar—HgCl + N_2 + 2\,CuCl$$

The Sandmeyer reaction is unsuitable for the preparation of aryl fluorides. According to Balz and Schiemann (*139*) these may be obtained by the decomposition of diazonium fluoborates, the addition of a catalyst being superfluous.

The reaction of diazonium salts with sulphur dioxide is interesting. Carried out by Gattermann's method (*780*) with copper powder, sulphinic acids result, the copper being oxidized (7.36). Recently, Meerwein *et al.* (*1398*) found that

$$ArN_2^{\oplus} + SO_2 + Cu \longrightarrow ArSO_2^{\ominus} + N_2 + Cu^{\oplus\oplus} \qquad (7.36)$$

$$ArN_2^{\oplus} + Cl^{\ominus} + SO_2 \xrightarrow{\text{CuCl}} ArSO_2Cl + N_2 \qquad (7.37)$$

sulphonyl chlorides can be formed if an aqueous solution of the diazonium chloride is added together with cuprous chloride to glacial acetic acid saturated with sulphur dioxide (7.37). If the diazo compound bears strongly negative substituents, the catalyst may even be omitted.

A comprehensive summary of the preparative uses of the Sandmeyer reaction and the underlying mechanisms has been presented by Cowdrey and Davies (*473*).

The clarification of the mechanism of Sandmeyer reactions is difficult above all because usually a series of side reactions occurs simultaneously and hence not all the stages have yet been proved unequivocally. It has already been mentioned that in several substitutions, such as in the preparation of aryl iodides, the addition of copper catalysts is unnecessary. Therefore these processes probably proceed by the S_N1 mechanism discussed in § 7.2 [equations (7.1) and (7.2)], that is, with the primary formation of an aryl cation to which an iodide ion or a tri-iodide ion is subsequently added. Recently, Carey, Jones, and Millar (*2312*) recorded two examples in which intermediate diazonium tri-iodides have been isolated.

The older investigations into the mechanism were concerned especially with the question of whether a complex between the cuprous and diazonium salts is produced (*932, 2090*). Hantzsch (*959*) let cuprous chloride act on diazonium bromide in dimethyl sulphide solution and obtained the aryl chloride. However, the conclusion that it is always the halogen atom of the cuprous salt which ends up in the aryl nucleus was later disproved experimentally by Hodgson and his co-workers (*1044*).

The investigation of the kinetics began with Waentig and Thomas (*2090*), who found that the rate of Sandmeyer reactions is proportional to the concentration of the diazo compound. In the most important paper on this topic,

Cowdrey and Davies (*472*) showed that the rate decreased inversely as the square of the concentration of chloride ions and this remarkable fact was confirmed by the simultaneous work of Pfeil and Velten (*1625, 1626*). It was deduced that the particles acting as catalyst were converted by the addition of two chloride ions into an ineffectual cuprous complex. Cowdrey and Davies, as well as later investigators of the Sandmeyer reaction (*576, 1245, 1246*), suppose that the ion $CuCl_2^\ominus$ is the catalyst and equation (7.38) the cause of deactivation, whilst Pfeil and Velten took CuCl to be the catalyst, which is converted into $CuCl_3^{\ominus\ominus}$.

$$CuCl_2^\ominus + 2\ Cl^\ominus \rightleftharpoons CuCl_4^{\ominus\ominus\ominus} \qquad (7.38)$$

Hodgson's proposal (*1040*) that cupric salts also catalyse Sandmeyer reactions and that therefore the metal salts act simply as halide carriers for an S_N2 substitution of the diazonium ion is to be discounted as Pfeil (*1624–1626*), Dittmar (*607*), Dickerman et al. (*576*), and Kochi (*1245, 1246*) showed that side reactions always bring about the reduction of a small proportion of the cupric salt to cuprous compounds able to act as catalyst. This also probably applies to salts of other heavy metals, for example ferrous chloride; apparently a free electron is necessary to start the Sandmeyer reaction and it is supplied by the metal ion in the first place, as had been supposed already by Waters (*2111*).

It seems therefore that the overall process follows the mechanism discussed for the Meerwein reaction, namely, steps (7.34a) and (7.34f), and such a scheme has indeed been postulated by Dickerman (*576*) for the Sandmeyer reaction, at least in the presence of acetone.

Pfeil (*1624–1626*) as well as Cowdrey and Davies (*472, 473*) attempted to gain deeper insight into the mechanism, for, although there is hardly any doubt but that the copper complexes of the Sandmeyer reaction decompose homolytically, the appearance of *free* radicals in aqueous solution is not certain. Cowdrey and Davies suggested the formation of a complex, $[Ar \cdot N : N \rightarrow CuCl_2]$, but this is unlikely for several reasons (*1580*). Firstly, in this complex the diazonium ion acts not as the usual electron acceptor, but as donor; secondly, it is hardly in agreement with the observation that electron-attracting substituents favour Sandmeyer reactions, the rate increasing in the series p-$OCH_3 < p$-$CH_3 < H < p$-$Cl < p$-NO_2; and finally, both azo nitrogens of the complex carry positive charges, which is electrostatically very disadvantageous. It therefore becomes much more probable, that in the Cowdrey and Davies complex $CuCl_2^\ominus$ is the electron donor and the formulation $[Ar \cdot N:N \leftarrow CuCl_2]$ accords with all the experimental data.

Presumably the electron transfer and the liberation of nitrogen take place within this complex, but whether the chlorine atom of the aryl chloride comes from the cuprous chloride in the complex or whether it derives from cupric chloride in the sense of Kochi and Dickerman's mechanism of the Meerwein reaction (equation 7.34f) cannot yet be stated with certainty.

The formation of the by-products of the Sandmeyer reaction, particularly of biaryls and azo compounds, depends on the square of the concentration of the catalyst (*472, 1625, 1626*) and hence these processes gain in significance as the amount of cuprous salt is increased. Cowdrey and Davies (*473*) have discussed the mechanism of the side reactions following on from their primary complex. Pfeil (*1624*) deduced the optimum conditions for the Sandmeyer reaction from a variety of kinetic studies, and, furthermore, Bogoslovskii (*278*) has concerned himself with obtaining the best yield of azobenzene derivatives from diazonium salts with copper catalysts. Clusius and Endtinger (*2314*) found by the N^{15} technique that the azo compound former from $Ar \cdot N : N^{15}$ contains one N^{15} atom.

7.7 Reduction and Oxidation of Aromatic Diazo Compounds

In the reduction of aromatic diazo compounds two fundamentally different reactions must be distinguished, namely, on the one hand, the replacement of the diazo group by hydrogen, and, on the other, the hydrogenation of the diazo residue leading to arylhydrazines via intermediates which can occasionally be isolated.

The replacement of the diazo group by hydrogen has already been partly dealt with in connection with the treatment of diazo compounds with boiling ethanol (§§ 7.2 and 7.4). According to Kornblum (*1260, 1265*) this method has only limited preparative significance. As a method of general applicability for the exchange of an amino, that is diazo, group for hydrogen, reduction with hypophosphorous acid (*1262–1265, 1443*) or with hydroquinone (*1559*) is suitable and proceeds by a radical mechanism. Kornblum (*1261*) proposed the scheme (7.39), which is supported by the kinetic isotope effect observed by

$$Ar^{\bullet} + H_3PO_2 \longrightarrow ArH + (H_2PO_2)^{\bullet} \qquad (7.39\,a)$$

$$(H_2PO_2)^{\bullet} + ArN_2^{\oplus} \longrightarrow Ar^{\bullet} + N_2 + (H_2PO_2)^{\oplus} \qquad (7.39\,b)$$

$$(H_2PO_2)^{\oplus} + H_2O \longrightarrow H_3PO_3 + H^{\oplus} \qquad (7.39\,c)$$

Alexander and Burge (*22*) (the rate is decreased about two to six times by working in heavy water).

Surprisingly good results are obtained when diazo compounds are heated in dimethylformamide to the point of nitrogen evolution. The process was first disclosed in patents (*2569, 2570*), but it is very suitable indeed for laboratory purposes also, as most remarkably very small amounts of by-products, such as diazo resins and phenols, are formed (*1149*).

Meerwein and his co-workers (*1392*) recently described a simple method of reduction by which the aromatic diazo compounds are smoothly converted into the corresponding hydrocarbons in dioxane buffered with acetate, in tetrahydrofuran, in 1,2-dimethoxyethane, or in 1,3-dioxolane. Tetrahydrofuran and dioxane become hydroxylated in the 2-position in the process.

Other methods of reducing diazo compounds have been dealt with by Saunders (*1776 s*) [see also (*1726*)].

Turning now to the preparation of aromatic hydrazines from diazo compounds, the usual reducing agent is sulphurous acid or sodium bisulphite, but secondarily stannous chloride also comes into consideration.

In the reduction with sulphurous acid or sodium bisulphite, the yellow diazosulphonic acids, $Ar \cdot N : N \cdot SO_3H$, are formed first, as was found by Emil Fischer (721, 722) in his comprehensive investigations a long time ago. These diazosulphonate intermediates can be isolated, but usually are not. In the case of anthraquinones they are especially stable (1456). Further reduction yields the colourless hydrazinesulphonic acids, $Ar \cdot NH \cdot NH \cdot SO_3H$, which are hydrolysed under acid conditions at elevated temperatures.

In practice, the diazo solution is run into a concentrated solution (40% w/w) containing excess of sodium bisulphite, previously brought to pH 7 with aqueous sodium hydroxide, with constant cooling. After ½ to 2 hours, if the hydrazinesulphonic acid is not to be isolated, the mixture is acidified with hydrochloric acid and slowly warmed. At 50° to 80° the hydrazinesulphonic acid usually hydrolyses smoothly in a short time. On neutralization the hydrazine normally precipitates and can be separated from the solution after cooling. When the hydrazine is to be used for the synthesis of a pyrazolone, the condensation with the β-diketone is frequently carried out directly without isolation of the hydrazine. The reduction of diazonium salts with sodium sulphite has been described in detail by Coleman (453), using diazobenzene as example. In the case of the relatively stable diazo compounds, such as p-diazobenzenesulphonic acid, the initial cooling is not required.

Davies (532) recommends reduction with ammonium sulphite solution, which permits the ready isolation of ammonium hydrazinesulphonates.

E. S. Lewis and Suhr (1336) studied the mechanism of the reduction of diazosulphonates with sulphite and they were able to determine the rates of the reactions both with the syn- and with the $anti$-diazosulphonate. It could be shown with the latter isomer that, contrary to E. Fischer's opinion (722), the primary product is the hydrazinedi- and not the mono-sulphonic acid [see equation (7.16), § 7.4; compare (2393)].

Reduction by means of stannous chloride is very convenient for laboratory purposes, but it does not possess the great range of applicability of the sulphite process (724). A whole series of diazo compounds, such as anthraquinone derivatives, remains unattacked and others react differently. Thus, for example, tetrazotized o-phenylenediamine does not give the dihydrazine, but reverts to the diamine (1838), providing one of the relatively few instances in which fission of the NN-bond of a diazo compound occurs. Splitting of the NN-link can be achieved in simple diazobenzenes by the use of sodium amalgam in dilute acetic acid (2105), but under alkaline conditions sodium amalgam produces the hydrazine (160, 176). Hantzsch (934, 939) showed that both syn- and $anti$-diazotates undergo this reduction and, because of the results of experiments using benzaldehyde (47) or ascorbic acid (2117) as interceptors, it has been supposed that aryldi-imides, $Ar \cdot N : NH$, are the primary products of the action of sodium amalgam.

Oxidation of diazo compounds in alkaline media leads to arylnitramines, $Ar \cdot NH \cdot NO_2$. As oxidizing agents for this reaction, studied particularly by Bamberger (*141, 142, 144, 145, 148, 152, 165, 172, 173, 177, 181*), potassium ferricyanide is the first choice, but oxidation with permanganate (*177*) and hydrogen peroxide (*172, 173*) has also been investigated. Diazoperoxides have been synthesized by Minisci and others (*2345–2347*).

Arylnitramines are strongly acid and only moderately stable. It is well known that they rearrange into *o*- and *p*-nitroarylamines, but at the same time several other compounds are formed, the constitution of which has only been partly elucidated (*170, 171, 297*).

Phenylnitramine is produced also in the autoxidation of benzenediazonium per-bromide in aqueous caustic alkali (*141, 142, 144, 145, 148, 152*). Oxidation in the presence of ammonia which results in azido compounds has already been discussed in § 7.4.

7.8 Photochemical Decompositions of Diazo Compounds

In general, solutions of diazonium salts are very sensitive to light. Every azo chemist knows, for example, that an acid solution of *p*-nitrodiazobenzene is stable for a long time at room temperature as long as it is kept in a dark bottle, but light soon causes nitrogen to be evolved. It is for this reason that in titrations with nitrodiazobenzene use of a brown burette is advisable.

Schmidt and Maier (*1818, 1819*) [see also (*1352*)] showed that in a medium sufficiently strongly acid nitrogen is liberated quantitatively. In contrast to the homolytic decomposition by means of heat, the evolution of gas is stronger at lower pH, which suggests that here radicals play no part and that the reaction does not start from either the diazohydroxide or the diazotate. The product consists essentially of phenols (*1558*), but at high halide ion concentration substitution by chlorine or bromine has been observed (*1881*). In all, it can be assumed that *photocatalysis of the heterolytic diazo decomposition* is occurring. On the contrary, in alcoholic solution, particularly in isopropanol, the photocatalysed, reductive diazo decomposition with replacement of the diazo group by hydrogen preponderates and this probably proceeds by a radical mechanism (*295, 1085*). The extensive literature of the photochemistry of diazo compounds has been summarized by Saunders (*1776b*); here only the most significant aspects will be considered.

The ring contractions observed by Süs (*1980*) on illuminating acid solutions of *o*-diazophenols (7.40) are interesting. The reaction probably corresponds to the Arndt–Eistert rearrangement of aliphatic diazoketones (see §§ 5.6 and 6.3). As illustrated by mechanism (7.40), a carbonium ion rearrangement of the Wagner–Meerwein type is taking place. This is supported by experiments by de Jonge, Alink, and Dijkstra (*537*), who showed that in 50% sulphuric acid, in which the diazophenol no longer exists as the mesomeric zwitterion, but as the diazonium ion with an undissociated phenolic hydroxy group, the product is catechol.

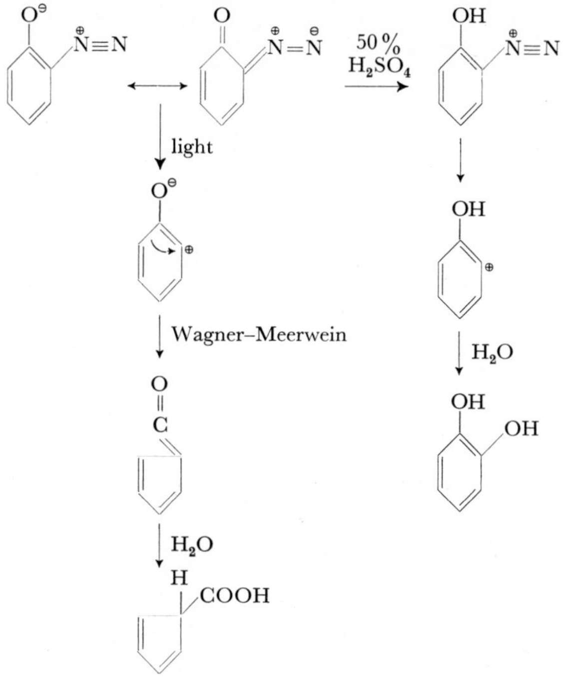

(7.40)

More recently, Süs (*1981–1983, 1985, 1986*) has described the photosynthetic preparation by this method of a variety of compounds, some of which are difficult or impossible to obtain in other ways. Thus indene derivatives substituted in the five- or six-membered ring have been made from 1-amino-2-naphthols (7.41). Similarly cyclopentadiene derivatives with fused on hetero-

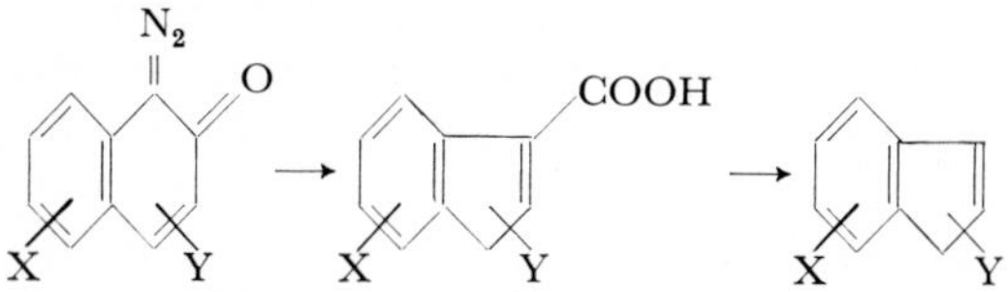

(7.41)

cyclic rings (**XXXIX, XXXX**) can be prepared and quinolines and pyridines yield the corresponding indole- and pyrrole-carboxylic acids (**XXXXI, XXXXII**), some of which can then be decarboxylated. Of interest is 3,6,7,8-tetrahydropentalene (**XXXXIV**) obtainable in this manner from the indan

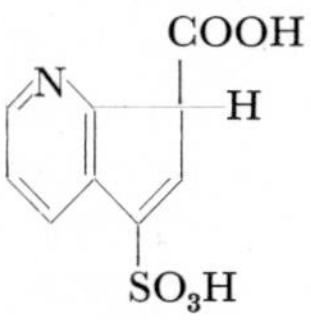

XXXIX 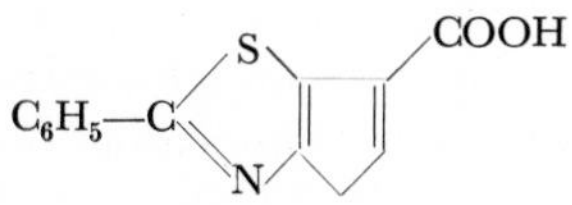   XXXX 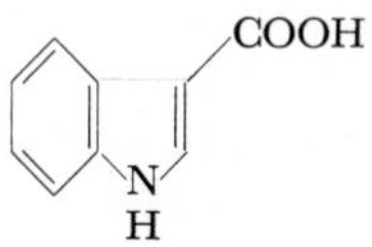   XXXXI 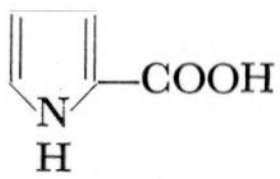   XXXXII

(XXXXIII). The skeleton of the steroids, cyclopentenophenanthrene, has been prepared analogously by Süs from a chrysene derivative.

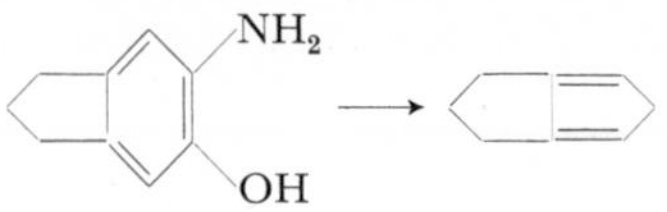

XXXXIII   XXXXIV

Photolysis of p-diazophenols yields high molecular weight compounds, which according to Süs (*1984*) probably possess the structure (XXXXV).

XXXXV

Experiments by Yates and Robb (*2201*) show that ring contraction of o-diazophenols can be achieved also by means of heat. In boiling xylene 1,2- as well as 2,1-diazonaphthol decomposes to compound (XXXXVI). Dewar (*570, 571*) investigated the thermolytic decomposition of a p-diazophenol.

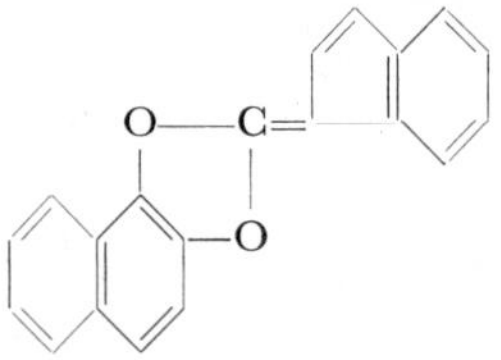

XXXXVI

The application of the diazo decomposition reactions in the preparation of light-sensitive papers (diazotype) is very important, but can here be treated only in outline. The paper is impregnated with a suitable diazo compound, such as an o-diazophenol or more frequently a p-phenylenediamine derivative, one amino group of which is alkylated or arylated. Naturally, the diazonium salts must be stable to heat and so they are applied either as zinc chloride double salts or together with suitable additives. In use the diazo compound is destroyed where it is exposed to light and by subsequent treatment with a coupling component (phloroglucinol, resorcinol, acetoacetanilide or naphthol derivatives) azo dyes are formed over the remaining area. The first paper of this kind to be marketed, Ozalid M of Kalle & Co., Wiesbaden-Biebrich, appeared in 1924. The process has since been replaced by one which avoids the wet treatment: the paper contains both the diazo and the coupling component together with substances, such as citric or tartaric acid, the acidity of which prevents dye formation. After exposure to light, coupling in ammonia vapour, that is by a dry method, is possible. The various diazotype processes have been reviewed by Brown (*340*), Saunders (*1776v*), and Holzach (*1071b*), and much information about the German industry is available (*2700, 2701, 2708*). Other potential applications have been studied by Suter and Häfeli (*1987*).

7.9 The Constitution of the Diazo Resins

Dark-coloured insoluble by-products are formed in the preparation of phenols by treatment of diazonium salts in boiling aqueous acid as well as occasionally in azo coupling, though here usually only to a small extent. They were described by Griess (877) as diazo resins. Depending on their origin and the reaction conditions, they exhibit quite different properties and it is certain that they consist of mixtures of several substances. Frequently, they are the cause of considerably lower yields of the desired products.

In spite of the marked practical importance of the resin-forming reactions, not much has been published about them. Apart from the efforts to lessen the consequences of the diazo decomposition during azo coupling by altering the rate relationships by means of the correct choice of pH, pyridine catalysis, kinetic salt effects, and addition of stabilizers, the literature discloses little about the chemistry of the diazo decomposition and the constitution of the diazo resins. Not until Gies and Pfeil's work (791) were these mixtures investigated in detail.

A few definite by-products of the phenol formation had been reported previously. Thus p-hydroxybiphenyl and diphenyl ether had been found among the products from benzenediazonium salts and apparently hydrocarbons regularly accompany the phenols (791). Nitrogen-containing compounds were observed by Jolles (1177, 1178) as well as by Oddo and Indovina (1547); for example, diazobenzenes bearing nuclear methyl groups yield indazoles and azoindazoles.

Pfeil (791) showed that, on boiling, solutions of purest diazonium bisulphates produce apart from phenol small amounts of diphenyl ether, partly also hydroxybiphenyl and p-hydroxyazobenzene, as well as always 6 to 15% of diphenyl sulphate, but typical diazo resins are obtained only by boiling solutions made by diazotization without isolation and purification of the solid diazonium salt. Pfeil discovered that the primary products of the formation of diazo resins are the o- and p-nitrosophenols, derived by the action of nitrous

Table 7.4

Formation of Resin on Boiling 1000 ml N Diazo Solution, containing
13·0 g Pure Benzenediazonium Bisulphate, in Presence of Sodium Nitrite According to Pfeil (791)

Sodium nitrite g	Resin g
0	0
1	0·48
2	0·86
5	1·3

acid on phenol. An excess of nitrous acid in the diazotization therefore favours the production of resins (see Table 7.4).

In consequence, Pfeil recommends that resin formation is repressed by diazotizing as carefully as possible, removing excess of nitrite by addition of permanganate, working in dilute solution, and continuously removing the phenol formed in the hydralysis stage by steam distillation.

The investigation of the composition of the resins from unsubstituted diazobenzene led to the isolation apart from *p*-nitrosophenol of some triphenodioxazine (XXXXVII), a condensation product of *o*-nitrosophenol (cf. § 9.1).

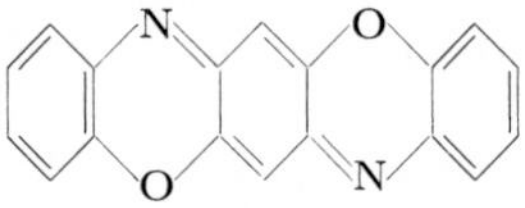

XXXXVII

Further insight into the constitution of the diazo resins was gained by means of an *o,o'*-disubstituted compound, a 1,3-xylene-2-diazonium salt. As illustrated by equation (7.42), 1,6,3',5'-tetramethylindophenol (IL) and the aminophenol (XXXXVIII) are formed. It is probable that in the case of unsubstituted nitro-

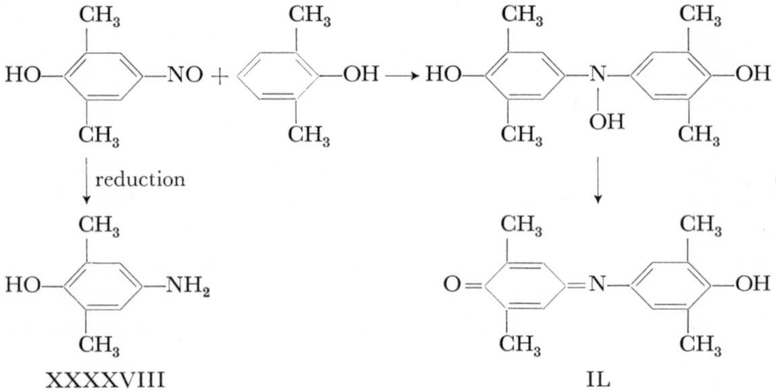

(7.42)

XXXXVIII   IL

sophenols the reaction takes a similar course, but is complicated by the fact that *o*- and *p*-nitrosophenol possess two and phenol three reactive positions, resulting according to Pfeil in a network of benzene and pyrazine rings of relatively high molecular weight (L).

Pfeil's researches allow older observations (*979, 1855, 1856*) of the unfavourable influence of an excess of nitrite on the stability of diazo solutions to be readily understood. The action of sulphamic acid, recommended in a patent (*2582*) as a stabilizing additive, probably depends on the destruction of any nitrite adventitiously present.

Ried (*2350*) recently investigated the thermal decomposition of *o*-diazophenols (see also p. 172).

L

7.10 Stabilization of Diazo Solutions by Arylsulphonic Acids

The addition of certain acids has a surprising effect on the stability of diazonium ions. Allan (23) found that the stability of 2,4-dinitrobenzenediazonium
sulphate in sulphuric acid solutions of different concentrations varied greatly.
Up to a content of about 80% sulphuric acid, the stability increases, but then
goes through a marked minimum in the region 90 to 95%.

Apart from this paper, many attempts have been made to reduce the decomposition of dissolved diazo compounds both for laboratory and industrial
purposes. The preparation of stabilized *solid* diazonium salts has already been
dealt with in § 3.6(a) and here will be considered only those investigations
which have led to an increase in the stability of diazo compounds in solution.

The stabilizing effect of arylsulphonic acids is of greatest practical importance. Becker (2527, 2529, 2531) discovered that the addition of α- or β-naph-
thalenesulphonic acid to a solution of tetrazotized benzidine or *p*-nitrodiazo-
benzene gave rise to precipitates which could be filtered off and dried without
danger. Even after longer storage, they can still be dissolved smoothly in water
and immediately exhibit the reactions typical of diazonium ions.

The effects of such additions of arylsulphonic acids to diazo solutions has
been described in very many patents, which have been reviewed by Saunders
(1776g), but it is most likely that practice has greatly exceeded the limits set
by the examples cited in the literature. In many cases, especially with difficultly soluble or weakly basic amines, not only is a sulphonic acid added to the
diazo solution after preparation, but much more frequently the amine is dissolved or suspended in a concentrated aqueous solution of a sulphonic acid and
is diazotized in such a medium. Particularly suitable for this purpose is a crude
sulphonation mixture from naphthalene, which contains mainly α-naphtha-
lenesulphonic and sulphuric acids and is diluted with 3 to 5 parts of water.
Apart from its stabilizing effect on the diazonium ions produced, such a medium is advantageous also because it possesses great solvent power for amines
and nitrous acid (formation of naphthalenenitrosylsulphonate, $C_{10}H_7 \cdot SO_3 \cdot NO$?). Some diazotizations can be carried out on the large scale in naphthalenesulphonic acid in good yield at 40° to 55° (see § 1.3).

Marriott (*1370*) investigated quantitatively the influence of 1,5-naphtha-lenedisulphonic and *p*-anisolesulphonic acids on the rate of decomposition of several substituted diazobenzenes. The most important conclusion was that no predictions can be made about the effectiveness of the additives in relation to the constitution of the diazo component. In general the naphthalenedisul-phonic acid is more helpful than anisolesulphonic acid and this is confirmed by technical experience. In the case of *p*-nitrodiazobenzene anisolesulphonic acid even exhibits the opposite action and catalyses the decomposition. Marriott carried out his experiments at 2 to 3 different acidities in the range of pH of 5·2 to 8·3. Although from his data no generalizations can be drawn for prac-tical application or about the mechanism of the stabilization by sulphonic acids, it is worth noting that the effect of pH in this region varies greatly with the nature of the diazo compound. Whilst the decomposition of 4-chloro-2-diazotoluene is only insignificantly more rapid in alkaline solution, an increase in pH has a very marked action on the 5-chloro isomer.

Unusual side reactions occur on the addition of 2-naphthol-1-sulphonic acid to diazo solutions. With strongly electrophilic diazo components, such as nitro-diazobenzenes, the aryldiazonium residue displaces the sulpho group in the normal manner for the naphthalene series, a compound of constitution (LI) appearing as intermediate according to Rowe (*1746, 1747*). It has not been proved unequivocally that this substance is neither simply a difficultly soluble salt of the two reactants nor an *O*-azo derivate of the Bucherer type (*356, 357*).

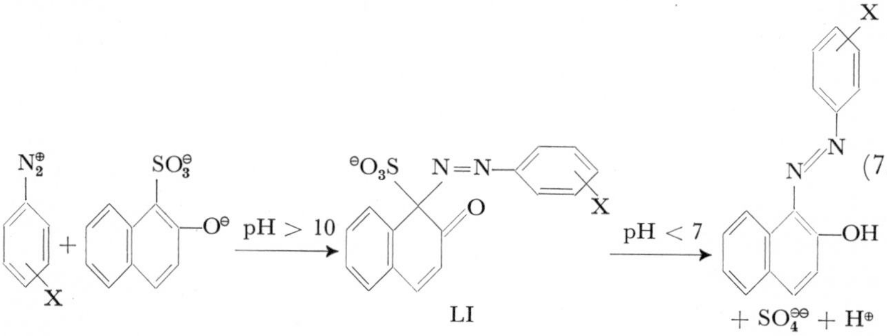

$$(7.43)$$

In alkaline solution this intermediate behaves differently, as demonstrated by Rowe *et al.* (*1741–1744, 1746–1753*) in a succession of papers: the hydro-xylated nucleus of the naphthalene system is opened with the formation of a cinnamic acid derivative (LII), which is converted into the corresponding phthalazine (LIII).

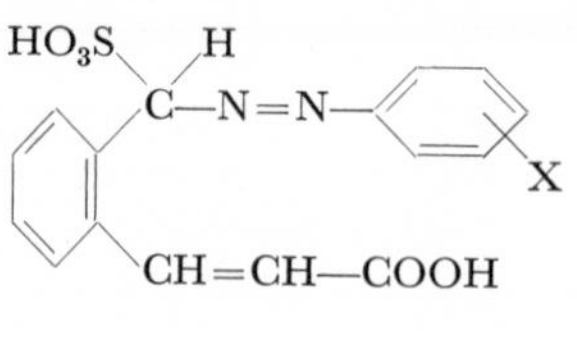

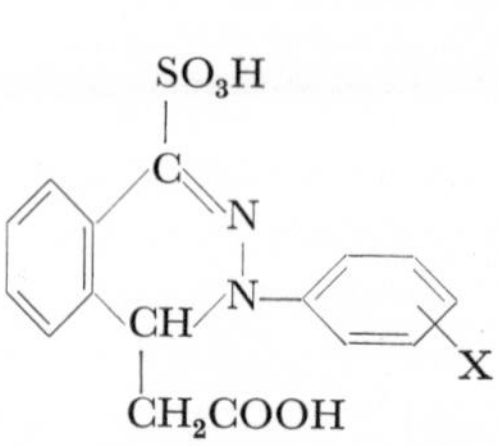

8. Diazoamino Compounds

8.1 Preparation of Diazoamino Compounds

Diazoamino compounds result from the interaction of a diazonium ion with ammonia, a primary, or a secondary amine (8.1). Formally they can be consi-

$$\text{Ar} \cdot \overset{\oplus}{\text{N}} \text{:} \text{N} + \text{HN} \diagup_{R'}^{R} \rightleftarrows \text{Ar} \cdot \text{N} \text{:} \text{N} \cdot \text{N} \diagup_{R'}^{R} + \text{H}^{\oplus} \tag{8.1}$$

dered to be derivatives of the unknown substance *triazene*, $\text{HN:N} \cdot \text{NH}_2$, on which their nomenclature is usually based. Substitution of some or all of the hydrogen atoms of triazene by aliphatic, alicyclic, aromatic, or heterocyclic groups gives rise to several types of derivatives, of which the following are especially important or noteworthy:

(a) *Diazoamino compounds*, $\text{Ar} \cdot \text{N:N} \cdot \text{NH} \cdot \text{R}$, are obtained when primary amines act as the nucleophilic component. They are characterized by the possession of a tautomeric system to be discussed in detail in § 8.2.

(b) *Diazoimino compounds*, $\text{Ar} \cdot \text{N:N} \cdot \text{NRR'}$, are similarly derived from secondary amines. Prototropy is naturally not possible here.

(c) *2-Tetrazenes*, $\text{RR'N} \cdot \text{N:N} \cdot \text{NRR'}$, are the oxidation products of hydrazines substituted only on one nitrogen atom.

(d) *Bisdiazoamino compounds or pentaz-1,4-dienes*, $\text{Ar} \cdot \text{N:N} \cdot \text{NR} \cdot \text{N:N} \cdot \text{Ar}$, normally result from the reaction of diazonium ions with ammonia or primary aliphatic amines.

(e) *Hexaz-1,5-dienes*, $\text{Ar} \cdot \text{N:N} \cdot \text{NX} \cdot \text{NX} \cdot \text{N:N} \cdot \text{Ar}$, are similarly formed from those hydrazine derivatives in which each nitrogen carries at least one hydrogen atom.

Wholly aliphatic diazoamino compounds are known, though so far only few have been studied. Dimroth (*596–598, 601*) obtained them by the action of Grignard reagents on azido compounds (8.2a). For isolation was used the cuprous compound (I), from which the 1,3-dialkyltriazene was liberated by means of diazoaminobenzene (8.2c).

$$\text{R}-\text{N}_3 + \text{R}'-\text{MgCl} \longrightarrow \left(\begin{array}{c} \text{R}-\text{N}=\text{N}-\text{N}-\text{R}' \\ | \\ \text{MgCl} \end{array} \right) \xrightarrow{+ \text{H}_2\text{O}} \text{R}-\text{N}=\text{N}-\text{NH}-\text{R}' + \text{Mg(OH)Cl} \tag{8.2a}$$

$$R\text{—}N\text{=}N\text{—}NH\text{—}R' \xrightarrow{+\,Cu^{\oplus}} R\text{—}N\text{=}N\text{—}\underset{\underset{Cu}{\vert}}{N}\text{—}R' \qquad (8.2\,b)$$

I

$$(8.2\,c)$$

$$R\text{—}N\text{=}N\text{—}\underset{\underset{Cu}{\vert}}{N}\text{—}R' \xrightarrow{+\,C_6H_5\text{—}N\text{=}N\text{—}NH\text{—}C_6H_5} R\text{—}N\text{=}N\text{—}NH\text{—}R' + C_6H_5\text{—}N\text{=}N\text{—}\underset{\underset{Cu}{\vert}}{N}\text{—}C_6H_5$$

1,3-Dimethyltriazene is a colourless liquid, miscible with water, and has an odour resembling that of alkaloids. It explodes on heating. In air methylamine is formed with evolution of nitrogen, the decomposition being catalysed by acid. In presence of hydrochloric acid methyl chloride is obtained as well as methylamine and nitrogen.

The most important method of preparing diazoamino compounds, the reaction (8.1), was described already by Griess (869). He allowed an alcoholic solution of aniline to react with an amount of nitrous fumes insufficient to effect complete diazotization of all the amine, to obtain diazoaminobenzene, $C_6H_5 \cdot N{:}N \cdot NH \cdot C_6H_5$. The same compound results if diazotization is carried out with an equimolecular quantity of nitrite, but with not enough acid. Several publications deal with the generally applicable methods of preparation (534, 646, 2704).

With aromatic *primary* amines triazenes are usually formed and pentaz-1,4-dienes bearing aromatic substituents exclusively can be obtained only by indirect routes (1604). When the nucleophilic reactivity of the aryl residue of an aromatic amine is raised by substituents or fused rings, as in m-toluidine, 1-, or 2-naphthylamine, C-coupling takes place preferentially and the N-azo bodies cannot be isolated. Several investigators (186, 232, 1403, 2079) have studied the relationship between C- and N-substitution on derivatives of aniline, N-methylaniline, and other arylamines. The observation, due to Bamberger (186) and Mehner (1403), that the same components favour nuclear coupling the more strongly acid (or less basic) the medium, must be due to acid catalysis of the back-reaction to the formation of the diazoamino compound (8.1). In contrast to reaction (8.1), nuclear substitution under normal conditions is not reversible, as shown in § 10.5. These facts allow diazoamino compounds to be differentiated from the corresponding aminoazo derivatives. In the presence of acid and a reactive coupling component, such as 2-naphthol, triazenes undergo the back-reaction (8.1) and the diazonium ion formed interacts with the coupling component to yield the azo dye. Contrary to Bamberger (179), this transformation does not occur with aminoazo compounds. With reaction products from secondary aromatic amines, infra-red spectra provide a certain method of determining the constitution. In the spectrum of the aminoazo compound (II) is present an NH-band in the 3μ region, which is missing from that of the corresponding diaziomino isomer (III) (2238).

$$\underset{\text{II}}{\text{Ar}'\text{---N=N---Ar---}\underset{\underset{\text{H}}{|}}{\text{N}}\text{---R}} \qquad\qquad \underset{\text{III}}{\text{Ar}'\text{---N=N---}\underset{\underset{\text{R}}{|}}{\text{N}}\text{---Ar}}$$

The tendency to form aminoazo compounds is greater with secondary than with primary aromatic amines, but, in both series, whenever all the positions *ortho* and *para* to the amino group are substituted already, the diazoamino bodies are obtained without any complications.

When diazonium ions interact with aliphatic or alicyclic amines, the 1:1 product, the diazoamino compound, cannot usually be isolated. The second hydrogen atom of the amino group is substituted almost as rapidly, so that 3-alkylpentaz-1,4-dienes (bisdiazoamino compounds) result. It is therefore preferable to obtain 1-aryl-3-alkyltriazenes from Grignard and azido compounds according to Dimroth's method (*596–598, 601*). 1-Phenyltriazene, $C_6H_5 \cdot N:N \cdot NH_2$, cannot be made from diazobenzene and ammonia because of the formation of the corresponding bisdiazoamino compound (*1604*), but Dimroth (*599*) was able to prepare it by reduction of azidobenzene with stannous chloride in ether. However, 1-anthraquinonyltriazene can be isolated from the products of the interaction of 1-diazoanthraquinone and ammonium carbonate (*2089*), though pentazdienes are formed even in the anthraquinone series (*2543*).

The preparation of very pure diazoamino compounds is not easy, and Dwyer (*634, 635*) has shown that the colour of triazenes is due in part to the presence of small amounts of diazoaminoazobenzenes of the type of (IV). Campbell and

IV

Day (*406*) recommend chromatographic purification of diazoamino compounds on alumina. R. Kuhn and co-workers (*2399*) took advantage of the formation of the almost insoluble diazoamino compounds from 1-deoxy-1-arylaminoketoses to isolate Amadori products from reaction mixtures.

The kinetics of the formation of diazoamino compounds have been studied by Kruger (*1276*), who determined the rates of reaction of diazobenzene with substituted anilines relative to that with aniline itself. It is unfortunate that he apparently did not consider it necessary to keep the hydrogen ion concentration constant.

The first *tetrazene* was isolated by Renouf (*1694*), who oxidized 1,1-dimethylhydrazine to obtain tetramethyltetrazene, a yellow oil, with low solubility in water and strongly basic properties. It reduces silver nitrate solutions and with dilute acids yields formaldehyde, methylamine, dimethylamine, and nitrogen. The analogous decomposition of tetraethyltetrazene (*723*) was studied by H. Wieland (*2153*) and interpreted to occur according to equation (8.3). According to Watson (*2115*), heat or light causes tetrazenes to undergo a similar, but homolytic, decomposition (8.4). In attempting to hydrogenate

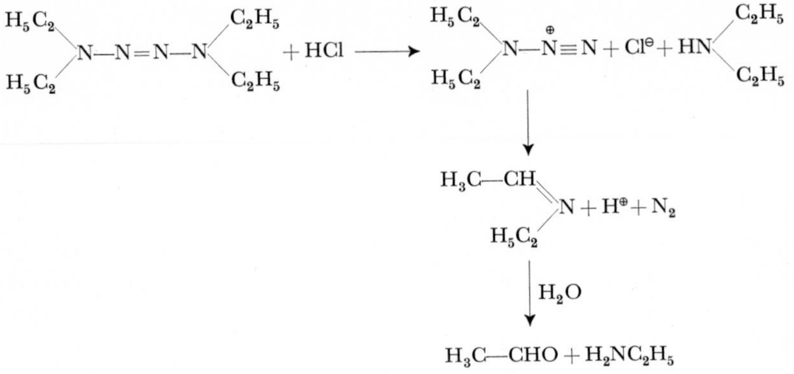

$$H_5C_2 \diagdown \atop H_5C_2 \diagup N-N=N-N \diagup C_2H_5 \atop \diagdown C_2H_5 + HCl \longrightarrow \quad H_5C_2 \diagdown \atop H_5C_2 \diagup N-N\equiv\overset{\oplus}{N} + Cl^{\ominus} + HN \diagup C_2H_5 \atop \diagdown C_2H_5$$

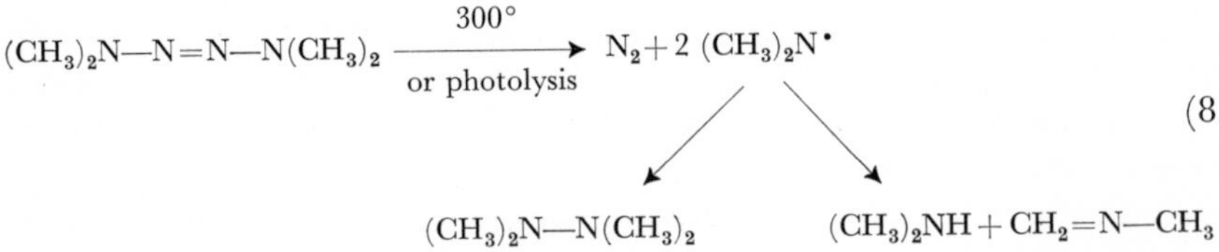

$$H_3C-CH \diagdown \atop H_5C_2 \diagup N + H^{\oplus} + N_2 \tag{8.3}$$

$$\downarrow H_2O$$

$$H_3C-CHO + H_2NC_2H_5$$

$$(CH_3)_2N-N=N-N(CH_3)_2 \xrightarrow[\text{or photolysis}]{300^\circ} N_2 + 2\,(CH_3)_2N^{\bullet} \tag{8.4}$$

$$(CH_3)_2N-N(CH_3)_2 \qquad\qquad (CH_3)_2NH + CH_2=N-CH_3$$

tetrazenes, Birkofer (*255*) obtained the secondary amine and nitrogen. Audrieth *et al.* (*380*) have compared the spectra of tetrazenes with those of their mercury complexes, which presumably have the structure (V).

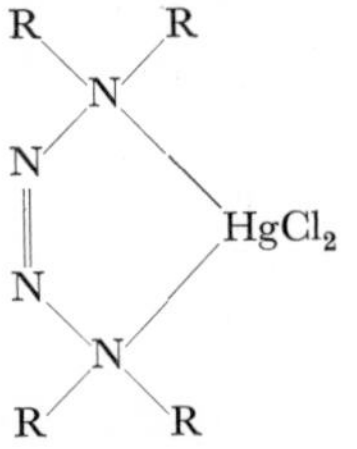

V

The *hexaz-1,5-dienes* (VI) were discovered by K. A. Hofmann and Hock (*1065*). Diazonium ions interact with 1,2-diacylhydrazines, $RCO \cdot NH \cdot NH \cdot COR$, leading to the compounds in which X is an acyl residue (*1088*), but Theilacker and Fintelmann (*2027*) have prepared hexaz-1,5-dienes bearing

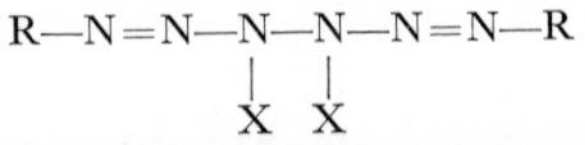

$$R-N=N-\underset{\underset{X}{|}}{N}-\underset{\underset{X}{|}}{N}-N=N-R$$

VI

aromatic substituents only (R=X=Ar) by oxidation of diazoaminobenzene derivatives with potassium permanganate (8.5).

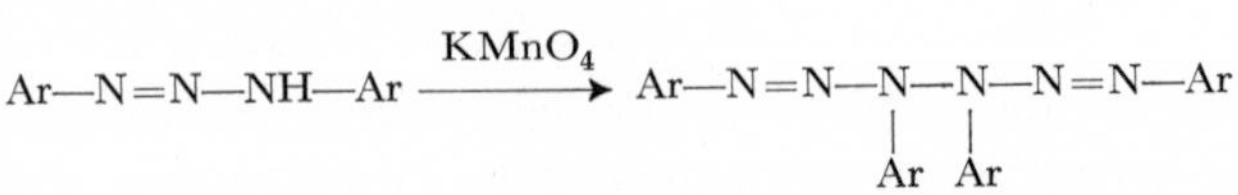

$$Ar-N=N-NH-Ar \xrightarrow{\text{KMnO}_4} Ar-N=N-\underset{\underset{Ar}{|}}{N}-\underset{\underset{Ar}{|}}{N}-N=N-Ar \tag{8.5}$$

8.2 Tautomerism in Diazoamino Compounds

Diazoamino compounds derived from primary amines belong to the large number of substances which can exist in two tautomeric forms. As the structures differ only in the position of a hydrogen atom, this type of isomerism is also described as *prototropy*.

Griess (*880*) already recognized this complication. The action of *p*-diazotoluene on aniline (8.6a) leads to the same product as that of diazobenzene on *p*-toluidine (8.6b).

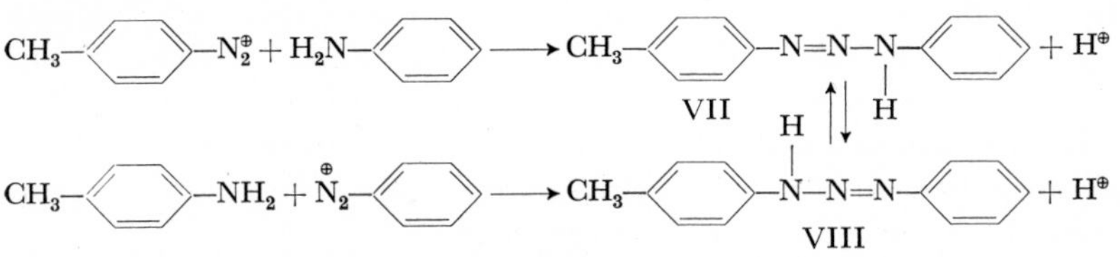

$$CH_3-\langle\;\rangle-N_2^\oplus + H_2N-\langle\;\rangle \longrightarrow CH_3-\langle\;\rangle-N=N-N-\langle\;\rangle + H^\oplus \quad (8.6a)$$

$$\text{VII} \quad H \updownarrow H$$

$$CH_3-\langle\;\rangle-NH_2 + \overset{\oplus}{N_2}-\langle\;\rangle \longrightarrow CH_3-\langle\;\rangle-\underset{H}{N}-N=N-\langle\;\rangle + H^\oplus \quad (8.6b)$$

$$\text{VIII}$$

The question of whether the product is a mixture of (VII) and (VIII) or whether only one of these formulas is appropriate for it has been tackled frequently, but without so far giving an unequivocal answer. The relevant work has been reviewed by Campbell and Day (*406*).

Nölting and Binder (*1536, 1537*) studied chemical methods of degradation. They obtained products which were to be expected partly on the basis of the presence of both tautomeric structures, partly on that of either the one or the other form. Thus acid reduction with zinc gave not only aniline and *p*-tolylhydrazine, but also *p*-toluidine and phenylhydrazine. Again, acid hydrolysis yielded all the four possible products, namely, aniline, *p*-toluidine, phenol, and *p*-cresol, but bromination led solely to *p*-tolyldiazonium bromide and 2,4,6-tribromoaniline, implying structure (VII) only. On the other hand, interaction with phenol, by resulting in *p*-hydroxyazobenzene and *p*-toluidine, indicated (VIII).

Meldola and Streatfield (*1415–1419*) tried to settle the problem by means of *N*-alkylation in alkaline solution and Smith and Watts (*1905*) later showed that the product consists of an equimolecular mixture of the 1- and the 3-alkyltriazene. It is now known that this method cannot give the answer, because the alkylation proceeds via the anion (IX), which is common to both of the tautomeric diazoamino compounds.

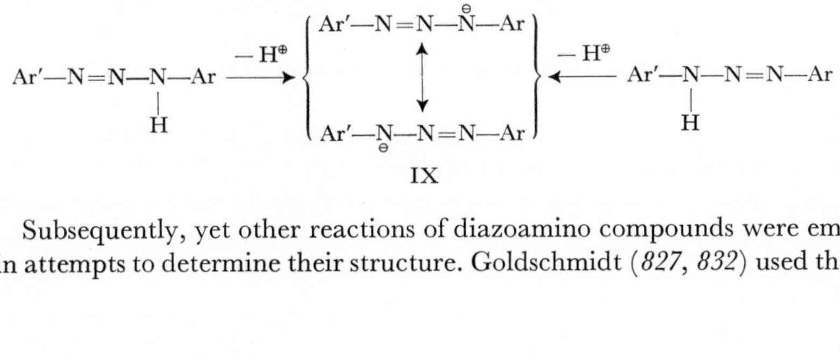

$$Ar'-N=N-N-Ar \xrightarrow{-H^\oplus} \left\{ \begin{array}{c} Ar'-N=N-\overset{\ominus}{N}-Ar \\ \updownarrow \\ Ar'-\underset{\ominus}{N}-N=N-Ar \end{array} \right\} \xleftarrow{-H^\oplus} Ar'-N-N=N-Ar \quad (8.7)$$

$$\underset{H}{|} \qquad\qquad\qquad\qquad\qquad\qquad\qquad\qquad \underset{H}{|}$$

$$\text{IX}$$

Subsequently, yet other reactions of diazoamino compounds were employed in attempts to determine their structure. Goldschmidt (*827, 832*) used that with isocyanates, whilst Dwyer (*634–637*) studied metal–complex formation, but the problem of distinguishing between formulas (X) and (XI) is not soluble chemically.

In summarizing these efforts to assign a structure by purely chemical means, it can be said that a solution of the problem with their help alone remains most improbable. The relationship between the degradation products formed from the two isomers is not only a function of the position of the tautomeric equilibrium, but depends also on the rate of reaction with each form. Only if both tautomers happen to react equally rapidly would it be possible to draw conclusions about the equilibrium between them.

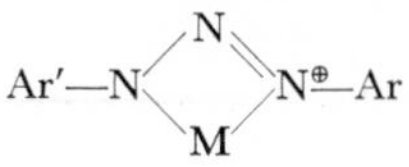

The situation is made even more difficult by the fact that diazoamino compounds tend to associate in solution. Hunter (*1145*) has shown that triazenes derived from primary amines exhibit average molecular weights greater than expected, but that N-alkylated triazenes behave normally. The associated form has been suggested to have the dimeric, cyclic structure (XII). Dipole moments (*1317*) also indicate the presence of di- or poly-mers. Contrary to Davidson (*530*), Le Fèvre (*1317*), as well as Campbell and Day (*406*), stresses that the dipole moments do not allow structures to be assigned unequivocally.

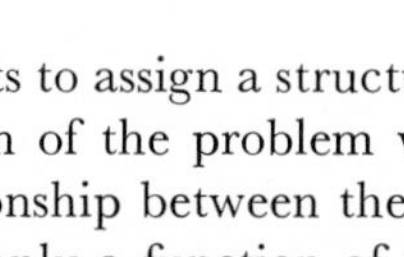

Because of present knowledge of the action of substituents on aromatic nuclei through M and I effects, it can be deduced that negative groups in the 1-phenyl ring of 1,3-diphenyltriazenes should favour the tautomeric form in which the hydrogen atom is in position 3. Ershov and Joffe (*686*) arrived at an analogous conclusion, but Goldschmidt and Molinari (*832*) propounded the opposite.

8.3 The Diazoamino Rearrangement

The rearrangement of diazoamino compounds in the presence of acid, which leads according to equation (8.8) to the aminoazo isomers, is of great technical significance. The reaction is important particularly for the preparation of azo compounds involving primary or secondary amines of the benzene series as coupling components. Only in a few cases, such as that of *m*-toluidine, does

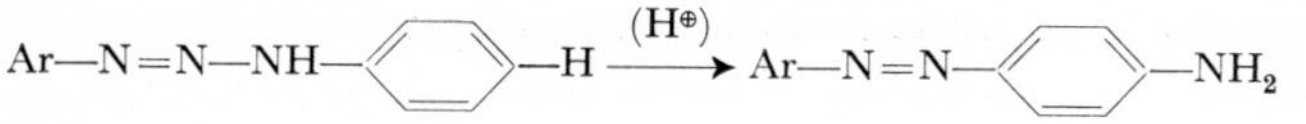

$$Ar—N=N—NH—\langle\ \rangle—H \xrightarrow{(H^\oplus)} Ar—N=N—\langle\ \rangle—NH_2 \qquad (8.8)$$

coupling give the azo derivative directly, and normally the diazoamino compound is formed. The latter, on heating in an acid medium, for preference with addition of the corresponding amine, rearranges to the desired azo dye. During the process the arylazo group migrates to the *p*-position, *o*-rearrangement occurring usually only with *p*-substituted amines. The reaction finds industrial application above all in the manufacture of *p*-aminoazobenzene and aminoazotoluenes. The rearrangement has practically no importance in the naphthalene series, as diazoamino compounds of the type (XIII) can be iso-

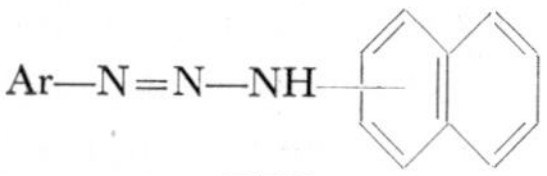

$$Ar—N=N—NH—$$

XIII

lated only when the positions of the naphthalene nucleus *ortho* and *para* to the amino group are occupied or strongly hindered sterically. Thus, for example, 2-naphthylamine-8-sulphonic acid, in which the *peri*-sulphonic group obstructs *C*-coupling, could be shown to give rise to a diazoamino derivative, which has even been isolated (*2238*).

The mechanism of the diazoamino rearrangement has been clear for a long time. The reaction was discovered by Griess and Martius (*885*) and Friswell and Green (*771, 772*) suggested that it proceeded stepwise, fission into amine and diazonium ion being followed by recombination of these fragments through *C*-coupling. In other words, the rearrangement is an intermolecular process. Experimental support for it had already been provided by Nietzki (*1529*). 4-Diazoaminotoluene on treatment in the presence of anilinium or *o*-toluidinium chloride yields aminoazo compounds, in which aniline or *o*-toluidine, respectively, serve as coupling components and *p*-diazotoluene as the electrophilic partner (8.9). If the reaction is carried out in the presence of phenols or

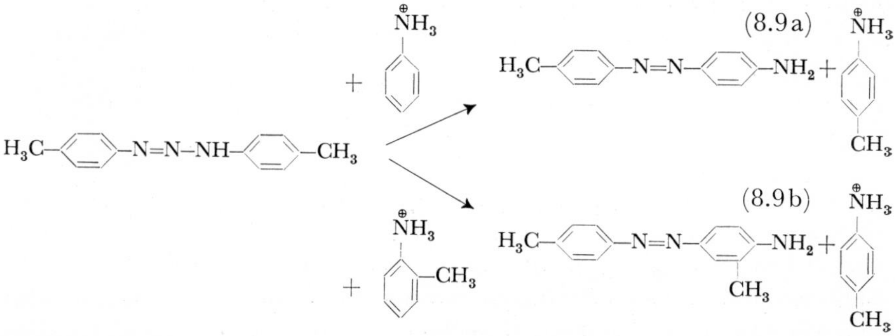

$$H_3C—\langle\ \rangle—N=N—NH—\langle\ \rangle—CH_3$$

$$(8.9a) \qquad H_3C—\langle\ \rangle—N=N—\langle\ \rangle—NH_2 +$$

$$(8.9b) \qquad H_3C—\langle\ \rangle—N=N—\langle\ \rangle—NH_2 +$$

N-dialkylanilines, hydroxyazo and *N*-dialkylaminoazo derivatives result in an analogous manner (*720, 1017, 1211, 1734*).

The rearrangement must therefore be formulated as follows:

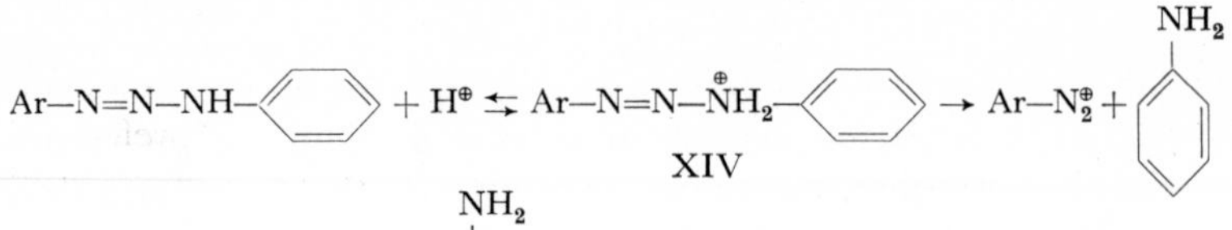

$$\text{Ar—N=N—NH—}\bigcirc + \text{H}^{\oplus} \rightleftharpoons \underset{\text{XIV}}{\text{Ar—N=N—}\overset{\oplus}{\text{N}}\text{H}_2\text{—}\bigcirc} \rightarrow \text{Ar—N}_2^{\oplus} + \overset{\text{NH}_2}{\bigcirc} \qquad (8.10\,\text{a})$$

$$\text{Ar—N}_2^{\oplus} + \overset{\text{NH}_2}{\bigcirc} \longrightarrow \text{Ar—N=N—}\bigcirc\text{—NH}_2 + \text{H}^{\ominus} \qquad (8.10\,\text{b})$$

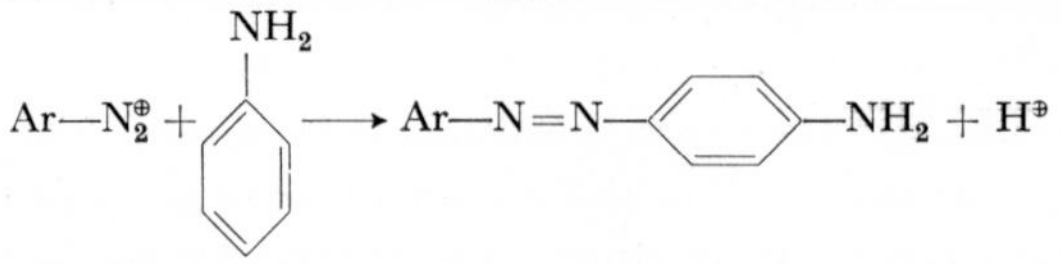

The scheme corresponds to the mechanism postulated by Friswell and Green. The diazonium ion appearing as intermediate couples in the second step to other coupling components present in so far as their concentration and reactivity are sufficiently great to enable the reaction with them to have preference. The formation of the diazoammonium ion (XIV) in the preliminary equilibrium has been proved to occur by Suizu and Yokozima (*1979*).

Goldschmidt's school was able to show that, although Friswell and Green's mechanism is fundamentally correct, under certain conditions the reaction can proceed somewhat differently (*823, 824, 828, 833–835*). It is striking, that the diazoamino rearrangement is not only catalysed by acid, but that also the addition of the appropriate amine greatly facilitates it. This could be explained by supposing that, after the formation of the diazoammonium ion (XIV), fission according to equation (8.10a) does not occur, but that the base is added with splitting off, either simultaneously or immediately thereafter, of a proton and of the amine originally present in the diazoamino compound (8.11).

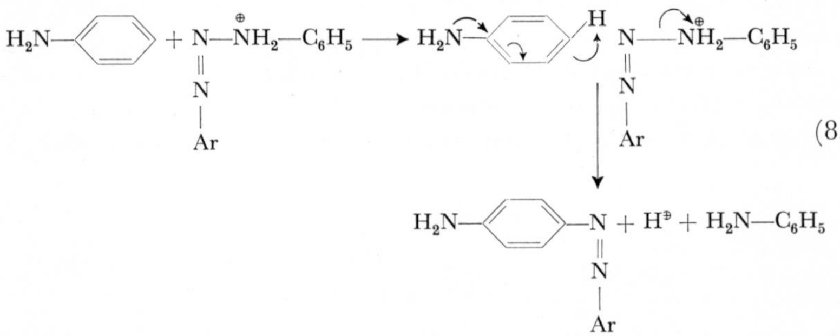

$$\text{H}_2\text{N—}\bigcirc + \underset{\overset{|}{\text{N}}\overset{|}{\underset{\text{Ar}}{}}}{\overset{\oplus}{\text{N}}\text{—}\overset{\ominus}{\text{N}}\text{H}_2\text{—C}_6\text{H}_5} \longrightarrow \text{H}_2\text{N—}\bigcirc \cdots \overset{\text{H}}{\underset{\overset{\|}{\text{N}}\overset{|}{\underset{\text{Ar}}{}}}{\text{N—}\overset{\oplus}{\text{N}}\text{H}_2\text{—C}_6\text{H}_5}} \qquad (8.11)^{[1]}$$

$$\text{H}_2\text{N—}\bigcirc\text{—}\underset{\overset{\|}{\text{N}}\overset{|}{\underset{\text{Ar}}{}}}{\text{N}} + \text{H}^{\ominus} + \text{H}_2\text{N—C}_6\text{H}_5$$

Hughes and Ingold (*1104, 1153h*) have demonstrated that Goldschmidt's mechanism is a special case of a more comprehensive form of the classic proposal of Friswell and Green. The scheme (8.12a to 8.12c) represents a slight modification of the views of Hughes and Ingold. It will be seen that in Goldschmidt's formulation the base $X^{\ominus}$ is the aniline molecule.

---

[1] The formulas for the diazoamino and azo compounds are written in an angular manner only for the sake of clarity.

$$\text{Ar—N=N—NH—C}_6\text{H}_5 + \text{H}^\oplus \rightleftharpoons \text{Ar—N=N—}\overset{\oplus}{\text{N}}\text{H}_2\text{—C}_6\text{H}_5 \qquad (8.12\,\text{a})$$

$$\text{Ar—N=N—}\overset{\oplus}{\text{N}}\text{H}_2\text{—C}_6\text{H}_5 + \text{X}^\ominus \rightleftharpoons \left\{ \begin{array}{c} \text{Ar—N=N—X} \\ \updownarrow \\ \text{Ar—}\overset{\oplus}{\text{N}}\equiv\text{N} + \text{X}^\ominus \end{array} \right\} + \text{C}_6\text{H}_5\text{NH}_2 \qquad (8.12\,\text{b})$$

$$\text{Ar—}\overset{\oplus}{\text{N}}\equiv\text{N} + \text{C}_6\text{H}_5\text{NH}_2 \longrightarrow \text{Ar—N=N—}\!\!\left\langle\!\!\bigcirc\!\!\right\rangle\!\!\text{—NH}_2 + \text{H}^\oplus \qquad (8.12\,\text{c})$$

If the reaction proceeds via the diazonium ion in step (8.12 b), it would be expected to be of second order. If Ar·N:N·X becomes an intermediate, the reaction would be dependent not only on the concentration of hydrogen ions and of the diazoamino compound, but also on that of particles $\text{X}^\ominus$, that is, it would become of third order.

In fact, Goldschmidt was able to show that this is so. Since he employed aniline as the solvent, it was impossible to demonstrate experimentally the dependence on the concentration of aniline expected according to equation (8.11). On the other hand, the reaction proved to be in the main of first order with respect to the concentration of acid as far as mineral acids (hydrochloric, hydrobromic, nitric) were concerned. However, the very accurate experimental data suggested that, apart from the principal reaction with direct proportionality to the acid concentration, a fraction took place with second order in respect of acid. If instead of mineral acid, weaker acids (nitrobenzoic acids) were employed, the order of the reaction increased, leading to the conclusion that now the reaction proceeds mainly via Ar·N:N·X, where $\text{X}^\ominus$ is the anion of the nitrobenzoic acid.

All these observations are in agreement with the scheme (8.12). Apart from the diazoamino compound, a proton and a nucleophilic component are necessary for the reaction. When mineral acid is used, the particle $\text{X}^\ominus$ which it provides is only extremely weakly basic and the solvent aniline predominantly serves as the electron donor. On the contrary, in the case of carboxylic acids, the more basic carboxylate anions play a greater part according to the strength of their electrophilic character.

An analogous investigation of the diazoamino rearrangement in aqueous medium has not yet been carried out. It would excite interest, because, on the one hand, it should give information on the ability of the covalent diazo compounds Ar·N:N·X to exist in aqueous acid solution. On the other hand, it might bring about the clarification of the problem of why, under the conditions of the preparative diazoamino rearrangements (60° to 100°), diazonium ions, which are slowly added to a solution of the amine, will not undergo direct C-coupling in good yield. According to the classic mechanism of Friswell and Green, it should be possible in this way to prepare aminoazo compounds in one step.

8.4 Diazo Migration

As long ago as 1866, Griess (873, 883) had observed that diazobenzene and ammonia gave, instead of the expected 1-phenyltriazene, among other substances diazoaminobenzene, the product of the interaction of diazobenzene with

aniline. Later, he showed that in an acid solution *p*-diazobenzenesulphonic acid
and *p*-toluidine quantitatively yield *p*-diazotoluene and sulphanilic acid. The
isolation of *p*-nitroaniline from *p*-nitrophenyl*anti*diazotate and ammonium chloride by von Pechmann and Frobenius (*1604*) is analogous.

   The phenomenon is described as diazo migration. Both Schräube and Fritsch
(*1841*), as well as Hantzsch and Perkin (*972*), interpreted it as a consequence
of the formation of diazoamino compounds (8.13).

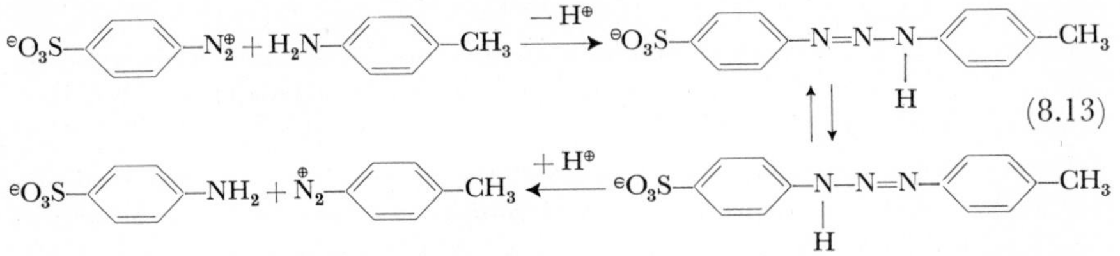

$$\text{(8.13)}$$

   In quite a number of technically important azo coupling processes, diazo migration, although often not recognized as such, constitutes an undesirable side
reaction which lowers the yield. It would be expected to occur particularly
when a reactive diazo compound is to be coupled to a strongly basic amine of
the benzene series, such as *m*-toluidine, for example. Simultaneously with *C*-
coupling is formed the diazoamino compound; this is then protolytically split
into *p*-diazotoluene and the amine from which the original diazo compound had
been derived.

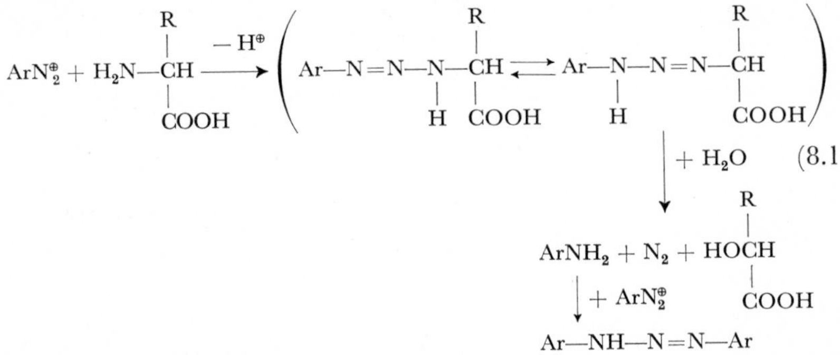

$$\text{(8.14)}$$

   The formation of 1,3-diphenyltriazenes, observed by Zahn, Wollemann, and
Waschka (*2207*) in the reaction between aryldiazonium salts and glycine or
alanine, is also due to diazo migration (8.14).

   According to Schraube and Fritsch, in neutral solution the interaction of
p-diazobenzenesulphonic acid and *p*-toluidine does not stop at the stage of the
mixed triazenes of equation (8.13); on the contrary, the two quasisymmetrical
diazoamino compounds (XV) and (XVI) can be isolated. This surprising result

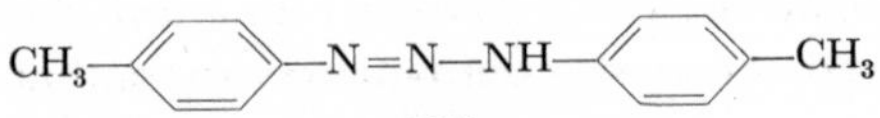

$$CH_3-\langle\rangle-N=N-NH-\langle\rangle-CH_3$$

XV

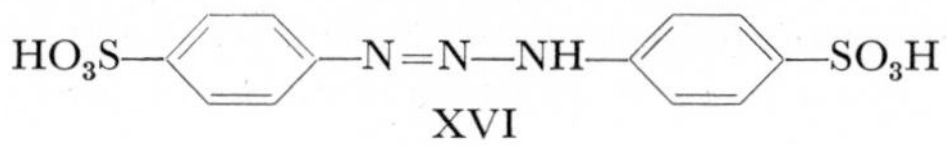

$$HO_3S-\langle\ \rangle-N=N-NH-\langle\ \rangle-SO_3H$$

XVI

may be interpreted as follows. Primarily the mixed diazoamino compounds, both 1,3- and 3,1-*p*-sulphophenyl-*p*-tolyltriazene, are formed. As the hydrogen ion concentration is low, the triazenes split so slowly that the subsequent reactions can be neglected. However, a 4-sulphophenyldiazonium ion, which is, after all, a Lewis acid, can add on to the nitrogen atom at position 1 or 3 (XVII–XVIII). These adducts may then dissociate back to the primary products, but alternatively fission may occur at the bonds indicated by the dotted lines in formulas (XVII) and (XVIII). In the case of (XVIII), this still leads

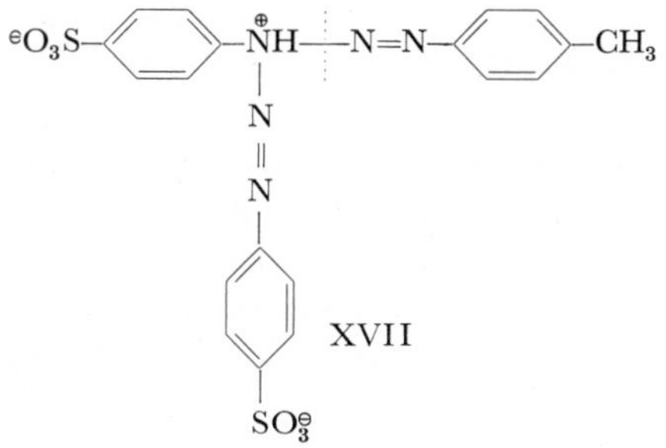

XVII 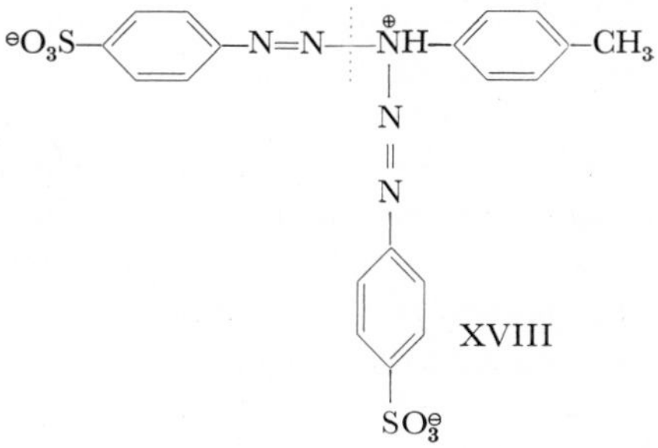   XVIII

back to the primarily formed triazene, but (XVII) gives the disulphotriazene (XVI) and a *p*-tolyldiazonium ion, which with the *p*-toluidine still present yields ditolyltriazene (XV).

8.5 Technical Application of Diazoamino Compounds

Quite apart from the industrial importance of the diazoamino rearrangement in the manufacture of aminoazo compounds, triazenes have attained great significance in connection with the formation of insoluble azo colouring matters on the fibre.

As already described when discussing the diazoamino rearrangement, the action of acids on diazoamino compounds leads in the first place to the liberation of diazonium ions. The rate of dissociation is proportional to the hydrogen ion concentration (*823, 824, 828, 833–835, 1104, 1153h*), that is, by lowering the pH by one unit, diazonium ions are formed ten times more rapidly. Thus, on acidification a mixture of a diazoamino compound with a coupling component yields an azo dye. Although the technical usefulness of this principle had already been foreshadowed in 1886 (*2524*), it did not become exploited on a large scale until the I. G. Farbenindustrie introduced the Rapidogen colours in 1930 (*2551, 2553*). The Rapidogens are water-soluble mixtures of coupling components of the Naphtol AS type (3-hydroxy-2-naphthanilides and others in the form of their alkali salts) with diazoamino compounds, derived from an aromatic amine free from anionic substituents and an amine bearing a sulpho or carboxy group. Along with the Rapid Fast colours mentioned in discussing the diazotates (see § 4.3), they are of interest especially in textile printing. In the classic Rapidogen process, the prints are developed by acid steaming. Compared with the Rapid Fast colours, they cover a wider range of hues and are more stable.

This difference is based on the fact that the stability of a given diazo component as *anti*-diazotate (Rapid Fast type) cannot be varied. Strongly negative substituents thus make a diazo compound unsuitable for the Rapid Fast series, as the difficulty of reverting to the diazonium ions would be too great. The opposite is the case with diazo components with electron-releasing substituents, such as several OCH_3 or NR_2 groups, the *anti*-diazotates of which yield the cations all too readily. In the Rapidogens, however, such a great contrast in the ease of formation of diazonium ions can be avoided by combining negatively substituted diazo components with weakly basic amines and less reactive diazo derivatives with more strongly basic amines. Examples for this rule can readily be found among the constitutions of the diazoamino compounds which are now known to make up the Rapidogen range (*1380, 1776m, 2077d, 2704a*). Five amines, sarcosine (XIX), methyltaurine (XX), and the three aromatic amines (XXI to XXIII) sufficed for a total of thirty five azoic compositions

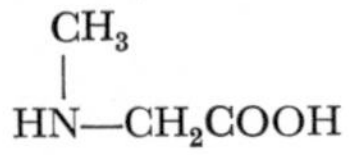

$$CH_3$$
$$HN-CH_2COOH$$
$$XIX$$

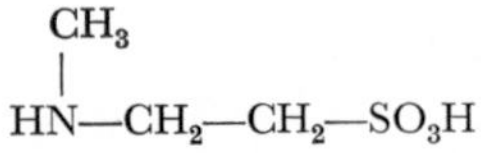

$$CH_3$$
$$HN-CH_2-CH_2-SO_3H$$
$$XX$$

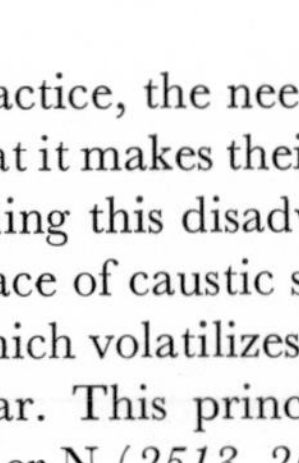

$$CH_3$$
$$HN$$
COOH
$$XXI$$ 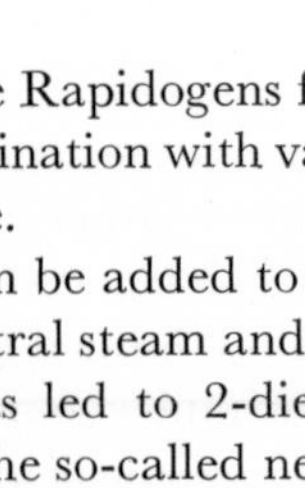
$$SO_3H$$

$$C_2H_5$$
$$HN$$
COOH
$$XXII$$ 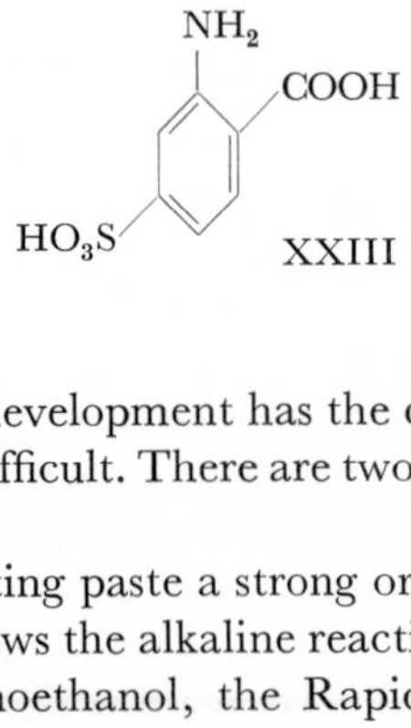
$$SO_3H$$

$$NH_2$$
COOH
$$HO_3S$$
$$XXIII$$

In practice, the need of the Rapidogens for acid development has the drawback that it makes their combination with vat dyes difficult. There are two ways of avoiding this disadvantage.

In place of caustic soda can be added to the printing paste a strong organic base, which volatilizes in neutral steam and thus allows the alkaline reaction to disappear. This principle has led to 2-diethylaminoethanol, the Rapidogen Developer N (*2513, 2514*). The so-called neutral developers depend on the use of ammonium salts, from which steam liberates ammonia by hydrolysis and so makes the printing paste more acid.

Recently, products have been marketed in which the rate of dissociation of the diazoamino compounds is balanced so carefully that they can be developed under neutral conditions (*2517, 2520*) [Neutrogenes of Fran, Rapidogen N types of By, and Cibaneutrenes of Ciba[2]]. Amongst others, they contain as amine 2-*o*-carboxyphenylglycine (XXIV). In these products it is important that

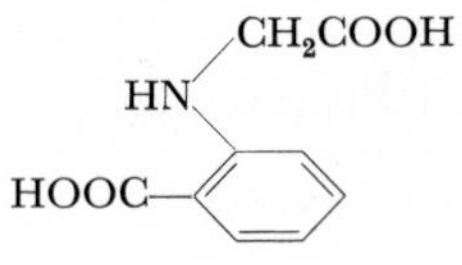

$$
\begin{array}{c}
\text{CH}_2\text{COOH} \\
\text{HN} \diagup \\
\text{HOOC} \diagdown \\
\end{array}
$$

XXIV

the reactivity of the diazo component shall be counterpoised accurately with the basicity of the amine (*2578*). As can be seen from equations (8.15) and (8.16), the diazoamino equilibrium remains completely analogous to the acid–base equilibrium of the corresponding aniline derivative.

$$\text{Ar—N}_2^{\oplus} + \text{R—NH}_2 \rightleftharpoons \text{Ar—N=N—NH—R} + \text{H}^{\oplus} \qquad (8.15)$$

$$\text{Ar—NH}_3^{\oplus} + \text{H}_2\text{O} \rightleftharpoons \text{Ar—NH}_2 + \text{H}_3\text{O}^{\oplus} \qquad (8.16)$$

In addition, diazoamino compounds play a part as blowing agents in the manufacture of foamed synthetic rubbers. Before the thermoplastic stage, there is added to the mass an agent able to liberate gases on heating. Apart from ordinary diazoamino compounds, substances recently proposed for this purpose are of the type of (XXV) (*2596*), obtained from diazobenzenes and nitroamides of arylsulphonic acids, or they are diazoaminobenzenes bearing acid azide groups (*2595*). The diazido derivative (XXVI) evolves three equivalents of nitrogen on heating.

$$
\begin{array}{c}
\text{Ar—N=N—N—SO}_2\text{Ar}' \\
| \\
\text{NO}_2
\end{array}
\qquad\qquad
\text{N}_3\text{—CO} \diagup \diagdown \text{—N=N—NH} \diagup \diagdown \text{—CO—N}_3
$$

XXV   XXVI

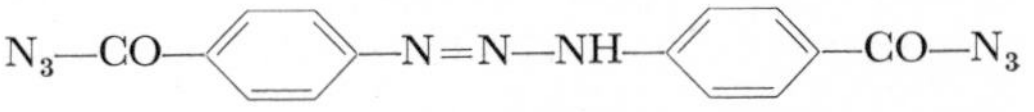

---

[2] For abbreviations of dyestuff manufacturers' names see appendix, page 406.

9. Methods of Preparing Azo Compounds

9.1 The Preparation of Aromatic Azo Compounds

This chapter deals with the methods of preparing the azo compounds themselves, that is, those substances in which the group —N:N— is joined at each end to the carbon atoms of organic residues to give $R \cdot N : N \cdot R'$. Compounds in which both R and R′ are aromatic or *quasi*aromatic differ considerably both in preparation and properties from those in which one or both azo nitrogen atoms are linked to aliphatic radicals, or, more correctly, to sp^3-hybridized carbon atoms. The methods available for obtaining aliphatic azo compounds will be described in § 9.2.

Among the routes to the aromatic azo derivatives, by far the greatest importance attaches to the coupling reaction between an aromatic diazo compound and a so-called coupling component. Discussion of it is deferred to §§ 9.3 and 9.4 and the next two chapters. For the preparation of azo bodies in which either or both R and R′ are heterocycles, apart from the normal coupling reaction, oxidative coupling (§ 9.5) is sometimes suitable.

In this section will be mentioned briefly all the other methods of formation available for aromatic azo compounds. Except for the now obsolete synthesis of Tartrazine due to J. H. Ziegler, the oxidation of aminostilbene derivatives and their precursors which leads to dyes such as Mikado Yellow (L), containing azoxy and probably azo groups (*863, 864, 1237, 2539, 2709*), and the preparation of Chloramine Yellow (FBy) (see below), none of these has any direct technical significance in colour chemistry, but they are important preparatively in circumstances in which an azo compound inaccessible by coupling is to be made.

The parent substance of the azo dyes, azobenzene, was prepared by Mitscherlich (*1452*) by the action of alcoholic potassium hydroxide on nitrobenzene almost a quarter of a century before the discovery of the diazo compounds. Some patents (for example *2525, 2593*) and a Russian paper (*2024*) deal with modifications of this process. It is well known that the reduction of nitrobenzene proceeds via azoxybenzene and hydrazobenzene eventually to aniline, but, whilst acid reduction cannot usually be arrested at an intermediate stage, in caustic alkaline medium azobenzene can be obtained. For preparative purposes reduction with zinc dust in methanol (9.1) is recommended especially

$$2\,Ar—NO_2 + 4\,Zn + 8\,NaOH \longrightarrow Ar—N=N—Ar + 4\,Na_2ZnO_2 + 4\,H_2O \qquad (9.1)$$

(*251*), but sodium amalgam (*2126*), aluminium sodium hydride (*719*), sodium sulphide (*2541*), D-glucose (*1553*), or other reagents (*251*) may also be used.

Nitrosobenzene can be reduced to azobenzene by means of aluminium lithium hydride (2119).

Martynoff (1373, 1374) has investigated a method of preparing azo derivatives from nitro compounds and amines [cf. (131)], in which the amine reacts with nitrobenzene and sodium hydroxide at 170° to 200° with good yield, although the reaction is not well understood. For example, m-anisidine and nitrobenzene gave m-methoxyazobenzene, demethylated with aluminium chloride to m-hydroxyazobenzene. The condensation of 4,4'-dinitrostilbene-2,2'-disulphonic acid with two molecules of 4-aminoazobenzene derivatives in aqueous sodium hydroxide is technically important (2539). A part of the amino compound is used up as reducing agent. Through a reductive or oxidative aftertreatment (glucose or hypochlorous acid, respectively) a degree of purification is achieved. According to research work carried out at Farbenfabriken Bayer (2709) the commercial products are essentially tetrakisazo dyes containing azoxy compounds as impurities.

Under some conditions reducing agents do not convert diazonium salts into the hydrazines expected, but into azobenzene derivatives. Thus, by the action of potassium ferrocyanide on diazobenzene Griess (881, 1354) obtained a mixture, containing azobenzene and (phenylazo)biphenyl, $C_6H_5 \cdot N:N \cdot C_6H_4 \cdot C_6H_5$. This reaction has recently been studied in greater detail by Waters and co-workers (738). Vorländer and Meyer (1046, 2087) investigated the reduction of a series of diazo compounds by ammoniacal cuprous oxide and found that in the case of some compounds, such as 2,4-xylidine derivatives, the yield of the corresponding azobenzene is surprisingly good. Saunders and Waters (1777) suppose that aryl radicals formed primarily and diaryl radicals produced from them react with diazonium ions in the presence of a reducing agent.

In a more extensive study of the formation of azobenzenes by the action of copper catalysts on diazonium salts, Bogoslovskii (278, 279) found that by adding the diazo solution quickly to the solution of the copper salt a large number of symmetric azobenzenes can be obtained in good yield (55 to 90%). A mixture of two aryldiazonium salts gives the unsymmetric azo compound if the two components bear substituents differing clearly in their electronic effects. For example, 4-methylazobenzene-2'-carboxylic acid can be made from 2-diazobenzoic acid and 4-diazotoluene.

The mechanism of formation of such unsymmetric azo derivatives has been studied by Holt (1067), who carried out the reaction between ordinary diazo-

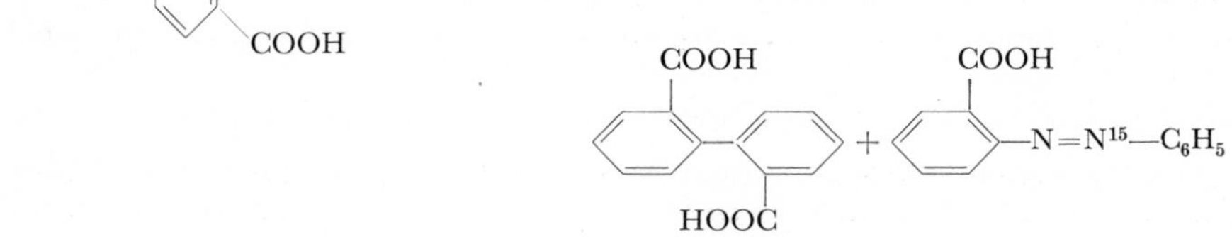

$$C_6H_5N_2^{\oplus} + \ \ \xrightarrow{\text{Cu (NH}_3)_4^{\oplus\oplus}} \ C_6H_5 \!-\! N \!=\! N \!-\! C_6H_5 + \qquad (9.2)$$

benzene and 2-(β-N^{15}-diazo)-benzoic acid in the presence of the tetrammino-cupric ion. He obtained, apart from diphenic acid and diazobenzene, which was free from N^{15} as expected, azobenzene-2-carboxylic acid in which the β-nitro-gen again bore the heavy isotope (9.2).

The preparation of azo compounds by oxidation of amines is possible by various processes, for instance, using air (*1273, 2024*), potassium permanganate (*2024*), lead tetra-acetate (*1593*), hydrogen peroxide and other peroxy compounds (*296, 805, 1404, 1592, 2593*). Yields vary greatly with the nature of the substituents [cf. (*1592, 2024*)]. The oxidation of phenylhydrazine with benzoyl peroxide also leads to azobenzene (*1080*). The reaction of amines of the benzothiazole series with hypochlorite has technical significance [Chloramine Yellow NN from 2-(*p*-aminophenyl)-6-methylbenzothiazolesulphonic acid (*709f*)].

The thermal and photolytic disproportionation of hydrazobenzene to azobenzene and aniline possesses interest not preparatively, but from the point of view of mechanism. Holt and Hughes (*1069, 1070*) were able to show by means of N^{15} that the two nitrogen atoms of hydrazobenzene are not parted, thereby confirming the mechanism which depends on the dehydrogenation of hydrazobenzene by $C_6H_5 \cdot NH \cdot$ radicals and which had already been suspected by H. Wieland (*2151*) and postulated by Dewar (*568*).

More important to the azo chemist are those methods which permit the synthesis of unsymmetric derivatives.

Zincke and Bindewald (*2224*) showed that 4-phenylazo-1-naphthol, normally made by coupling diazobenzene to α-naphthol, can also be obtained by interaction of phenylhydrazine and 1,4-naphthoquinone. The method has some importance for the preparation of a few hydroxyazo compounds accessible not at all or only with difficulty by means of azo coupling, an example being 2-phenylazo-1-naphthol (*2224*). In investigations of the problem of whether *p*-hydroxyazo dyes exist as such (I) or as the tautomeric quinonehydrazones (II) (cf. § 13.2) the corresponding *N*-methylhydrazones are significant (*706, 707*).

Ziegler's Tartrazine synthesis (*50, 808, 2218, 2523*) is based on the hydrazine route. The reaction of tetrahydroxysuccinic acid, which probably takes part as the diketone, and two equivalents of the hydrazine gives an osazone, immediate ring closure to the pyrazolone occurring (9.3). It is not known whether the product consists of the ketohydrazone (III), the azoketone (IV), or the hydroxyazo compound (V). The structure (IV) is improbable because of the break in the conjugation.

A further way of preparing azo derivatives is the condensation of nitroso compounds with amines used by A. von Baeyer (*131*) and by Bamberger (*158, 175*). Whilst the formation of hydrazones from quinones leads only to *o*- and

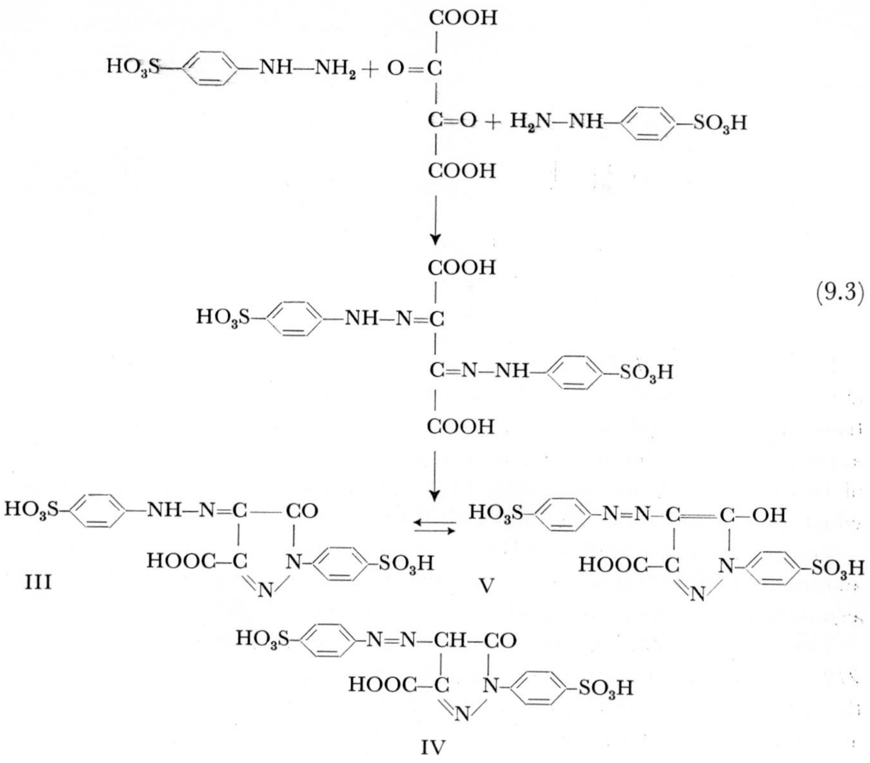

COOH
|
HO₃S—⟨＿⟩—NH—NH₂ + O=C
|
C=O + H₂N—NH—⟨＿⟩—SO₃H
|
COOH

↓

COOH
|
HO₃S—⟨＿⟩—NH—N=C   (9.3)
|
C=N—NH—⟨＿⟩—SO₃H
|
COOH

↓

HO₃S—⟨＿⟩—NH—N=C—CO   HO₃S—⟨＿⟩—N=N—C══C—OH
      | | ⇌ | |
  HOOC—C   N—⟨＿⟩—SO₃H   HOOC—C   N—⟨＿⟩—SO₃H
III   ＼N／   V   ＼N／

HO₃S—⟨＿⟩—N=N—CH—CO
         | |
  HOOC—C   N—⟨＿⟩—SO₃H
      ＼N／

IV

p-hydroxyazo dyes, by this method azo bodies with *meta* hydroxy or amino groups are accessible. A whole series of papers by Ruggli's school (*1759, 1761–1767*) deals with the applications of this process, which was used to obtain the three isomeric o-, m-, and p-(phenylazo)azobenzenes, as well as tris- [3,3'- and 4,4'-bis(phenylazo)azobenzenes] and tetrakis-azobenzenes (4,4''-phenylenebis-azobisazobenzene) and their derivatives. The spectra of these substances were evaluated by Dahn and von Castelmur (*522*). Japanese workers (*1549, 2057*) have investigated the kinetics of these reactions.

Contrary to the prevalent opinion that the condensation of nitrosobenzene with primary amines to azo compounds is a smooth reaction of general applicability, it must be stressed that it is restricted in the main to the benzene series, and even then is not invariably successful. Thus, nitrosobenzene acts as an oxidizing agent towards o-aminophenols, triphenodioxazines being formed partially or exclusively (9.4) (*105, 1271*). The condensation is usually unsuitable for naphthalene derivatives, for, according to Merian (*1426*), nitrosobenzene will not react with 2-naphthylamine, neither will 2-nitrosonaphthalene with aniline. However, in the course of their studies on mercaptoazo compounds, Burawoy et al. (*2309*) were able to synthesize 1-benzylthio-2-phenylazonaphthalene from 1-benzylthio-2-naphthylamine and nitrosobenzene.

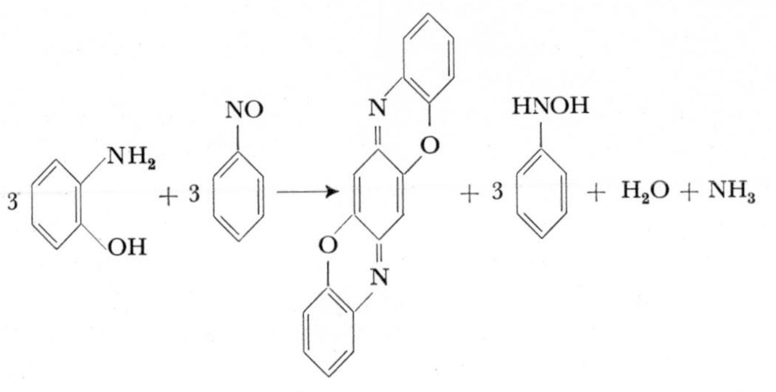

$$3 \quad \text{NH}_2/\text{OH} + 3 \quad \text{NO} \longrightarrow \quad \text{(azoxy product)} \quad + 3 \quad \text{HNOH} + \text{H}_2\text{O} + \text{NH}_3 \qquad (9.4)$$

Michaelis (*1438–1440*) allowed aromatic amines to interact with thionyl chloride and converted the sulphinylamines formed into azobenzene derivatives with phenylhydroxylamine. The course of the reaction is not clear and arylides of arylsulphamic acids appear as by-products. Advantage was taken of this reaction by Merian (*708, 1426*) to prepare 2-phenylazo-3-naphthol, which proved to be inaccessible by all the other routes.

Very recently, Suckfüll and Dittmer (*2443*) described the interaction of diazosulphonates and *anti*-diazotates with diazonium compounds which yield asymmetric azo compounds under certain conditions.

The so-called Wallach rearrangement of azoxybenzene (*124, 167, 844, 2100*), known for many years, in which *o*-hydroxyazobenzene is obtained by the action of light and its *p*-isomer by means of warm concentrated sulphuric acid, is hardly of interest preparatively, as it fails to give the *m*-derivatives not open to direct synthesis. Azoxy compounds are converted into azo bodies also by Grignard reagents (9.5) (*1286*).

$$\text{Ar}\!-\!\text{N(O)}\!=\!\text{N}\!-\!\text{Ar} + 2\,\text{RMgX} \longrightarrow \text{Ar}\!-\!\text{N}\!=\!\text{N}\!-\!\text{Ar} + \text{R}\!-\!\text{R} + (\text{MgX})_2\text{O} \qquad (9.5)$$

According to Horner (*1072*), photolysis of aryl azides gives azo derivatives.

A route to azo dyes related to azo coupling has recently been described by W. Pelz (*2500*): interaction of two equivalents of a nucleophilic component with a sulphonyl azide yields the symmetric azo compound with liberation of the alkyl- or arylsulphonamide (9.6). Particularly suitable as coupling components are α- and β-naphthol, and heterocyclic compounds with reactive methyl or methylene groups, for example, 1,3,3-trimethyl-2-methyleneindoline, pyrazolone, and other enolizable substances. It is noteworthy that the re-

$$\text{SO}_2\text{N}_3 + 2 \quad \text{(naphthol)} \xrightarrow[\text{NaOH}]{\text{CH}_3\text{OH}} \quad \text{(azo naphthol)} \!-\!\text{N}\!=\!\text{N}\!-\! \text{(naphthol)} + \quad \text{SO}_2\text{NH}_2 \qquad (9.6)$$

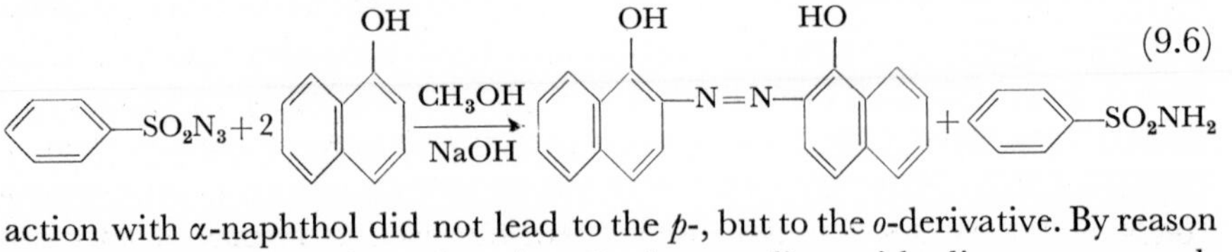

action with α-naphthol did not lead to the *p*-, but to the *o*-derivative. By reason of the investigations into the *o*/*p*-ratio in coupling with diazo compounds (§ 11.3), it may be concluded that sulphonyl azides are only weakly electrophilic reagents.

9.2 The Preparation of Aliphatic Azo Compounds

Aromatic and aliphatic azo compounds are derivatives of di-imide, HN:NH, which Thiele (*2029*), Raschig (*1680*), and Diels (*585*) unsuccessfully attempted to prepare. Only recently have indications been obtained that this compound may be formed under certain conditions. Dows, Primentel, and Whittle (*623*) suppose, on account of infra-red spectra, that the material which condenses on a surface cooled to 90° K during the decomposition of nitrogen–hydrogen mixtures by means of a glow discharge contains di-imide among other products.

The most important method of preparing di-imides doubly substituted by aliphatic radicals is provided by the dehydrogenation of the corresponding hydrazines. A series of oxidizing agents has been employed for this purpose, but preparative significance attaches particularly to bromine, mercury compounds, and peroxides. All these oxidations had been described already for a few examples by the turn of the century.

Thus, Tafel (*1996*) and E. Fischer (*725, 726*) obtained compounds of the type $Ar \cdot N : N \cdot R$, such as phenylazomethane and phenylazoethane, from the appropriate hydrazines by reaction with mercuric oxide. In a great number of subsequent researches, this oxidizing agent has been used again and again, Renaud and Leitch (*1693*), for example, only recently converted 1,2-diethyl-hydrazine into azoethane in 97% yield. Also azoalkanes with longer aliphatic chains, such as azoheptane (*2063*), can be prepared in good yield by this method.

Benzoyl peroxide and hydrogen peroxide have been used frequently as well [e. g. (*446, 447, 450, 1080, 1678, 1999*)].

The oxidation of hydrazines with bromine is especially important because Thiele and Heuser (*2033*) employed this route in 1896 to synthesize azodi-isobutyronitrile, the most extensively investigated aliphatic azo compound at present. From readily available starting materials, the desired azo compound was obtained in two steps according to equation (9.7). The dinitrile can be

$$
2\,(CH_3)_2CO + 2\,HCN + H_2NNH_2 \longrightarrow (CH_3)_2\text{---}\underset{\displaystyle CN}{C}\text{---}NH\text{---}NH\text{---}\underset{\displaystyle CN}{C}(CH_3)_2
$$

$$
\Big\downarrow + Br_2 \tag{9.7}
$$

$$
(CH_3)_2\text{---}\underset{\displaystyle CN}{C}\text{---}N{=}N\text{---}\underset{\displaystyle CN}{C}(CH_3)_2
$$

converted into esters and amides in the usual way. If in place of acetone cyclohexanone is used, the product is 1,1'-azobis(cyclohexanecarbonitrile), also originally described by Thiele and Heuser (*2033*). Full details of its preparation have been recorded (*1572, 1577*).

Azodi-isobutyronitrile has been investigated so intensively because, on the one hand, it is readily obtained according to (9.7) and, on the other, its rate of decomposition lies in a very favourable region. At room temperature, the compound is stable, but at about 60° to 120° radical formation occurs at a rate convenient for kinetic determination and for preparative purposes (radical transfer processes such as polymerizations; compare §§ 12.1 and 12.3). In consequence, derivatives of azodi-isobutyronitrile have been described in a considerable number of patents [for example (2504, 2589)], but this type of preparative approach to these compounds also has its scientific uses. Bevington, Melville, and their co-workers (236, 238, 240) synthesized azodi-isobutyronitrile labelled with C^{14} in the methyl groups. Substances of structure (VI) were obtained by Overberger (1563, 1566) both in meso- and DL-forms and he made a series of products of general formula (VII) by varying the p-substi-

$$
\begin{array}{cc}
\overset{\displaystyle R}{\underset{\displaystyle CN}{|}} & \overset{\displaystyle R}{\underset{\displaystyle CN}{|}} \\
CH_3{-}C{-}N{=}N{-}C{-}CH_3 &
\end{array}
\qquad\qquad
X{-}\langle\ \rangle{-}CH_2{-}\overset{\displaystyle CH_3}{\underset{\displaystyle CN}{|}}C{-}N{=}N{-}\overset{\displaystyle CH_3}{\underset{\displaystyle CN}{|}}C{-}\langle\ \rangle{-}X
$$

$$
\text{VI} \qquad\qquad\qquad\qquad\qquad\qquad\qquad \text{VII}
$$

tuents. Goldschmidt (838) isolated compounds in which the cyano groups were replaced by CH_2OH, CH_2NH_2, or CH_2Cl.

In many cases, atmospheric oxygen suffices for the oxidation of hydrazines, an example being the preparation of compounds with one or two azo groups contained in otherwise saturated rings (1573, 2106) [cf. (IX) and (X)]. Naturally, such oxidations with oxygen also possess technical interest [for instance (2585, 2588)].

In earlier work, yet other oxidizing agents were employed, but now these are only of secondary significance. Thus, Thiele (2030) first prepared azomethane, the parent compound of aliphatic azo compounds, by the action of potassium chromate on N,N'-dimethylhydrazine. As shown long ago by Thiele (2031, 2033) and by Knorr (1240), N,N'-dinitroso compounds, obtainable from hydrazines, also decompose with the formation of azo derivatives.

Some importance attaches to the oxidation of hydrazines with cupric compounds. According to Diels (585), Noyes (1355), and others (2121), the cuprous complex of the azoalkane, which is considerably more stable than the azoalkane itself, is obtained in the first place. Its constitution will be discussed in § 14.4.

The conversion of N,N'-bis(triphenylmethyl)hydrazine into the unknown azobis(triphenylmethane), originally attempted by Wieland (2150), could still not be achieved in more recent times (449, 1631).

The key position occupied by the hydrazines in the preparation of azoalkanes justifies a brief review of some special methods of synthesizing these compounds. Often it is preferable to make the detour via diformylhydrazine rather than to alkylate directly, as in this way the entry of more than one alkyl group per nitrogen atom can be avoided (*2121*). An important synthesis of hydrazines starts with the preparation of azines from ketones, as illustrated by equation (9.8) which leads from acetophenone to 1,1′-diphenyl-1,1′-azoethane (*2585*). Azo compounds with neophyl groups (VIII) were obtained by Over-

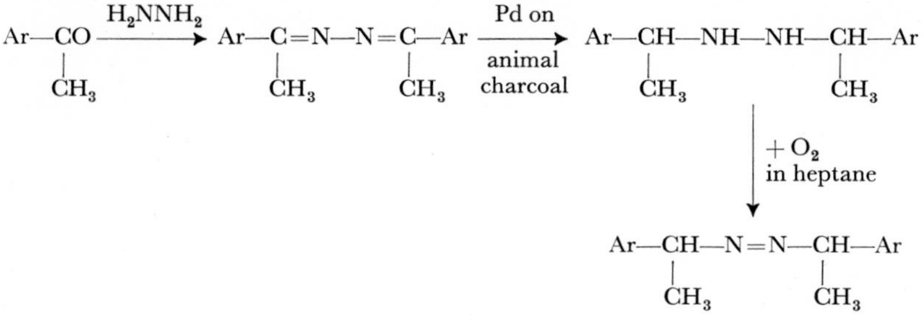

$$
\text{Ar—CO} \xrightarrow{\text{H}_2\text{NNH}_2} \underset{\overset{|}{\text{CH}_3}}{\text{Ar—C}} = \text{N—N} = \underset{\overset{|}{\text{CH}_3}}{\text{C—Ar}} \xrightarrow[\substack{\text{animal} \\ \text{charcoal}}]{\text{Pd on}} \underset{\overset{|}{\text{CH}_3}}{\text{Ar—CH}} \text{—NH—NH—} \underset{\overset{|}{\text{CH}_3}}{\text{CH—Ar}}
$$

$$
\Big\downarrow \substack{+\,O_2 \\ \text{in heptane}} \qquad (9.8)
$$

$$
\underset{\overset{|}{\text{CH}_3}}{\text{Ar—CH}} \text{—N} = \text{N—} \underset{\overset{|}{\text{CH}_3}}{\text{CH—Ar}}
$$

berger and Gainer (*1570*) in an analogous manner. Cyclic azines of type (IX) and cyclic bisazines of type (X) were also prepared by Overberger *et al.*

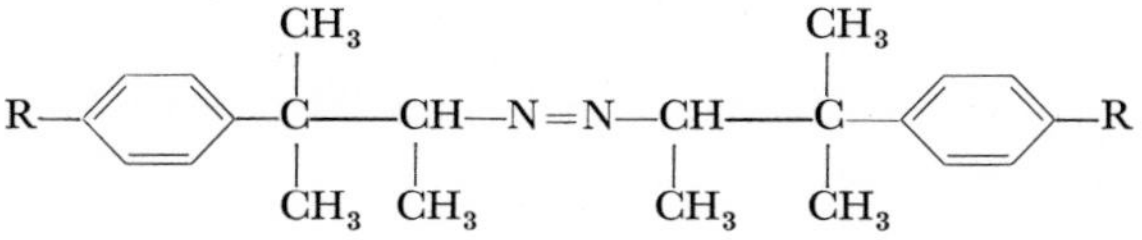

$$
\text{R—}\langle\bigcirc\rangle\text{—}\underset{\overset{|}{\text{CH}_3}}{\overset{\overset{\text{CH}_3}{|}}{\text{C}}}\text{—}\underset{\overset{|}{\text{CH}_3}}{\text{CH}}\text{—N}=\text{N—}\underset{\overset{|}{\text{CH}_3}}{\text{CH}}\text{—}\underset{\overset{|}{\text{CH}_3}}{\overset{\overset{\text{CH}_3}{|}}{\text{C}}}\text{—}\langle\bigcirc\rangle\text{—R}
$$

VIII

(*1573–1576*, *1579*), using hydrazine and 1,5- and 1,6- or 1,10- and 1,12-diketones, respectively. Another route (9.9) to cyclic hydrazines useful as star-

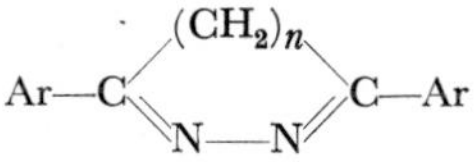

IX   n = 3 or 4

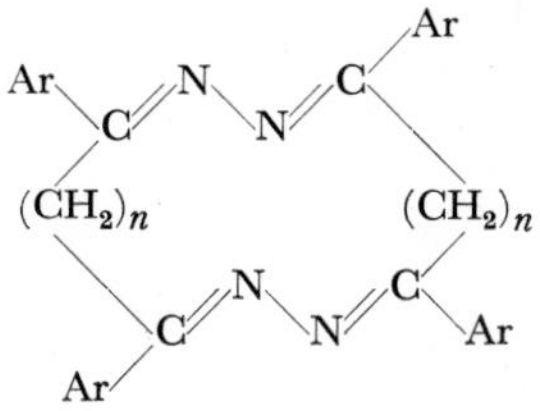

X   n = 8 or 10

ting materials for the synthesis of cyclic azoalkanes has been employed by Wang, Cohen, *et al.* (*2106*).

N-Phenyl-*N*′-alkylhydrazines are usually prepared from phenylhydrazine, which is allowed to interact at the unsubstituted nitrogen either directly with an alkyl chloride, such as triphenylmethyl chloride (*446*, *2588*), or with a ketone to yield a phenylhydrazone reducible to the corresponding hydrazine with aluminium lithium hydride (*447*, *450*).

Yet another way of converting azines into azo compounds has been described by S. Goldschmidt (*836*, *837*). Chlorine at —60° yields α,α′-dichloroazoalkanes directly (9.10a), but preliminary reaction with hydrocyanic acid

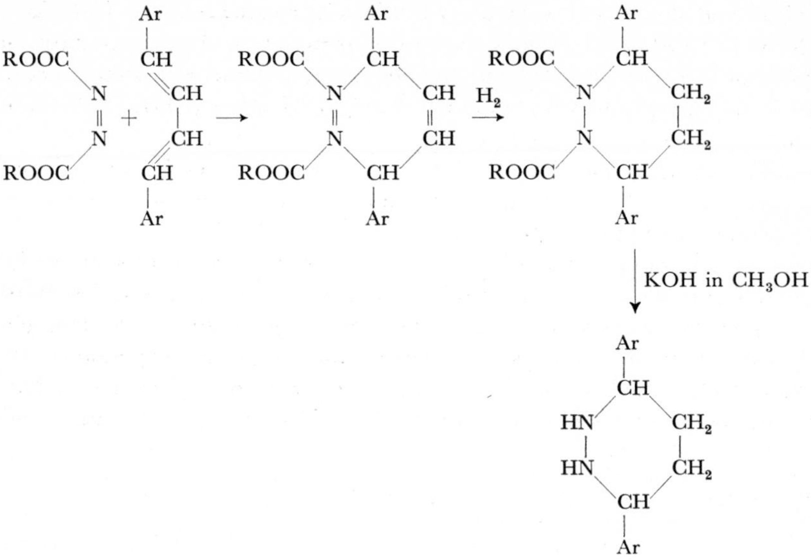

$$
\begin{array}{ccc}
\underset{\text{ROOC}}{} \overset{\text{Ar}}{\underset{}{\text{CH}}} & & \\
\text{N} \quad \text{CH} & & \\
\| \;+\; | & \longrightarrow & \\
\text{N} \quad \text{CH} & & \\
\underset{\text{ROOC}}{} \overset{}{\underset{\text{Ar}}{\text{CH}}} & &
\end{array}
\qquad \xrightarrow{\;\text{H}_2\;}
$$

(9.9)

$$\xrightarrow{\;\text{KOH in CH}_3\text{OH}\;}$$

enables α-chloro-α′-cyanoazoalkanes to be obtained (9.10b). Benzing (*226*) has made similar compounds.

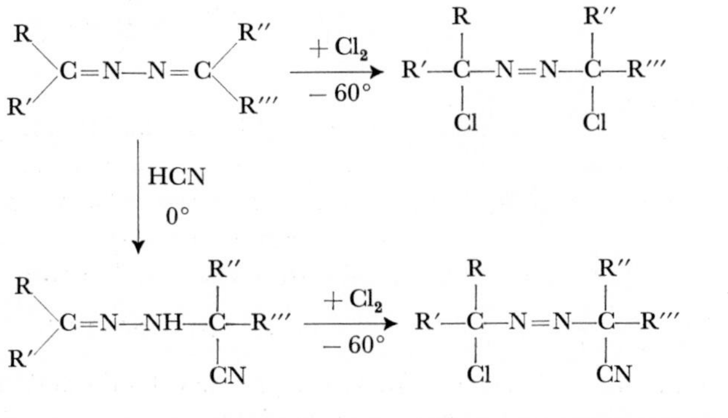

$$
\underset{R'}{\overset{R}{>}}C=N-N=C\underset{R'''}{\overset{R''}{<}} \;\xrightarrow[-60°]{+\,Cl_2}\; R'-\underset{\underset{Cl}{|}}{\overset{\overset{R}{|}}{C}}-N=N-\underset{\underset{Cl}{|}}{\overset{\overset{R''}{|}}{C}}-R'''
$$

(9.10 a)

$$\Big\downarrow \;\; \text{HCN} \atop 0°$$

$$
\underset{R'}{\overset{R}{>}}C=N-NH-\underset{\underset{CN}{|}}{\overset{\overset{R''}{|}}{C}}-R''' \;\xrightarrow[-60°]{+\,Cl_2}\; R'-\underset{\underset{Cl}{|}}{\overset{\overset{R}{|}}{C}}-N=N-\underset{\underset{CN}{|}}{\overset{\overset{R''}{|}}{C}}-R'''
$$

(9.10 b)

Occasionally, the oxidation of alkylamines can also lead to azoalkanes. Thus, Farenhorst and Kooyman (*696*) prepared azo-t-butane from t-butylamine by means of potassium hypobromite followed by silver oxide (9.11) and 2-ami-

$$
(CH_3)_3CNH_2 \xrightarrow{\;\text{KOBr}\;} (CH_3)_3CNHBr \xrightarrow{\;\text{Ag}_2\text{O}\;} (CH_3)_3C-N=N-C(CH_3)_3
$$

(9.11)

noisobutyronitrile interacts with sodium hypochlorite at −8° to yield azodi-isobutyronitrile (*2592*).

Azocarbonamides (R·N:N·CONH₂, RNH·CO·N:N·CO·NHR, etc.) can be made by oxidation of semicarbazides (*1189, 2034*), diacylhydrazines (*1157, 1958, 1960*), or from acid amides (*1322*). A method of preparing unsymmetrically substituted dibenzoyldi-imides (ArCO·N:N·COAr′) has been described

by Leffler and Bond (*1322*). Symmetric esters ot azodicarboxylic acid (RO·
CO·N:N·CO·OR) were synthesized by Curtius (*515, 516*) from those of
chloroformic acid via the hydrazodicarboxylates, but the oxidation is more
conveniently carried out with bromine (*1204*) or chlorine (*1494, 1670*) than
with the concentrated nitric acid originally used by Curtius.

Hexafluoroazomethane ($F_3C·N:N·CF_3$) has been obtained by methods not
clearly understood (*807, 1662*) and is of interest because its decomposition gives
rise to trifluoromethyl radicals (see § 12.2).

Under certain circumstances, the interaction of diazo with organometallic
compounds can lead to azo derivatives, though diazoalkanes and Grignard
reagents give hydrazones (*454, 743*). The mechanism postulated by Huisgen
(*1114*) shows that this happens only because the Grignard compound of the
azoalkane (XI), which is formed as an intermediate in the reaction (9.12),
rearranges on hydrolysis into the tautomeric hydrazone (XII). Hodgson and

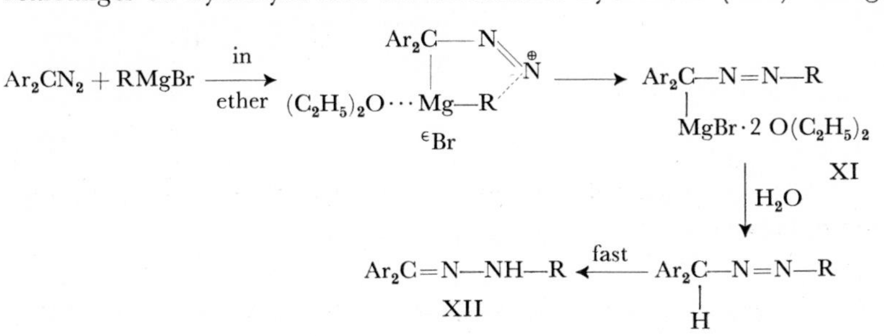

$$Ar_2CN_2 + RMgBr \xrightarrow[\text{ether}]{\text{in}} \underset{^{\ominus}Br}{\overset{Ar_2C\!-\!N}{\underset{(C_2H_5)_2O\cdots Mg\!-\!R}{\big|}}}\!\!\!\!\!\!\overset{\oplus}{N} \longrightarrow \underset{MgBr\cdot 2\,O(C_2H_5)_2}{\overset{Ar_2C\!-\!N=N\!-\!R}{\big|}}$$

$$\Big\downarrow H_2O \qquad \overset{XI}{\qquad} \qquad (9.12)$$

$$Ar_2C=N\!-\!NH\!-\!R \xleftarrow{\text{fast}} \underset{H}{\overset{Ar_2C\!-\!N=N\!-\!R}{\big|}}$$

$$\qquad XII$$

Marsden (*1056*) report that from the zinc chloride double salts of aryldiazonium chlorides and methylmagnesium iodide or ethylmagnesium bromide
methyl- or ethyl-azobenzene, respectively, is obtained in poor yield. According
to Curtin and Ursprung (*503*), azo derivatives are formed from organozinc
compounds and diazonium salts (9.13) with considerably better yields.

$$R\!-\!ZnCl + Ar\!-\!\overset{\oplus}{N}\!\equiv\!N \longrightarrow R\!-\!N=N\!-\!Ar + Zn^{\oplus\oplus} + Cl^{\ominus} \qquad (9.13)$$

In a recent patent (*2574*), azoalkanes are prepared by the action of hydrogen
peroxide on isocyanates or isothiocyanates (9.14).

$$2\,R\!-\!N=CO + 2\,H_2O_2 \longrightarrow (2\,R\!-\!N^{\bullet}) + 2\,CO_2 + 2\,H_2O \qquad (9.14)$$

$$\downarrow$$

$$R\!-\!N=N\!-\!R$$

9.3 The Azo Coupling Reaction of Compounds with Reactive
Methylene or Methyl Groups

Azo coupling is the interaction of an aromatic diazo compound, the so-called
diazo component, and one of a series of aromatic or otherwise unsaturated
compounds capable of reacting.

In the chapter dealing with the mechanism of the process, it will be shown that this consists of an electrophilic aromatic substitution. The diazonium ion, normally acting as the electrophilic reagent, attacks that atom of the (nucleophilic) coupling component which exhibits the greatest electron density. The point of reaction need not necessarily be at a carbon atom and, in principle, amino nitrogen and oxygen provide even more suitable sites, leading to diazoamino compounds and diazoethers (see § 7.4). However, the term azo dye is taken to imply exclusively such compounds in which the arylazo residue is bound to carbon. Occasionally it is useful to distinguish substitution by a diazo component at a nitrogen, oxygen, or carbon atom by designating these processes as *N*-, *O*-, or *C*-coupling, respectively.

Diazo compounds are relatively weakly electrophilic. Therefore to be suitable as coupling components, substances must possess a structure able to build up a very high electron density at one or more carbon atoms. H. C. Brown and Nelson (*344, 1511*) recently carried out systematic investigations, according to which an increase in the electron-attracting character of the electrophilic reagent causes not only a higher rate of substitution ('activity' in Brown's nomenclature), but also a reduction in the so-called selectivity as regards choice of site of substitution on the nucleophilic component. It must be stressed, however, that for the detailed treatment of the reactivity of nucleophilic particles consideration of the distribution of the electron density *alone* is insufficient.

In Brown's classification, a diazo component is a reagent of very low activity and correspondingly high selectivity. This follows from the fact that diazo compounds do not react at all with weakly nucleophilic benzene derivatives, such as toluene, which are readily substituted by more active, electrophilic particles, such as the nitronium ion ($NO_2^\oplus$, nitration). In the latter type of process, in spite of the *o/p*-directing nature of the methyl group, considerable substitution occurs in *all* three positions, including the *meta*. Benzene derivatives, such as phenol, which because of the presence of appropriate substituents exhibit greater electron density at *all* nuclear carbon atoms, are capable of coupling, but only in the *p*- and little in the *o*-position. *m*-Azo derivatives of phenols are not even obtained in traces, whilst with more strongly electrophilic reagents *m*-substitution can be shown to occur.

Coupling of paraffin derivatives can be used to illustrate the need for a relatively high electron density at the atom to be substituted, which is expressed more qualitatively by saying that the atom has a pair of electrons in reserve or is able to make one available for the formation of the new homopolar bond. For example, n-propane shows no signs of coupling. However, if a nitro group is introduced, the product reacts smoothly with diazo components. This is quite unexpected on the basis of the experience of azo chemists, as in coupling components, such as phenols, naphthols, and naphthylamines, a nitro substituent hinders coupling greatly and can even prevent it altogether. A review of diazo coupling reactions at aliphatic carbon atoms has been published recently (*2402*).

The ability of nitroparaffins to couple has been known for a long time (*987, 1436, 1776o,r*) and depends on two factors. On the one hand, the normal nitro compound (XIII) is in equilibrium with the tautomeric aci-form (XIV). Whilst in (XIII) the carbon atom is surrounded by σ-bonds (sp^3-hybridization

XIII   XIV

of electrons) which are hardly reactive, (XIV) contains a double bond and so the electrons about the carbon atom are sp^2-hybridized. These electrons move in the plane of the formula as written, but the remaining p-electron of the carbon atom has its orbital perpendicular to this plane and so can overlap with the corresponding p-electron of the nitrogen atom to form a π-bond. It is the electron cloud due to the π-bond which attracts the electrophilic reagent.

Although the ability to couple of the aci-form of nitroparaffins can thus be understood and has been proved experimentally (*811*), another factor also plays a part. It is known that coupling can proceed from the nitro form, although this would not appear to be possible from the above argument. The reactivity is due to the acid character of the CH-bond which is made relatively strongly polar by the neighbouring nitro group [—I-effect (*1153 c*)]. As the proton splits off, the anion (XVa–XVb) is formed and can be attacked

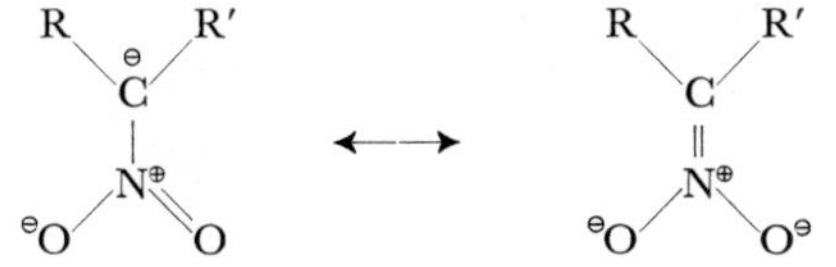

XVa   XVb

because of its lone pair of electrons. It is apparent that the nitro- and aci-forms have a common anion, always a consequence of prototropy. According to Hünig and Boes (*1136*), the rate of coupling of the nitro form is limited by the relatively slow dissociation of the CH-bond, but the rate of the actual coupling step involving the anion (XVa–XVb) is probably considerably greater than that of the aci-form.

Other *compounds with reactive methylene and methyl* groups are completely analogous to the nitroparaffins. Substances with ketonic carbonyl groups are the most important. Their simplest representatives, formaldehyde and acetone, seem something of a contradiction as it is stated that they do not couple although acetone has formally great similarity to nitromethane. To say that acetone is incapable of coupling is not correct, as its reactivity is small but sufficient to have been demonstrated recently (*2442*). The reason is as follows. Just as nitromethane couples only as the anion or in the aci-form, but not in the nitro form, so acetone (XVI) reacts only as the enol (XVIII) and even more readily as the mesomeric anion (XVIIa–XVIIb). Determinations by Schwarzenbach

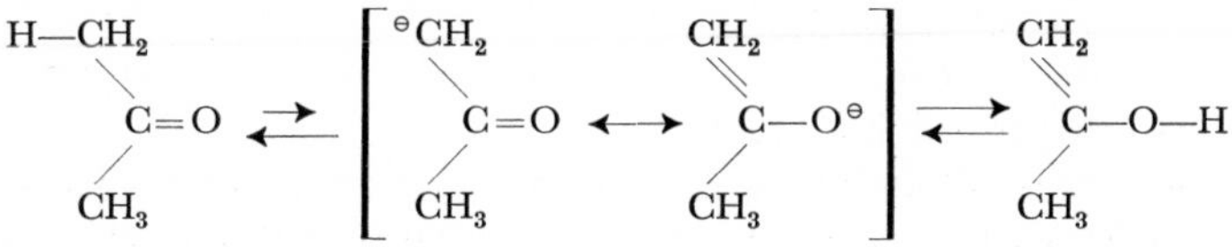

$$\begin{array}{ccccc}
\text{H---CH}_2 & & ^{\ominus}\text{CH}_2 & \text{CH}_2 & \text{CH}_2 \\
\diagdown & & \diagdown & \diagup\diagup & \diagup\diagup \\
\text{C=O} & \rightleftharpoons & \text{C=O} \leftrightarrow \text{C---O}^{\ominus} & & \text{C---O---H} \qquad (9.15) \\
\diagup & & \diagup \qquad\quad \diagup & & \diagup \\
\text{CH}_3 & & \text{CH}_3 \qquad \text{CH}_3 & & \text{CH}_3 \\
\text{XVI} & & \text{XVII a} \qquad \text{XVIIb} & & \text{XVIII}
\end{array}$$

ability
to couple :   none   great   moderate

and Wittwer (*1874*) have shown that an aqueous acetone solution contains only $2 \cdot 5 \times 10^{-4}\%$ enol and that the enolate concentration at about neutrality is even lower. The poor coupling power of acetone is thus not a fundamental phenomenon, but only a consequence of too low an equilibrium concentration of the reactive species and the slowness of reaching equilibrium in the protolysis of the ketone [indicated in equation (9.15) by the lengths of the arrows].

As the inductive effect of a nitro is greater than that of a carbonyl group, so the CH-acidity and therefore the reactivity of nitroalkanes is higher. In ketones such a level of activity can only be attained by the introduction of further acidifying residues. Acetoacetic ester (XIX) provides the classic example, in which the methylene group is activated not solely by the carbonyl, but also by the ester substituent.

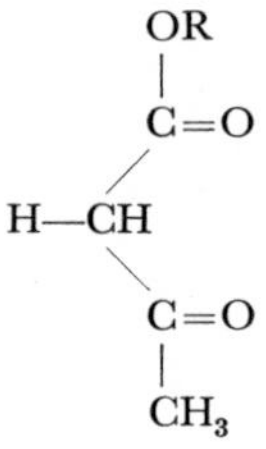

$$\begin{array}{c}
\text{OR} \\
| \\
\text{C=O} \\
\diagup \\
\text{H---CH} \qquad \text{XIX} \\
\diagdown \\
\text{C=O} \\
| \\
\text{CH}_3
\end{array}$$

In the application of acetoacetic acid derivatives in azo coupling, the investigations of Dimroth and Hartmann (*603*) are specially noteworthy, apart from the original work of V. Meyer (*1435*). The former were able to show that it is the enol and not the keto forms which react, though now it can be stated more precisely, that under the conditions used by Dimroth and Hartmann, the reactive entity is the *common anion* of both forms and this anion is obtained more easily, that is, more rapidly from the enol than from the keto form.

Technically important above all are the acetoacetanilides, originally as pigments of the type of Hansa Yellow (IG) (*712*), but today indispensable also as yellow metal–complex and azoic dyes. The preparation of acetoacetic acid derivatives by means of ketene has considerably enlarged the possibilities of their use on the large scale.

The α-methylene group of ketones can be activated not only by neighbouring carbonyl residues, but also, of course, by other substituents with a —I effect, such as —CN, —SO—, and —SO$_2$—. Even one halogen atom suffices: according to Favrel (698), 1-chloro-2-propanone is able to couple. A large number of coupling components of this type is listed by Holzach (1071a) and by Saunders (1776n) in their respective monographs and each year many new examples are cited in the literature.

β-Dicarbonyl compounds do not always couple in the manner described above. When one of the carbonyl residues is part of a carboxy group, this is split off as CO_2, as in β-oxoglutaric acid (acetonedicarboxylic acid) (1606) and cyclic 2-oxocarboxylic acids, for instance, 2-oxocyclopentane- and 2-oxocyclohexane-

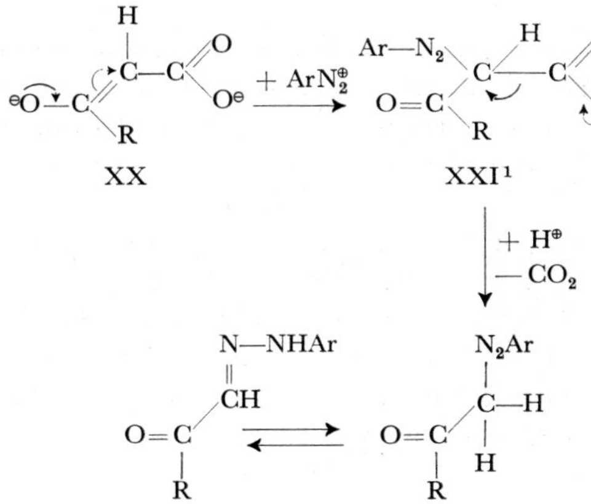

$$(9.16)$$

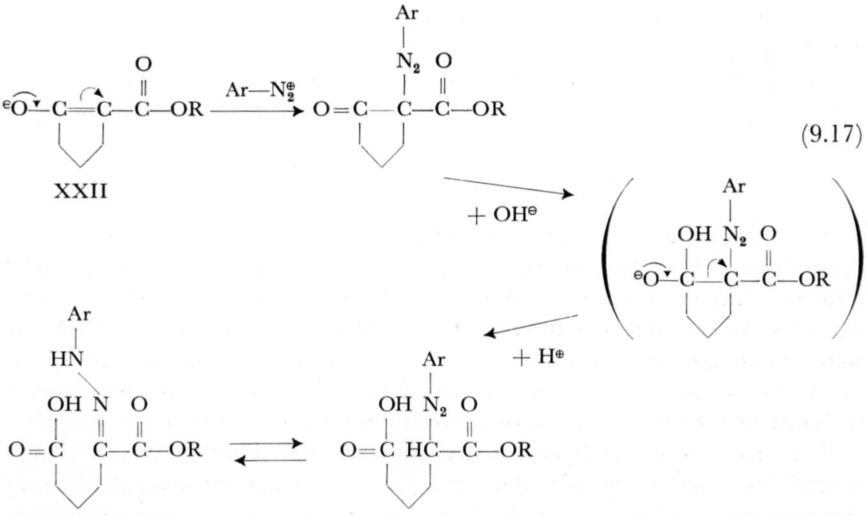

$$(9.17)$$

----

[1] Before decarboxylation the intermediate might be deprotonated.

carboxylic acids (*577, 1348*). The mechanism can be illustrated on the enolate of β-oxoglutaric acid (XX, R = CH$_2$COO$^\ominus$). The entry of the acidifying aryl-azo residue polarizes both the adjacent C-C-bonds in the intermediate (XXI) formed in the first stage and thus facilitates decarboxylation. If, however, —CO$_2^\ominus$, an electrophilic leaving group readily eliminated, is not available, it can happen that the link to the carbonyl group is severed heterolytically for preference, as the example of the anion of ethyl 2-oxocyclopentanecarboxylate (XXII) shows (*1192, 1193*). The resultant hydrazone of β-oxoadipic acid monoester (XXIII) easily yields compound (XXIV) by a sort of Fischer

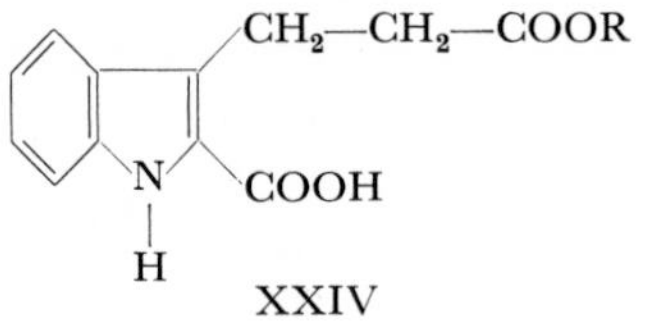

XXIV

indole synthesis (*1158, 1369*). Such derivatives of indolepropionic and indole-butyric acids have been prepared in this manner on several occasions (*1192, 1193*). Clusius and Weisser (*441*) have shown that it is the β-nitrogen of the phenylhydrazone (XXIII) which is split off as NH$_3$, thus making it practi-cally certain that the mechanism proposed by the Robinsons (*1723, 1724*) for such indole syntheses is valid.

As indicated, the azo compounds produced by reactions (9.16) and (9.17) tautomerize readily to the corresponding monohydrazones of α-ketones. Since these hydrolyse with ease, this is one of the best routes to α-diketones.

Another substituent which greatly increases the acidic nature of a methyl or methylene group is the diazonium residue. Its acidifying effect is so intense that in the formation of alkyldiazonium cations a proton is lost immediately to give zwitterions of the type of (XXV). In analogy with the argument used in

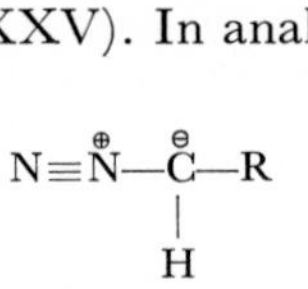

$$N \equiv \overset{\oplus}{N} - \overset{\ominus}{\underset{\underset{H}{|}}{C}} - R$$

XXV

deducing the coupling power of nitroparaffins, one would expect the aliphatic diazo compounds to act as nucleophilic reagents towards aromatic diazo com-ponents and therefore to couple with them. The reaction has been realized by Huisgen and Koch (*1120*), who found that diazoacetic ester and *p*-nitro-diazobenzene interact in methanolic solution with loss of nitrogen from the aliphatic component. The formation of the hydrazide of chloroglyoxylic ester in good yield is readily explained by azo coupling (9.18). The parent compound, diazomethane, undergoes the same type of reaction only at extremely high concentrations of chloride ions. Otherwise a new kind of rearrangement occurs at the stage of the intermediate carbonium ion (XXVI), yielding the aryl-

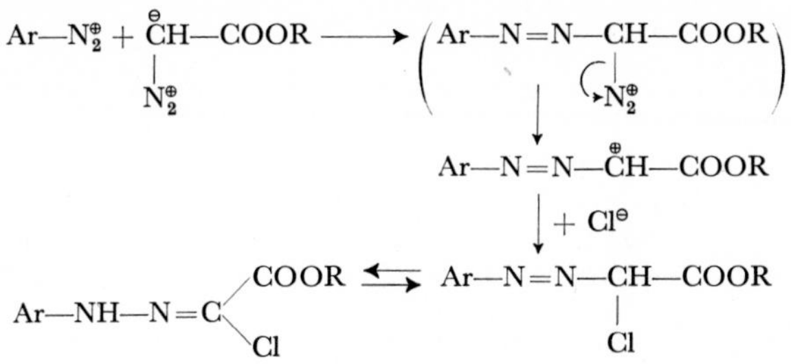

$$Ar—N_2^{\oplus} + \overset{\ominus}{C}H—COOR \longrightarrow \left(\begin{array}{c} Ar—N=N—CH—COOR \\ \big| \\ N_2^{\oplus} \end{array} \right)$$

$$\Big\downarrow$$

$$Ar—N=N—\overset{\oplus}{C}H—COOR \qquad (9.18)$$

$$\Big\downarrow + Cl^{\ominus}$$

$$Ar—NH—N=C\Big\langle \begin{array}{l} COOR \\ Cl \end{array} \rightleftarrows \begin{array}{c} Ar—N=N—CH—COOR \\ \big| \\ Cl \end{array}$$

cyanamide (XXVII) which is methylated by the excess of diazomethane. The scheme (9.19) is supported by the results of experiments with N^{15} (*434*).

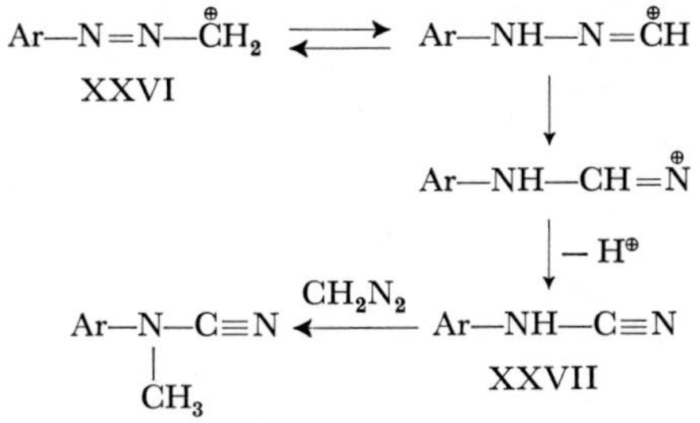

$$Ar—N=N—\overset{\oplus}{C}H_2 \rightleftarrows Ar—NH—N=\overset{\oplus}{C}H$$
$$\text{XXVI} \qquad\qquad \Big\downarrow$$

$$Ar—NH—CH=\overset{\oplus}{N} \qquad (9.19)$$

$$\Big\downarrow - H^{\oplus}$$

$$Ar—N—C\equiv N \xleftarrow{CH_2N_2} Ar—NH—C\equiv N$$
$$\big| \qquad\qquad\qquad\qquad \text{XXVII}$$
$$CH_3$$

Yet a third type of reaction may follow the loss of nitrogen and this was encountered by Huisgen and Fleischmann (*1115*) in the interaction of *o*-diazo-phenols with aryl derivatives of diazomethane or diazoacetic esters. The pre-sence of the strongly basic phenolate oxygen in the immediate vicinity of the carbonium group causes ring closure to a $2H$-1,3,4-oxadiazine to take prece-dence over addition of an extraneous base as in equation (9.18). For example, 2-diazo-5-nitrophenol and diazodiphenylmethane give 2,2-diphenyl-7-nitro-$2H$-1,3,4-benzoxadiazine in more than 90% yield (9.20). In coupling to diazo-

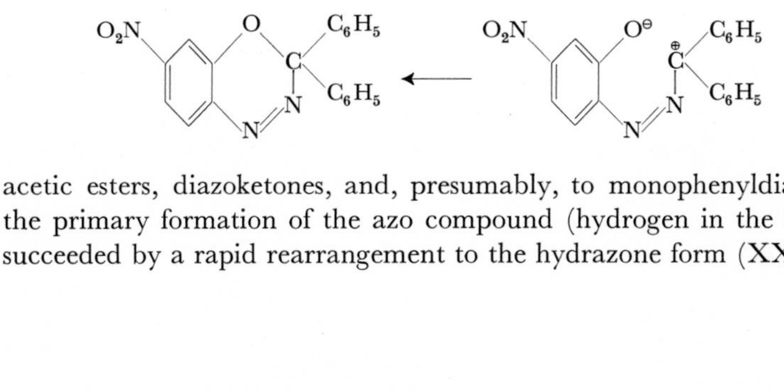

$$(9.20)$$

acetic esters, diazoketones, and, presumably, to monophenyldiazomethanes, the primary formation of the azo compound (hydrogen in the 2-position) is succeeded by a rapid rearrangement to the hydrazone form (XXVIII).

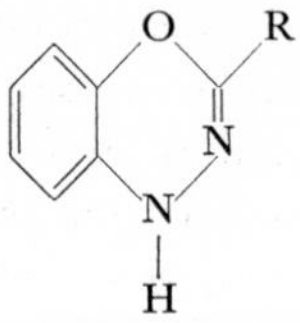

$R = COOC_2H_5, COC_6H_5, COCH_3$, or C_6H_5

XXVIII

When *p*-diazophenols are employed as the electrophilic component, quinone-azines are formed according to equation (9.21) (*1115*).

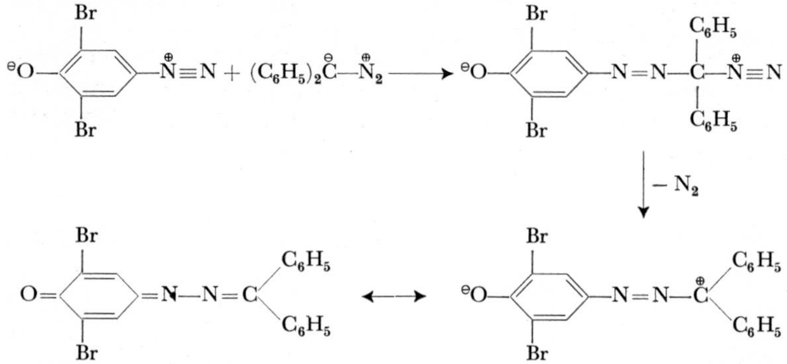

(9.21)

The reactivity of methylene groups is also increased by neighbouring nitrogen atoms in the ammonium form, an example being the phenacylpyridinium ion (XXIX) which is capable of coupling (*1272*, *1274*).

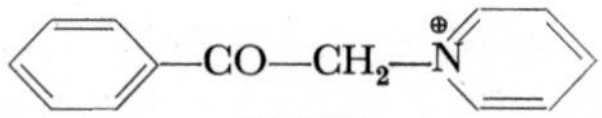

XXIX

It has been known for several decades that some compounds containing heterocyclic quaternary nitrogen and a methyl substituent in α-position to it can have 1 to 2 hydrogen atoms of the methyl group replaced by arylazo

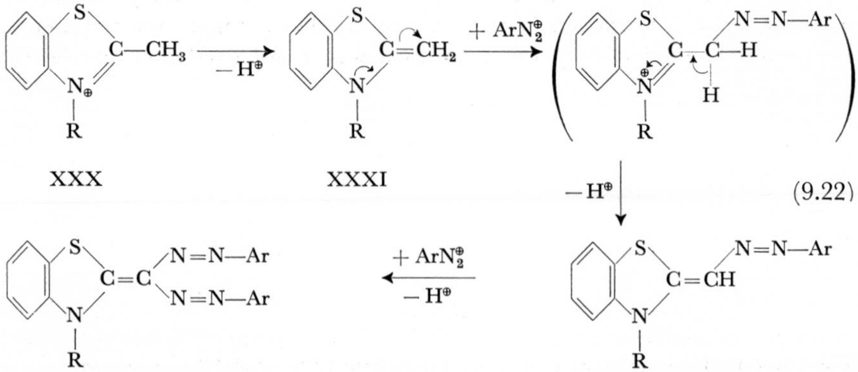

(9.22)

XXX XXXI XXXIII XXXII

residues (*1252, 1652, 1733*). Such substitutions have been investigated systematically in recent years, particularly by H. Wahl and co-workers (*1303, 1630, 2091–2095, 2098, 2337*). Thus 2-methylbenzothiazolium ions (**XXX**) couple smoothly with two equivalents of a diazo component to give the disazo compounds (**XXXIII**). The monoazo stage (**XXXII**) can be isolated only under certain circumstances, for example when diazoamino compounds (*1241, 2096, 2097*) or *anti*-diazotates (*1133, 2184*) are used as electrophilic components. It would be of interest from the point of view of the mechanism of azo coupling, whether these compounds take part in the actual substitution step as such or as diazonium ions, which are formed from them by a slow reaction, but the question has not yet been decided. There are signs that it is not the 2-methylbenzothiazolium ion itself, but the ethylenic compound (**XXXI**) derived from it by loss of a proton, which is substituted (*912*). It has not yet been settled whether coupling to the non-quaternary 2-methylbenzothiazole (**XXXIV**) (*1629*) also proceeds via the tautomeric ethylene (**XXXVI**).

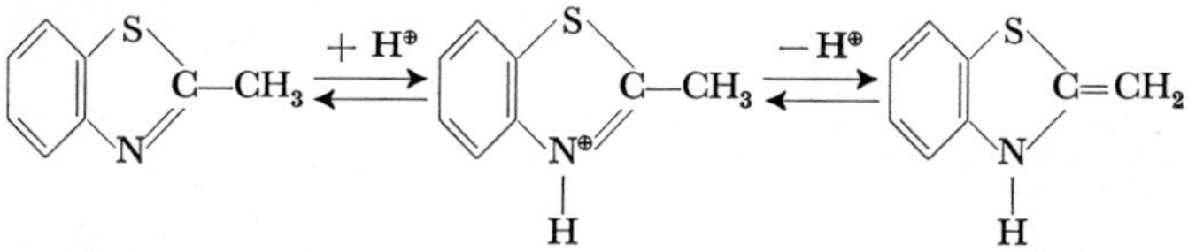

$$\text{XXXIV} \qquad \text{XXXV} \qquad \text{XXXVI} \qquad (9.23)$$

Kharkharov (*1209*) has reported that other heterocyclic compounds with methyl groups in α- or γ-position, such as 9-methylacridine or 2-picoline, can couple and, according to him, even the methyl group of 2,4,6-trinitrotoluene is able to react with diazo components because of the acidifying effect of the three nitro substituents. However, the latter observation is contrary to Huisgen's experience (*1124*).

Derivatives of 5-pyrazolone, another class of coupling components with activated methylene groups, are of great importance technically. Especially 3-methyl-1-phenyl-5-pyrazolone (**XXXVII**) and the closely related compounds bearing a variety of substituents in the benzene nucleus have become indispensable for the manufacture of yellow acid dyes as well as yellow, orange, and red metal-complexes. The older literature of this field was summarized by Cohn (*452*).

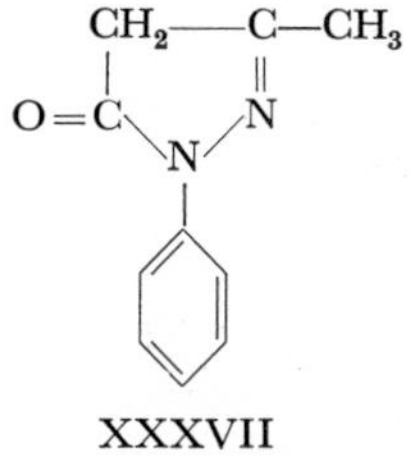

XXXVII

The corresponding derivative of 5-iminopyrazole also possesses industrial significance, though to a much lesser extent (*2558*).

The products of coupling to methyl and methylene groups are tautomeric with the hydrazones of the corresponding carbonyl compounds. As already mentioned, on occasion it is possible to replace two hydrogen atoms by arylazo residues and such disazo compounds (**XXXVIII**) can be obtained also by coupling to the hydrazones (*393, 1171*). Von Pechmann [(*1595*), see also (*1533*)] dubbed these products *formazyls*, but this designation (for example **XXXVIII**, with R = H, Ar = Ar' = C_6H_5 would be described as formazyl-

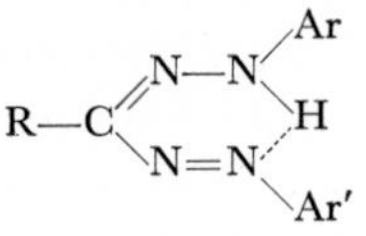

$$R-C \genfrac{}{}{0pt}{}{\underset{N=N}{\overset{N-N}{\diagdown}}}{} \genfrac{}{}{0pt}{}{Ar}{\underset{Ar'}{H}}$$

$$(R = H, \text{ alkyl, aryl})$$

XXXVIII

hydrogen) is being replaced by a more rational nomenclature based on calling

$$\overset{1}{HN}:\overset{3}{N}\cdot CH:\overset{5}{N}\cdot NH$$

the hypothetical substance formazan (formazylhydrogen = 1,5-diphenyl-formazan).

With the help of Hünig's oxidative coupling (see § 9.5), dehydroformazans can be prepared (*1139*) by the reaction of the hydrazones of aldehydes with heterocyclic hydrazones in ammoniacal solution in the presence of oxidizing agents (9.24).

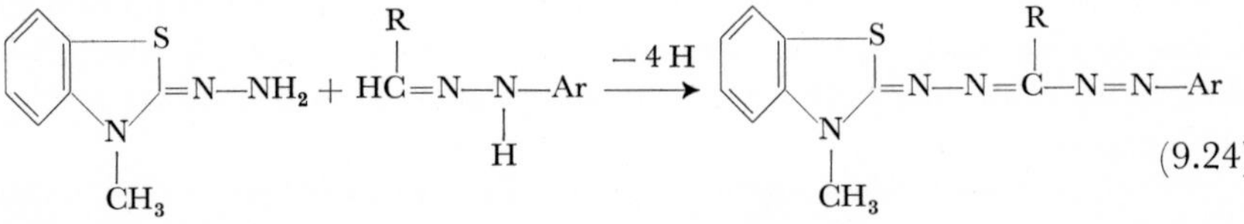

$$\text{(9.24)}$$

Formazans are of interest in several respects. According to Bamberger (*183–185*) formazyl compounds undergo an acid-catalysed cyclization to triazines, which probably follows scheme (9.25).

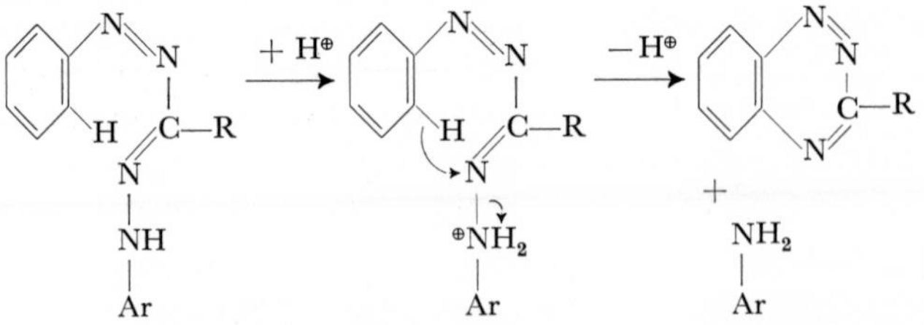

$$\text{(9.25)}$$

By means of oxidizing agents, the intensely coloured formazans are converted into tetrazolium salts (**XXXIX**) (*1707*), which are colourless or, at most, light coloured. Usually they can be smoothly reduced back to the starting material.

Tetrazolium salts have attracted attention as bioindicators; thus, grain stains red with 1,3,5-triphenyltetrazolium chloride if capable of germination (*1284*). Tetrazolium salts are also useful in the paper chromatography of steroids and other classes of compounds in order to make oxidizable substances visible.

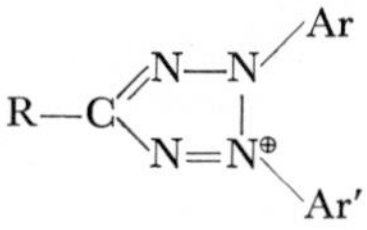

XXXIX

Complex formation by formazans follows from structure (XXXVIII), as the proton completing the six-membered ring can be replaced by metal ions. Such complexes were investigated by Hunter (*1146*) and, more recently, in particular by Wizinger (*2182*). Apart from the monocyclic metal–complexes derived from the parent compound (XXXVIII), derivatives with complexing substituents, such as OH or COOH, in *o*-position in one or both of the 1,5-phenyl residues lead to bi- and tri-cyclic complexes (XXXX, XXXXI). For the method used here to represent complex formation see § 14.1.

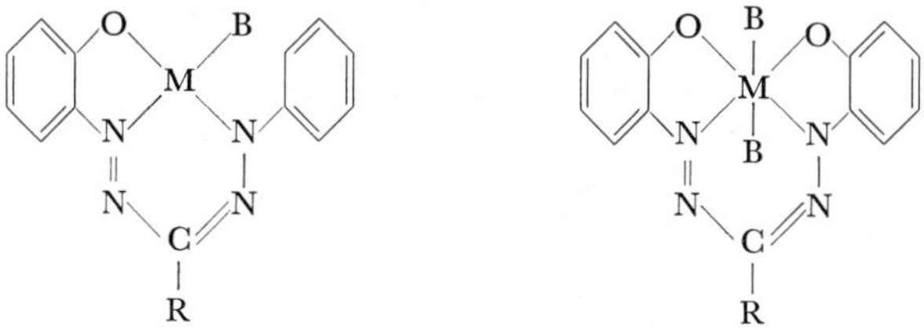

XXXX   XXXXI

B = ligand supplied by the solvent

M = Ni or Cu   M = Cr or Co

Knox (*1242*) has just reported the reaction of 5-diazocyclopentadiene with methyl-lithium. The dark red solid produced, which presumably possesses structure (XXXXII), yields 1,1'-bis(methylazo)ferrocene (XXXXIII) with anhydrous ferrous chloride. 1,1'-Bis(phenylazo)ferrocene can be prepared analogously. Thus the azoferrocenes, searched for in vain by Broadhead and Pauson (*319*) as well as by Nesmeyanov and Perevalova (*1521*), have become available. Diazopyrazoles, which are comparable to 5-diazocyclopentadiene, have since been described by Farnum and Yates (*2382*).

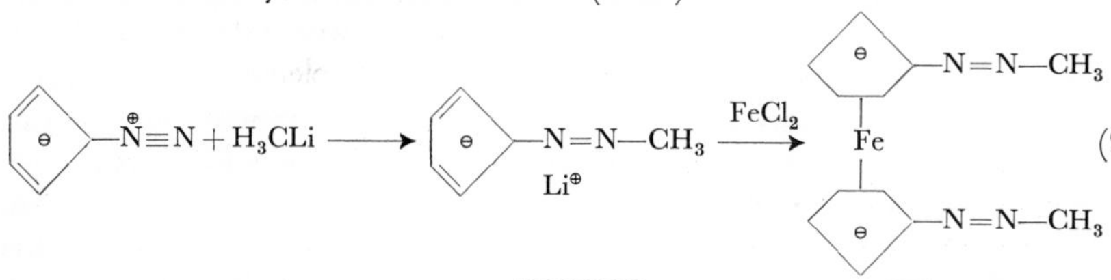

$$(9.26)$$

XXXXII   XXXXIII

9.4 Coupling of Aromatic Compounds

The term coupling reaction suggests in the first place not the substitution in methylene and methyl groups dealt with in the previous section, but the reaction with substituted aromatic hydrocarbons, especially phenol and aniline derivatives.

In principle, the coupling of phenols in o-position corresponds to that of ketones, which react as the enol or enolate according to equation (9.15). The only, but not fundamental, difference consists of the fact that the keto-enol equilibrium in the case of phenols lies at least as extremely far over in favour of the enol as that in the case of a simple carbonyl compound, such as acetone, is on the side of the ketone (*1874*). The enol-form of phenols is thermodynamically the more

$$
\text{(9.27)}
$$

(as well as further quinonoid limiting structures)

stable because the resonance energy of the benzene ring is not available to the keto-form. The π-electrons of the latter are part of a $2,4$-pentadien-1-one system, the resonance energy of which is lower. The conditions for the existence of the corresponding γ-ketone of phenol are probably even less favourable. However, the keto-form of phenols does play a part in the intermediate formed in aromatic electrophilic substitution (see § 10.4).

For the above reasons, in considering the coupling to phenols the keto-form can be completely disregarded. The increase of reactivity produced by acidifying α-substituents in methylene compounds (greater CH-acidity) is therefore not required in phenols and aromatic amines; on the contrary, here, groups, such as NO_2 and SO_3H, depress the ability to couple. Although they shift the phenol–phenolate equilibrium to the side of the anion, which couples more energetically, this action is greatly outweighed by the lowering of the electron density on the carbon atoms of the aromatic ring brought about by their —M and —I effects. Thus nitronaphthols, in which both substituents are in the same nucleus, and especially nitrophenols couple practically not at all or only very sluggishly. A technically important example is salicylic acid, in which not only the effect of the carboxy group on the π-electrons of the ring, but also the lower acidity of the phenolic proton due to hydrogen bonding, are responsible for depressing the ability to couple. On the other hand, positive substituents, such as alkyl, alkyloxy, and amino residues, facilitate reaction; thus the second hydroxy group of resorcinol enables this component to be used for syntheses, which in practice could not be carried out with phenol.

Normally coupling occurs at the position *para* to the hydroxy group. If this is occupied by a substituent not readily eliminated, as in p-cresol or β-naphthol, the diazo component attacks the *o*-position. The relationship between *o*- and *p*-coupling and how it is affected by structure and medium are subjects of great importance in the manufacture of azo dyes and will be discussed after the mechanism of the reaction has been considered (see § 11.3). When both *o*- and *p*-positions are free, two arylazo residues can be introduced, but with phenols the second coupling occurs with considerably more reluctance. Even so, phenol itself can give rise to 2,4,6-trisazo derivatives (*859, 961, 1004, 1005, 1009*).

The kinetic investigations to be dealt with in § 10.1 have shown that it is the phenolate ion which enters into the substitution proper, but that undissociated phenol does exhibit ability to couple, even if only to an extremely small degree. It follows that *phenol ethers* should also react and K.H.Meyer (*1431, 1432*) demonstrated that anisole and phenetole yield azo compounds with energetic diazo components in solution in glacial acetic acid. Polyalkoxybenzenes, such as ethers of resorcinol and phloroglucinol, are known to couple with less electrophilic diazo compounds. Recently, Goerdeler and co-workers (*2386*) used coupling to phenol ethers to examine the reactivity of the diazonium salts of some heterocyclic compounds.

In coupling to phenol ethers the alkyl group is frequently split off either partially or wholly, arylazo derivatives of the corresponding phenol being produced. The problem was studied by von Auwers (*100, 104*) and by Jambuserwala and Mason (*1165*) and more recently by Haginiwa and Murakoshi (*904–906*), who found that in coupling to the ether of resorcinol only the methoxy group *para* to the azo residue is affected. Bunnett and Hoey (*381*) were able to show that the fission of the ether group follows the actual coupling reaction and is influenced by acid in the sense of a specific (proton) catalysis. The process can be formulated as (9.28). Recently, Bunnett and Buncel (*2414*) determined the kinetics for 4-(4′-sulphophenylazo)-1-methoxynaphthalene and for the corresponding benzene derivative at different acid concentrations (up to 9 M hydrochloric and 4 M perchloric acid). From the same school (*2415*) comes the discovery that, when the hydrolysis is carried out with O^{18} labelled water, the product contains O^{18}.

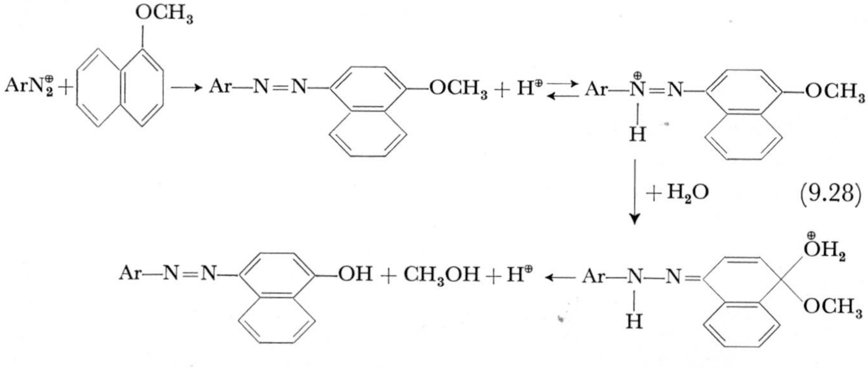

$$+H_2O \qquad (9.28)$$

The behaviour of aromatic primary, secondary, and tertiary amines as coupling components is fundamentally similar to that of phenols. Their reactivity is also based on the relatively high electron density at the carbon atoms in *o*- and *p*-positions, but the rates of reaction of amines are distinctly slower throughout than those of the corresponding phenolate ions at the same concentration. Readiness to couple increases with amines in the sequence primary, secondary, tertiary, as long as apart from the one aryl nucleus only alkyl groups are present on the nitrogen atoms. Diarylamines couple with considerably more difficulty than alkylarylamines.

Certain dialkylarylamines apparently provide exceptions to this rule as they couple not at all or only reluctantly, but their behaviour is to be considered in connection with the mechanism of coupling (§ 10.2). The tendency to *N*-coupling, present in secondary and especially in primary amines, makes it necessary in many instances to prepare the aminoazo compounds by the detour using the diazoamino rearrangement.

It is surprising that *β*-dialkylaminostyrene (**XXXXIV**), which can be regarded as the vinylogue of an *N*-dialkylaniline (*481*), couples not in the nucleus, but at the *α*-carbon atom. The primary product (**XXXXV**) hydrolyses to the hydrazonealdehyde (**XXXXVI**).

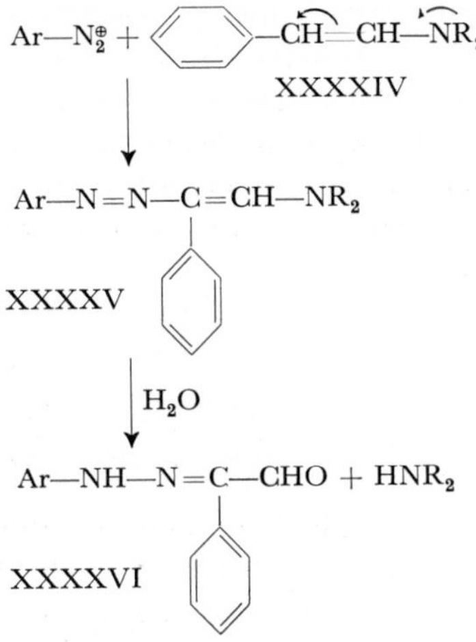

$$Ar\!\!-\!\!N_2^{\oplus} + \langle\text{aryl}\rangle\!\!-\!\!CH\!\!=\!\!CH\!\!-\!\!NR_2$$

$$\text{XXXXIV}$$

$$\downarrow$$

$$Ar\!\!-\!\!N\!\!=\!\!N\!\!-\!\!C\!\!=\!\!CH\!\!-\!\!NR_2$$

XXXXV

(9.29)

$$\downarrow H_2O$$

$$Ar\!\!-\!\!NH\!\!-\!\!N\!\!=\!\!C\!\!-\!\!CHO + HNR_2$$

XXXXVI

N-Dimethylvinylamine (**XXXXVII**) can be regarded as the counterpart of *β*-dialkylaminostyrene for, as K. H. Meyer and Hopff (*1430*) briefly mentioned, it is able to form azo compounds on reaction with diazo components.

$$CH_2\!\!=\!\!CH\!\!-\!\!NR_2$$

XXXXVII

Eigenmann (*655*) has investigated the coupling of *o*-, *m*-, and *p*-dialkylaminostyrenes (**XXXXVIII**), isomers of the *β*-dialkylamino compound. The *m*-derivative couples in the nucleus *para* to the dimethylamino group, but the *p*-isomer is substituted at the *β*-carbon atom of the side chain. In the case of *o*-dimethylaminostyrene coupling may occur either in the ring or in the ethylene group, depending on the conditions and the diazo component used.

XXXXVIII

On the other hand, *o*- and *p*-vinylanisole react with *p*-nitrodiazobenzene with evolution of nitrogen. According to Dale (*523*) 1-*o*-methoxyphenyl-2-*p*-nitro-phenylethanol and 4-methoxy-4'-nitrostilbene, respectively, are formed in small yield. The process may be used for the synthesis of substituted 4-methoxy-stilbenes otherwise not readily accessible.

Acylation in general takes away the ability of amines to couple, but occasionally under energetic conditions reaction can be forced to occur. Known examples of this are provided by the toluenesulphonamides of naphthylamines and by 1,8-naphthosultam, which can be regarded as an internal sulphonamide of α-naphthylamine. Acetyl- and especially benzoyl-α-naphthylamine possess the ability to couple only to the very slightest degree (*1254–1256*), yet the coupling of 2-acetamidothiophene and ethyl 2-furancarbamate (*1147*) occurs in spite of the presence of acyl groups.

Of the other *N*-substituted aromatic amines capable of coupling, the cyanamides, the sulphamic acids, and the nitroamines (XXXXIXa–c) must be mentioned. The ω-methylsulphonic acids (XXXXIXd) have technical significance. They are obtained simply by means of formaldehyde and bisulphite and couple easily in *p*-position, the sulphomethyl group being readily removed from the products by hydrolysis. They provide an alternative to the detour over the diazoamino compounds.

$$\text{Ar—NH—X} \qquad \text{X = CN} \qquad \text{XXXXIXa}$$
$$= \text{SO}_3\text{H} \qquad \text{XXXXIXb}$$
$$= \text{NO}_2 \qquad \text{XXXXIXc}$$
$$= \text{CH}_2\text{—SO}_3\text{H} \qquad \text{XXXXIXd}$$

Comparison of the effect of substituents on the ability to couple shows that the reactivity of benzene and naphthalene derivatives decreases in the order $O^{\ominus} > NR_2 > NHR > OR \sim OH$. The methyl group is an even weaker electron donor, yet aromatic compounds bearing solely alkyl residues are capable of coupling. However, their reactivity is low; hence the process is smooth only when several alkyl groups are present and favourably oriented, the diazo component used having to be very energetic. K. H. Meyer and Tochtermann (*1434*) demonstrated that 2,4,6-trinitrodiazobenzene couples to mesitylene but, surprisingly, although the same diazo component reacts with isodurene (1,2,3,5-tetramethylbenzene) and pentamethylbenzene, it will not attack durene (1,2,4,5-tetramethylbenzene) (*1909*, cf. *2386*). Under similar conditions an azo compound cannot be obtained from t-butylbenzene either (*1543*). This has some significance in comparison with mesitylene, which possesses three methyl substituents in the nucleus, whereas t-butylbenzene carries them in the side chain, hyperconjugation being impossible in the latter case. Several polynuclear aromatic hydrocarbons, such as benzo[a]pyrene, yield crystalline azo derivatives even with moderately electrophilic diazo compounds (4-nitrodiazobenzene) (714) and it is probable that the coupling power becomes greater as the basicity increases.

A characteristic example for this correlation is the smooth substitution of azulene and its derivatives by diazonium ions (27, 787, 790, 1638, 1790, 2048, 2049, 2051), azulene being converted into azulenium ions ($C_{10}H_9^\oplus$) even in rather dilute mineral acid (421, 1002, 1643).

There is evidence of a very weak tendency to couple in compounds with unsaturated substituents, such as styrene and indene (2022), and phenylacetylene yields an arylhydrazone of phenylglyoxal, probably according to equation (9.30) (10). In 4-propenylanisole (L) substitution occurs at the α-carbon atom of the side chain, the rest of which is converted into the corresponding aldehyde (9.31) (1667, 1668).

$$\langle\!\!\langle \rangle\!\!\rangle\!-\!C\!\equiv\!CH + Ar\!-\!N_2^\oplus \longrightarrow \left(\langle\!\!\langle \rangle\!\!\rangle\!-\!\overset{\oplus}{C}\!=\!CH\!-\!N\!=\!N\!-\!Ar\right)$$

$$\downarrow +\,H_2O \qquad\qquad (9.30)$$

$$\langle\!\!\langle \rangle\!\!\rangle\!-\!\underset{\overset{\|}{O}}{C}\!-\!CH\!=\!N\!-\!NH\!-\!Ar \;\rightleftharpoons\; \langle\!\!\langle \rangle\!\!\rangle\!-\!\underset{\overset{|}{OH}}{C}\!=\!CH\!-\!N\!=\!N\!-\!Ar$$

$$RO\!-\!\langle\!\!\langle \rangle\!\!\rangle\!-\!CH\!=\!CH\!-\!CH_3 + Ar\!-\!N_2^\oplus \xrightarrow{\;+OH^\ominus\;} RO\!-\!\langle\!\!\langle \rangle\!\!\rangle\!-\!CH\!=\!N\!-\!NH\!-\!Ar + CH_3CHO \;(9.31)$$

L

According to Razumovskii (1682), unsubstituted 1,1-diphenylethylene, its 1'-methyl derivative, and 1-methyl-1-phenylethylene couple at the 1'-position with 4-nitrodiazobenzene in a medium containing acetic acid. In pyridine, however, arylation occurs at the same carbon atom. Coupling at the 1'-position is extraordinarily facilitated when electron-releasing substituents, such as NR_2, are present in the p-positions of the aryl nuclei. The investigation carried out by Wizinger and Cyriax (2185) in this connection has significance for the understanding of the mechanism of the actual substitution of the coupling process (see § 10.4).

Noteworthy as a field of application for the azo coupling reaction is the behaviour of the quasiaromatic system of cyclic phosphinemethylenes (9.32), studied by Ramirez (1673–1675).

$$\underset{\|}{P(C_6H_5)_3} \qquad\qquad \underset{\|}{P(C_6H_5)_3} \qquad\qquad \overset{\oplus}{P}(C_6H_5)_3$$

$$\langle\!\!\langle \rangle\!\!\rangle + ArN_2^\oplus \xrightarrow{\;-H^\oplus\;} \langle\!\!\langle \rangle\!\!\rangle\!-\!N\!=\!N\!-\!Ar \xrightarrow{\;+H^\oplus\;} \langle\!\!\langle \rangle\!\!\rangle\!=\!N\!-\!\underset{\overset{|}{H}}{N}\!-\!Ar \qquad (9.32)$$

Although not strictly within the compass of the present section, the action of diazo compounds on unsaturated aliphatic hydrocarbons is worth mentioning for comparison. As long ago as 1919, K. H. Meyer (*1428*) discovered that energetic components couple with 1,3-butadiene and its homologues and more recently the study of the reaction has been taken up by Terentiev and his colleagues (*2019–2021, 2023, 2025, 2026*) in connection with petrochemical investigations.

9.5 Oxidative Coupling

Diazotization can be applied to aromatic heterocyclic amines, but the diazonium salts obtained are not stable in every instance. Thus, in general, heterocyclic compounds behave like the analogous carbocyclic ones when the diazo group and the hetero atom of the ring are in the 3-position to each other, for example, as in β-diazopyridine. Such diazo compounds are able to couple to phenols and amines in quite the normal manner. However, if the original amino group is in the 2-position (in five- or six-membered rings) or in the 4-position (in six-membered rings), stable diazo compounds can be obtained only exceptionally, for instance, in the case of 2-aminobenzothiazole. In the more strongly basic heterocyclics, the freshly formed diazonium group undergoes rapid nucleophilic substitution (solvolysis, etc.), as happens with 4-aminopyridine. Such instability is probably due to the fact that in the relatively acid diazotization medium the conjugate acid (LII, protonation of the cyclic nitrogen) is present in a considerable equilibrium concentration (9.33). This ammonium nitrogen

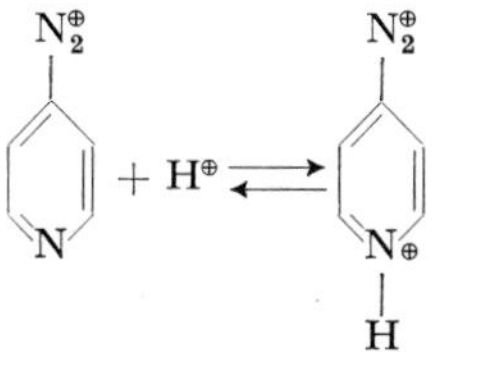

$$(9.33)$$

$$\text{LI} \qquad \text{LII}$$

facilitates nucleophilic substitution and therefore preparation of diazo derivatives of the corresponding quaternary salts, such as from 4-amino-N-methyl-pyridinium chloride, is also hardly possible.

The oxidative coupling of heterocyclic hydrazones, discovered by Hünig (*1134, 1135, 1138–1143, 2395, 2575, 2597*), has opened the way to the preparation of azo derivatives of these unobtainable diazo compounds. The reaction occurs as illustrated by equation (9.34) for the interaction of 1-methylcarbostyril hydrazone (LIII) and dimethylaniline, the overall process constituting an

$$(9.34)$$

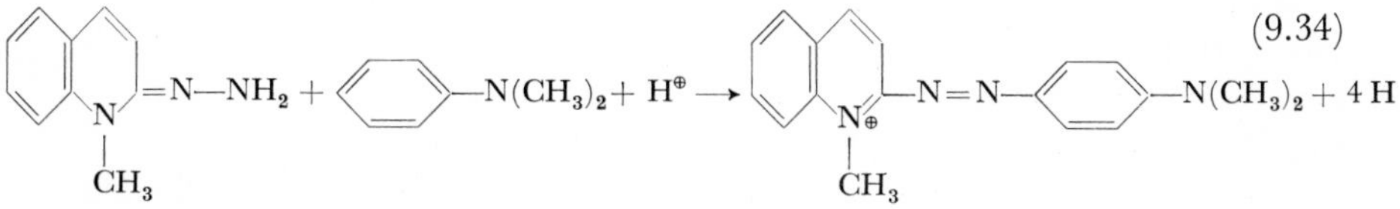

$$\text{LIII} \qquad\qquad\qquad\qquad\qquad \text{LIV}$$

oxidation. The most suitable oxidizing agent is potassium ferricyanide, but ferric chloride, hydrogen peroxide in the presence of ferrous salts, ammonium peroxydisulphate, lead dioxide, lead tetra-acetate, chromate, silver and cupric salts may be useful. Water mixed, for example, with methanol, dimethylformamide, or glycol ethers, is employed as reaction medium.

In principle, all phenols, aromatic amines, and other compounds, which can take part in the classic azo coupling reaction, can also be used here. Nuclear substituents exert the same activating and deactivating effects, but the presence of the oxidizing agent does provide difficulties, as it may cause attack on the coupling component rather than on the hydrazone.

In practice, coupling has been observed with phenol [see equation (9.35a)], 1- and 2-naphthol, 8-hydroxyquinoline, as well as with a series of compounds with reactive methyl or methylene groups, such as malononitrile, 3-methyl-1-phenyl-5-pyrazolone, 2,4-pentanedione, 1-(4-dimethylaminophenyl)-1-phenylethylene (LV), 1,2-dimethylindole (LVI), and 1,3,3-trimethyl-2-methyleneindoline (LVII, Fischer base), apart from dimethylaniline and other aromatic amines.

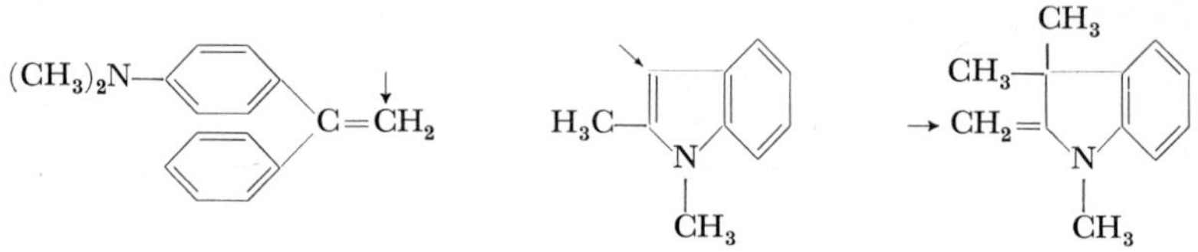

LV   LVI   LVII

The arrows indicate the positions of coupling.

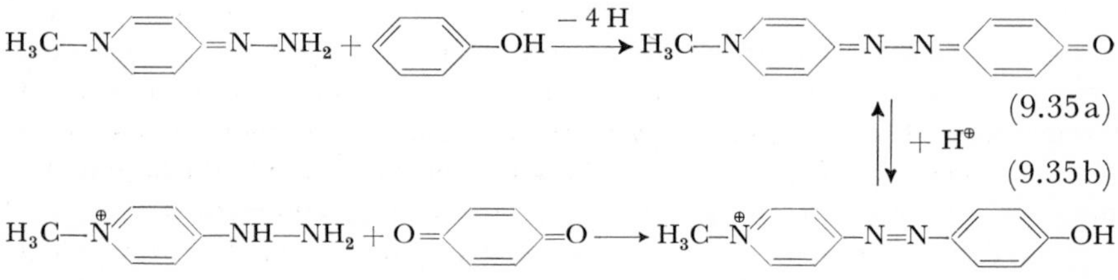

(9.35a)

(9.35b)

The azo derivatives of phenols which can be prepared by oxidative coupling can also be made from the corresponding hydrazines and quinones according to equation (9.35b) by a process analogous to Zincke's method (2224) (see § 9.1). Since the oxidative coupling of N-alkylpyridonehydrazones to phenol (9.35a) gives only a poor yield, Hünig (1142) recommends the hydrazine–quinone condensation (9.35b) in such cases.

As diazo components a very large number of hydrazones comes into consideration, Hünig's school alone having used over a hundred of them (1134). The most important groups of hydrazones are those of N-alkylated α- and γ-pyridones, 2(1)- and 4(1)-quinolones, and 2(3)-benzothiazolone derivatives.

As regards the range of pH in which oxidative coupling is best carried out, much the same rules are valid as in the classic reaction: amines are coupled in weakly acid, for example acetate-buffered, solution, whereas phenols and enols are employed in media made alkaline with bicarbonate or ammonia. The use of stronger bases is not advisable as it encourages the decomposition of the hydrazones to get out of hand, but, according to Hünig and Rauschenbach (*1144*), oxidative coupling can be carried out at high alkalinity, if the hydra-

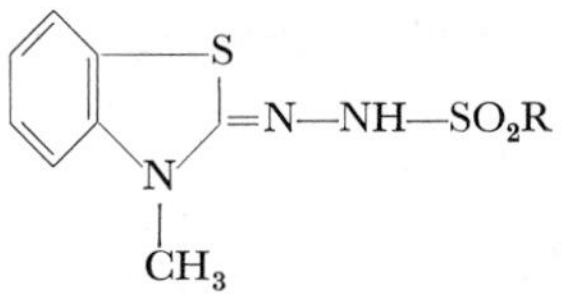

R = aryl or alkyl

LVIII

zones are replaced by their *N*-sulphonyl derivatives, such as (LVIII). In § 10.7, which deals with the mechanism of oxidative coupling, the pH dependence of the reaction will be discussed further.

That the preparation of dehydroformazans is possible by means of oxidative coupling has been mentioned in § 9.3.

9.6 The Classification of Azo Colouring Matters

The most authoritative compilation covering the constitution, properties, preparation, manufacturers, and other data of colouring matters, which are or have been commercially available, is the second edition of the *Colour Index*, published from 1957 onwards (*458*). Colouring matters are readily classified in two ways, either by chemical constitution or by technological use. In the Colour Index nearly 3600 constitutions are listed, more than 2250 colouring matters of different constitution being currently marketed, and of these more than half are of the azo class chemically. Azo colouring matters are not only the largest chemical class by number, but also by value and weight manufactured.

To indicate the constitution of azo colouring matters in the conventional manner becomes much too cumbersome, particularly with polyazo dyes. Apart from using trade names, the colour chemist has developed a kind of shorthand, which simultaneously provides some information about the synthesis of the azo compound concerned. A system of arrows is employed, linking the intermediates used, the arrow pointing from the amino compound to be diazotized to the substance acting as the coupling component. With polyazo compounds numbers show the order in which the processes are carried out and it is usually indicated whether the reaction is performed in acid or alkaline solution when aminohydroxy compounds are used as coupling components. For example, Diamine Green B (C, LIX) is written as:

$$\text{phenol} \xleftarrow{\ \ 3\ \ } \text{benzidine} \xrightarrow[\text{alkaline}]{\ \ 2\ \ } \text{H acid} \xleftarrow[\text{acid}]{\ \ 1\ \ } p\text{-nitroaniline}$$

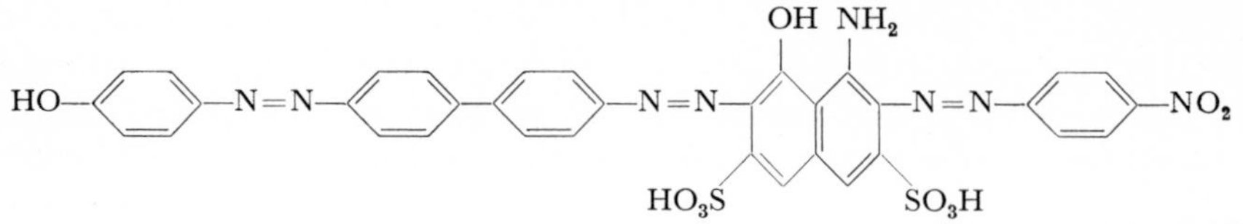

$$\text{HO} - \langle\!\!\bigcirc\!\!\rangle - \text{N}{=}\text{N} - \langle\!\!\bigcirc\!\!\rangle\langle\!\!\bigcirc\!\!\rangle - \text{N}{=}\text{N} - \overset{\text{OH NH}_2}{\underset{\text{HO}_3\text{S} \quad\quad \text{SO}_3\text{H}}{\langle\!\!\bigcirc\!\!\bigcirc\!\!\rangle}} - \text{N}{=}\text{N} - \langle\!\!\bigcirc\!\!\rangle - \text{NO}_2$$

LIX

Chemically the azo class is subdivided according to the number of azo groups present into mono-, dis-, tris-, tetrakis-, ...azo derivatives. Mono- and dis-azo colouring matters are about of equal importance, trisazo ones of rather less, and from tetrakisazo dyes onwards significance attaches only to specific compounds. Hence substances with more than three azo groups are generally lumped together as polyazo dyes. Further subdivision is achieved, first according to whether the compounds are water-soluble or not and secondly according to the types of component used.

The second method of subdivision is particularly important in the disazo group. Here primary and secondary types are distinguished. The former covers compounds made from two molecules of a diazo derivative and one of a bifunctional coupling component or from a tetrazo compound and two molecules of a coupling component. In both cases the monofunctional reagent may consist of two molecules of *one* compound or of one molecule of each of two substances used stepwise, the first alternative yielding 'symmetric' products. In stepwise reactions it is the rule to carry out the coupling occurring with greater difficulty first, since generally when components contain one or more azo groups they become progressively more inert.

The following dyes will serve as examples of the four types of primary disazo compounds:

Congo Red (A) —
symmetric primary disazo dye from a tetrazo component (benzidine)

$$\overset{\text{NH}_2}{\underset{\text{SO}_3\text{H}}{\langle\!\!\bigcirc\!\!\bigcirc\!\!\rangle}} - \text{N}{=}\text{N} - \langle\!\!\bigcirc\!\!\rangle\langle\!\!\bigcirc\!\!\rangle - \text{N}{=}\text{N} - \overset{\text{NH}_2}{\underset{\text{SO}_3\text{H}}{\langle\!\!\bigcirc\!\!\bigcirc\!\!\rangle}}$$

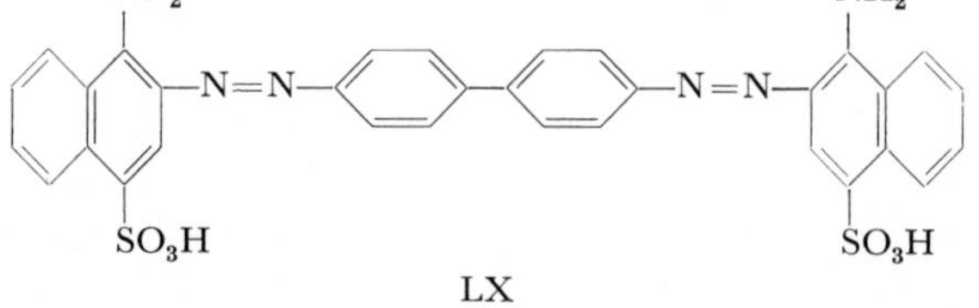

LX

Diamine Fast Red F (C) —
unsymmetric primary disazo dye from a tetrazo component (benzidine)

$$\text{HO} - \overset{\text{HOOC}}{\langle\!\!\bigcirc\!\!\rangle} - \text{N}{=}\text{N} - \langle\!\!\bigcirc\!\!\rangle\langle\!\!\bigcirc\!\!\rangle - \text{N}{=}\text{N} - \overset{\text{H}_2\text{N}}{\underset{\text{HO} - \langle\!\!\bigcirc\!\!\bigcirc\!\!\rangle - \text{SO}_3\text{H}}{\langle\!\!\bigcirc\!\!\rangle}}$$

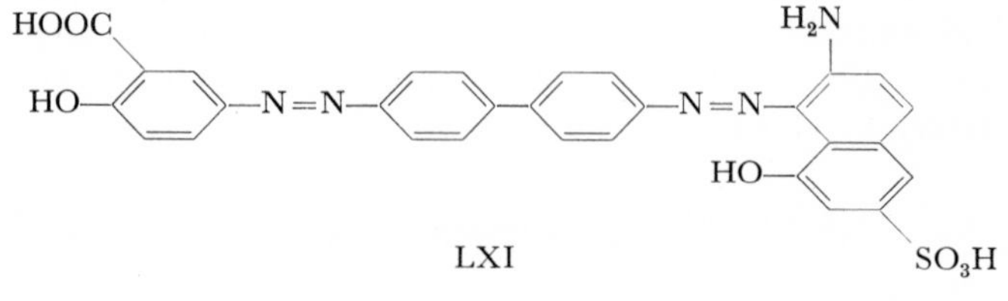

LXI

Resorcine Dark Brown (A) —
symmetric primary disazo dye with bifunctional coupling component (resorcinol)

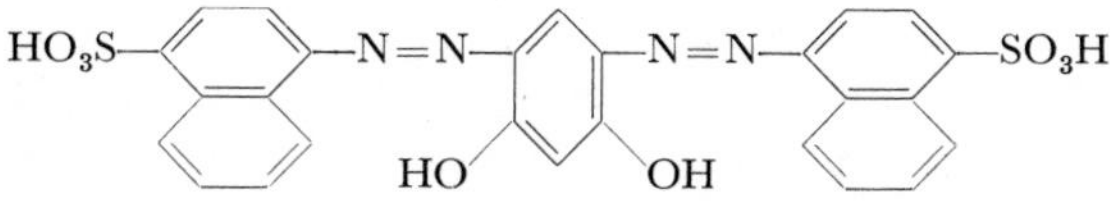

$$HO_3S-\text{[naphthalene]}-N{=}N-\text{[benzene]}-N{=}N-\text{[naphthalene]}-SO_3H$$

with HO and OH substituents on the central benzene ring

LXII[2]

Naphthol Blue Black B (C) —
unsymmetric primary disazo dye with bifunctional coupling component

$$\text{aniline} \xrightarrow[\text{alkaline}]{2} \text{H acid} \xleftarrow[\text{acid}]{1} p\text{-nitroaniline}$$

[structural formula (XVII), § 11.4]

The secondary disazo dyes are made by diazotizing an aminoazo compound,
the amino group of which derives from the original coupling component, and
coupling it to a suitable intermediate. Sulphon Cyanine GR (FBy) is an example:

$$\text{metanilic acid} \xrightarrow{1} \text{1-naphthylamine} \xrightarrow{2} \text{8-}p\text{-toluidino-1-naphthalenesulphonic acid}$$

Yet another group of disazo dyes is prepared by condensation of two identical
or different aminoazo compounds, the linking being achieved normally by
means of phosgene, cyanuric chloride, and, most recently, fumaryl dichloride
(*2507–2509*).

It will have been noted that in the structural formulas above sulphonic
groups have been written as the free acids, although the commercial articles are
almost invariably salts. This is usual since, as aromatic sulphonic acids are
strong acids, in aqueous solution they exist almost exclusively as anions and so
it does not matter whether one sets out from the free acids or their salts.

The chemical classification and the constitution of azo colouring matters is
treated much more fully in textbooks of the chemistry of dyes and pigments
(*2077, 2237, 2341*).

From the point of view of use, azo colouring matters can be classed into acid,
mordant, direct, disperse, azoic, and solvent dyes, as well as into pigments, and
a few azo compounds appear among basic and vat dyes. Acid, mordant, direct,
and basic dyes are water-soluble, the others are not. Examples of acid dyes,
so-called because they are generally applied to protein and protein-like fibres
from solutions on the acid side of neutrality, are Resorcine Dark Brown, Naphthol Blue Black, and Sulphon Cyanine GR (above), Tartrazine (§ 9.1), and
Orange I and II (§ 13.2). Some acid dyes are metal complexes and a few of
these will be found in § 14.4. Mordant dyes are essentially acid dyes capable of
forming metal complexes on the fibre. Examples are Eriochrome Black A und T
and Diamond Black PV (§ 11.3). Direct dyes derive their name from the fact

---

[2] According to recent investigations (*846, 1062*), coupling to resorcinol takes place in the
4- and 6-positions, not in the 2- and 4-positions, as formulated in the *Colour Index*, 2nd edition.

that they can be applied directly to cellulosic fibres. Illustrations are Diamine Green B, Congo Red, and Diamine Fast Red F (above), Mikado Yellow and Chloramine Yellow NN (§ 9.1), Benzo Fast Blue 8 GL and Coprantine Violet BLL (§ 11.2), and Benzo Fast Copper Red GGL (§ 14.4). In azoic dyeing and printing an insoluble azo compound is formed by carrying out the coupling reaction on the fibre. The preparation of specially stabilized diazo components for this purpose arose in §§ 4.3 and 8.5. The insoluble products of coupling azoic components may also be made in substance and used as pigments, as are Hansa Yellows (§ 9.3). Some pigments, termed lakes, are made from water-soluble dyes by precipitation with metallic salts and Orange II, for example, is so treated. Compounds to be employed as solvent dyes must be free from sulphonic groups: Butter Yellow (cf. § 13.1) is one. Disperse dyes are very similar, being used to dye man-made fibres from dispersions in water, but to retard settling out N-hydroxyalkyl groups are frequently introduced.

10. The Mechanism of the Coupling Reaction

10.1 The Reactive Equilibrium Forms of Coupling and Diazo Components

From the eighties of the last century onwards, the mechanism of the coupling process has received more attention than diazotization. The earlier hypotheses regarding the course of the reaction, propounded before 1930 by Hantzsch (*974*), Dimroth (*600, 602, 603*), Karrer (*1196*), K. H. Meyer (*1429, 1431, 1433*), and others, will not be considered here in detail. These older theories were essentially concerned only with the actual substitution, that is, with the replacement by the diazo residue of a hydrogen atom bound to an aromatic or *pseudo*-aromatic carbon atom. The experimental investigation of the problem of which equilibrium forms of diazo and coupling components are those in fact taking part in the substitution was largely neglected. However, the researches since 1930 have made it clear that the study of the equilibria to which *each* of the reactants is subject is the *conditio sine qua non* for the understanding of the substitution proper. These equilibria are also of great importance in interpreting several empirically developed rules of long standing for the preparation of azo dyes.

The clarification of the mechanism of coupling is based mainly on determinations of the rate of reaction. In current kinetic work two possible methods of estimation are utilized in particular (*2227*): polarography for the decrease in diazo concentration (*676*) and colorimetry of the azo compound formed (*459, 2076, 2173, 2178, 2242*).

In a series of communications at about the turn of the century, Goldschmidt (*825, 826, 829–831*) described the kinetics of coupling simple diazobenzenes to phenol, dimethylaniline, and some of their derivatives. As at the time the use of buffer solutions was still unknown and as it is now realized that the rate of coupling depends greatly on the acidity of the medium, his work has lost much of its significance, but Goldschmidt did recognize the reaction to be of second order. The kinetic equation (10.1) is thus implied. (Az), (D), and (C) represent

$$\frac{d(Az)}{dt} = k_s (D) (C) \tag{10.1}$$

the concentrations of the azo dye, the diazo, and the coupling component, respectively, whilst k_s is the rate constant. The subscript s implies the use of stoichiometric total concentrations of the reactants irrespective of the preliminary equilibria (*2227*). In that which follows, k without subscript will be employed to describe the rate constant when, instead of the stoichiometric concentrations, the equilibrium concentrations under the particular conditions obtaining of the actual species taking part in the substitution proper are entered into the equation.

Several qualitative observations on the *effect of acidity* are recorded in the scientific and patent literature and the methods of preparing azo dyes both in the laboratory and on the large scale are based on the fact that for every combination of components there exists an *optimum pH range*.

The first attempt to discover the fundamental connection between acidity and the rate of reaction was made by Conant and Peterson (*459*), who demonstrated that the rate of coupling of a series of naphtholsulphonic acids is proportional to the $OH^{\ominus}$ concentration in the range of pH of 4·50 to 9·15. This shows that the constant k_s is being affected by an acid–base equilibrium in *one* of the two reactants. Conant and Peterson concluded that the substitution proper occurred between free (undissociated) phenol and diazohydroxide, preceded by equilibration of the diazohydroxide with the diazonium ion according to equa-

$$\text{Ar—N}_2^{\oplus} + OH^{\ominus} \; \rightleftharpoons \; \text{Ar—N}=\text{N—OH} \qquad (10.2)$$

tion (10.2). Such an interpretation was in harmony with the mechanism of coupling generally accepted at that time (1930) (*704, 713, 2110*).

Eleven years later it was pointed out by Wistar and Bartlett (*2173*) that this scheme did not represent the only mechanism which accords with the experimental determinations and that another existed. Not only the diazo, but also the coupling component is subject to acid–base equilibrium, and in coupling to phenols or amines the following systems are involved:

$$\text{ROH} \; \rightleftharpoons \; \text{RO}^{\ominus} + H^{\oplus} \qquad (10.3)$$

$$\text{RNH}_3^{\oplus} \; \rightleftharpoons \; \text{RNH}_2 + H^{\oplus} \qquad (10.4)$$

For the relationship between the hydrogen ion concentration and the rate of reaction there are in principle four possibilities for coupling either to phenols or

Table 10.1

Combinations of Equilibrium Forms Possible for the Rate-determining Step of the Coupling Reaction

Case	Diazo component	Coupling component	
		Amine coupling	Phenol coupling
A	Diazohydroxide	Ammonium ion	Free phenol
B	Diazonium ion	Free amine	Phenolate ion
C	Diazonium ion	Ammonium ion	Free phenol
D	Diazohydroxide	Free amine	Phenolate ion

to amines, depending on which of the species of equilibria (10.2) and (10.3) or (10.2) and (10.4), respectively, are those which take part in the substitution proper. Table 10.1 lists the eight combinations. Wistar and Bartlett have illustrated the four cases A to D for model reactions by graphs, which show that plots of log k_s against pH give similar curves for A and B. In a series of couplings to naphthylaminesulphonic acids they found the rate of reaction to be proportional to the effective concentration of the base, that is, the naphthylaminesulphonate anion. For example, in the interaction of diazobenzene with 1-naphthylamine-8-sulphonic acid the rate decreases roughly ten times when the pH is lowered by one unit on the acid side of the buffer region of the amine (pK of 1-naphthylamine-8-sulphonic acid = 5·03). On the other hand, above pH 5 the reaction practically ceases to speed up.

This proves that in coupling to amines it is the free amine and not the ammonium ion which enters into the substitution step proper. Also implied is that the reacting form of the electrophilic component is not the diazohydroxide, but the diazonium ion.

By analogy the same behaviour would be expected in coupling to phenols. Conant's work leaves the choice between the combinations diazohydroxide + free phenol (case A) and diazonium ion + phenolate ion (case B). Although electronic theory makes B appear more probable, insufficient *experimental* material was available in 1941 to demonstrate whether undissociated phenol or the phenolate ion is more reactive towards electrophilic substitution.

The answer was provided a few years ago in two ways. Pütter (*1666*) applied Bartlett's method to several naphtholsulphonic acids, which differed greatly in the equilibrium constant for the dissociation of their phenolic group. He chose for study the reaction of 4-acetamidodiazobenzene-2-sulphonic acid with 1,4-, 1,2-, and 1,8-naphtholsulphonic acids, the pK values of which are 8·2, 9·4, and 12·6, respectively. The kinetic determinations carried out with these combinations in the region of pH 7·4 to 9·8 showed the proportionality expected between the rate and the concentration of the naphtholate ion, but none with that of the undissociated naphthol. This result corresponds with Bartlett's mechanism B (diazonium ion + phenolate ion), but contradicts Conant's hypothesis.

Qualitatively the greater reactivity of the phenolate ion compared with the free phenol is apparent also in coupling to 1,8-dihydroxynaphthalene-4-sulphonic acid (*2239*).

Semiquantitative experiments using coupling in very acid media (60 to 80% sulphuric acid) suggest, however, that the undissociated phenol too is capable of reaction (*24, 2228*), but the rate of coupling to it is at least 10^{10} times less than that to phenolate and so remains practically undetectable even in moderately acid solution.

Elofson et al. (*676*) investigated the kinetics of coupling to 3-methyl-1-phenyl-5-pyrazolone and also found that at about neutrality the rate increases ten times per pH unit. It must be concluded that the enolate ion is the reactive form of pyrazolones. As the enolate ion is the mesomeric base of enol *and* ketone, the previously much disputed point of whether the ketone or the enol is the coupling component proper loses greatly in significance (cf. § 9.3). From this it would be expected that pyrazolones substituted with an alkyl group in position 4 can no longer couple and hence it seems doubtful whether the product of the reaction between *p*-nitrodiazobenzene and 3,4-tetramethylene-1-phenyl-5-py-razolone really possesses the structure (I) postulated by Linstead and Wang (*1348*). The ready splitting off of the diazo residue suggests the formation of a diazoether of the enol (II) by *O*-coupling.

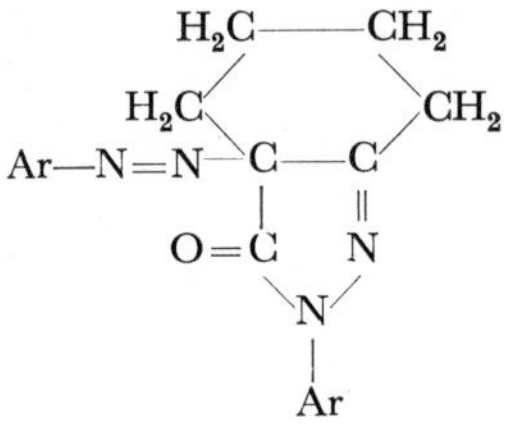

In the case of amines which are already able to lose a proton in dilute aqueous alkali with the formation of an ammoniate anion, Allan (*24*) supposes that these particles couple considerably more rapidly than the free amine. Confirmation comes from the work of R. D. Brown, J. H. Ridd, *et al.* (*351*) with glyoxaline (III). The increase in the rate of reaction in the region of pH of 7·1 to 11·0 corresponds to the coupling of the anion (IV) in the 2-position and iodination proceeds analogously at the same hydrogen ion concentration (*1705*). In electrophilic substitutions which involve (III) and not the anion (IV), attack occurs

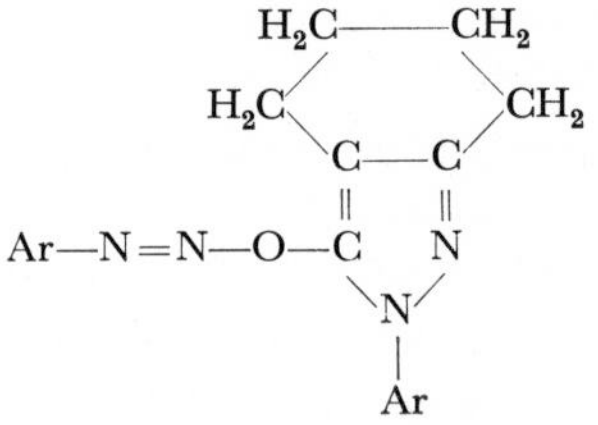

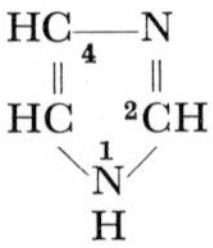

at position 4. This behaviour agrees remarkably well with the electron densities calculated for the various ring atoms in the different states of ionization of this heterocycle (*204*, see also *2326, 2404*). According to Ridd (*254*) indole similarly couples as the anion.

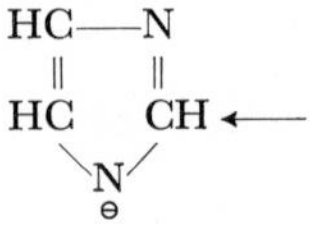

It has already been stated that Bartlett proved the free amine to be the nucleophilic partner in coupling and that from his work it followed indirectly that the *diazonium ion* and not the diazohydroxide is probably the electrophilic reagent. Two other investigations will now be discussed in detail as these provide direct experimental proof of the function of the diazonium ion in the raction.

For this purpose, Zollinger (*2229*) investigated the dependence of the rate of coupling on the ionic strength of the medium for the interaction of 2-naphthyl-amine-6-sulphonic acid with three diazo components in order to determine the sign and magnitude of the ionic charge on the latter. Brönsted's equation for primary salt effects (*331–333*) takes the form (10.5) for the case of azo coupling, z_D and z_C being the charges on the reactive forms of the diazo and coupling components, respectively, I the ionic strength, and k_0 and k_I the rate constants at ionic strengths 0 and I, respectively. α and β are constants and a is the average minimum distance between the ions.

$$\log k^I = \log k_0 + \frac{2\,z_D\,z_C\,\alpha\,I^{1/2}}{1+\beta a\,I^{1/2}} \qquad (10.5)$$

The coupling of 4-diazotoluene to 2-naphthylamine-6-sulphonic acid was studied first. From Bartlett's researches it is certain that the coupling component enters the substitution as a simple anion (V, $z_C = -1$), but the diazo compound may react as the diazonium ion (VI, $z_D = +1$), as the diazohydroxide (VII, $z_D = 0$), or as the diazotate (VIII, $z_D = -1$). By using these z_C and z_D values in Brönsted's equation it becomes apparent that increasing ionic strength would cause a decrease in the rate of reaction in the case of the diazonium ion (negative salt effect), but an increase in the case of the diazotate ion (positive salt effect). When the diazohydroxide or another electrically neutral species of diazo compound, such as the diazoacetate, is the reacting entity, the rate of coupling should be independent of the ionic strength.

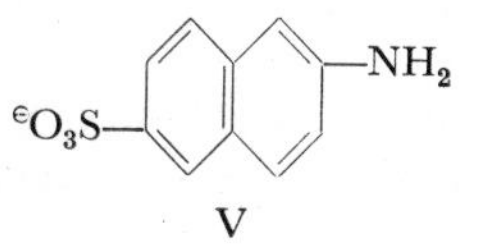

V

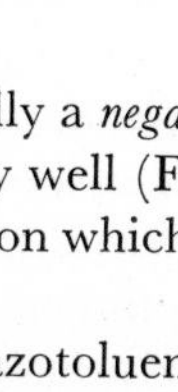

VI 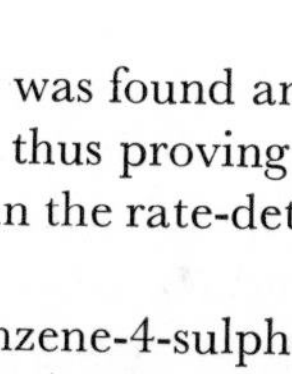   VII 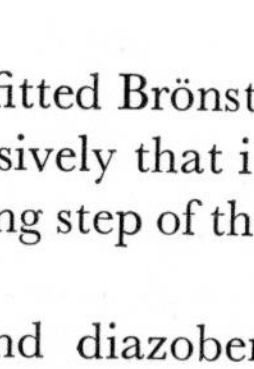   VIII

Experimentally a *negative salt effect* was found and this fitted Brönsted's equation surprisingly well (Figure 10.1), thus proving conclusively that it is indeed the diazonium ion which takes part in the rate-determining step of the coupling process.

Besides 4-diazotoluene, diazobenzene-4-sulphonic and diazobenzene-2,5-disulphonic acid were also employed. As the reactions with these components exhibited no and a positive salt effect, respectively (Figure 10.1), the reactive species here are the zwitterion (IX, $z_D = 0$) and the anion (X, $z_D = 1$), respectively.

$\overset{\oplus}{N}\equiv N$

$\overset{\oplus}{N}\equiv N$

$^{\ominus}O_3S$— —$SO_3^{\ominus}$

$SO_3^{\ominus}$

IX   X

More recently, the analogous dependence of the rate of reaction on ionic strength was confirmed for coupling to phenols (*2236*), but if sulphonic groups are present in the vicinity of the site of reaction the behaviour departs greatly from that expected by theory.

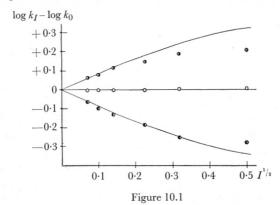

Figure 10.1

Dependence of the rates of reaction of couplings to 2-naphthylamine-6-sulphonic acid on the ionic strength (*2229*)

Circles indicate constants determined experimentally; the curves are those calculated according to Brönsted's equation

◐ 4-diazotoluene   ○ diazobenzene-4-sulphonic acid   ◑ diazobenzene-2,5-disulphonic acid

The determination of the nature of the equilibrium form of the diazo component which takes part in the substitution proper has also been carried out by Bartlett's method of comparing the rate of coupling with the acid–base system of the diazo compound. As described in § 3.5, Wittwer and Zollinger (*2178*) showed that the diazohydroxide is a metastable intermediate of the diazo equilibrium. On reaching the point of rearrangement, the diazonium ion not only takes up a hydroxyl ion, but the diazohydroxide produced immediately dissociates into the diazotate ion. In consequence, in the strongly alkaline region the concentration of the diazonium ions decreases per pH unit not merely ten, but a hundred times. According to the experiments of Wittwer and Zollinger, the rate of coupling decreases by a factor of 10^2 per pH unit in strongly alkaline solution, thus demonstrating the parallel between the stoichiometric rate constant k_s and the concentration of the diazonium ions (see Figure 10.2).

For the by far the most important two types of reaction, that is, coupling to amines and phenols, the equilibrium forms which enter into the substitution process have therefore been determined unequivocally. For the later discussion of the reaction of bifunctional coupling components and especially for the explanation of the mechanism of the substitution proper and for the comparison of the reactivity of different components, it is advantageous to amend Goldschmidt's original kinetic equation (10.1). As shown by Conant, the so-called stoichiometric rate constant k_s is dependent on the acidity of the medium because it is a function of the preceding equilibria. As these rapid preliminary changes are of no real concern to the coupling reaction proper, it was proposed (*2227, 2242*) to replace equation (10.1) by one which emphasizes the relationship between the effective concentrations of the reactive equilibrium forms, that is, the diazonium ion and the phenolate ion or the free amine. This leads to equations (10.6) and (10.7).

$$\frac{d(Az)}{dt} = k \, [Ar-N_2^\oplus] \, [RO^\ominus] \tag{10.6}$$

$$\frac{d(Az)}{dt} = k \, [Ar-N_2^\oplus] \, [RNH_2] \tag{10.7}$$

The constant k, in contrast to k_s, is independent of the acidity of the medium and this is brought out clearly in the evaluation of kinetic data published by various authors (Table 10.2). Very accurate constants can, of course, only be expected in those cases in which the kinetic determinations as well as those of the acid dissociation constants of the reactants were carried out under identical conditions (ionic strength, temperature, etc.). Of the coupling reactions listed in Table 10.2, this applies only to the last two examples. It should be noted that, except in the last instance, the determinations were carried out in a region of acidity in which the diazo compound exists almost entirely as the diazonium

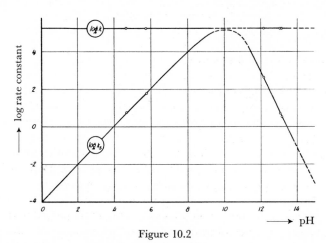

Figure 10.2

pH dependence of the rate constants of coupling diazotized metanilic acid to 2-naphthol-6-sulphonic acid (*2178*).

Rate constant k is from equation (10.6), k_s, the stoichiometric constant, is from equation (10.1).

ion. The relationship between the two rate constants k and k_s, on the one hand, and the hydrogen ion concentration on the other is illustrated for yet another coupling reaction in Figure 10.2.

Table 10.2

Rates of Coupling to Amines or Phenols at Various pH Values

Diazo component[1]	Coupling component[1]	pH	Rate constant		Reference
			$\log k_s$	$\log k$	
Diazobenzene (11.90)	1-Naphthylamine-8-sulphonic acid (5.03)	4·32	2·82	3·5	(2173)
		4·95	3·30	3·6	
		6·25	3·48	3·5	
4-Diazotoluene (12.59)	2-Naphthol (9.91)	6.4	1·57	5·5	(676)
		6·6	2·11	5·4	
		7·0	2·57	5·5	
		7·4	2·99	5·5	
4-Diazotoluene (12.59)	2-Naphthol-6-sulphonic acid (8.94)	5·09	—0·15	3·71	(2242)
		5·71	0·42	3·65	
		6·24	1·02	3·72	
		6·71	1·45	3·68	
		7·18	1·91	3·67	
3-Diazobenzene-sulphonic acid (10.84)	1-Naphthol-4-sulphonic acid (8.18)	4·58	—0·30	3·30	(2178)
		12·16	0·55	3·20	
		13·21	—1·31	3·44	

[1] The figures in parentheses represent the rearrangement constants in the case of the diazo components $[(pK_1 + pK_2)/2]$ and the acid dissociation constants in the case of phenols and ammonium ions [pK].

10.2 Discussion of the Reaction Mechanism on the Basis of the Electronic Theory

It has already been pointed out that up to the 'thirties the diazohydroxide was regarded as the most reactive form of the diazo component. This attitude was derived mainly from Hantzsch's work, which had been carried out at a time when the application of the ionic theory to the reactions of organic chemistry was practically unknown. The views on the course of heterolytic substitution, developed since about 1924, when brought to bear consistently on the coupling reaction, must, however, lead to the conclusion that the most acid equilibrium form of the diazo component, the diazonium ion, attacks the most basic form of the coupling component, the free amine or the phenolate ion. Ingold (*1153f*) has rightly stressed this point. In spite of it, the old opinions have been retained in textbooks and even in some volumes which deal with diazo compounds in detail. This is most clearly illustrated by the way diazo isomerism is discussed: almost without exception one finds in the literature the statement that the *syn*-diazotate couples in contrast to the *anti*-isomer. This assertion derived from Hantzsch is incorrect. The apparent reactivity of the *syn*-diazotate is due to the fact that it takes part in a rapidly established equilibrium with the diazonium ion, the latter being produced from the *anti*-form only by a slow rearrangement (*1335*).

Already in the 'thirties some authors (*520, 593, 2185*) formulated the coupling reaction so as to involve diazonium ions, but this point seems to have been overlooked subsequently, perhaps because the reasons for the reactivity of the diazonium ions were not considered in detail. However, in Hammett's classic book of physical organic chemistry (*914g, h*) the diazonium ion was recognized explicitly as the most electrophilic species taking part in the diazo equilibria and Hauser and Breslow (*989*) fully discussed the reactivity of the diazonium ion on the basis of the electronic theory. It is apparent from the mesomeric limiting structure (XIb) that the β-nitrogen possesses only a sextet of electrons

$$\text{Ar}-\overset{\oplus}{\text{N}}\equiv\overline{\text{N}} \longleftrightarrow \text{Ar}-\overline{\text{N}}=\overset{\ominus}{\text{N}}$$
$$\text{XI\,a} \qquad\qquad \text{XI\,b}$$

and therefore is strongly electrophilic. An analogous form of the diazohydroxide is much less probable as opposite charges would be present on two neighbouring atoms.

Hodgson (*1039, 1052, 1053, 1055*) has criticized the considerations advanced by Hauser and Breslow, as well as Wistar and Bartlett's researches, but Zollinger (*2227*) has pointed out that Hodgson's arguments can readily be refuted.

The mesomeric limiting structures for the free phenol and the phenolate ion, (XIIa, XIIb) and (XIIIa, XIIIb) respectively, show that the latter should provide the more reactive substrate for electrophilic substitutions, as zwitterionic forms are absent. The difference between the ammonium ion (XIV)

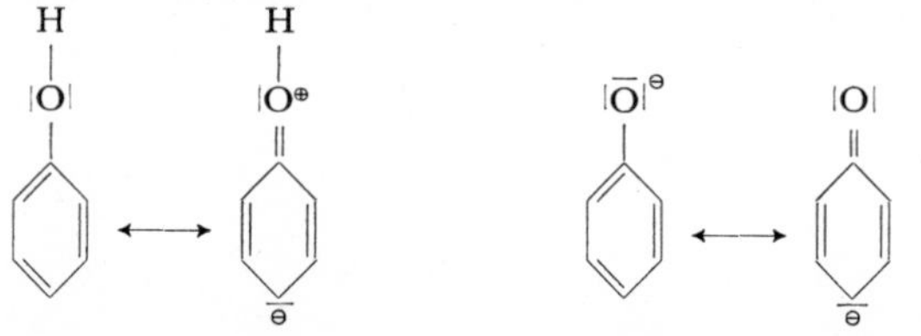

XIIa   XIIb[2]   XIIIa   XIIIb[2]

---

[2] The corresponding *o*-quinonoid structures have been omitted.

and the amine (XV) is probably still more marked. As supposed by Allan (*24*), the ammoniate anion (XVI) which results on ionization of the amine should be an even better coupling component.

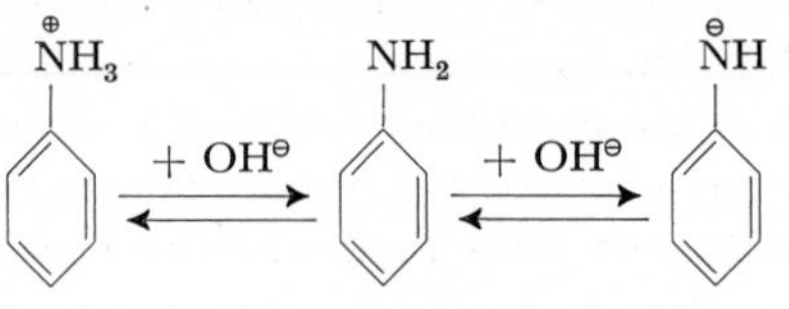

(10.8)

XIV   XV   XVI

By now the greater reactivity of the phenolate ion compared with the free phenol has been demonstrated for a whole series of electrophilic substitutions other than azo coupling, for example, halogenation (*539, 540, 1582*), hydroxymethylation (*536*), and deuteration (*234, 1154, 1155*). Still larger than with the pair phenol–phenolate is the difference in reactivity between the base and its conjugate acid in the electrophilic substitution of the system aniline–anilinium ion, as shown by R. P. Bell (*221*) in the case of bromination.

Resonance theory makes it possible to understand several observations of abnormal behaviour of some components in coupling. The great difficulty of coupling to *o*-substituted *N,N*-dimethylaniline derivatives known for a long time (*769, 2120*) is due to steric hindrance in the quinonoid limiting structures of these compounds. In (XVIIb) both methyl groups as well as the sub-

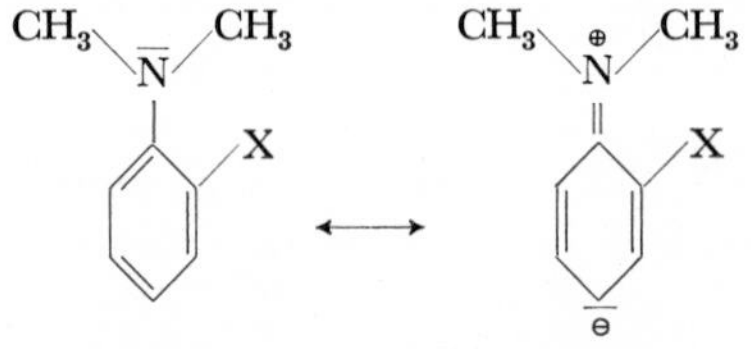

XVIIa   XVIIb

stituent X must lie in the plane of the benzene ring, but, in contrast to the *m*- or *p*-isomers, here this is only sterically possible to a limited extent. This phenomenon can be demonstrated not only by azo coupling, but also by many other methods, for example, by halogenations (*539, 540, 1582*), by deuteration (*234, 352, 1154, 1155*), by basic strengths (*908, 2308*), by ultra-violet spectra (*1692*), and by dipole moments (*1151*). The difficulties in coupling *p*-substi-

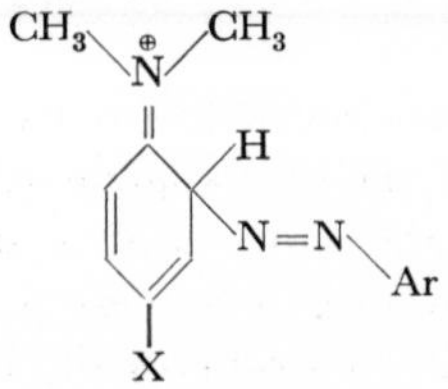

XVIII

tuted N,N-dimethylanilines, contrary to their o-isomers, is not caused by steric hindrance in *limiting structures*, but by unfavourable steric influences on the formation of the *intermediate* (XVIII) in the coupling reaction, the N-methyl groups obstructing the addition of the diazonium ion. The lack of reactivity in N,N-dimethyl-2-naphthylamines is to be interpreted analogously. Earlier explanations (*1054*), which assumed that the lower reactivity of both the o- and the p-isomers had the same origin, did not go deep enough. The unpublished observation (*2401*) that 1,3-bisdimethylaminobenzene can be coupled in the 4-position seems to be contradictory to the above statements. It can be understood, however, by assuming that reaction occurs *para* to that dimethylamino group which becomes an ammonium group in the limiting structure corresponding to XVIIb. The other dimethylamino residue cannot resonate with the benzene ring in the intermediate formed and therefore does not have to be co-planar.

That in comparison with other substitution processes azo coupling is sensitive to relatively small differences in electron density distribution follows from the fact that β-naphthol couples only in the 1-, and never in the 3- or even the 6-position (*716*). According to Wheland (*2142, 2143a*), the intermediate for 1-coupling possesses the two limiting structures (XIXa, XIXb), whereas that for 3-coupling has the isomeric form (XX). From valence-bond theory (XIX) would be expected to be more stable than (XX), as it retains the whole of the resonance energy of one benzene nucleus (shaded in the formulas). Contrary to the older ways, this one explains the behaviour of β-naphthol

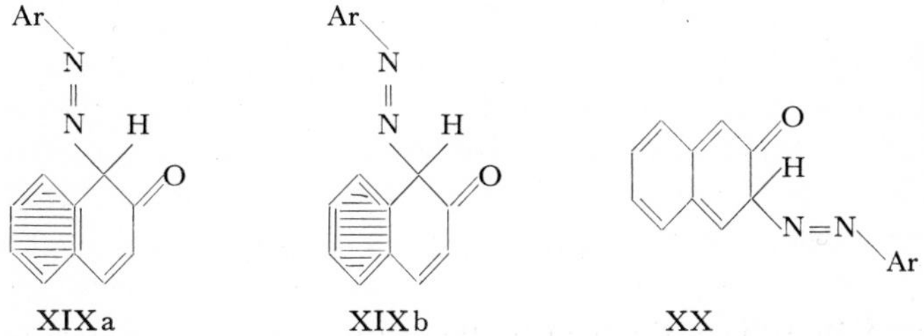

XIXa   XIXb   XX

without involving bond fixation. A similar interpretation of the mode of reaction of β-substituted naphthalenes was given by Pauling (*1591b*) and MO-calculations have arrived at parallel results (*469d, 470*).

10.3 Coupling Reactions in Non-Aqueous Media

Azo coupling in non-aqueous media has not yet been investigated systematically, but Huisgen's work on the rearrangement of nitrosoacylanilines provides some pointers to the mechanism of coupling in non-polar and weakly polar solvents. Huisgen studied the rate of conversion of the nitrosoacylanilines into the isomeric diazoacetates by colorimetrically determining the azo dyes produced from them (*1111, 1113, 1117, 1121, 1122*) (see § 7.5).

As coupling is much more rapid than rearrangement, the increase in concentration of the azo compound can be used to assess the rate of the first step. The following observations by Huisgen are relevant to the subject of this section. He demonstrated that in mixtures of benzene and glacial acetic acid the diazoacetate is in equilibrium with the diazonium ion ('diazonium acetate'). In benzene alone the system is wholly over on the side of the diazoacetate but,

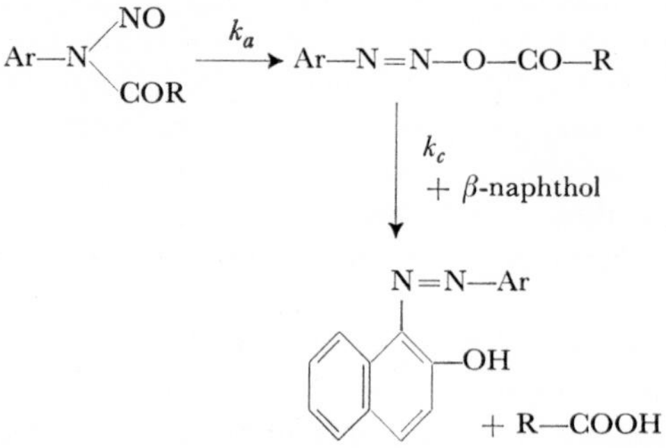

$$
\begin{array}{c}
\text{Ar—N}\!\!\begin{array}{c}\nearrow\text{NO}\\[2pt]\searrow\text{COR}\end{array}\xrightarrow{k_a}\ \text{Ar—N=N—O—CO—R}\\[14pt]
\Big\downarrow\ \begin{array}{l}k_c\\[2pt]+\ \beta\text{-naphthol}\end{array}\\[14pt]
\end{array}
\tag{10.9}
$$

$$
\text{N=N—Ar}
$$

[naphthol ring structure]—OH

$$
+\ \text{R—COOH}
$$

as the content of acetic acid is increased, the rate of coupling and the concentration of the diazoacetate decrease. Huisgen concludes that it is the diazoacetate and not the diazonium ion which reacts. However, Bradley and Thompson (*301*) report that diazonium salts, substituted with long alkyl chains and therefore soluble in non-polar media, couple smoothly with β-naphthol in benzene.

The detailed experimental investigation of these problems is very desirable from the point of view of theoretical organic chemistry. Such a study should include consideration of the possibility of forming *ion pairs* in the case of diazonium salts. It does not seem impossible that, on analogy with Winstein's observations on the equilibria and reactions of carbonium ions (*2170*), a system could be found containing diazo compounds, in which one or possibly more ion-pair-like intermediates of the diazo equilibria are present. The following formulas represent these ideas schematically:

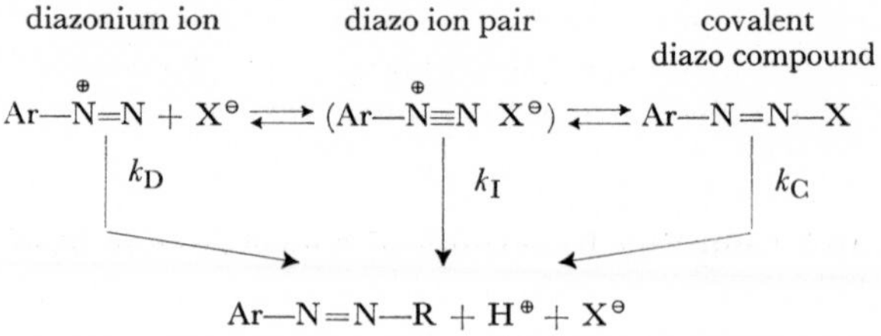

$$
\begin{array}{ccc}
\text{diazonium ion} & \text{diazo ion pair} & \begin{array}{c}\text{covalent}\\\text{diazo compound}\end{array}\\[6pt]
\overset{\oplus}{\text{Ar—N}}\!=\!\text{N} + \text{X}^{\ominus} \rightleftarrows & (\text{Ar—}\overset{\oplus}{\text{N}}\!\equiv\!\text{N}\ \text{X}^{\ominus}) \rightleftarrows & \text{Ar—N=N—X}\\[4pt]
\Big\downarrow k_{\mathrm{D}} & \Big\downarrow k_{\mathrm{I}} & \Big\downarrow k_{\mathrm{C}}
\end{array}
\tag{10.10}
$$

$$
\text{Ar—N=N—R} + \text{H}^{\oplus} + \text{X}^{\ominus}
$$

The investigation of such a system requires a series of preliminary experiments to prove whether or not an equilibrium form corresponding to the diazochloride exists. Only then can the production of ion pairs and the relationships between the reactivities of the various species be discussed. The greater coupling power of the diazoacetate, which Huisgen found in benzene

$(k_D < k_C)$, can perhaps be attributed to the ability of the acetyl residue, split out of the intermediate formed during coupling, to act simultaneously as acceptor of the proton from the coupling component (concerted mechanism with intramolecular base catalysis).

10.4 The Mechanism of the Substitution Proper

If it is asked what is the most significant result of the theories of organic chemistry developed since the 'twenties, it must be admitted that it is not the clarification of reaction mechanisms, even though this is based on much work on the fundamentals of the physical properties of chemical compounds, but that it is the possibility of classifying systematically the tremendous multiplicity of organic substances and reactions. Organic chemistry, which previously consisted largely of an endless number of specialized and apparently unconnected investigations, was transformed through the new theoretical framework into a logical science.

In this sense, the concepts introduced by Ingold are of particular importance for the coupling reaction, which belongs to the group of *electrophilic aromatic substitutions*.

This classification of azo coupling is relevant not only for the sake of being systematic, but above all because the knowledge gained in the study of other electrophilic aromatic substitutions, such as nitration, halogenation, Friedel–Crafts reactions, nitrosation, and deuteration, can therefore be applied to coupling. For the same reason results obtained with coupling allow deductions to be made about the mechanism of *all* substitutions of this class.

The historical development of the views on the mechanism of electrophilic aromatic substitution will not be gone into here, but some parallels between these reactions and additions to the double bond of olefins soon led to the explicit suggestion of a stepwise mechanism. It is especially worth stressing, that even in 1901 Lapworth (*1298*) in voicing his ideas on benzene substitution predicted results only recently obtained experimentally. Lapworth supposed that the intermediate (**XXI**) plays a role in the bromination of phenol. Although no definite proof of the structure of this intermediate has been supplied in the meantime, (**XXI**) is the most probable one on the basis of the present knowledge of the mechanism of bromination [see (*541*)].

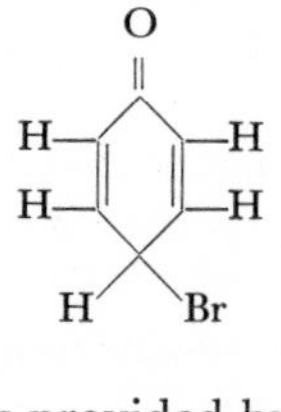

A considerable advance was provided by Pfeiffer and Wizinger's isolation of an ionized intermediate from the bromination of 1,1-bis(*p*-dimethylaminophenyl)ethylene (*1623, 2181*), the hypothesis that the substitution of benzene and other aromatic compounds proceeds by the same mechanism being propounded in consequence. The investigation of the azo coupling of diarylethylenes by Wizinger and Cyriax (*2185*) has particular interest in this connection, as here also was isolated a compound corresponding to the intermediate in the bromination.

Before dealing with the more recent research on the actual substitution process, it is necessary to discuss of the older work only the mechanism of coupling postulated by Dimroth and Hartmann (*600, 602, 603*). Dimroth examined in detail the diazoethers discovered by von Pechmann and Frobenius (*1603*) and exposed their close relationship to azo dyes and diazoamino compounds (*C*- and *N*-azo compounds) by describing them as *O*-azo compounds (*604*). Analogous terms have been employed since by Ingold (*1152*) for the products of nitrosation.

Dimroth and Hartmann showed that in the first place the enol of 2-benzoyl-1,3-diphenyl-1,3-propanedione (tribenzoylmethane) yields with diazonium salts yellow diazoethers, which are converted by dry heat into the red *C*-azo compounds. They assumed that such ethers are the essential preliminary to coupling with all phenols or enols, a suggestion already made by Kekulé (*1202*). It speaks against this mechanism that the analogous reaction with amines, the diazoamino rearrangement, certainly does not proceed intramolecularly, at least at low temperatures (see § 8.3). It must be supposed that also in the case of the diazoethers the rearrangement to the *C*-azo compounds does not occur directly, but only after dissociation into enolate and diazonium ions, that is, intermolecularly in two steps. The formation of an azonaphthol dye from the diazoether in presence of β-naphthol, mentioned by Dimroth and Hartmann, tends to confirm this, but so far no absolute proof excluding as well a *partially* intramolecular diazoether rearrangement has been provided.

Of cardinal importance is the discussion of the experimental support for the stepwise mechanism of electrophilic aromatic substitutions. First it must be shown that in the initial step (10.11 a) the diazonium ion adds to the aromatic compound and that the hydrogen atom to be substituted is only split off *subsequently* as a proton, leaving behind the pair of electrons by which it had been bound (10.11 b). As free protons possess an unmeasurably short life from

$$\text{R—N}_2^{\oplus} + \text{Ar—H} \longrightarrow \text{R—N}_2\text{—}\overset{\oplus}{\text{Ar}}\text{—H} \qquad (10.11\,\text{a})$$

$$\text{R—N}_2\text{—}\overset{\oplus}{\text{Ar}}\text{—H} + \text{B} \longrightarrow \text{Ar—N}_2\text{—R} + \text{HB}^{\oplus} \qquad (10.11\,\text{b})$$

a chemical point of view, it seems likely that the release of the proton takes place through immediate addition to a base B. It will be necessary to revert to this process later.

That the two steps do not occur synchronously is apparent from the fact that the rate of the substitution proper in azo coupling is not normally affected by changes in the concentration of the base B (*2232, 2242*). This cannot be explained by a single-step mechanism (10.12), but is in agreement with a two-stage bimolecular mechanism (10.11 a–b) as long as its second step, the protolysis, is considerably more rapid than its first.

$$X^{\oplus} + Ar{-}H + B \longrightarrow (X^{\oplus}..Ar...H...B) \longrightarrow Ar{-}X + HB^{\oplus} \qquad (10.12)$$
$$\text{transition state}$$

The most important and elegant support for this so-called (*1153d*) S_E2 mechanism (10.11 a–b) comes from Melanders's investigations of the electrophilic substitution of aromatic compounds, carrying at the position of reaction isotopic hydrogen, namely, the radioactive tritium (T). He demonstrated that for a series of benzene derivatives the tritiated hydrocarbons were nitrated and brominated equally as rapidly as the corresponding compounds containing only H^1. If the splitting off of hydrogen had belonged to the rate-determining part of the reaction (S_E3 mechanism 10.12) or if the second stage of the two-step mechanism had been slower than the first, a *kinetic isotope effect* would have been expected.

It is appropriate to indicate briefly the causes of kinetic isotope effects in general. A reaction, the rate-determining step of which is the fission of the bond between A and B, proceeds more slowly when a heavier isotope is substituted for either A or B. This phenomenon has been observed with a large number of isotopes, for example, those of carbon, nitrogen, and, particularly, hydrogen. By the kinetic isotope effect is understood the ratio of the rate constants of the reactions involving the different isotopes.

The size of the isotope effect depends on the element in question, the bond, the temperature, and other factors. Thus, a reaction in which hydrogen is released in the rate-determining step becomes 5 to 8 times slower on replacing protium (H) by deuterium (D) and 15 to 30 times slower on replacing protium by tritium. Elements of higher atomic weight give rise to calculated and observed isotope effects which are considerably smaller.

Of the various physical causes of the isotope effect only the most important will be mentioned here—the zero point energy of the bond concerned. Quantum theory designates with this term the lowest energy state of the vibrations of the link, because even at $0°\text{K}$ it cannot have a smaller value. At room temperature all bonds are still preponderantly in this state. The zero point energy is proportional to the vibration frequency, which, in turn, is inversely proportional to the square root of the reduced mass. As a first approximation, the hydrogen isotope effect is related to the zero point energies (E_0^H and E_0^D) and

$$\frac{k_H}{k_D} \simeq \exp\left(\frac{E_0^H - E_0^D}{RT}\right) = \exp\left(\frac{\nu_H - \nu_D}{1{\cdot}38\,T}\right) \qquad (10.13)$$

the vibration frequencies of the appropriate CH- and CD-bonds (ν_H and ν_D) according to equation (10.13). More detailed treatments (*227, 228, 248–250, 1405, 2148*) give the other factors on which the isotope effects are dependent.

Normally azo coupling exhibits *no* isotope effects. For example, 2-methoxy-diazobenzene reacts with 1-naphthol-4-sulphonic acid equally as rapidly as with 1-naphthol-2-*d*-4-sulphonic acid. However, the coupling of 4-chloro-diazobenzene with 2-naphthol-6, 8-disulphonic acid behaves totally differently, Zollinger and co-workers (*685, 2232*) finding an isotope effect which approximates closely to the theoretical value ($k_H/k_D = 6\cdot55$) when the protium of the 1-position in the coupling component is replaced by deuterium. The same reaction is very strongly catalysed by a series of bases, such as pyridine, but its rate is not directly proportional to the concentration of the base, as would be expected from an S_E3 mechanism. Especially remarkable is the observation that the magnitude of the isotope effect decreases as the concentration of base is increased.

All these facts are in agreement with the occurrence of an *S_E2 mechanism with a steady state intermediate*. This implies that during the course of the reaction the intermediate $R\cdot N_2\cdot \overset{\oplus}{Ar}\cdot H$ of the substitution process (10.11 a–b) does not accumulate but, except for a short initial and final phase, it is present in a *small* and *constant* concentration. According to Bodenstein (*273*), the explanation lies in bringing into consideration the back-reaction to the first step (10.14 a–b). In

$$R-N_2^{\oplus} + Ar-H \underset{k_{-1}}{\overset{k_1}{\rightleftarrows}} R-N_2-\overset{\oplus}{Ar}-H \qquad\qquad (10.14\,a)$$

$$R-N_2-\overset{\oplus}{Ar}-H + B \xrightarrow{k_2} Ar-N_2-R + HB^{\oplus} \qquad\qquad (10.14\,b)$$

the case of azo coupling, it was Pütter (*1666*) who first drew attention to the importance of this back-reaction in qualitatively interpreting base catalysis.

The reaction system (10.14 a–b) is kinetically represented by equation (10.15), k_2 being the only constant which is reduced by the theoretical factor of 5 to 8, mentioned above, on replacement of the reacting protium atom by deuterium. If the back-reaction to the first step can be neglected, that is, if k_{-1} is very small, it

$$\frac{d\,[Ar-N_2-R]}{dt} = \frac{k_1 \dfrac{k_2}{k_{-1}}\,[B]}{1 + \dfrac{k_2}{k_{-1}}\,[B]}\,[Ar-H]\,[R-N_2^{\oplus}] \qquad\qquad (10.15)$$

can be seen from equation (10.15) that the rate becomes practically independent of k_2 and [B] since —

$$1 + \frac{k_2}{k_{-1}}\,[B] \simeq \frac{k_2}{k_{-1}}\,[B]\,.$$

In other words, when this condition obtains, the reaction exhibits neither isotope effect nor base catalysis. The reverse is the case if the back-reaction to the first step is very rapid, that is, if k_{-1} is large; in the extreme the rate can become directly proportional to the concentration of the base and to the constant k_2, the isotope effect being great.

As the three factors, k_2, k_{-1}, and [B], vary so all the many possible cases lying between these two limits may be encountered. The *same* mechanism thus gives rise to reactions which may exhibit a large, a small, or no isotope effect, and this has been found experimentally *(685, 2233)*. From the results it could be shown mathematically that, in spite of the strong dependence of the isotope effect determined for the total process on the concentration of the base, the isotope effect of the second step, which alone is responsible for it, possesses in all instances practically the same value ($k_{2,H}/k_{2,D} = 6\cdot4 \pm 0\cdot3$) in accordance with theory.

Unfortunately, only the constant k_1 and the ratio k_2/k_{-1} can be calculated, but not the values of k_2 and k_{-1} separately. However, it could be shown that the rate of protolysis (k_2) is very great, though it cannot yet be stated whether it is smaller than usual in a reaction which exhibits isotope effects due to neighbouring sulphonic groups, because the negative charge of the $SO_3^\ominus$ residue electrostatically hinders the release of the proton $H^\oplus$.

But it is certain that this factor *alone* is not responsible for the isotope effect. The substantially smaller isotope effect in coupling to 1-naphthol-3-sulphonic acid *(685)* ($k_H/k_D = 3\cdot1$), where (XXII) appears as intermediate, shows that the steric action of the sulphonic group is considerable. The greater steric hindrance between the entering diazo residue and the *peri*-sulphonic group of 2-naphthol-6,8-disulphonic acid [see formula (IV), § 11.2] causes k_{-1} of that reaction to be larger than in the case of the only moderately hindered intermediate (XXII). The significance of the steric relationships in the intermediate becomes apparent also in the effect of the steric requirements of the catalysing base (B) (see § 11.2).

XXII

The kinetic investigations with benzene and naphthalene derivatives described above have experimentally proved with certainty the two-step mechanism of substitution, first mooted by Lapworth and explicitly postulated by Pfeiffer and Wizinger. Melander's nitration without isotope effect, azo coupling with and without isotope effect, Berglund–Larsson's sulphonation characterized by the small influence of tritiation *(227, 228)*, as well as the diarylethylene substitutions of Pfeiffer and Wizinger, are all based on the same mechanism.

Recently, Kresge and Chan *(2416)* demonstrated that the most fundamental of electrophilic substitutions, the hydrogen isotope exchange, proceeds by the same two-step mechanism: the rate of substituting tritium by protium is proportional to the concentration of $H_3O^\oplus$ for relatively basic aromatic compounds like 1,3,5-trimethoxybenzene. In contrast to these results, Gold and Satchell *(2418–2421)* some years ago described an H_0 dependence of the hydrogen isotope exchange reaction in benzene and proposed a three-step mechanism with two intermediates. Further investigations are necessary to explain the causes of these results, but Melander (*2417*) has discussed the possible reasons for the change in the relation to acidity from an H_0 to an $H_3O^{\oplus}$ dependence.

The benzene and naphthalene reactions are distinguished from those of the diarylethylenes by the lower stability of the intermediate. The addition product of the electrophilic reagent with the diarylethylene, which can be isolated, is incomparably more stable because it is a *carbonium ion stabilized by mesomerism*. Its tendency to lose a proton is thus lowered, that is, its acidity is less or, expressed the other way round, the basic nature of the diarylethylenes is much greater than that of the aromatic compounds, as demonstrated by Gold *et al.* (*812, 818–820*).

The intermediate of benzene substitution no longer possesses the aromatic character of the starting material, energetically a great disadvantage. Two of the six original π-electrons, which provided the stability of the aromatic system, have been claimed for the bond to the electrophilic reagent. The intermediate is thus more unstable, that is, its energy content is higher.

In the sense of classic chemistry, which was concerned more with isolation and proof by chemical reaction, the intermediate must be described as a very unstable particle, but, according to the exact, thermodynamic definition it is stable, because it corresponds to an energy *minimum*. It is therefore an actual intermediate and not merely a transition state. This must be stressed, for in some papers, even recent ones, the intermediate is described as a transition state. Lately a series of researches has been carried out using various methods, all leading to the conclusion that the intermediate of substitution is indeed a stable particle. A detailed discussion would be out of place here, but references to some relevant physicochemical work (*341, 342, 346–348, 409, 410, 815–817, 1407, 2235*) and to attack by the methods of quantum chemistry (*207, 1478*) may be given.

From the preparative side support for the reality of the intermediate comes from the intramolecular coupling reaction (10.16), investigated by Stiles and Sisti (*1956*). On treating the amine (XXIII) with nitrous acid the azo compound (XXV) is formed, apart from a product which results via the carbonium ion and so is not of interest here. That (XXV) is obtained becomes comprehensible if it is assumed that intramolecular coupling gives the intermediate (XXIV). By working at low temperatures, Olah and co-workers (*2422–2424*) were able to isolate the corresponding intermediates of some electrophilic substitutions of the Friedel-Crafts type.

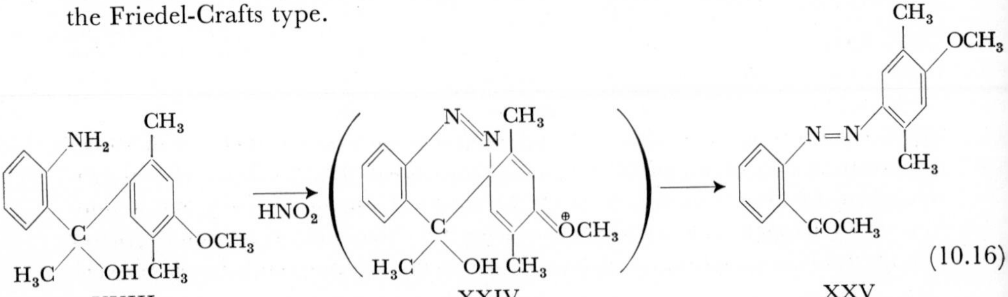

(10.16)

10.5 Substitution in the Wider Sense and the Reversal
of the Coupling Reaction

By substitution in the wider sense is understood the replacement of residues other than hydrogen by means of electrophilic reagents. The mechanism of the substitution proper described in the previous section makes it easy to forecast which groups are particularly suitable for such an exchange with diazonium ions. In substitution in the narrow sense hydrogen is released as a proton, that is, as a Lewis acid, the pair of σ-electrons being left behind with the aromatic substrate. All substituents which readily form such electrophilic particles can therefore be smoothly replaced by electrophilic reagents, in the present case, the diazonium ion. A sulphonic group, $SO_3^\ominus$, is eliminated as sulphur trioxide, a carboxy group, $COO^\ominus$ or COOH, as carbon dioxide. Many such reactions have been encountered and exploited technically (*359, 394, 645, 1530, 2048, 2510–2512, 2518, 2540, 2542*). *p*-Hydroxybenzoic acid even couples more readily in the *p*-position with liberation of carbon dioxide than in the *o*-position (*860*). A whole series of examples of the replacement of the halogen atoms of phenols by diazo residues is recorded in the literature (*1776p*). As here the strongly electrophilic halogen cations may perhaps be formed primarily, several of these papers are of more general interest. Important is the demonstration by Pollak and Gebauer-Fülnegg (*1648*) that 1-halogeno-2-naphthols easily give diazoethers, but not always *C*-azo compounds. It is possible that occasionally these diazoethers have been mistaken for azo dyes. The difficulty of eliminating halogen as a cation can be avoided according to Joffe (*1174, 1175*) by reducing it to halide with thiosulphate. In general, alkyl groups cannot be replaced by diazo residues (*716*), but Ziegler and Zigeuner (*2212–2217*) recently showed that methyl groups can be eliminated in certain cases, such as when they are joined to hydroxy or tertiary amino groups either directly, as in CH_2OH, or by means of a system of conjugated double bonds, as, for example, in (XXVI) (*307, 1132, 1457, 1458, 2211*). It must be supposed that the hydroxy group facilitates the substitution by mesomerically stabilizing the alkylcarbonium ion

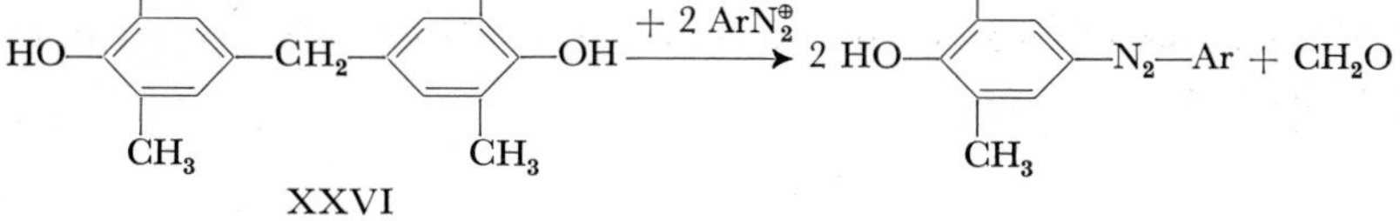

split off. Freeman and Scott (*765*) compared the replacement of methylol groups with that of hydrogen and found that it was more difficult with diazonium ions when in the *p*-position. On the contrary, an *o*-methylol group is more readily exchanged than hydrogen, because it is linked to the phenolic hydroxy group through a hydrogen bond, as had been demonstrated in other work (*1703, 1921*).

Triarylmethane dyes react with diazonium ions in a way similar to that of methylol compounds and on the reaction can be based a method for determining the constitution of these dyes. It was first described by Suais (*1976*) and later briefly mentioned by Green (*865*). F.M.Smith (*1906*) developed the technique with unsulphonated basic and mordant dyes and showed that the course of the reaction is modified both by the proportion of diazo compound used and by the structure of the dye. With one molecular proportion, the diazo compound combines with one aromatic nucleus as if it were free, forming an azo compound with replacement of the aromatic nucleus by a hydroxy group to give a hydrol. A further molecule of diazo compound then attacks the hydrol, yielding another molecule of azo dye and leaving a substance, which on elimination of water produces an aromatic aldehyde. If in the aldehyde a substituent is present in the *p*-position which normally causes coupling, a third molecule of diazo compound displaces the aldehyde group, the latter probably giving rise to formic acid. Side reactions do occur, for instance, if the original triarylmethane bears dialkylamino residues, *N*-methyl groups may be converted into formaldehyde, *p*-nitrodiazobenzene giving nitrobenzene in the process, and *N*-ethyl groups may lead to acetaldehyde.

The reaction of bilirubin (**XXVII**) with diazo compounds is analogous to reaction (10.17), involving coupling twice together with the replacement of a methylene or methylol group (*727, 1562*). The carbinol (**XXIX**), obtained as a fission product from the first step, is attacked by a second equivalent of diazonium ions to yield another molecule of azobilirubin (**XXVIII**).

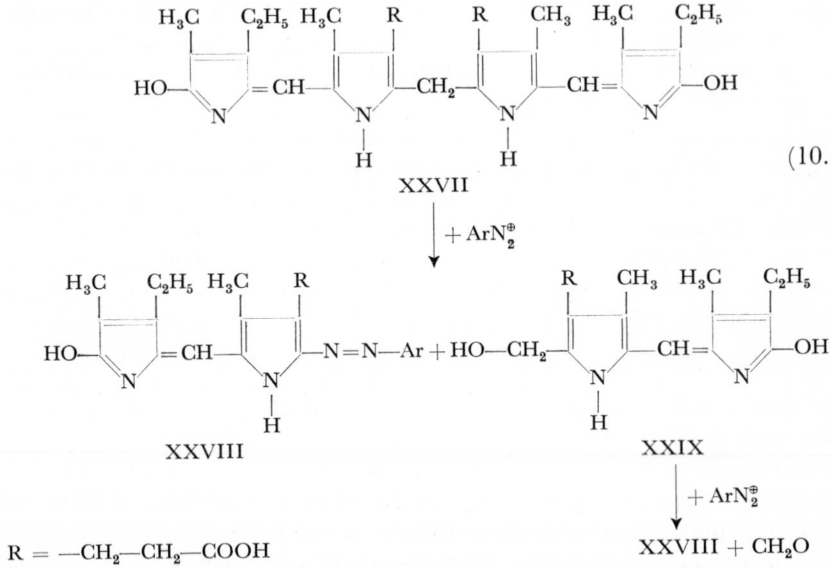

$$(10.18)$$

$$R = -CH_2-CH_2-COOH$$

The replacement of an arylazo group of an azo dye by another diazo residue was first achieved by Nölting and Grandmougin (*1538*) on bringing together 4-phenylazo-1-naphthol and 4-diazobenzenesulphonic acid (10.19).

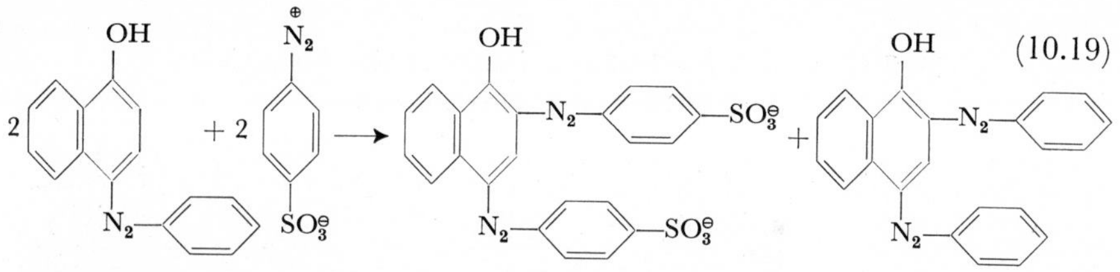

(10.19)

Filippytschew and Tschekalin (718) also studied the substitution of an aryl-azo group by diazonium ions and found that the reaction occurs more easily as the reactivity of the incoming component increases. This would be expected on the basis of the stepwise mechanism of coupling and its reversal, which has ousted earlier interpretations. The reaction thus proceeds via the metastable compound (XXX), which corresponds to the intermediate of the coupling process according to equation (10.14a–b).

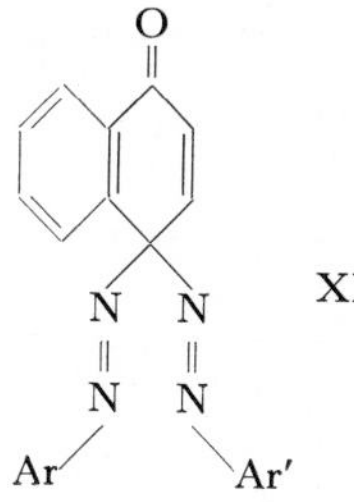

XXX

That diazo exchange reactions of this type have been observed only so rarely is rather surprising, as the diazo residue is a group readily eliminated as an electrophilic diazonium ion. This applies also to the *reversal of the coupling reaction*. Stamm and Zollinger (1927) recently showed that the acid catalysed re-arrangement of 4-arylazo-1-naphthol-3-sulphonic acid into the 2-isomer con-sists in the first place of the addition of a proton and splitting off of the diazo-nium ion, that is, of a reversal of coupling. Older observations (1745, 1821) can probably be interpreted similarly.

Whether the fission of hydroxyazo and aminoazo compounds by means of oxidizing heavy metal oxides (PbO_2, CrO_3) in the presence of mineral acid also uses reversal of coupling as the first step cannot be decided on the evidence available (1301, 1408).

That the reversal of coupling does not take place more smoothly in spite of the helpful nature of the electrophilic group to be eliminated is probably due to the fact that the acid medium immediately alters the equilibrium of the reactive phenolate in the case of hydroxyazo compounds and the free amine in the case of aminoazo bodies in favour of the corresponding acids. In consequence, *p*-hydroxyazo dyes being stronger acids are more readily split protolytically than their *o*-isomers, which are stabilized through hydrogen bonds.

According to Huisgen (1111, 1113, 1117, 1121, 1122), the displacement of the arylazo by a nitroso group is the cause of the decolorization of a solution of phenylazo-2-naphthol in glacial acetic acid on addition of sodium nitrite.

16 Zollinger

10.6 Quantitative Comparisons of the Reactivity
of Different Components

From the determinations of the rate constants of coupling reactions, it becomes possible to obtain quantitative assessments of the electrophilic reactivity of diazonium ions and of the nucleophilic reactivity of aromatic amines and phenols. Comparisons then give the effects of substituents on reactivity.

Already Conant and Peterson (*459*) tried to correlate the reactivity of various combinations with the structures of the components. As the rate constants depend on the acidity of the medium, they chose to carry out their comparisons at a pH such that $\log k_s$ of equation (10.1) has the value 1. This method does not always lead to correct results and the use of the effective rate constant k of equations (10.6) and (10.7) is an improvement.

The influence of substituents on the reactivity of the benzenediazonium ion can be described quantitatively with the help of Hammett's equation (10.20) (*913, 914c, 1160*). By means of this equation have been evaluated a large num-

$$\log k - \log k_0 = \varrho\,\sigma \tag{10.20}$$

ber of reactions and equilibria involving one group attached to a benzene ring as regards the dependence on further substituents present in the *m*- or *p*-position.

In the case of azo coupling, k represents the rate constant for the substituted diazobenzene, k_0 that for diazobenzene and the same coupling component, σ a quantity characteristic for the particular substituent, and ϱ the so-called reaction constant. The last must have the same value for all coupling reactions carried out with the same nucleophilic component (phenol, amine, etc.) under

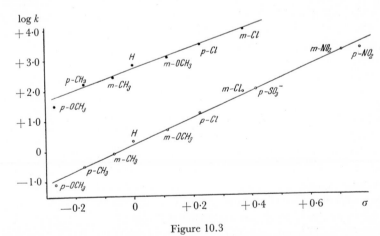

Figure 10.3

The dependence of the rate constants of coupling (k) of substituted benzenediazonium ions with 2-naphthol-6-sulphonic (•) or 2-naphthylamine-6-sulphonic acid (o) on Hammett's substituent constants (σ) (*2231*).

identical conditions, if Hammett's equation is to be recognized as being valid for the process in question.

From determinations carried out with eleven differently substituted diazobenzenes and 2-naphthol- and 2-naphthylamine-6-sulphonic acids, it can be seen that the dependence of the reactivity of these diazo components on the substituents does follow Hammett's equation (Figure 10.3) (2230). Once the validity of Hammett's equation is established for these processes, it becomes possible to calculate the rates of reaction of about 80 in *m*- or *p*-position differently substituted diazobenzenes with these two coupling components. The application of the equation to the selective coupling of aminonaphthols will be discussed in § 11.4.

The reactivity of naphtholsulphonic acids bearing the sulphonic group in various positions has been studied by Pütter (1666) through the rate of coupling to 4-acetamidodiazobenzene-2-sulphonic acid. Table 10.3 records the experimentally determined rate constants of the substitution *proper* according to equation (10.6), together with the acid dissociation constants of the naphthols. So far these results have not yet been evaluated quantitatively. Apart from the steric hindrance evident with the 1,3- and 1,5-derivatives, the great reactivity of the weakly acid 1,2- and 1,8-compounds is striking. Such relatively high pK values are probably due to hydrogen bonding with the *o*- and *peri*-sulphonic groups, respectively. It is possible that these bonds are also responsible for the rapid rates of coupling.

Table 10.3

Relative Rates of Coupling of 4-Acetamidodiazobenzene-2-sulphonic Acid with Isomeric Naphtholsulphonic Acids (1666)

	pK of the naphtholsulphonic acid	Relative rate constant
1-Naphthol-2-sulphonic acid	9·4	1 200
1-Naphthol-3-sulphonic acid	8·5	2
1-Naphthol-4-sulphonic acid	8·2	1
1-Naphthol-5-sulphonic acid	9·0	11
1-Naphthol-8-sulphonic acid	12·6	120 000
2-Naphthol-6-sulphonic acid	9·15	3·2

10.7 The Mechanism of Oxidative Coupling

Oxidative coupling by Hünig's method (1134), the preparative aspects of which were dealt with in § 9.5, exhibits great similarity to classic coupling as regards the nature of the coupling components and the orientation of the products. Hence it may be supposed that here also electrophilic aromatic substitution is occurring. The essential difference in mechanism lies in the formation of the electrophilic component.

A parallel to oxidative coupling exists in the reaction of p-phenylenediamines with aromatic amines and phenols in the presence of oxidizing agents leading to indamine and indophenol dyestuffs according to equations (10.21) and (10.22), respectively. Products of this type have achieved considerable import-

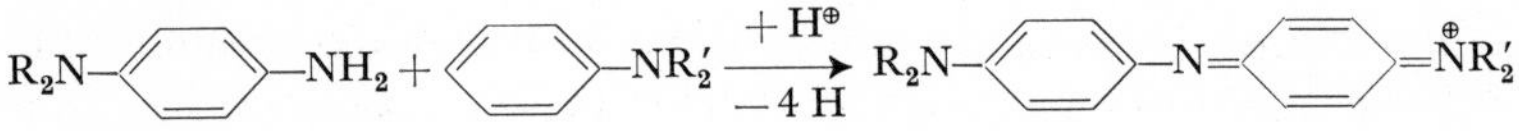

$$R_2N-\!\!\left\langle\;\right\rangle\!\!-NH_2 + \left\langle\;\right\rangle\!\!-NR_2' \xrightarrow[-4\,H]{+H^\oplus} R_2N-\!\!\left\langle\;\right\rangle\!\!-N=\!\!\left\langle\;\right\rangle\!\!=\overset{\oplus}{N}R_2' \quad (10.21)$$

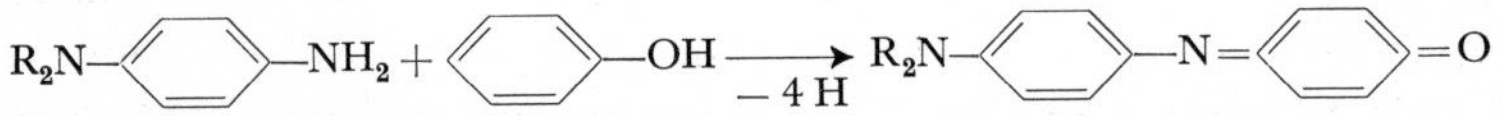

$$R_2N-\!\!\left\langle\;\right\rangle\!\!-NH_2 + \left\langle\;\right\rangle\!\!-OH \xrightarrow[-4\,H]{} R_2N-\!\!\left\langle\;\right\rangle\!\!-N=\!\!\left\langle\;\right\rangle\!\!=O \quad (10.22)$$

ance especially in colour photography and, in consequence, the reaction discovered by Koechlin and Witt (2522) in 1881 has recently been subjected to detailed study. In photographic emulsions the silver halides serve as oxidizing agents for the indamine and indophenol formation and this process is due to R. Fischer (733, 2544).

A series of suggestions has been advanced about the mechanism of the oxidative attack of p-phenylenediamine derivatives on amines and phenols and these have been critically summarized by Vittum and Weissberger (2080). The real basis for a discussion is provided by Michaelis (1442) in his investigations of the redox equilibria of p-phenylenediamine, Wurster's Red, and analogous compounds. According to him, the oxidation of p-phenylenediamines proceeds in two steps (10.23), in each of which one electron is lost. Formed first is a

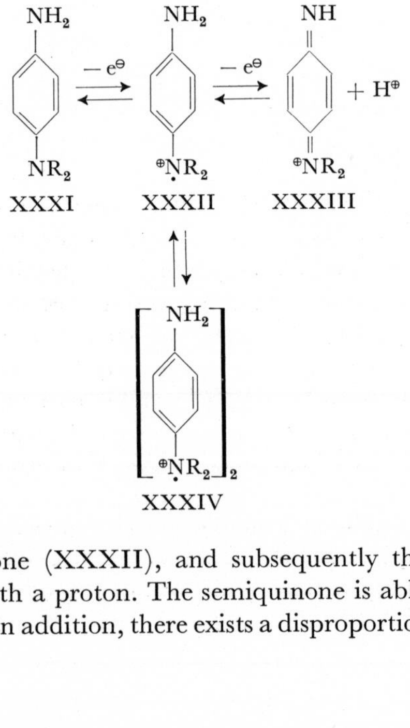

$$
\underset{\substack{|\\NR_2\\ \text{XXXI}}}{\overset{\substack{NH_2\\|}}{\bigcirc}}
\underset{-e^\ominus}{\overset{-e^\ominus}{\rightleftarrows}}
\underset{\substack{\oplus\\ \overset{\cdot}{N}R_2\\ \text{XXXII}}}{\overset{\substack{NH_2\\|}}{\bigcirc}}
\underset{-e^\ominus}{\overset{-e^\ominus}{\rightleftarrows}}
\underset{\substack{\oplus\\ \overset{\cdot}{N}R_2\\ \text{XXXIII}}}{\overset{\substack{NH\\||}}{\bigcirc}} + H^\oplus
\qquad (10.23)
$$

$$
\left[\underset{\substack{\oplus\\ \overset{\cdot}{N}R_2}}{\overset{\substack{NH_2\\|}}{\bigcirc}}\right]_2
$$
XXXIV

radical, the semiquinone (XXXII), and subsequently the quinonedi-imine (XXXIII) together with a proton. The semiquinone is able to go over into a dimer (XXXIV) and, in addition, there exists a disproportionation equilibrium with the diamine and the quinonedi-imine: $2 \text{ XXXII} \rightleftarrows \text{XXXI} + \text{XXXIII}$. The understanding of such an interconnected system has been considerably facilitated by the investigation of the half-wave potentials of nuclear substituted *N,N*-dialkyl-*p*-phenylenediamines by Weissberger *et al.* (*224*). It became apparent that the equilibrium system (10.23) is greatly influenced by substitution *ortho* to the dialkylamino group because it hinders the co-planarity and thus the mesomerism between this group and the benzene ring.

Thomas and Weissberger (*2035*), as well as Lyalikoff (*1363*), have proposed mechanism (10.24) for the oxidative combination of *N,N*-dialkyl-*p*-phenylenediamines with aromatic amines. It agrees with all the observations made of this type of reaction. In it the substitution proper (10.24a–b) consists of the interaction of the quinonedi-imine (XXXIII) and the basic form of the coupling component (XXXV, free amine or the anion in the case of phenols and enols) to yield the *leuco*compound of the indamine dye (XXXVII), presumably via

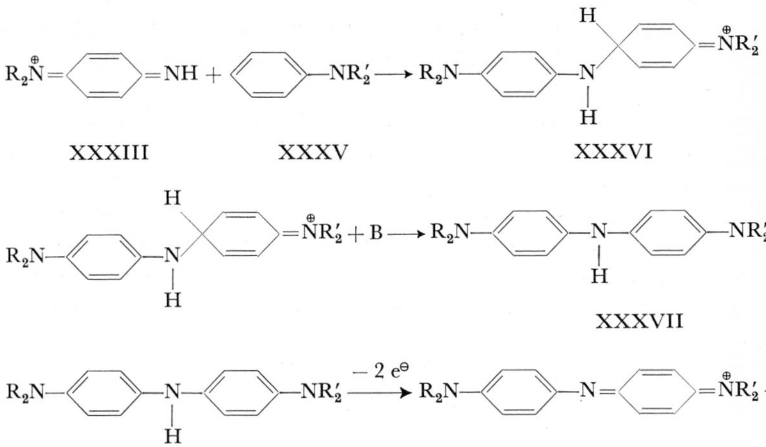

$$R_2\overset{\oplus}{N}=\langle\rangle=NH + \langle\rangle-N R_2' \longrightarrow R_2N-\langle\rangle-\underset{H}{\overset{H}{\underset{|}{N}}}\langle\rangle=\overset{\oplus}{N}R_2' \qquad (10.24\,a)$$

XXXIII XXXV XXXVI

$$R_2N-\langle\rangle-\underset{H}{\overset{H}{\underset{|}{N}}}\langle\rangle=\overset{\oplus}{N}R_2' + B \longrightarrow R_2N-\langle\rangle-\underset{H}{\overset{|}{N}}-\langle\rangle-NR_2' + HB^{\oplus} \qquad (10.24\,b)$$

XXXVII

$$R_2N-\langle\rangle-\underset{H}{\overset{|}{N}}-\langle\rangle-NR_2' \xrightarrow{-2\,e^{\ominus}} R_2N-\langle\rangle-N=\langle\rangle=\overset{\oplus}{N}R_2' + H^{\oplus} \qquad (10.24\,c)$$

XXXVIII

the usual intermediate (XXXVI) of an electrophilic substitution. The oxidation of the *leuco*compound which follows is rapid (10.24c).

This mechanism has been proved to hold kinetically by Eggers (*652, 653*) and also by Tong and Glesman (*2043–2046*). The dependence of the rate of reaction on the acidity of the medium was interpreted in a manner similar to that applied to diazo coupling by Wistar and Bartlett (*2173*) and by Pütter (*1666*): the more nucleophilic, basic form of the coupling component takes part in the substitution. The Brönsted salt effects can be understood only if a cation is the electrophilic component and the kinetics exhibit the same behaviour as was observed in the oxidative deamination of *N,N*-disubstituted *p*-phenylenediamines (*2041, 2042*).

Although the formation of indamines und indophenols does not belong to the reactions of diazo and azo compounds, it has fundamental significance for oxidative azo coupling. The former process is dependent on the constitution of *p*-phenylenediamine, which represents a special case of a compound in which two amino groups are situated at the ends of a conjugated system of double bonds (**XXXIX**). Replacement of one of the methine groups of (**XXXIX**) by

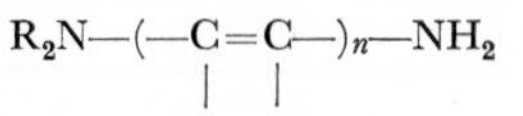

$$R_2N\text{---}(\text{---}C\text{=}C\text{---})_n\text{---}NH_2$$

XXXIX

$$H_3C\text{---}N\overset{}{\underset{}{\bigcirc}}\text{=}N\text{---}NH_2$$

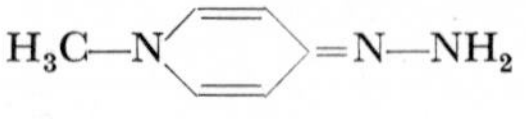

XXXX

nitrogen gives hydrazones of ω-dialkylaminopolyenealdehydes, of which the hydrazone of 1-methyl-4(1)-pyridone (**XXXX**) is an example. This last compound is, of course, one of the heterocyclic hydrazones which Hünig (*1141, 1143*) successfully employed in oxidative coupling. All the other hydrazone components which can be used for this reaction (see § 9.5) can be regarded also as derivatives of (**XXXIX**).

Although to date no unequivocal kinetic determinations have been carried out, a series of experiments indicates that the mechanism here is analogous to that proved to apply to indamine formation. The hydrazone (**XXXXI**) first gives the radical (**XXXXII**) equivalent to the semiquinone and, in the second step (10.25 b), this is converted into the quinonedi-imine-like cation (**XXXXIII**) and a proton. Both states of oxidation are stabilized by mesomerism. Compound (**XXXXIII**) would be expected to act as the electrophilic component since in one of its limiting structures (**XXXXIII**b) the β-nitrogen of the hydrazone group carries only a sextet of electrons. The attack of (**XXXXIII**) on the coupling component takes place by a normal two-stage substitution (10.25 c), the *leuco*compound formed quickly yielding the dye (10.25 d).

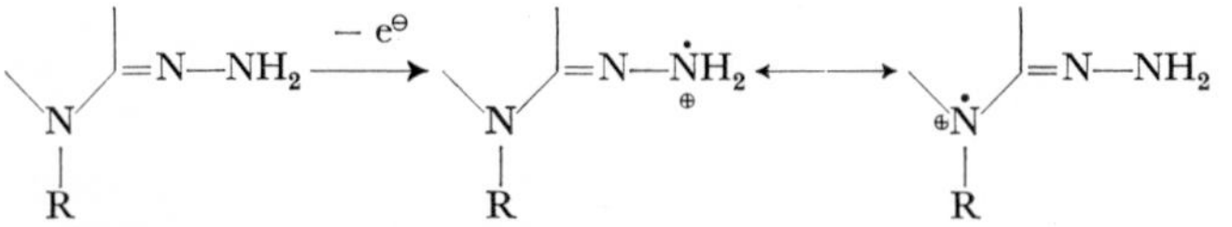

(10.25 a)

XXXXI   XXXXII a   XXXXII b

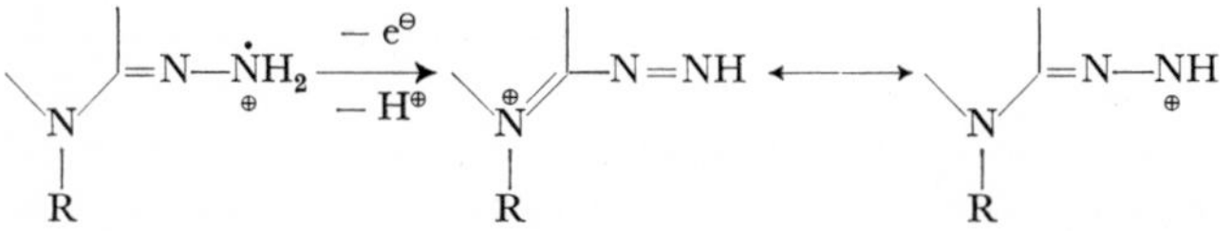

(10.25 b)

XXXXIII a   XXXXIII b

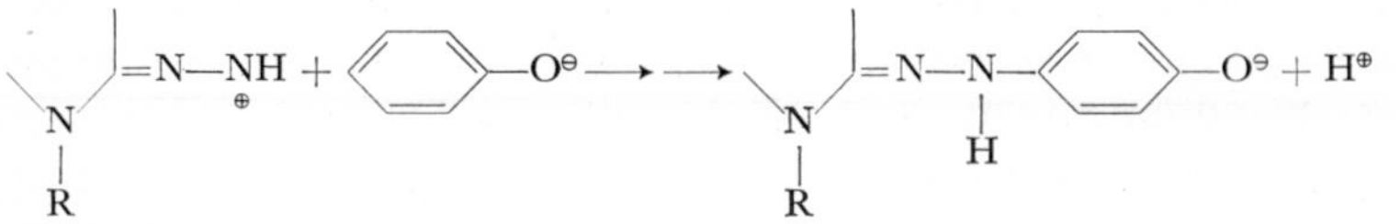

(10.25 c)

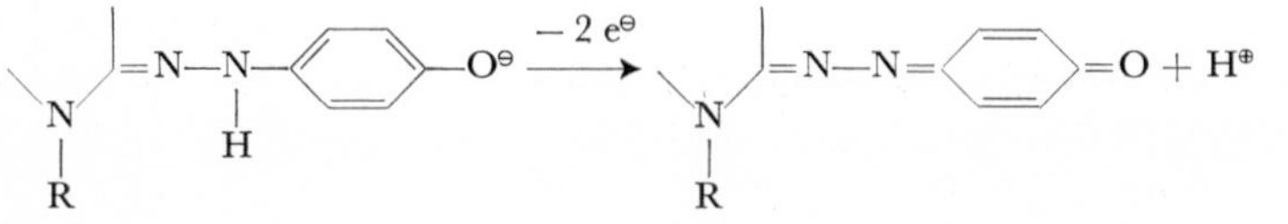

(10.25 d)

The cation (**XXXXIII**) is also produced by reduction of nitrosoimino compounds of the type (**XXXXIV**; 10.26). The reductive coupling of *N*-methyl-2-nitrosoiminobenzothiazoline (**XXXXV**) with dimethylaniline in the presence of zinc dust (10.27) (*1534*) can be understood on this basis. The *leuco*-compound (**XXXXVI**) formed is oxidized to the dye (**XXXXVII**) by air.

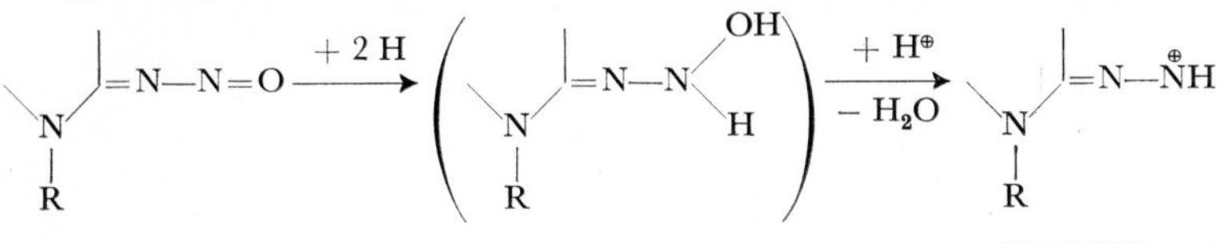

$$\text{XXXXIV} \xrightarrow{+2\text{H}} \left(\text{...}\right) \xrightarrow[-\text{H}_2\text{O}]{+\text{H}^\oplus} \text{XXXXIII} \quad (10.26)$$

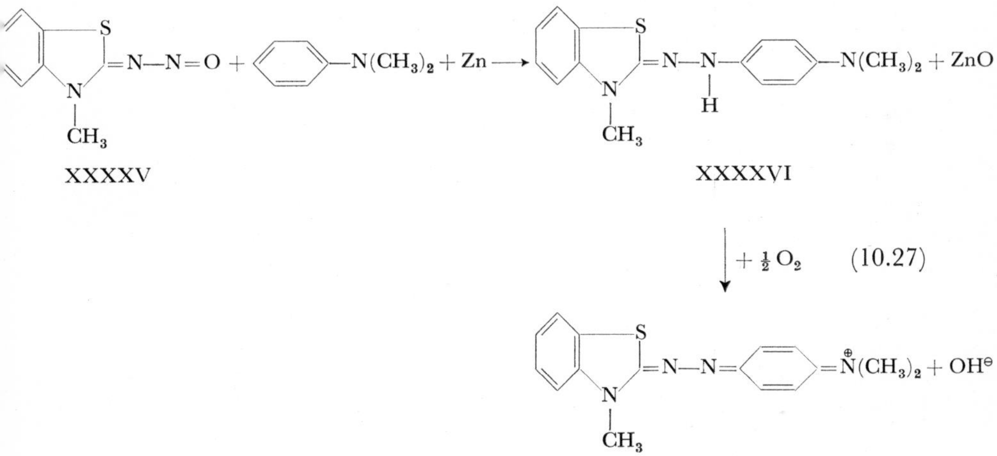

XXXXV $\quad$ XXXXVI

$$\left|\ +\tfrac{1}{2}\text{O}_2 \quad (10.27)\right.$$

XXXXVII

The yield obtained by oxidative coupling usually exhibits a well marked optimum at a particular pH. In coupling to phenols, it lies at about pH 9 (*1141, 1143*), in coupling to amines, at pH 2 to 5 (*1535*). The drop in yield at lower pH values is due to the preliminary equilibrium of the coupling component, but on the alkaline side the cause is probably to be found in the competing reaction of the quinonedi-imine-like intermediate (**XXXXIII**) with hydroxyl ions. That this is so is suggested by the parallel between the optimum pH for coupling and the acid dissociation constant of some hydrazones, the reaction of which with dimethylaniline has been investigated by Noether (*1535*) (Table 10.4). The optimum yield of weakly basic hydrazones occurs at higher pH values because their lower acidity allows the side reaction with hydroxyl ions to assert itself only at greater hydroxyl ion concentrations. The mechanism of this side reaction has not been examined more closely, but similar relationships between yield and the pH of the medium have been observed by Hünig and Daum (*1137*) in the formation of indamines.

Table 10.4

pK$_a$ Values of Hydrazones and the Region of pH for Optimum Yield in Oxidative Coupling to Dimethylaniline (1535)

	pK$_a$	pH
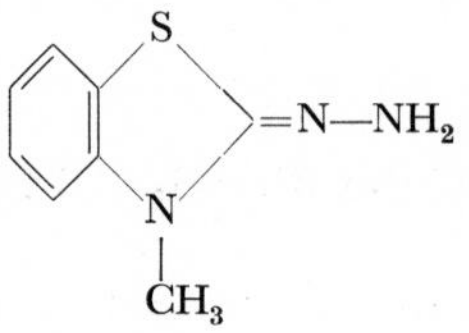	5·7	1·8
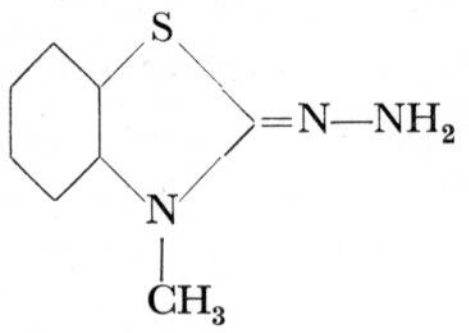	7·8	3·0
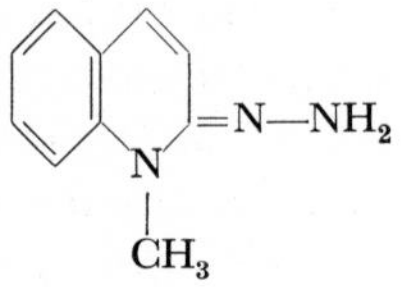	8·8	3·9
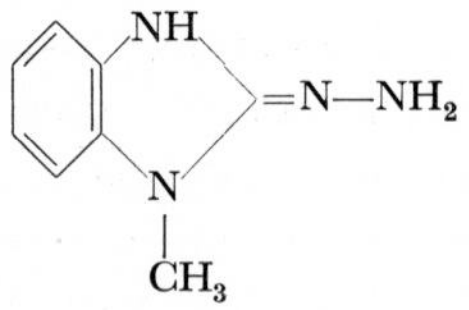	9·0[3]	3·9

---

[3] Estimated

11. Applications of the Theory of Coupling to the Technology of Azo Dyestuffs

11.1 The Role of the Reaction Rate

One of the most fundamental problems in technology is to increase reaction rates. Surprisingly, the case which immediately comes to mind, namely, that of a reaction which takes hours or days to complete and needs to be performed more quickly for the sake of economy, is not so important. On the other hand, there are very many instances in which it is necessary to speed up processes which exhibit times of half reaction under works conditions of only a few minutes or even seconds.

Under certain circumstances an *increase in yield* follows, since the yield of any reaction is determined by two factors: firstly, by the losses during separation and purification (extraction, salting out, filtration, etc.), and secondly, by the relationship of the rate of the main reaction to the sum of the undesirable side reactions. Technological processes almost always consist of a so-called system of *competitive reactions*. In the simplest case, when each of the competitive reactions is of the same order with respect to all the reactants present in not too great an excess, the yield is related to the rate constants by equation (11.1), as long as the losses mentioned above are left out of consideration. Increasing the rate of the main reaction without accelerating the side reactions must then always lead to greater yields. If the main and side reactions are not of the same order, this

$$\text{Yield in } \% = \frac{100 \, k_\mu}{k_\mu + \underset{\sigma}{\Sigma} k_\sigma} \tag{11.1}$$

k_μ = rate constant of the main reaction
k_σ = rate constant of the side reactions

statement is still valid in principle, though the mathematical relationship becomes much more complicated than equation (11.1).

Now comes the question of how such a specific influence over the main reaction is to be achieved. Limits are usually set to increasing the stoichiometric concentrations of the starting materials by solubility and other factors, but one aspect, often decisive for the most important reaction medium, water, is frequently given insufficient attention: the exploitation of the equilibria which precede the substitution proper.

In the previous chapter these acid–base equilibria, which are so fundamental for the kinetics of azo coupling, were discussed in detail. From these considerations can be drawn a simple conclusion of the greatest practical significance for azo technology: *coupling reactions should be carried out in a medium such that the equi-libria of the diazo and coupling components favour as much as possible the diazonium ions and the phenolate ions or the free amine, respectively* [see equation (3.9) and equations (10.3) and (10.4)].

If, for example, a simple diazobenzene derivative is coupled to a naphthol-sulphonic acid, the hydroxy group of which possesses a pK of 9·0, it can be predicted with certainty that in the pH range below 8 an increase in alkalinity by one pH unit will increase the rate tenfold. However, above pH 10 the rate of coupling will be independent of the hydroxyl ion concentration as far as the naphthol–naphtholate equilibrium goes, but coupling in too alkaline a solution is not recommended because the diazo equilibrium fails to remain on the side of the diazonium ions. In consequence, there exists for each combination an *optimum pH region for coupling*, which is limited by the acidities, expressed in pH units, which correspond to the pK value of the coupling component and the constants of the diazo equilibria, respectively.

Increasing the temperature usually does not have a favourable effect, as the diazo decomposition reactions possess greater energies of activation and hence a larger temperature gradient than azo coupling. According to Crossley *et al.* (*496*), the energy of activation of the former is 22·8 to 33·2 kcal/mole, whereas Conant and Peterson (*459*) determined that of several azo coupling reactions to be 14·2 to 17·2 kcal/mole. It follows that for every 10° rise in temperature, the rate of coupling increases 2·0 to 2·4 times, whereas that of the decomposi-tions rises 3·1 to 5·3 times.

In some technological azo coupling reactions, sodium chloride is added *before* the reaction takes place. This is not immediately comprehensible, because neither sodium nor chloride ions are required in the actual reaction and salt has no buffering action. If it is merely a question of salting out the product, then it should be equally effective to add salt *after* completion of the reaction, as usual. In fact, the addition causes an increase in yield and the reason has been traced in a model experiment (*2236*) to lie in the differences in the dependence of the rates of coupling and of decomposition on ionic strength (Brönsted salt effects).

11.2 Catalysis by Pyridine

A series of technological azo coupling reactions, especially in the manufacture of polyazo dyestuffs, can be carried out satisfactorily only in the presence of pyridine or of one of its homologues, such as 5-ethyl-2-methylpyridine (*2594*). This applies in particular to the coupling of diazotized aminoazo and aminodis-azo compounds containing a 2-alkoxy-1-naphthylamine-6-sulphonic acid as end component. A typical example built up in this manner is the dye Benzo Fast Blue 8 GL (IG, I). Another group of dyes, prepared by a pyridine-catalysed reaction, consists of the disazo compounds obtained from tetrazotized 3,3′-di-hydroxybenzidine, Coprantine Violet BLL (Ciba, II) being representative. In the absence of pyridine, decomposition occurs preferentially.

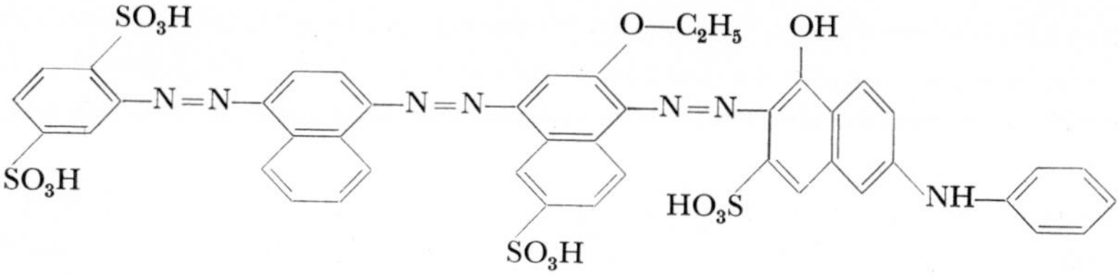

I

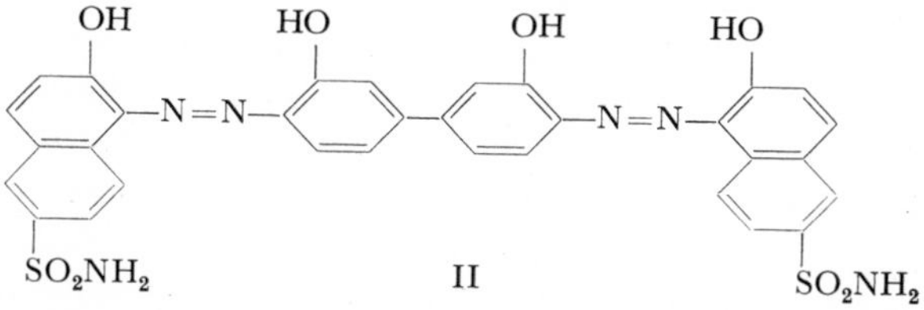

II

It has been claimed that the action of the pyridine bases can also be achieved through other additives. As far as its chemical influence goes, quinoline (*1004*) must be classed as a pyridine derivative, but catalysis with acetone (*2501*), employed by Imperial Chemical Industries Ltd for a time in place of pyridine, can hardly depend on the same mechanism. This must also apply to the more recently used sulphonic acids of xylene and other aromatic compounds (*2581*), as well as to derivatives of formamide (*2563, 2564*).

Hodgson and Marsden (*1052*) thought that the action of pyridine could be attributed to a stabilization of the diazo compound in alkaline solution through the formation of a diazopyridinium ion (III) (*729–731, 1467, 1776q, 2077a*). This experimentally unsupported supposition has since been made untenable by the work of Pütter (*1666*) and of Zollinger (*2232*).

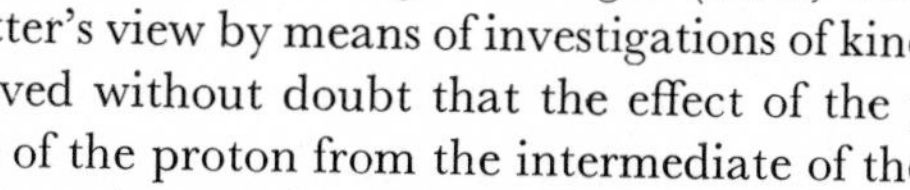

$$\text{(pyridine)} + Ar-N_2^{\oplus} \rightleftharpoons Ar-N=N-\overset{\oplus}{N}\text{(pyridinium)} \tag{11.2}$$

III

The interpretation of this catalytic action advanced by Pütter (*1666*) on the basis of unequivocal, kinetic evidence is able to explain all the phenomena observed in practice. Some years ago Zollinger (*2232, 2234*) complemented and confirmed Pütter's view by means of investigations of kinetic isotope effects.

It has been proved without doubt that the effect of the pyridine is due to catalysing the loss of the proton from the intermediate of the substitution proper, the base acting as the proton acceptor B in the second step of the reaction system (10.14a–b) of § 10.4. From the kinetic equation (10.15), there fully discussed, it follows that an alteration in the concentration of B can only affect the kinetics of the total process if the ratio k_2/k_{-1} has a low value. This happens when the back-reaction to the first step (k_{-1}) is fast compared with the protolysis of the intermediate (k_2). This condition is fulfilled when the presence of voluminous substituents *ortho* or *peri* to the position of coupling favours the splitting off of the diazonium ion from the intermediate.

The practical conclusion can be drawn that in principle the addition of pyridine should be tried in the case of reactions with coupling components in which substitution occurs in the immediate vicinity of sulphonic and other groups composed of several atoms.

Kinetic determinations on the coupling of *p*-nitrodiazobenzene to *N*,*N*-diethylaniline were made by Kozlov and Stepanov (*1270*) in the presence of increasing amounts of pyridine or quinoline and the results show these two proton acceptors to behave almost identically.

It was shown (*2234*) for substituted pyridines that their catalytic effect was directly proportional to their basic dissociation constant. General base catalysis in Brönsted's nomenclature (*220*) is therefore occurring. In consequence, 2- and 3-picoline are more active catalysts than pyridine. However, the behaviour exhibited by α-substituted pyridines diverges, as they increase the rate of coupling less than expected from their basic strength. The cause is to be found in steric hindrance of the proton transfer from the naphthalene nucleus to the heterocyclic nitrogen atom, the transition state of such a protolysis being illustrated by (IV). The catalysis of azo coupling by α-substituted pyridines is one of the relatively rare cases of steric hindrance of a protolysis.

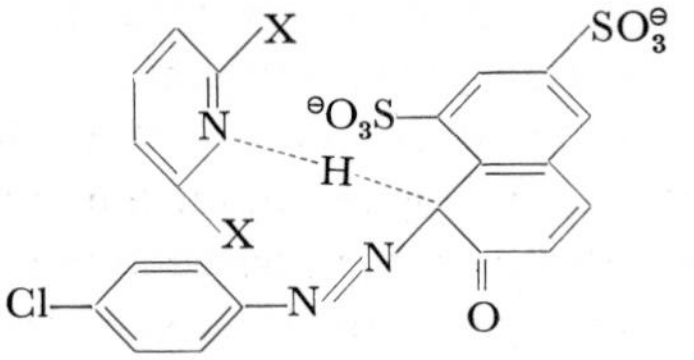

IV

The experiments demonstrate that the outstanding suitability of the pyridine molecule as proton acceptor is due to steric factors. Unlike in tertiary aliphatic amines, the basic centre here, namely, the free pair of electrons of the nitrogen, is relatively easily accessible. A position intermediate between pyridine and the aliphatic tertiary amines is taken by quinuclidine (V), models of which readily show that its nitrogen is less protected by the methylene chains.

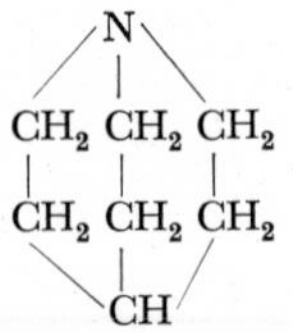

V

The question of in which range of pH the *hydroxyl ion* can act as base for the protolysis of the substitution proper has been investigated experimentally for two coupling reactions with 2-naphthol-6,8-disulphonic acid (*2178*). When simple diazobenzene derivatives are used as electrophilic components, the rate constant *k* becomes proportional to the hydroxyl ion concentration only above pH 11. The indication is that below this region the proton acceptor is a particle the concentration of which is independent of pH, probably the H_2O molecule, but in strongly alkaline solution the hydroxyl ion does take over.

11.3 The *o/p* Ratio in Azo Coupling

In principle, coupling components, in which the position *ortho* as well as that *para* to the directing substituent (OH, NH_2) is free, can be attacked at both by diazo compounds. The technologically most important representatives of such components are 1-naphthylamine and also 1-naphthol and its sulphonic acids. Special mention must be made of the derivatives of 1-naphthol-3-sulphonic acid, such as H (1-amino-8-naphthol-3,6-disulphonic acid), J, and γ acid (2,5,7- and 2,8,6-aminonaphtholsulphonic acid, respectively). Their importance in the synthesis of innumerable acid mono- and dis-azo dyes as well as substantive dis- and poly-azo dyes can hardly be overestimated. In 'alkaline coupling', it matters greatly whether the azo group enters in the *o*- or *p*-position to the hydroxy residue, as in the *o*-derivatives an intramolecular hydrogen bond is formed. In hydroxyazo dyes, removal of the phenolic proton always leads to a change in colour, that is, indicator-like behaviour, but the presence of a hydrogen bond shifts the protolytic equilibrium into a region of pH (> 11), which in practice is not reached by textiles dyed with these compounds. However, the hue of the isomeric *p*-hydroxyazo dyes alters even in weakly alkaline solution, the pK of the hydroxy group being 7 to 9 (see § 13.3). This constitutes a serious disadvantage from the point of view of the demands made on dyed materials in use, e. g. by washing with soap. Also, *p*-hydroxyazo compounds are unable to form stable complexes with metals.

The problem of the *o/p* ratio is therefore technically important in the sense of having to recognize and exploit those factors which either favour reaction in the *o*-position or hinder *p*-coupling.

Phenol is the simplest example of a coupling component which is capable of substitution in the *o*- or *p*-position and Bamberger (*166*) already investigated the ratio of *o/p*-coupling. The separation of the two isomers is relatively easy, since *o*-arylazophenols unlike the *p*-compounds are volatile in steam, as long as substituents making them soluble in water are absent. This is one of the consequences of the lowered solvation of the hydroxy group brought about by the hydrogen bond to the β-nitrogen atom. Bamberger found that in aqueous alkaline medium the *p*-dye is the main product, being formed in about 98% yield and accompanied by 1% each of the *o*-isomer and the *o,p*-disazo compound. It has been shown repeatedly [cf. (*861*)] that under the appropriate conditions the 2,4-disazo and the 2,4,6-trisazo dyes can readily be obtained.

Of greater interest and import is the behaviour of 1-naphthol and certain of its sulphonic acids, the *o/p*-ratio here being dependent on several factors:

1. The nature of the diazo component
2. The nature of the solvent
3. The hydrogen ion concentration of the medium
4. The temperature of coupling
5. The presence of catalysts
6. The position of substituents.

1-Naphthol itself couples to simple diazobenzenes preferentially at its 4-position, but Bamberger (157, 178) found that the yield of o-isomer can be increased to 22% in the case of p-nitrodiazobenzene on working in 85% alcohol in the presence of sodium acetate and to 90% in benzene solution. Technically important is the observation, briefly mentioned by Fierz-David and Brütsch (354, 710), that 1-naphthol couples to simple derivatives of diazobenzene, free from hydroxy groups, in acid and weakly alkaline solution almost exclusively in the p-position with only about 1% o-reaction, but that in strongly alkaline media considerable quantities of the 2,4-disazo dye are formed.

The ratio between the isomers obtained in coupling with 1,3- and 1,5-naphtholsulphonic acids was studied in detail by Gattermann et al. (782, 783), who showed that it is dependent on the reactivity of the diazo component. Energetic ones, such as 2,4-dinitrodiazobenzene, couple with 1-naphthol-3-sulphonic acid practically only in the p-position, but p-chlorodiazobenzene and still weaker diazo compounds attack the o-position. Both isomers result when mononitrodiazobenzenes are used. The tendency to couple *para* is greater in 1-naphthol-5-sulphonic acid.

However, the ratio between the isomers is dependent not only on the nature of the diazo component, but also on the reaction conditions, as demonstrated by Stamm and Zollinger (1926, 1927) for the combination o-nitrodiazobenzene and 1-naphthol-3-sulphonic acid. In an acetate buffer at pH 4·58 and 10°, a mixture is formed consisting of 76·2% o- and 23·8% p-dye, equivalent to an o/p-ratio of 3·20. At higher temperatures the proportion of o-isomer increases,

Table 11.1

Dependence on the Buffer Concentration of the o/p-*Ratio in Coupling* o-*Nitrodiazobenzene to 1-Naphthol-3-sulphonic Acid (1926, 1927)*

Expt No.	Buffer system[1]	pH	o/p-Ratio	$k_o \times 10^5$ (l. mole^{-1} sec^{-1})	$k_p \times 10^5$ (l. mole^{-1} sec^{-1})
1	0·05 M NaOAc / 0·05 M AcOH	4·59	14·2	2·9	0·21
2	0·17 M NaOAc / 0·17 M AcOH	4·61	9·65	3·6	0·37
3	0·50 M NaOAc / 0·50 M AcOH	4·64	4·35	4·4	1·04
4	0·50 M NaOAc / 0·05 M AcOH	5·60	4·56	4·2	0·88

[1] Ionic strength brought to 0·5 by appropriate addition of potassium chloride.

the o/p-ratio becoming 4·35 at 20° and 7·55 at 30°. More remarkable still is the dependence on the medium, there being evidence not only of the direct influence of the hydrogen or hydroxyl ion concentration, but also of an apparently inexplicable, specific effect of the nature and concentration of the buffer used. Experiments 1, 2, and 3 of Table 11.1 show that a tenfold increase in the concentration of acetate ions produces five times more of the p-, but only 1·5 times more of the o-compound. Experiment 4 proves that the relationship between the isomers is a function of general base catalysis, in this case by the acetate ion, and not of the hydroxyl ion concentration.

Investigation of the causes of the differences in the action of bases on o- and p-coupling leads to the result that, apart from an inductive effect, the steric conditions are again decisive. The intermediate formed in the p-substitution is sterically more strained and so the proton acceptor finds greater difficulty in attacking it. 'Good' bases, such as pyridine, therefore favour p-coupling and should be avoided if possible but, fortunately, the behaviour of proton acceptors varies widely and there are bases which increase the o/p-ratio. In order to obtain more o-hydroxyazo dye, it is in general advantageous to employ low concentrations of base, as illustrated by experiments 1 to 3 of Table 11.1.

In this work a problem arose with regard to the mechanism which should be discussed briefly. If the rate constants of Table 11.1 are extrapolated to zero concentration of acetate ions, that part of the reaction is obtained which is catalysed by other bases. Above all, this embraces the effect due to the water molecule as proton acceptor and it is found that this part is much larger in the case of o-coupling than in the p-reaction. As the direct transfer of a proton from carbon to the naphtholate oxygen is hardly likely because of the distance involved, the explanation for the much greater effectiveness of water in the o-substitution is probably to be found in a concerted mechanism, in which a water molecule solvated by the naphtholate oxygen accepts the proton from the 2-position and in exchange gives up one of its own protons to the naphtholate group. For an equivalent proton transfer from the 4-position a long chain of water molecules would be necessary, a condition most unlikely to be fulfilled. The cyclic mechanism is supported by determinations of the entropies of activation of o- and p-coupling ($\Delta S_o^{\ddagger} - \Delta S_p^{\ddagger} = 28$ cal mole^{-1} deg.$^{-1}$) and by solvent effects. The transition state for an o-phenolate coupling is best represented by formula (VI).

VI

The significance of the neighbouring phenolate oxygen in the protolysis was first discussed by Pütter (1666), and a further, small amount of data on in-

fluencing the o/p-ratio can be gleaned from the literature (*705, 710, 1460, 1650, 1755*).

Coupling with diazophenols appears to contradict this explanation of how the o/p-ratio is altered. These components attack 1-naphthol in weakly alkaline solution preponderantly in the p-position but, as the hydroxyl ion concentration is increased, formation of the o-isomer is favoured and frequently it can become almost the sole product (*2560*). The so-called 1,2,4 acid (1-amino-2-naphthol-4-sulphonic acid) on diazotization and coupling to 1-naphthol yields the important Eriochrome Black A (Gy, VIIA), which according to Fierz-David (*705, 710*) is a mixture of o- and p-isomers. The corresponding diazo component with a 6-nitro substituent gives Eriochrome Black T (Gy, VIIB), which is supposed to consist almost exclusively of the o-compound.

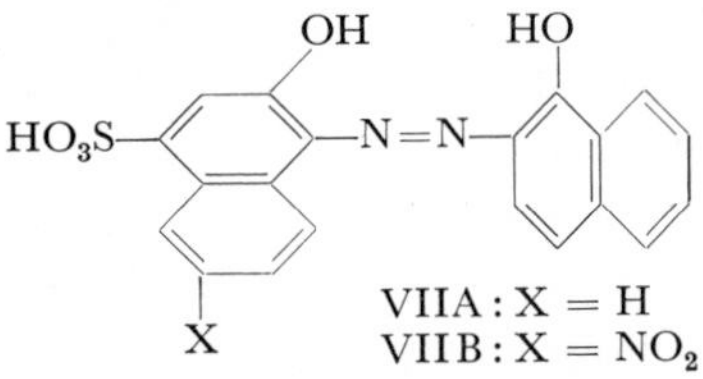

VIIA : X = H
VIIB : X = NO$_2$

1,5-Dihydroxynaphthalene behaves similarly, simple diazo components attacking mainly in the 4-position, but diazophenols in the 2-position (*731, 2710*). Diazotized 2-aminophenol-4-sulphonic acid couples with it to produce the important mordant dye, Diamond Black PV (FBy).

That 6-nitro-1-diazo-2-naphthol-6-sulphonic acid prefers the 2-position in spite of the nitro group and that increasing alkalinity favours o-coupling with diazophenols is presumably due to the dissociation of the hydroxy group of the diazophenols. In weakly alkaline media the phenoldiazonium cation (VIII), which couples relatively more energetically and attacks the p-position preferentially, is present in a small absolute concentration, but in an amount greater by several powers of ten than at very high pH values. Throughout the region

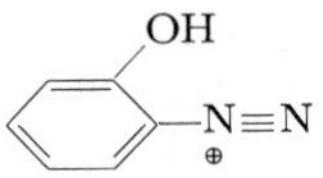

VIII 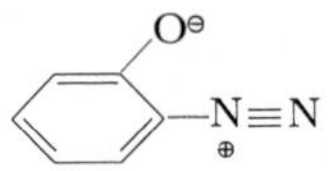   IX

the diazoniumphenolate zwitterion (IX) constitutes more than 99% of the diazo component and so the concentration of this equilibrium form can be regarded as practically constant between about pH 7 and 13. Zwitterion (IX) couples considerably more slowly than the ion (VIII) and it seems possible that at pH 7 to 9 the concentration of the latter is sufficient for a substantial proportion of the total reaction to proceed via this form, thus yielding the p-dye. However, in caustic alkali, this route can be neglected, coupling taking place only with the zwitterion (IX) in the o-position.

The position of the equilibrium (VIII) $\rightleftarrows$ (IX) has been determined for p-diazophenol by E.S. Lewis and Johnson (1331), who found the pK value of the phenolic group to be 3·40 at 25°. The acidity of the o-isomer, which is of more interest here, would be expected to be even greater. Hence this work supports the above interpretation of the o/p-ratio in the coupling of o-diazo-phenols as a consequence of the dissociation of the hydroxy group.

Behaviour in coupling to amino compounds is essentially analogous to that in the case of phenols and naphthols. Turner (2053) has investigated the products of coupling to 1-naphthylamine in acetate buffers at pH 5·6 (see also 2362).

Naphthalene-1-sulphamic acid (2548) (Ar·NH·SO₃H) and l-nitraminonaph-thalene (2556) (Ar·NH·NO₂) couple exclusively in the p-position. Presumably the acidifying residues SO_3H and NO_2 reduce the basic nature of the amino group to such an extent that it can no longer act as a proton acceptor. Hence the solvation of the nitrogen by water and the concerted mechanism discussed above for 1-naphthol and similar compounds (formula VI) recede in importance.

Gattermann (782, 783) described not only coupling to 1,3- and 1,5-naph-tholsulphonic acids, but also that to the corresponding naphthylaminesulphonic acids. The dependence of the o/p-ratio on the substituents in the diazo component proved analogous to that found with the hydroxy compounds, but naphthylamines exhibit a greater tendency to couple in the o-position than the naphthols.

As an appendix to the discussion of the orientation phenomena, the *Mills–Nixon effect* must be mentioned. Mills and Nixon (1450) found that 5-hydroxy-indan (X) couples in the 6- and not the 4-position, as does 6-hydroxy-1,2,3,4-tetrahydronaphthalene (XI), for example. The original explanation through

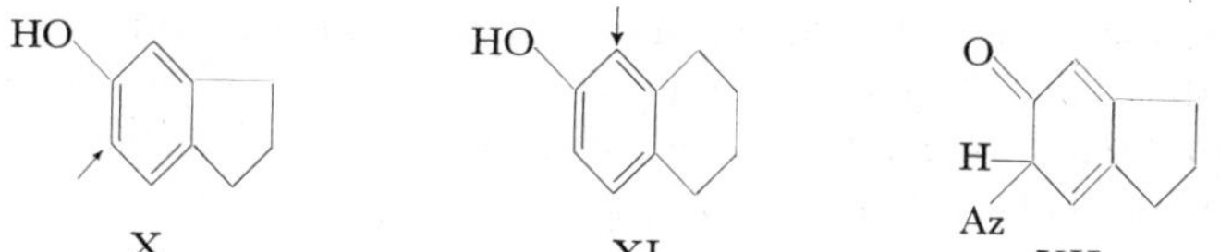

X   XI   XII

$\longrightarrow$ indicates position of coupling

double bond fixation is no longer tenable and, according to recent quantum theoretical calculations (1356), the Mills–Nixon effect depends on the ring strain in the benzene nucleus produced by the presence of the five-membered ring. In consequence the 5,6-link in (X) is stretched, thus approaching the state which exists in the intermediate for coupling in position 6 (XII), but not in that for position 4. The intermediate (XII) is therefore more stable than the isomeric compound with the azo group in the 4-position.

The influence of the medium on the site of coupling in reactions involving resorcinol and m-phenylenediamine will be dealt with in the next section, which is concerned with bifunctional components.

11.4 Kinetics of Coupling with Bifunctional Components

Coupling with reactants which possess two reactive substituents is of great technological importance. On the one hand, there are compounds with two diazo groups, such as tetrazotized benzidine; on the other, there are the bifunctional coupling components, firstly, the various aminonaphtholsulphonic acids, mentioned in § 11.3, and, secondly, compounds such as resorcinol and m-phenylenediamine. With all these components it is possible by correct choice of reaction conditions to conduct the coupling in such a manner as to yield practically homogeneous, monosubstituted products. For the preparation of azo dyes from such compounds there is known a series of rules empirically based on many years' experience. It can be shown that all of them can be derived from the fundamental principles of kinetics.

Conant and Peterson (*459*) observed that in coupling with *resorcinol* the rate increases by *more* than ten times when the pH is raised by one unit and this result was confirmed by the determinations of Elofson *et al.* (*676*). The apparent divergence from behaviour according to rule is readily explained with the help of kinetic equations (10.6) and (10.7), in which the preliminary equilibria of the reactants have been eliminated from the rate constant. Resorcinol is a dibasic acid and in aqueous solution a doubly charged anion ($R^{\ominus\ominus}$) will be present as well as a singly charged one ($RH^{\ominus}$) and the undissociated molecule (RH_2). It is to be expected that the three equilibrium forms of equation (11.3)

$$RH_2 \underset{\longleftarrow}{\overset{+ \ OH^{\ominus}}{\longrightarrow}} RH^{\ominus} \underset{\longleftarrow}{\overset{+ \ OH^{\ominus}}{\longrightarrow}} R^{\ominus\ominus} \qquad (11.3)$$

do not possess identical rates of coupling. The kinetic implication is that *three* reactions occur in parallel, namely, coupling to the ion $RH^{\ominus}$, coupling to the ion $R^{\ominus\ominus}$, and coupling to the undissociated resorcinol molecule RH_2. Assuming that the rate of the last reaction is small enough to be neglected, the kinetic equation (11.4) follows for coupling to resorcinol. From determinations of the

$$\frac{d(Az)}{dt} = [Ar{-}N_2^{\oplus}] \ (k_1 \ [RH^{\ominus}] + k_2 \ [R^{\ominus\ominus}]) \qquad (11.4)$$

total rate at two different hydrogen ion concentrations, the constants k_1 and k_2 can be calculated. In this way it was shown (*2242*) that the doubly charged anion couples roughly 10000 times more rapidly than the singly charged one, which is qualitatively in agreement with expectations based on the electronic theory. The rate of coupling with resorcinol therefore increases more quickly than normally as the pH is raised because greater alkalinity favours the formation of an even more reactive entity.

The site of substitution in the resorcinol nucleus has been investigated by Gore and Venkataraman (*846*), who obtained with one equivalent of diazo component the 4-monoazo compound (**XIII**) apart from about 10% of the 2,4-disazo body. With excess of diazo component in solutions of pH 5 to 8, the second coupling occurs in the 2-position, but in more strongly alkaline media the 4,6-disazo derivative is formed. Gore and Venkataraman attempted to explain this through double bond fixation in the benzene nucleus caused by the hydrogen bond of (XIII).

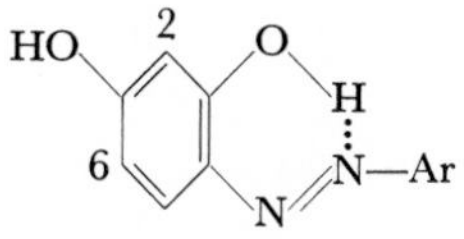

XIII

The case of coupling to *m*-phenylenediamine has been clarified paperchromatographically by Mužík and Allan (*1501, 1502, 2300*) and turns out to be similar to that of resorcinol. In acid solution the 2,4-, in alkali the 4,6-disazo compound (XIV and XV, respectively) is formed preferentially, besides the 4-monoazo and the 2,4,6-trisazo derivative.

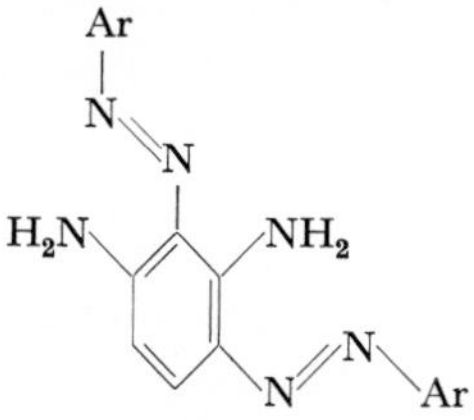

XIV 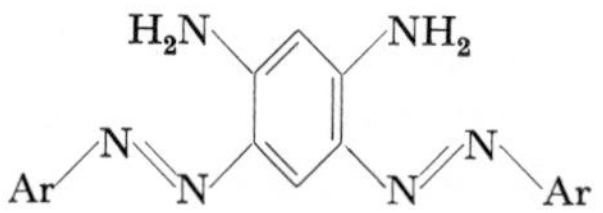   XV

As the opening of the hydrogen bond between the amino and azo groups, which is undoubtedly present in the monoazo dye, is hardly likely, it is difficult to apply Gore and Venkataraman's reasoning here. Since the reaction behaviour of resorcinol is very similar to that of *m*-phenylenediamine and since hypotheses which postulate double bond fixation are always rather risky, it seems that Gore and Venkataraman's explanation for the pH dependence of coupling to resorcinol is incorrect.

From more recent investigations of the reactivity of resorcinol (*1062*) it has become apparent that the 2,4/4,6-ratio is not purely a function of pH, as would be expected from previous work (*846*). At constant pH the ratio between the isomeric disazo dyes can be varied within wide limits by alterations in the buffer, an increase in the concentration of the basic component of the buffer or use of a 'good' base (pyridine) favouring the 4,6-compound. Hence general base catalysis is occurring, probably equivalent to that found in the case of the *o*/*p*-ratio of 1-naphthol derivatives.

The reactions of resorcinol, *m*-phenylenediamine, and aminonaphthols correspond to scheme (11.5). In this, C and D represent the coupling and diazo component, respectively, CD and DC the two isomeric monoazo derivatives,

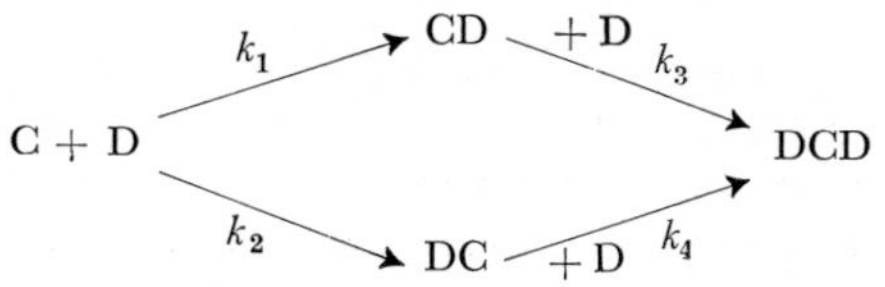

$$(11.5)$$

and DCD the disazo product. It is surprising that this system, so important for the technology of azo dyestuffs, has been fully analysed kinetically not for this purpose, but for a biochemical reaction, the coupling of diazobenzene-*p*-sulphonic acid with histidine (XVI) (*1029*), *1030*). Of general interest is particu-

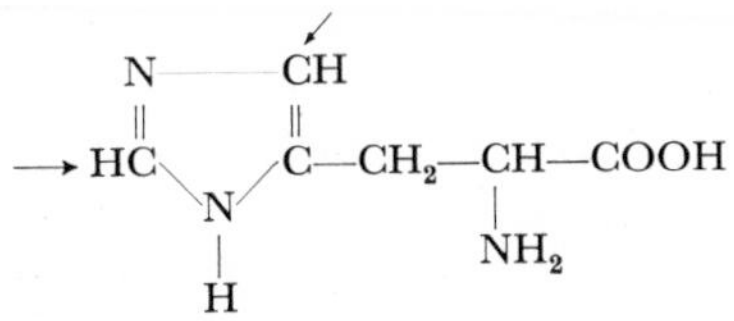

XVI $\longrightarrow$ indicates position of coupling

larly the fact that with this imidazole derivative the second coupling(k_3 or k_4) proceeds 1·4 times more rapidly than the first (k_1 or k_2). In coupling to aromatic compounds the second coupling is always slower. This divergent behaviour may be connected with the acidification of the imidazole nucleus brought about by the presence of the first phenylazo residue, which would be expected to alter the preliminary equilibrium in the direction favourable to coupling.

Kinetic evidence presented by R. D. Brown et al. (*350*) suggests that in the reaction of indazole with 4-diazobenzenesulphonic acid the monoazo derivative formed initially is attacked by another molecule of diazonium compound.

Selective coupling of aminonaphtholsulphonic acids has already been mentioned. In acid solution the reaction takes place in that ring of the naphthalene nucleus which bears the amino group, in alkali the site of coupling is governed by the hydroxy residue.

The cause of selective coupling has been determined unequivocally (*2242*). The basis is provided by the kinetic equation (11.6), which is valid for the total reaction, that is, for both phenol *and* amine coupling of the aminonaphthol.

$$\frac{d(Az_{NH_2} + Az_{OH})}{dt} = [Ar\!-\!N_2^{\oplus}]\,(k_{NH_2}[HORNH_2] + k_{OH}[{}^{\ominus}ORNH_2]) \quad (11.6)$$

In this equation, Az_{NH_2} and Az_{OH} represent the two dyestuffs formed, i.e. aminoazo and hydroxyazo compound, respectively, k_{NH_2} and k_{OH} are the rate constants of the corresponding coupling reactions, and ${}^{\ominus}ORNH_2$ is the phenolate ion derived from the aminonaphthol $HORNH_2$. As the system consists of two simultaneous reactions of the diazonium ion, it is possible to determine experimentally the ratio between the isomeric products formed and hence the ratio between the two rate constants from equation (11.7).

$$\frac{(Az_{NH_2})}{(Az_{OH})} = \frac{k_{NH_2}[HORNH_2]}{k_{OH}[{}^{\ominus}ORNH_2]} \quad (11.7)$$

Since the acid dissociation constants of the ammonium and hydroxy groups of aminonaphthols are about 10^{-4} and 10^{-9}, respectively, these compounds will exist almost entirely in the form of $HORNH_2$ in weakly acid media (pH 4 to 6), i.e. $(HORNH_2) \simeq [HORNH_2]$, whilst the effective concentration of the amino-naphtholate ion $^{\ominus}ORNH_2$ will constitute less than one thousandth of the stoichio-metric concentration. For this reason the ratio of azo dyes formed in weakly acid solution favours the aminoazo compound even when the constant of its formation k_{NH_2} is smaller than k_{OH}. In (11.7), the product $k_{NH_2}[HORNH_2]$ exceeds $k_{OH}[^{\ominus}ORNH_2]$, because $[^{\ominus}ORNH_2]$ possesses such a low value.

Very different conditions obtain in alkaline solution. Above pH 9 practically the whole of the coupling component is present as naphtholate. Since this equi-librium form is at least as capable as the aminonaphthol with undissociated hydroxy group of producing aminoazo dye, k_{OH} must be *greater* than k_{NH_2} in order to allow equation (11.7) to account for preparative experience. Experi-mental proof was provided by studying the coupling of a diazo component under the identical conditions (solvent, temperature, ionic strength, etc.) with 2-naphthol-6-sulphonic acid, on the one hand, and with the analogous amino compound, 2-naphthylamine-6-sulphonic acid, on the other.

The ratio of the rate constants determined for coupling to 2-naphthol-6-sul-phonic and 2-naphthylamine-6-sulphonic acids (k_{OH}/k_{NH_2}) is 540, but this value applies only to the reaction with p-diazotoluene. It possesses the same order of size, but not exactly the same value, for other diazo components and, indeed, seven differently substituted diazobenzenes gave variations between 540 and 120 (*2230*). This is especially well illustrated by Figure 10.3 of § 10.6, in which the logarithms of the rate constants are plotted as functions of Hammett's sub-stituent constant σ [equation (10.20) of § 10.6]. The straight lines for naphthol and naphthylamine coupling do not possess the same slope and they approach each other as σ increases, which implies that the ratio k_{OH}/k_{NH_2} is smaller for more negatively substituted diazobenzenes, such as p-nitrodiazobenzene. The slopes of the two straight lines correspond to Hammett's reaction constant ϱ. Coupling to phenols has the smaller reaction constant ($\varrho_{OH} = +3\cdot85$, $\varrho_{NH_2} = +4\cdot26$), that is, coupling to 2-naphthol-6-sulphonic acid is less strongly influen-ced by substituents in the diazo component.

These considerations have practical significance for the selective coupling to aminonaphthols. From the reaction constants it can be deduced that negative substituents in the diazonium ion favour acid, positive residues alkaline coupling to aminonaphthols (*25*). The preparation of pure monoazo compounds by amino coupling from these components is therefore more difficult with positively substituted diazo compounds than with the reactive negatively substituted ones. The situation is reversed for phenolic coupling of the aminonaphthols.

The application of these facts is illustrated by the manufacture of dyes of the Naphthol Blue Black type (C, XVII), derived from H acid by coupling first in

XVII

acid solution with *p*-nitrodiazobenzene, then alkaline with diazobenzene. All commercial products of this type (*2077c*) have been obtained by coupling with the more reactive component in the ring bearing the amino group. An apparent exception is provided by Azo Dark Green A (Gy, XVIII), but this is made by reduction of the nitro group of (XVII). From the effects of substituents in diazo components deduced above it follows that if (XVIII) were prepared by coup-

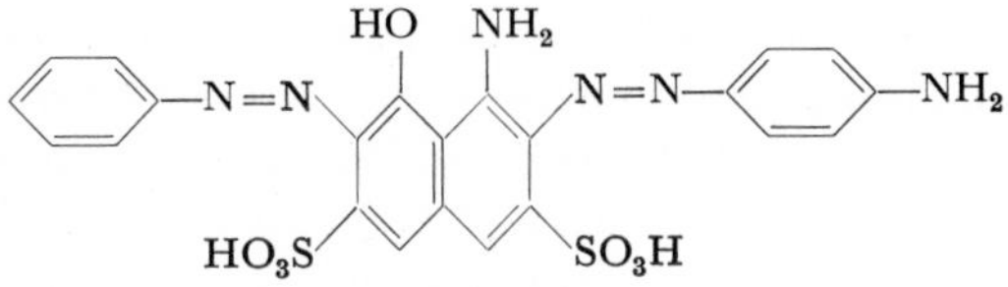

XVIII

ling H acid with 4-acetamidodiazobenzene (acid) and diazobenzene (alkaline), with subsequent hydrolysis to remove the acetyl residue, the product would be less pure than that obtained via the nitro compound. This is of decisive significance, as in the manufacture of disazo dyes of the Naphthol Blue Black type even under the optimum conditions substantial amounts of isomeric disazo and of monoazo derivatives are formed. Brode *et al.* (*52, 320*) described a method for the analytical determination of the various components of such commercial products.

Aromatic diamines are of great practical importance as *tetrazo components*, tetrazotized benzidine being outstanding. The two diazo residues are able to react in stages with two distinct coupling components and Schoutissen (*1835, 1836, 1838*) investigated in detail the apparently different reactivities of the two completely equivalent groups. The fact that one diazo substituent in *p*-tetrazobenzene is able to couple in concentrated sulphuric acid, whereas the other requires the more usual region of acidity (pH >2) has been interpreted by Schoutissen as being due to constitution (XIX) in very acid media. He supposed that only the 'un-ionized diazo salt' (right hand group in XIX) couples. In moderately acid solution the 'un-ionized diazonium salt' (left hand group in XIX) rearranges to —N:N$^\oplus$ X$^\ominus$ and so becomes capable of coupling.

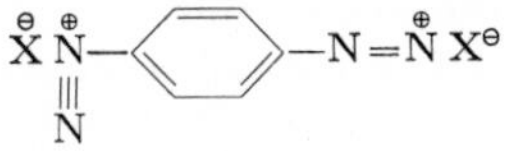

XIX

However, already Stephenson and Waters (*1953*) pointed out that it is incorrect to assume the existence of two isomeric diazonium cations, that is, the diazonium ion proper (Ar·$\overset{\oplus}{N}$: N) and a diazo ion (Ar·N:$\overset{\oplus}{N}$), as these two formulas merely represent mesomeric limiting structures for one and the same substance.

Actually, the apparent difference in reactivity between these two diazo residues follows from the fact that coupling of such tetrazo compounds with 2 equivalents of an amine or phenol takes place as a *stepwise reaction* not only in concentrated acid, but under all conditions. The rate of the first coupling is greatly increased by the presence in the same benzene or biphenyl system of the second diazonium group, because the latter is extraordinarily strongly negative [highly developed —M and —I effects according to Ingold (*1153a*)]. This shows itself, for example, when a diazonium residue facilitates nucleophilic aromatic substitution even more than the nitro group (*382*) (see § 7.3). Schoutissen himself mentions that the first diazo substituent of *p*-tetrazobenzene couples in concentrated acid equally as well as 2,4,6-trinitrodiazobenzene, the activating effect of the residue —$\overset{\oplus}{N}\!:\!N$ thus roughly corresponding to that of three nitro groups.

However, as soon as the first coupling of the tetrazo component has occurred, the remaining diazo residue is no longer activated by the presence of the other, which has, of course, been replaced by an arylazo group. The latter still activates the second diazonium group, but to a considerably reduced degree. The σ-value of an unsubstituted phenylazo residue in the *p*-position in Hammett's equation is $+0\cdot640$, whilst that of a diazonium group is $+1\cdot8$, as shown by Lewis (*1331*). The sole reason for the difference between the originally identical diazo groups in tetrazobenzene and tetrazobiphenyl lies therefore in the stepwise reaction in which a strongly activating substituent ($N_2^{\oplus}$) is replaced by one ($N_2\cdot Ar$) that encourages coupling activity much less.

Recently, E. S. Lewis and M. D. Johnson (*2411, 2412*) confirmed this explanation in two kinetic investigations of the reactions of tetrazobenzene with nucleophiles such as water, hydroxy, halide, thiocyanate, and azide ions. Here, too, the first diazonium group in the *p*-phenylenebisdiazonium ion has extremely high reactivity which is due to the strong influence of the second diazonium group.

11.5 The Formation of Primary Disazo Dyes from Dihydroxy- and Aminohydroxy-Naphthalene Derivatives

Apart from the matters treated in the last section, two further phenomena of importance in coupling to aminonaphthols must be dealt with briefly, although their causation is not yet understood.

It has been known for a long time that technically important aminonaphthol-sulphonic acids, such as J and H acid (XX and XXI, respectively), only yield disazo dyes if the first coupling occurs in the ring bearing the amino group. The isomeric monoazo compounds, in which the phenylazo residue is in the *o*-position to the hydroxy group, no longer react with a second equivalent of a diazo component. Scheme (11.8) illustrates this using H acid as the example.

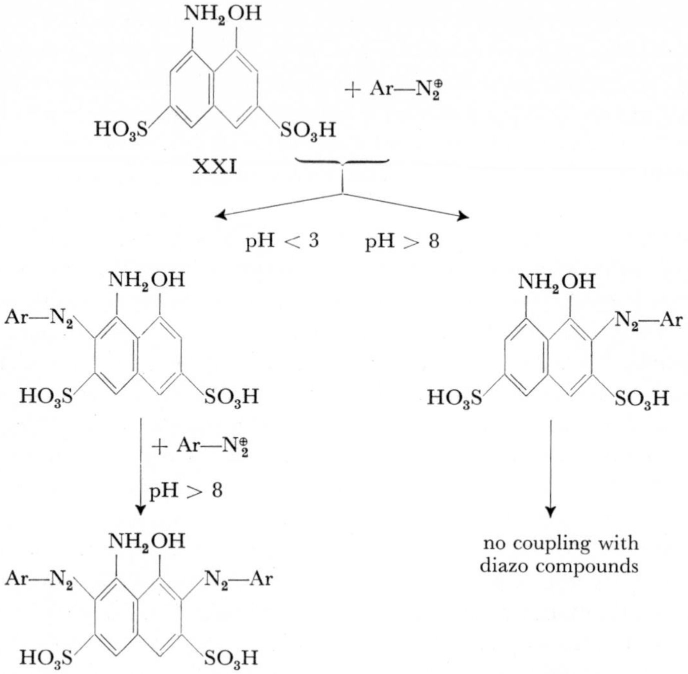

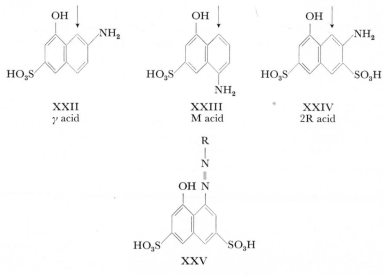

$$(11.8)$$

Related to this well known problem of azo technology is the observation that
some aminonaphtholsulphonic acids are almost incapable of forming primary
disazo dyes when they have reacted first with a diazo component in the ring

XXII
γ acid

XXIII
M acid

XXIV
2R acid

XXV

→ indicates position of coupling
R = amino- or hydroxy-aryl residue

bearing the amino group. This is the case with γ, M, and 2R acid. The characteristic common to these components is readily apparent from formulas (XXII to XXIV) and occurs also in the monoazo compounds derived from H acid as diazo component (XXV), which cannot couple in the H acid residue. All the monoazo dyes of this type contain the azo bridge in *peri*-position to the hydroxy group, which is expected to direct the second coupling. It is known that in analogous *peri*-hydroxy compounds, such as α-hydroxyanthraquinones (*1092*) and the monobasic ion from 1,8-dihydroxynaphthalene (*1093, 2239, 2240*), the proton of the hydroxy group is held by an extraordinarily strong hydrogen bond to the neighbouring oxygen atom, thereby greatly lowering the tendency of the proton to ionize. Hence it is not surprising that in the above monoazo dyes there is present an analogous O—H$\cdots$N bond (XXVI), which retards the dissociation of the hydroxy group. It has been found that coupling can occur again to dyes of the type of (XXVII) derived from γ acid when the amino group has been acetylated (*2515, 2516*) or when the pH is raised to above 13·5, i.e. to dissociate the *peri*-hydroxy group, as was demonstrated by Allan only recently (*2442*).

Perekalin (*1610*) has investigated in detail the question of the second coupling of aminonaphtholsulphonic acids and has come to the conclusion that the reactivity missing in monoazo derivatives is due to resonance phenomena and to steric effects of sulphonic groups. From more recent work by Perekalin (*1611*)

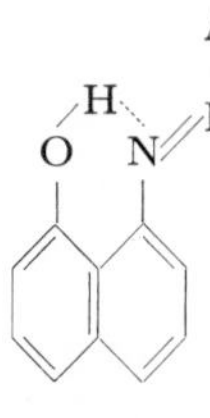

XXVI 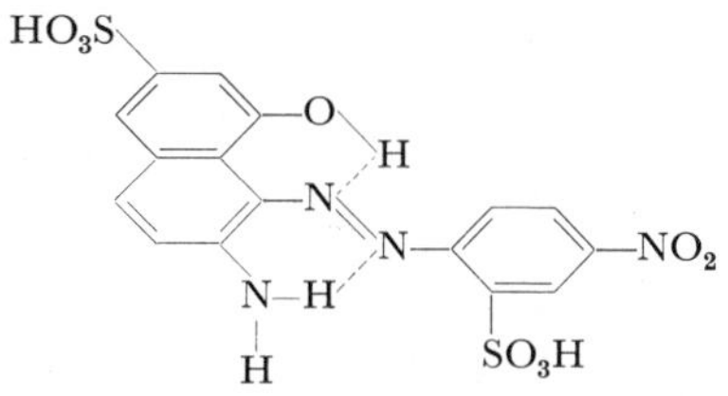   XXVII

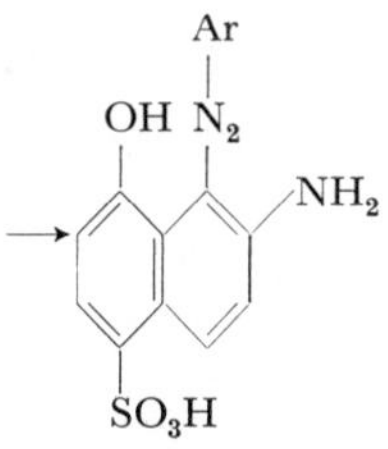

XXVIII 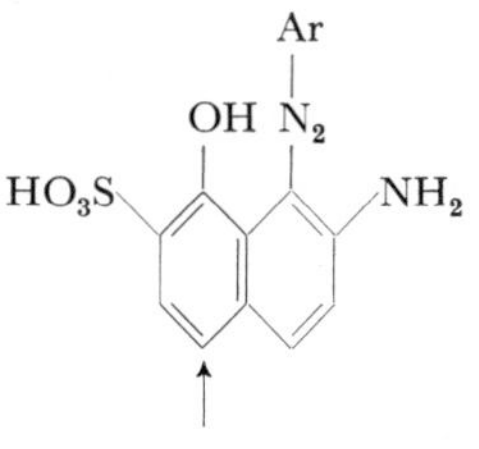   XXIX

it appears that a 1-hydroxy-8-azo structure *alone* does not necessarily prevent coupling for the second time. Compounds (XXVIII) and (XXIX) couple at pH 12 in the 2- and 4-position, respectively, to yield disazo dyes, but, surprisingly, 7-amino-1-naphthol, which is free from sulphonic groups, when coupled in position 8 will not react further (*1612*).

12. Reactions of Azo Compounds

12.1 The Homolytic Fission of Aliphatic Azo Compounds

In this section those reactions of aliphatic azo compounds are dealt with which proceed in solution by a homolytic mechanism. The term aliphatic azo compound is here taken to cover all those substances in which at least *one* of the two azo nitrogen atoms is linked to a tetrahedral, that is, an sp^3-hybridized, carbon atom.

Both chemically and technologically the most important reaction of these compounds is their thermolytic fission (12.1) into molecular nitrogen and two radicals, which subsequently can undergo further processes, such as recombination (12.2a; strictly speaking not a recombination as the nitrogen does not take part in it), or transfer reactions (12.2b–c) with the solvent or with other particles (X) present in the system. The reaction can also occur photolytically, as discussed in § 12.2.

$$R—N=N—R' \longrightarrow N_2 + R^{\cdot} + R''^{\cdot} \tag{12.1}$$
$$R^{\cdot} + R''^{\cdot} \longrightarrow R—R' \tag{12.2a}$$
$$R^{\cdot} + X \longrightarrow R—X^{\cdot} \longrightarrow \text{products} \tag{12.2b}$$
$$R''^{\cdot} + X \longrightarrow R'—X^{\cdot} \longrightarrow \text{products} \tag{12.2c}$$

The radical decomposition of azoalkanes has been known for a long time already. Thus in 1896 Thiele and Heuser (*2033*), the discoverers of azodi-isobutyronitrile [R = R' = $(CH_3)_2C(CN)$], now so useful industrially, described the quantitative evolution of nitrogen according to equation (12.1) as well as the formation of tetramethylsuccinonitrile (12.2a) and isobutyronitrile. The latter is produced through reactions (12.2b–c) by transfer of hydrogen atoms from the solvent to the radicals formed in the first place. However, since in general up to the middle 'thirties aliphatic azo compounds were investigated only sporadically, very little was done during this period as regards the study of their homolytic fission.

As interest increased in gas reactions, much attention was paid from 1935 onwards to the thermolysis at 200° to 400° of unsubstituted azoalkanes, particularly azomethane (see § 12.2). It is remarkable that this reaction also had been carried out very much earlier by Thiele (*2030*).

The third phase began in about 1949, when it was recognized how suitable azodi-isobutyronitrile is for the initiation of polymerization (*414, 1339, 1577, 2219, 2584*). Subsequently many schools conducted research on the broadest lines into the radical decomposition and application of this and related compounds. Previously peroxides (benzoyl peroxide, hydrogen peroxide, persulphates) were by far the most used radical-producing agents for polymerization, but by now the new class of azo compounds has achieved about equal importance as initiator both scientifically and technically.

Consideration of the thermolysis of gaseous azoalkanes and photolysis will be deferred to § 12.2, whilst the applications of these compounds will be discussed in § 12.3.

The experimental investigation of the decomposition of aliphatic azo compounds is relatively simple in comparison with that of other radical reactions. Fission is strictly of first order, it is little affected by the nature of the solvent, and suitable substituents enable the reactivity to be varied within wide limits. Lastly, it is noteworthy that the decomposition is not induced by radicals or oxygen already present in the system (1768), as occurs, for instance, when peroxides are used.

The kinetics of the fission can be followed by four methods, the best of which is the determination of the nitrogen evolved (69, 317, 1339, 1577, 2220). Most azo compounds absorb at relatively long wavelengths (see § 13.1) and so it is possible to follow spectrophotometrically the rate at which the concentration of the starting material is falling (2001). The concentration of azo bodies can also be measured polarographically and the kinetics of the decomposition can therefore be obtained in this way (2064). The fourth method consists of interception of the radicals formed according to equation (12.1) by means of stable radicals, the so-called scavengers. Particularly suitable for this purpose is the violet 2,2-diphenyl-1-picrylhydrazyl (I) which is changed in the process into the yellow hydrazine (II) (12.3), thus permitting the reaction to be followed

colorimetrically (209). However, this method of determining the kinetics suffers from the disadvantage of failing to assess those of the radicals formed according to (12.1) which recombine according to (12.2) (237, 916, 2102). In consequence the rate constants derived in this manner are too small, but the result together with kinetic determinations by other methods gives information about the mechanism of the recombination (see below). Hammond and Boozer (916) were able to show that in the presence of iodine and oxidation inhibitors agreement can be achieved with the other methods in certain solvents.

As regards the ability of the C-N bond of azo compounds to undergo homolytic dissociation, three groups of substances can be distinguished. In aromatic azo derivatives, such as azobenzene, the bond is so strongly stabilized by mesomerism that phenyl radicals are only formed far above 600° (429, 1168).

Table 12.1

Rates of Decomposition of Some Aliphatic Azo Compounds

Compound	Solvent	Rate $k \times 10^4$ sec^{-1}	Temperature	$\Delta H^{\ddagger} \simeq E_a$ kcal mole^{-1}	$\Delta S^{\ddagger}$ cal mole^{-1} deg.$^{-1}$	Reference
$CH_3-N=N-CH_3$	gas	5·6	300°	50·2	11	(448, 1700–1702)
$(CH_3)_2CH-N=N-CH(CH_3)_2$	gas	4·8	250°	40·9	1	(448, 1677)
$C_6H_5-CH(CH_3)-N=N-CH(CH_3)C_6H_5$	toluene	1·69	110°	32·6	7	(445)
$(C_6H_5)_2CH-N=N-CH(C_6H_5)_2$	toluene	3·40	64°	26·6	2	(448)
$(CH_3)_2C(CN)-N=N-C(CN)(CH_3)_2$	toluene	1·55	80·4°	31·1	3	(1577, 2001)
$(CH_3)_2C(COOEt)-N=N-C(COOEt)(CH_3)_2$	nitrobenzene	1·57	80°	30·9	5	(2220)
$C_6H_5-N=N-CH(C_6H_5)_2$	decahydro-naphthalene	2·69	144·5°	34·0	4	(450)
$C_6H_5-N=N-C(C_6H_5)_3$	toluene	2·25	53·5°	26·8	5	(21, 450)

Azomethane and other aliphatic azo compounds bearing no substituents with a —M effect at the α-carbon atoms possess moderate reactivity, reaching times of half reaction of the order of an hour at temperatures of 230° to 280°. Lastly, in the presence of appropriate substituents such times of half reaction are already obtained at room or slightly elevated temperatures, in extreme cases, as that of azobistriphenylmethane (*2152, 2154–2156*), the azo compound being too labile even for isolation.

This increase in reactivity of azoalkanes is achieved particularly by means of phenyl, cyano, and alkoxycarbonyl groups at one or both α-carbon atoms. The kinetic results for the decomposition of some azo compounds are listed in Table 12.1 and they have been discussed by Cohen and Wang (*448, 450*). The reactivity is increased when two hydrogen atoms of each α-carbon atom of azomethane are replaced by methyl groups and even more by phenyl residues. It can be seen that the energy of activation is lowered by 5 kcal/mole by each symmetrical introduction of two methyl groups and by 12 kcal/mole by two phenyl groups. Presumably the greater reduction in activation energy produced by phenyl groups is due to the stabilization of the diphenylmethyl and α-methylbenzyl radicals [$(C_6H_5)_2\dot{C}H$ and $(C_6H_5)(CH_3)\dot{C}H$] through mesomerism. To a lesser extent this could also be the case with isopropyl radicals in the sense of (III a–III b). If further phenyl residues are introduced, the energy

$$CH_3-\dot{C}H-CH_3 \longleftrightarrow H\cdot\ CH_2{=}CH-CH_3$$

$$\text{III a} \qquad\qquad \text{III b}$$

of activation is decreased so far as to make the compounds unstable and hence not isolatable (*2155*). The unfavourable entropies of the decomposition of 1,1'-dimethylazoethane and azobisdiphenylmethane are possibly caused by the fact that here the planarity required for the optimum stabilization of the transition state by mesomerism is achieved only with difficulty. If the whole alkyl group at a nitrogen atom is replaced by phenyl, the stability is increased as expected. The introduction of cyano or alkoxycarbonyl groups at each α-carbon atom greatly raises the reactivity ($\Delta E_a \simeq 10$ kcal/mole). Qualitative experiments carried out by S. Goldschmidt and his co-workers (*836, 838*) showed that other groups (CH_2OH, CH_2NH_2, Cl) at these positions do not facilitate fission, confirming that the stability of the radicals formed is increased only by —M substituents. Groups (X) in the *p*-position of compounds of the type of (IV) have only very little influence on the kinetics of the decompo-

$$X-\langle\ \rangle-CH_2-\underset{\underset{CN}{|}}{\overset{\overset{CH_3}{|}}{C}}-N{=}N-\underset{\underset{CN}{|}}{\overset{\overset{CH_3}{|}}{C}}-CH_2-\langle\ \rangle-X$$

$$\text{IV}$$

sition (*1566*), which is in agreement with the known poor transmission of electronic effects by methylene groups.

Cohen and Wang (*446*) determined the rates of fission of substituted phenyl-azotriphenylmethanes (V), all the substituents listed, except the methyl group, causing decomposition to occur more slowly than with the parent compound (X = H). Comparison with the corresponding investigation of benzoyl per-

$$X—\langle\bigcirc\rangle—N=N—C(C_6H_5)_3 \qquad\qquad X = OH, OCH_3, CH_3, H, NHCOCH_3, Br, NO_2$$
$$V$$

oxides (*1991*) leads to the conclusion that the fission of the azo compounds occurs by a concerted mechanism, i.e. that the first step consists of the synchronous splitting of both C-N bonds, whilst it is known that in the case of benzoyl peroxides (*444, 919*) the O-O link dissociates primarily yielding two benzoate radicals, which subsequently give phenyl radicals and carbon dioxide. Hence Bartlett terms azo compounds 'two-bond initiators' (*194*).

If they were 'one-bond initiators' like benzoyl peroxide, they would produce in the first place an alkylazo as well as an alkyl radical. Arnett and Peterson (*69, 70*) have investigated the initiator efficiency in polymerization of azodi-iso-butyronitrile labelled with C^{14} in the cyano groups. Since with vinyl compounds not all the radicals formed initiated chains, but only 50 to 80%, it was concluded erroneously that two different radicals ($R \cdot N:N^\cdot$ and $R^\cdot$) had been produced. The mistake in interpretation lay in the neglect of the recombination (12.2a). The absence of azo groups from the resultant chain molecules does not support the participation of alkylazo radicals either. Additional arguments against the formation of such radicals will be considered when the thermolysis of unsubstituted azoalkanes is discussed in § 12.2.

Seltzer (*2431*) measured the secondary kinetic isotope effect in the decomposition of 1,1'-diphenylazoethane-1,1'-d_2 in ethylbenzene as solvent. The value $k_H/k_D = 1.27$ is in accord with a concerted mechanism. The main product, 2,3-diphenylbutane-2,3-d_2, contains two deuterium atoms which shows that no appreciable reaction with the solvent takes place, that is, the cage effect (explained on p. 273) is very marked.

A series of investigations has thrown a flood of light on the character of the radicals produced from azo compounds. That the very stable triphenylmethyl radical is obtained in solution when phenylazotriphenylmethane decomposes was shown a long time ago by H. Wieland (*2157*). The much more reactive phenyl radical formed in competition attacks the solvent according to equation (12.3a), phenylation being the result. The triphenylmethyl radical does not react with the solvent. Hey (*1022*) and Huisgen (*1116, 1123, 2325*) were able to demonstrate that the proportions of the isomers obtained remain practically the same when pyridine, chlorobenzene, or naphthalene interacts with phenylazo-triphenylmethane instead of with one of three other phenylating agents (benzoyl peroxide, nitrosoacetanilide, Gomberg reaction with diazobenzene). Further, the decomposition of phenylazotriphenylmethane in benzene in the presence of oxygen yields triphenylmethyl peroxide (*1321b, 2157*), but the phenyl radical is too unstable to give the analogous product or to recombine with the triphenylmethyl radical and has to attack the solvent immediately.

$$H_5C_6—N=N—C(C_6H_5)_3 \longrightarrow N_2 + C_6H_5{\cdot} + {\cdot}C(C_6H_5)_3$$

$$\Big\downarrow + ArH \qquad\qquad (12.3\,a)$$

$$C_6H_5—Ar + H{\cdot}$$

There is no doubt that phenyl radicals are formed. It is possible that the dissociation of the complexes of the Sandmeyer reaction (see § 7.6), which perhaps proceeds by 'three-bond cleavage' according to equation (12.4), corresponds to the radical decomposition of compounds of the type of $Ar \cdot N : N \cdot R$.

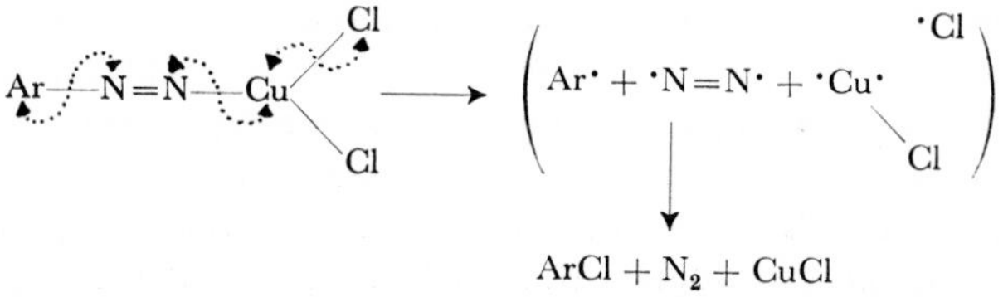

$$(12.4)$$

That *free* radicals are actually formed in the fission of azoalkanes has been elegantly proved by Overberger and Berenbaum (*1563, 1564*), who showed that the racemates and the *meso*-forms of optically active azonitriles not only decompose at the same rate, but yield identical mixtures of diastereomeric succinonitrile derivatives. Also a mixture of two azonitriles bearing different substituents gives not only the two symmetric products, but also the unsymmetric one.

Overberger *et al.* (*1573–1575, 1578*) as well as Wang and Cohen (*2106*) have investigated the rate of fission of series of azo compounds of the types of (VI), (VII), and (VIII). Of interest is the fact that the substance (VII, $n = 2$) decomposes 100 times more rapidly than the analogous, acyclic azo compound (VIIa) (*2106*). The reason obviously lies in the *cis*-configuration forced on the

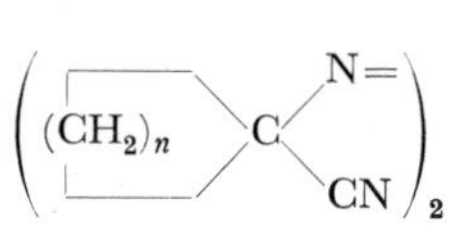

VI

$n=3,4,5,6,7,$ or 9

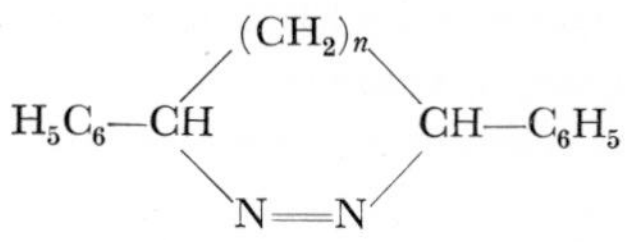

VII

$n=2,3,$ or 4

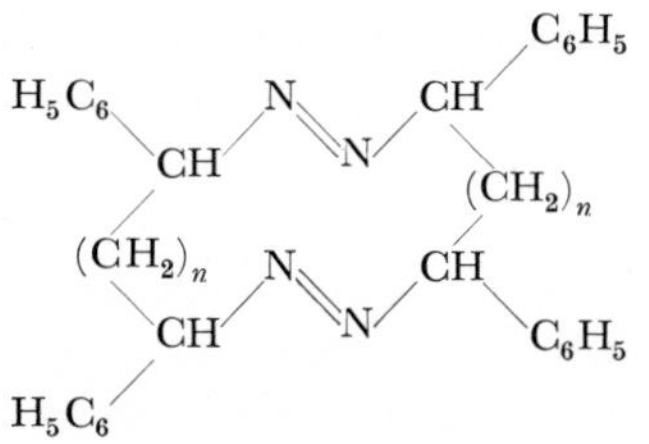

VIII

$n=6,8,$ or 10

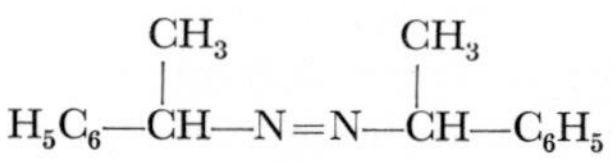

VIIa

ring compound. Cyclic azo derivatives in which the size of the ring is such as to enable them to take up the *trans*-configuration, as, for example, in (VIII, $n = 8$ or 10, that is 24- or 28-membered rings), exhibit on the contrary only unimportant differences of reaction rate from the comparable, open chain compounds (*1573, 1578*).

The kinetics of decomposition of aliphatic azo bodies depends only little on the solvent. In acetic acid, alcohols, aniline, nitrobenzene, and aromatic hydrocarbons, the rate determined for azodi-isobutyronitrile, for instance, remains constant within $\pm 13\%$ (*69, 317, 1339, 1577, 2001, 2220*). This indicates hardly any participation of other molecules in step (12.1) in which the radicals are formed. Thus when azo compounds are employed as initiators for polymerization, it is improbable that their fission should occur simultaneously with the interaction between the fragments and the monomer. However, that the solvent effects here, as in many of the reactions in organic chemistry, are by no means fully understood follows from Huisgen's work (*1116*) on the influence of the medium on the ratio of isomers obtained in phenylating with phenylazotriphenylmethane as well as from the researches of Leffler *et al.* (*21, 443, 1323*) into the rate of decomposition of the same compound and of *p*-nitrophenylazotri(*p*-methoxyphenyl)methane. It became apparent that in spite of the small overall effect of the solvent on the rate constant, considerable differences in the heats and entropies of activation are present, but that these just compensate for one another.

The effect of high pressure on the kinetics of the decomposition of azodi-isobutyronitrile in toluene solution has also been studied (*693*). The rate decreases markedly as the pressure is increased, falling to 40% of its value at atmospheric pressure when 10000 atm are applied. This is attributed to the fact that in the transition state of the radical formation the C—N bond is stretched about 10% and hence the process is hindered by increased pressure. The relation deduced by Stearn and Eyring (*806, 1946*) allows the volume difference between azodi-isobutyronitrile and the transition state of its radical decomposition to be calculated, giving a value of about 4 ml/mole, but it should be noted that the validity of the relation has been doubted in the case of other, heterolytic types of reaction (*355*).

The investigations discussed so far have been concerned essentially with the fission of the C—N bond, i.e. with step (12.1), but considerable interest attaches also to the subsequent reactions of the radicals produced (12.2a–c). The recombination (12.2a) assumes especial significance, both technically because it withdraws radicals from chain initiation and also from the point of view of the mechanism as it plays a role in explaining the structure and reactivity of the radicals.

In the case of azodi-isobutyronitrile the recombination leads via 2-cyanopropyl radicals (IX) to tetramethylsuccinonitrile (X) (*918, 1754, 2033*), which frequently constitutes 50 to 90% of the products, though this depends on the nature of the solvent and on whether other molecules capable of ready reaction with radicals are present. It is remarkable that even very effective radical

$$(CH_3)_2C\underset{\underset{CN}{|}}{-}N{=}N\underset{\underset{CN}{|}}{-}C(CH_3)_2 \longrightarrow N_2 + 2\ (CH_3)_2\overset{\cdot}{C}\underset{\underset{CN}{|}}{} \longrightarrow (CH_3)_2C\underset{\underset{CN}{|}}{-}C(CH_3)_2 \underset{\underset{CN}{|}}{}$$

$$\text{IX} \hspace{5cm} \text{X} \hspace{2cm} (12.5)$$

scavengers, such as mercaptans and diphenylpicrylhydrazyl (I), cannot suppress recombination completely (see above) and it follows that the tendency of 2-cyanopropyl radicals to reunite must be particularly strong. To explain such processes of recombination, Franck and Rabinowitch (752) postulated that the radicals formed are unable to separate sufficiently quickly because they are enclosed in a cage of solvent molecules. That this is indeed true is supported by the dependence of the cage effect on the nature of the solvent, as shown, for example, by Kooyman's investigation (1259) into the decomposition of dimesityl disulphide in presence of dihydroanthracene. He found that the ratio of the reaction products, hexamethylbiphenyl (recombination) to mesitylenethiol (reaction with dihydroanthracene), varies with the viscosity of the solvent.

Spectrophotometric study of the decomposition of azodi-isobutyronitrile has suggested that recombination does not lead directly to (X), but to a metastable intermediate (XI) in the first place (2000, 2001), that is, one of the two 2-cyanopropyl radicals attacks primarily not carbon, but the nitrogen atom of the cyano group. Bevington (236) found that the amount of the products of disproportio-

$$\text{IX} \longrightarrow (CH_3)_2C{=}C{=}N{-}C(CH_3)_2 \underset{\underset{CN}{|}}{} \longrightarrow X$$

$$\text{XI} \hspace{7cm} (12.6)$$

nation of the 2-cyanopropyl radicals decreases relatively as the scale on which the reaction is carried out is increased. Walling (2103) considers that the explanation may lie in the intermediate appearance of (XI).

Disproportionation always gives some isobutyronitrile (XII) and as Bevington showed that this product is formed also in solvents free from hydrogen atoms, the hydrogen taken up must come from a second radical, which would be converted into 2-cyanopropene (XIII). In this connection some experiments

$$\underset{\underset{CN}{|}}{(CH_3)_2CH} \hspace{3cm} \underset{\underset{CN}{|}}{CH_3{-}C{=}CH_2}$$

$$\text{XII} \hspace{3cm} \text{XIII}$$

of Cohen and Wang (451) are of interest: the decomposition of azobisdiphenylmethane in 1-C^{14}-diphenylmethane gives as recombination product tetraphenylethane which exhibits only 1·1% of the radioactivity of the solvent, demonstrating clearly that the recombination occurs much more rapidly than reaction with the solvent.

Overberger's work also contributes to the understanding of the cage effect. In contrast to the reaction with azobisphenylpropane, attempts to interfere with the decomposition of the similar, but cyclic disazo compound (VII, $n = 8$) by means of *cis*-stilbene were practically without success (*1573, 1578*). Hence cyclic azoalkanes are very subject to the cage effect. Overberger has also shown that neopentyl radicals rearrange partly during these reactions (*1565, 1571*).

Criegee (*2316*) studied the thermolysis of a small ring compound with a cyclic azo group, 2,3-diazabicyclo[2.2.1]hept-2-ene, and found that it yields bicyclo-[2.1.0]pentane (12.7) at 160°.

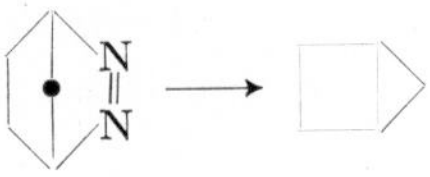

$$\text{(12.7)}$$

Apart from the aliphatic–aromatic azo compounds of the type $R \cdot N : N \cdot Ar$, such as phenylazotriphenylmethane, unsymmetric aliphatic azo bodies have only been prepared rarely (*778, 1679*). Other endeavours to synthesize them failed (*450, 2154*). Recently, Overberger and DiGiulio (*1567, 1568*) were able to make α,α-methylisobutylbenzylazo-2-(4-methylpentane) (XIV) and they proceeded to study its decomposition at 110° in xylene. Because of the cage effect the main product should be that of the unsymmetric recombination of the primarily formed α,α-methylisobutylbenzyl and methylisobutylcarbinyl radicals (XV and XVI), but 2,4,5,7-tetramethyl-4-phenyloctane (XVII) is obtained in a yield of only about 18% (12.8). On the other hand, the compounds due to interaction with the solvent, 2-methyl-4-phenylpentane (XVIII) and 2-methylpentane (XIX), are produced in greater amounts, namely, 38 to 51% and 31 to 46%, respectively. In addition, a series of further compounds of only partly known constitution results. The remarkably small proportion of the

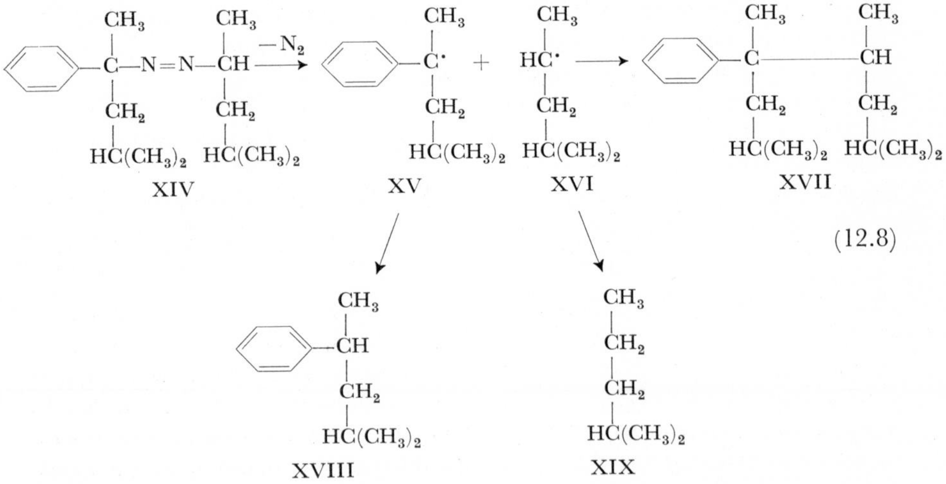

$$\text{(12.8)}$$

'normal' recombination product (XVII) and the absence of substances due to coupling of the α,α-methylisobutylbenzyl radical (XV) at the α-carbon atom indicate that the reactivity of (XV) is severely limited by steric factors.

Heilbronner, Wepster, and co-workers (2425) described an example where the HgO oxidation of a dibenzylhydrazine derivative did not stop at the azo-alkane step but proceeded to the recombination product, a 1,2-diphenylethane.

In the case of methyl azodi-isobutyrate (XX) the amount of disproportionation is relatively high (12.9). The methyl methacrylate (XXII) formed in this way reacts with radicals to yield compounds to which Bickel and Waters (246) have assigned the structures indicated. Due to its scavenging effect, the presence of iodine leads predominantly to 2-iodoisobutyrate, but in the case of azo-di-isobutyronitrile the substance corresponding to (XXIII) is still formed (739) [see also (247)].

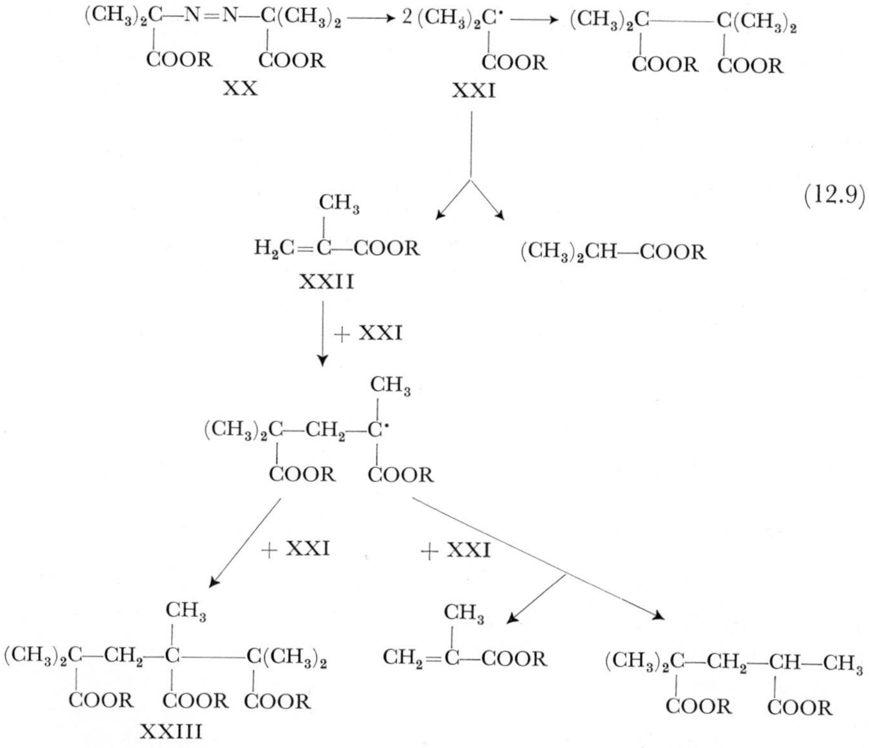

$$(CH_3)_2C-N=N-C(CH_3)_2 \longrightarrow 2\,(CH_3)_2C^\cdot \longrightarrow (CH_3)_2C\underset{COOR}{\overset{}{|}}\,\,C(CH_3)_2$$

(with COOR, COOR under XX, COOR under XXI, and COOR COOR)

XX   XXI

(12.9)

$$\underset{XXII}{H_2C=\overset{CH_3}{\underset{}{C}}-COOR}$$

$$(CH_3)_2CH-COOR$$

+ XXI

$$(CH_3)_2C-CH_2-\overset{CH_3}{\underset{}{C^\cdot}}$$
COOR   COOR

+ XXI   + XXI

$$(CH_3)_2C-CH_2-\overset{CH_3}{\underset{}{C}}-C(CH_3)_2$$
COOR   COOR   COOR

XXIII

$$CH_2=\overset{CH_3}{\underset{}{C}}-COOR$$

$$(CH_3)_2C-CH_2-CH-CH_3$$
COOR   COOR

Apart from the attack on aromatic hydrocarbons already discussed, radicals from aliphatic azo derivatives can react with a series of other compounds. Kooyman and his co-workers (244, 679, 697) have investigated in detail the addition to the *meso*-positions of anthracenes. The parent substance yields two isomers (XXIV, XXV), presumably because of the *cis*- and *trans*-arrangement of the 2-cyanopropyl residues (R), together with the dimer (XXVI). It seems that only one isomer of constitution (XXVI) is formed. If the 9-position of the anthracene is already substituted, the dimer is not obtained and only one of the two isomers (XXIV) or (XXV) results. The relative rates of addition were determined for nine anthracene derivatives.

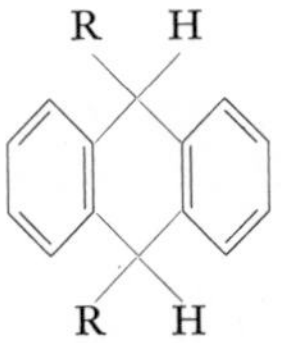

XXIV 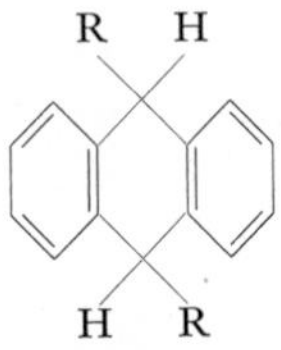   XXV 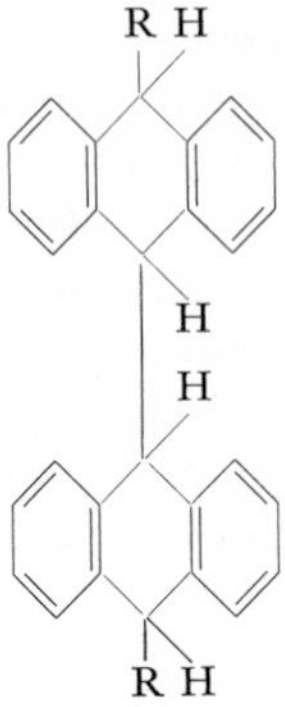   XXVI

Kice and Parham (*1210*) studied the attack of 2-cyanopropyl radicals on phenylated fulvenes, such as (**XXVII**), as regards the constitution of the products and the kinetics. They found apart from rubber-like by-products two diastereomeric dimers, presumably of structure (**XXVIII**).

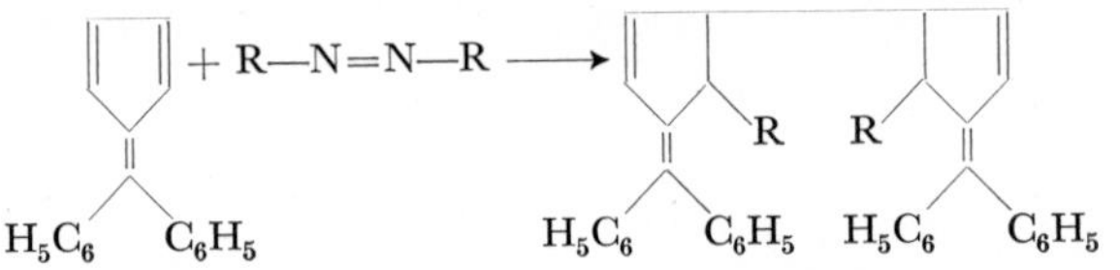

$$\text{(12.10)}$$

XXVII   R = (CH$_3$)$_2$C—   XXVIII
                    | (two diastereomers)
                    CN

Reactions with mercaptans and hydrogen sulphide (*243, 353, 918, 1787, 2587*), aldehydes (*981, 1504*), mercury (*1683*), diphenyltin (*1683*), iodine (*739*), and nitric oxide (*803*) have been described. Because of their significance in the technology of polymers the reactions with quinones (*235, 245, 917, 1358, 2219*), quinonimines (*803*), semiquinone-like compounds, such as Wurster salts (*755*), and oxygen have been subjected to detailed examination. Azodi-isobutyro-nitrile and methyl azodi-isobutyrate yield a series of products with *p*-benzo-quinone (12.11), Bickel and Waters (*245*) explaining the course of the process by means of the intermediate appearance of semiquinones (**XXX**) and (**XXXIV**). The latter result from the addition of the primarily formed radicals (**XXIX**) to the benzoquinone. Interaction with a second radical can occur either by disproportionation or addition to a hydroquinone mono- or di-ether (**XXXII, XXXI**), respectively. The acrylic acid derivative (**XXXIII**) also produced in the disproportionation gives by combination with two additional radicals and a molecule of benzoquinone a small yield (3%) of another hydro-quinone monoether, to which constitution (**XXXV**) is assigned. Experiments employing ten different quinones (*1358*) showed that the extent to which the reaction takes place is determined in general by the redox potential of the qui-none used.

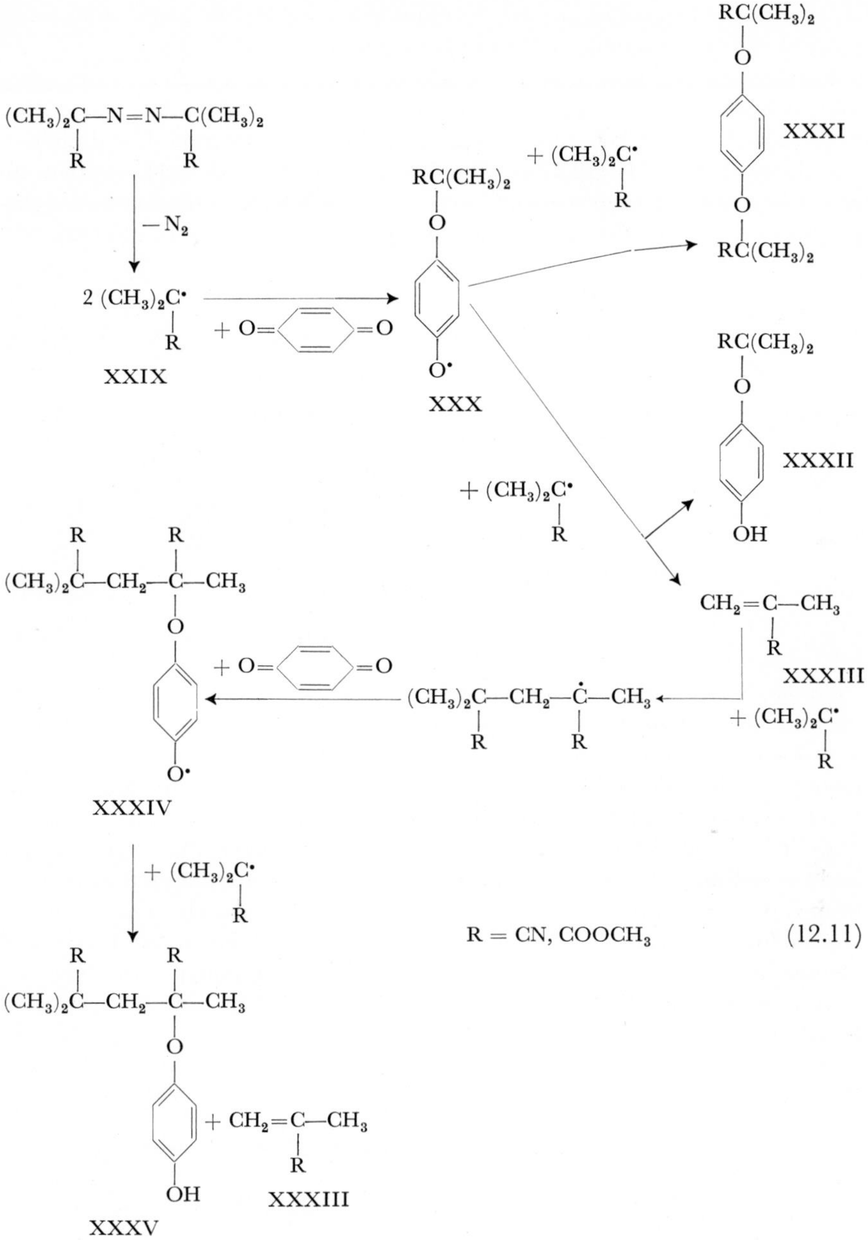

$$RC(CH_3)_2\text{—O—}\langle\text{ring}\rangle\text{—O—}RC(CH_3)_2 \qquad \text{XXXI}$$

$$(CH_3)_2C\text{—N}=\text{N—}C(CH_3)_2 \atop \quad R \qquad\qquad R$$

$$+ (CH_3)_2C^\bullet \atop R$$

$$\Big\downarrow -N_2$$

$$RC(CH_3)_2\text{—O—}\langle\text{ring}\rangle\text{—O}^\bullet \quad + (CH_3)_2C^\bullet \longrightarrow RC(CH_3)_2 \text{—O—}\langle\text{ring}\rangle\text{—O—}RC(CH_3)_2$$

$$2\,(CH_3)_2C^\bullet \atop R$$

XXIX

$$+\ O=\langle\text{ring}\rangle=O$$

XXX

$$+ (CH_3)_2C^\bullet \atop R$$

$$\longrightarrow RC(CH_3)_2\text{—O—}\langle\text{ring}\rangle\text{—OH} \qquad \text{XXXII}$$

$$CH_2=C\text{—}CH_3 \atop R \qquad \text{XXXIII}$$

$$+ (CH_3)_2C^\bullet \atop R$$

$$R \qquad\quad R \atop (CH_3)_2C\text{—}CH_2\text{—}C\text{—}CH_3$$

$$+\ O=\langle\text{ring}\rangle=O \qquad (CH_3)_2C\text{—}CH_2\text{—}\overset{\bullet}{C}\text{—}CH_3 \atop R \qquad\quad R$$

$$\text{O—}\langle\text{ring}\rangle\text{—O}^\bullet$$

XXXIV

$$\Big\downarrow + (CH_3)_2C^\bullet \atop R$$

$$R \qquad\quad R \atop (CH_3)_2C\text{—}CH_2\text{—}C\text{—}CH_3$$

$$\text{O—}\langle\text{ring}\rangle\text{—OH} \quad + CH_2=C\text{—}CH_3 \atop R \qquad \text{XXXIII}$$

XXXV

$$R = CN,\ COOCH_3 \qquad\qquad (12.11)$$

Autoxidation of cumene and 1,2,3,4-tetrahydronaphthalene in the presence of azodi-isobutyronitrile, investigated by Boozer *et al.* (*288–290*), is related by mechanism to the radical reactions induced by the fission of aliphatic azo compounds. The catalysis of the decomposition of hydroperoxides (*1930*) and the acceleration of brominations with *N*-bromosuccinimide (*740, 2506*) and similar halogen transfer reactions (*737*) also belong here.

Further, the reaction of aliphatic azo compounds with radicals from other sources has received attention. Thus Bickel and Kooyman (*243*) found that thiyl radicals (**XXXVI**) can abstract a hydrogen atom from 1,1′-diphenyl-azoethane (**XXXVII**) (12.12a). The radical formed (**XXXVIII**) contains an azo group and leads to acetophenone azine (**XXXIX**) presumably by disproportionation (12.12b and/or 12.12c). For the interaction of aliphatic azo

$$R-S^{\cdot} + H_5C_6-\underset{\underset{CH_3}{|}}{\overset{\overset{H}{|}}{C}}-N=N-\underset{\underset{CH_3}{|}}{\overset{\overset{H}{|}}{C}}-C_6H_5 \longrightarrow H_5C_6-\underset{\underset{CH_3}{|}}{\overset{\cdot}{C}}-N=N-\underset{\underset{CH_3}{|}}{\overset{\overset{H}{|}}{C}}-C_6H_5 + R-SH \quad (12.12a)$$

XXXVI   XXXVII   XXXVIII

$$H_5C_6-\underset{\underset{CH_3}{|}}{\overset{\cdot}{C}}-N=N-\underset{\underset{CH_3}{|}}{\overset{\overset{H}{|}}{C}}-C_6H_5$$

$$\overset{+R-S^{\cdot}}{\nearrow} \quad H_5C_6-\underset{\underset{CH_3}{|}}{\overset{}{C}}=N-N=\underset{\underset{CH_3}{|}}{\overset{}{C}}-C_6H_5 + R-SH$$

XXXIX (12.12b)

$$\overset{+XXXVIII}{\searrow} \quad H_5C_6-\underset{\underset{CH_3}{|}}{\overset{}{C}}=N-N=\underset{\underset{CH_3}{|}}{\overset{}{C}}-C_6H_5 + XXXVII \quad (12.12c)$$

compounds with trichloromethyl radicals Kooyman (*1258*) has determined the rate of reaction in comparison with those of ketazines, olefins, and other hydrocarbons. The considerably greater reactivity of the azo bodies is in agreement with MO calculations. Reactions similar to (12.12a–c) play a part in the thermolysis and photolysis of azomethane (§ 12.2).

Esters of azodi-isobutyric acid can be saponified under alkaline conditions and the sodium salt obtained is stable. However, if it is attempted to prepare from it the free acids, carbon dioxide is liberated immediately. The spontaneous evolution of carbon dioxide had already been observed by Thiele and Heuser (*2033*), when they tried to convert azodi-isobutyronitrile into azodi-isobutyric acid. According to Kooyman (*1259*) the decomposition is probably based on a concerted mechanism (12.13).

Benzing (*2378*) recently studied the decomposition of 1,1′-dichloro-1,1′-dimethylazoethane.

$$(CH_3)_2\underset{\underset{COO^{\ominus}}{|}}{C}-N=N-\underset{\underset{COOC_2H_5}{|}}{C}(CH_3)_2 + H^{\oplus} \longrightarrow \left((CH_3)_2\underset{\underset{O}{\diagdown}\underset{O}{C}\diagup}{C}\overset{N=N}{\underset{H}{-}}-\underset{\underset{COOC_2H_5}{|}}{C}(CH_3)_2 \right)$$

$$\downarrow \quad (12.13)$$

$$(CH_3)_2C=N-N-\underset{\underset{H}{|}\quad\underset{COOC_2H_5}{|}}{C}(CH_3)_2 + CO_2$$

To complete this section, the decomposition of *diaroyldi-imides* (azodiaroyls) will now be considered briefly. As it has been stated that aliphatic azo compounds comprise those substances in which at least one of the two azo nitrogen atoms is linked to an sp^3-hybridized carbon atom, the diaroyldi-imides should not really be classed with them, but the behaviour of the two groups does show some similarities. Horner and Naumann (*1079*) showed that photolysis of dibenzoyldi-imides (azodibenzoyls) carrying chloro substituents yields the corresponding benzils (12.14). As this decomposition does not catalyse poly-

$$Ar—CO—N{=}N—CO—Ar \xrightarrow{h\nu} Ar—CO—CO—Ar + N_2 \qquad (12.14)$$

merizations taking place concurrently, it may be concluded that *free* radicals do not appear (cage effect?). Surprisingly, the reaction does not occur with di-*p*-anisoyldi-imide. According to Stollé (*1964*), the thermal decomposition of diaroyldi-imides takes another course. The aroyl radicals add to starting material still present and the tetra-aroylhydrazine, which has not been isolated, disproportionates into diaryloxadiazole and the acid anhydride (12.15).

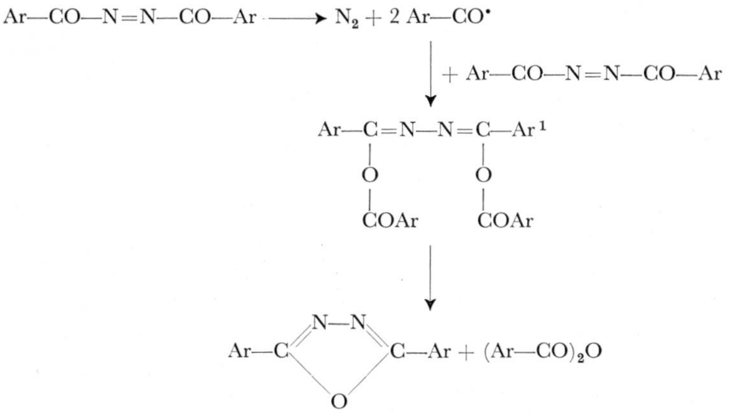

$$Ar—CO—N{=}N—CO—Ar \longrightarrow N_2 + 2\ Ar—CO^•$$

(12.15)

Rosenthal and Overberger (*2405*) recently studied the kinetics of the thermolysis of phenylphenylsulphonyldi-imide. The decomposition is autocatalysed by an acidic product, the rate being increased by scavengers. A radical mechanism is probable.

12.2 Thermolysis and Photolysis of Unsubstituted Azoalkanes and Related Compounds

As mentioned in the introduction to § 12.1, unsubstituted azoalkanes, such as azomethane, are so stable that they decompose at a measurable rate only at relatively high temperatures. In consequence such reactions occur in the

---

[1] Tetra-arylhydrazine as formulated by Stollé (*1964*).

gaseous state and the composition of the products differs partly from that of
the decomposition of azonitriles and other comparatively unstable azo compounds.

Already in 1909, Thiele (*2030*) heated azomethane with carbon dioxide to
400° and found that, apart from nitrogen, the main product was ethane, some
ethylene and methane being formed concomitantly. In the later 'thirties the
thermolysis of azomethane was investigated in greater detail and higher hydrocarbons were detected among the products (*1321a*), in agreement with the
results of photolysis at elevated temperatures (*397, 398*). If the work on thermolysis and photolysis of azomethane is compared, the reactions are found to run
parallel to a very large extent.

The formation of ethane from azomethane can be followed by determining
the changes in volume or pressure. The by-products, methane and ethylene,
however, cause the pressure to increase further than expected according to
equation (12.16a). This was confirmed experimentally, but in spite of it the

$$CH_3-N=N-CH_3 \longrightarrow C_2H_6 + N_2 \qquad (12.16a)$$

$$\longrightarrow CH_4 + \tfrac{1}{2}CH_2=CH_2 + N_2 \qquad (12.16b)$$

kinetics are approximately of the first order (*1000, 1698*). Although much
intensive research has been carried out, still relatively little is known about
the mechanism of such thermolyses. Some years ago already, H. A. Taylor
(*2008, 2009*) postulated that the methyl radicals formed primarily not only
combine directly to yield ethane, but that they also attack azomethane at the
nitrogens. In this way tetramethylhydrazine is produced as intermediate, but
it possesses little stability at 290° to 400° and cannot be isolated. The addition
of methyl radicals to azomethane cannot be suppressed with nitric oxide. In
the presence of hydrogen, formation of 1,2-dimethylhydrazine occurs at room
temperature and at 110° methane, nitrogen, and methylamine are obtained as
well, but above 195° the normal thermolysis of azomethane predominates
without the participation of hydrogen (*1012*). An important parallel to Taylor's hypothesis regarding the appearance of tetramethylhydrazine is provided
by the researches of Pritchard and his colleagues (*1662*) into the photolysis of
hexafluoroazomethane in the gas phase, in which the trifluoromethyl radicals
formed primarily also add on to the azo bridge (12.17b–c). H. O. Pritchard and
Trotman-Dickenson (*427, 1581*) have compared the energy and entropy of

$$F_3C-N=N-CF_3 \xrightarrow{h\nu} N_2 + 2\,F_3C^\bullet \qquad (12.17a)$$

$$F_3C-N=N-CF_3 + F_3C^\bullet \longrightarrow \begin{matrix} F_3C \\ \diagdown \\ N-\overset{\bullet}{N}-CF_3 \\ \diagup \\ F_3C \end{matrix} \begin{matrix} \nearrow (F_3C)_2N-N-N-N(CF_3)_2 \\ \qquad\quad \underset{CF_3}{\overset{|}{}}\ \underset{CF_3}{\overset{|}{}} \\ \searrow (F_3C)_2N-N(CF_3)_2 \end{matrix} \begin{matrix} (12.17b) \\ \\ (12.17c) \end{matrix}$$

activation of the decomposition of hexafluoroazomethane with those of the corresponding reaction of azomethane and those of other radical processes.

Kodama and Takezaki have studied the thermolysis of azomethane in the presence of methanol (*1248*) and formaldehyde (*1249*). Methanol leads to ethane, methane, carbon monoxide, and formaldehyde at 300°, whereas with formaldehyde methane, carbon monoxide, glyoxal, 1,2-dimethylhydrazine, and hydrogen are formed, the following scheme being proposed in consequence:

$$H_3C-N=N-CH_3 \xrightarrow{\;300°\;} N_2 + 2\ \dot{C}H_3 \qquad (12.18\,a)$$

$$\dot{C}H_3 + HCHO \longrightarrow CH_4 + \dot{C}HO \qquad (12.18\,b)$$

$$\dot{C}HO + \dot{C}H_3 \longrightarrow CH_4 + CO \qquad (12.18\,c)$$

$$\dot{C}HO \longrightarrow CO + H^{\bullet} \qquad (12.18\,d)$$

$$H^{\bullet} + HCHO \longrightarrow H_2 + \dot{C}HO \qquad (12.18\,e)$$

$$2\ \dot{C}HO \longrightarrow O=CH-CH=O \qquad (12.18\,f)$$

$$2\ H^{\bullet} + H_3C-N=N-CH_3 \longrightarrow H_3C-NH-NH-CH_3 \qquad (12.18\,g)$$

The appearance of radicals in the thermolysis and photolysis of azomethane can be demonstrated by means of lead or tellurium mirrors, which are removed in the process (*1306, 2085*). Further, azomethane catalyses the cracking of ethane (*1954*).

The photolytic decomposition of azomethane proceeds by a mechanism largely analogous to that of thermolysis. Naturally, fission is catalysed especially by light which azomethane is capable of absorbing and Forbes, Heidt, and Stickman (*736*) have shown that the quantum yield is greatest at 335 to 366 mμ, that is, in the region of the long wavelength absorption band of azomethane (see § 13.1). Several determinations of the quantum yield all lead to a value of roughly unity (*262, 413, 1181*). X-rays also can initiate the same decomposition (*892*).

As in the decomposition by heat, the primary products are nitrogen and methyl radicals, the latter dimerizing subsequently to ethane. According to Jones and Steacie (*1181*), the formation of methane is due to the attack of a methyl radical on azomethane which is supposed to yield the unstable radical $H_3C\cdot N{:}N\cdot \dot{C}H_2$. This particle corresponds to the intermediate postulated by Kooyman and Bickel (*243, 1258*) for the reaction of azonitriles with trichloromethyl and thiyl radicals (see § 12.1).

From their experiments on the effect of light of 366 mμ on azoethane, Weininger and Rice (*2121*) concluded that absorption first gives an activated azoethane molecule, the minimum lifetime of which was calculated to be $2\cdot5 \times 10^{-11}$ sec. For the decomposition of this species these authors suggest not only synchronous cleavage of both C-N bonds, but also the formation of a diazoethyl radical (12.19a), nitrogen being liberated only subsequently (12.19b).

$$H_5C_2\!-\!N\!=\!N\!-\!C_2H_5 \xrightarrow{\,h\nu\,} \left[H_5C_2\!-\!N\!=\!N\!-\!C_2H_5 \right]^* \longrightarrow H_5C_2\!-\!N\!=\!N^{\boldsymbol{\cdot}}+ \dot{C}_2H_5 \qquad (12.19\,\mathrm{a})$$

$$H_5C_2\!-\!N\!=\!N^{\boldsymbol{\cdot}} \longrightarrow N_2 + \dot{C}_2H_5 \qquad (12.19\,\mathrm{b})$$

Diazoethyl radicals have also been postulated to take part in the photolysis of azomethane (629, 1581). Such mechanisms have so far not been found to apply to the thermal decomposition of azoalkanes in solution, even in favourable cases (e.g. R·N:N·Ar), as already discussed in § 12.1. Certainly diazoalkane radicals would be very unstable, since reaction (12.19b) is strongly exothermic. All the same, their appearance as intermediates is somewhat more likely in photolysis than in thermolysis, as light at 366 mμ is hardly absorbed by these radicals in contrast to the parent azoalkane. Cohen and Wang (448, 450) were able to show that the rate of the thermal decomposition of unsubstituted azoalkanes increases in roughly equal steps from azomethane to 2-(methylazo)-propane to 1,1'-dimethylazoethane (azoisopropane). Such a result is readily understood on the basis of a concerted mechanism because of the greater stability of the isopropyl radical. If, however, R—N=N· radicals are produced in the first place, 2-(methylazo)propane would be expected to possess practically the same rate of decomposition as the di-isopropyl compound.

Steacie and his co-workers (88, 629) have concerned themselves with the fate of the alkyl radicals from azoethane and 1,1'-dimethylazoethane (azo-isopropane) and found that ethyl radicals dimerize about seven times more rapidly than they undergo disproportionation to ethane and ethylene. In the photolysis of azomethane at greater temperatures higher hydrocarbons, probably propane, are obtained as by-products (397, 398, 533).

The photolysis of substituted azoalkanes has received some attention. Note-worthy are experiments with hexafluoroazomethane (521, 1662): according to Pritchard tetrakis(trifluoromethyl)hydrazine and hexakis(trifluoromethyl)te-trazane are formed [see equations (12.17a–c)]. The photolysis of azodi-isobutyro-nitrile in benzene solution using filtered ultra-violet light exhibits a very high quantum yield (0·43) (119). A detailed kinetic study of this reaction has been published recently by P. Smith et al. (1911, 2356).

Frequently the photolysis of azomethane has been employed, particularly by Steacie [cf. (89–92)], as a source of methyl radicals, when the reactivity of the latter towards other compounds was to be studied. Others (89–92, 533, 1063, 1789, 2007) have carried out the decomposition in the presence of hydrogen, oxygen, nitric oxide, or oxygen–propane mixtures. The primary process, namely, the formation of nitrogen and two methyl radicals, is not affected by hydrogen, nitric oxide, or oxygen. Oxygen reacts with the methyl radicals to give methanol and formaldehyde, which subsequently polymerizes (1063). The addition of azomethane to oxygen–propane mixtures enables cold flames to be obtained at temperatures (255° to 270°) at which they normally do not yet appear (1789). In the presence of nitric oxide, methyl radicals combine with it to form nitrosomethane which dimerizes subsequently (2426).

12.3 The Applications of Aliphatic Azo Compounds

It has already been mentioned in § 12.1 that the interest in aliphatic azo compounds increased greatly after 1949, when the suitability as polymerization initiator of the readily available azodi-isobutyronitrile became recognized.

Even before then the fact that nitrogen is evolved in the thermolysis of azo-di-isobutyronitrile had been exploited technically. The I.G. Farbenindustrie marketed this compound under the name Porophore N as a blowing agent for resins based on polyvinyl chloride and it is still manufactured by Farbenfabriken Bayer. Porophore N is worked into the mass in the cold and behaves in the process rather like a plasticizer, that is, it presumably dissolves to become molecularly dispersed. On heating, the liberation of nitrogen leads to light foams with very fine pores. The action is much better than that of additives, such as sodium bicarbonate, which are only mixed in mechanically and have an effect like that of baking powder.

From a purely chemical point of view, the use of aliphatic azo compounds as chain initiators in polymerization holds much greater interest. It is surprising that this aspect of the azoalkanes had been almost totally neglected before 1949, though Schulz (*1851, 1852*) already described the polymerization of styrene by means of phenylazotriphenylmethane in 1939. From a report about the dangers in handling azodi-isobutyronitrile (*414*) it can be concluded that the application of this compound to polymerization on the large scale must have set in towards the end of the 'forties. After the appearance of the decisive publications of K. Ziegler (*2219*) and Overberger (*1577*), as well as that of Lewis and Matheson (*1339*), aliphatic azo compounds, especially azodi-iso-butyronitrile and 1,1'-azodicyclohexanecarbonitrile, became widely used for polymerization both scientifically and technologically.

The essential question is why this class of substances has achieved such importance for this purpose. The reason is connected with the characteristics of the homolytic fission of azo compounds: as is apparent from Table 12.1 of § 12.1, azodi-isobutyronitrile decomposes at moderate temperatures at a rate technically interesting. However, unsubstituted azoalkanes are not reactive enough and even benzoyl peroxide, the classic polymerization initiator, needs a temperature about 15° higher than that required by azodi-isobutyronitrile. The rule that substituents which mesomerically stabilize the radicals to be formed increase the rate of the homolysis has general validity, but for the same reason the radicals obtained are too stable to attack other molecules and so to start a chain reaction. This applies quite generally to compounds which are 'one-bond initiators' in Bartlett's terminology (*194*).

However, as explained in § 12.1, azo compounds exhibit simultaneous homolytic fission of *two* links ('two-bond initiators'), two radicals being formed as well as a molecule of nitrogen. Here also the rate of decomposition is determined principally by the stability of the products. But whilst in the case of one-bond initiators a high rate of formation of radicals must be bought with the great stability of the radicals obtained, in the case of azo compounds the rapidity of decomposition is determined by the enormous stability of *one* of the products, the nitrogen molecule. This permits the formation at low temperatures (40° to 70°) of relatively unstable radicals, that is, those well suited to initiate chains.

The rate of decomposition of initiators is very important in polymerizations because it exerts considerable influence on the kinetics of the overall process. In the steady state, the rate of polymerization depends according to equation (12.20) on the square root of the concentration of the initiator as well as on that of its rate of decomposition [see, for example, (*187, 735, 1278, 2103a*)].

$$v_{\text{total}} = \frac{-\,\mathrm{d}\,[M]}{\mathrm{d}t} = k_p \left[\, f k_i / 2\, k_t \,\right]^{\frac{1}{2}} [M]\,[I]^{\frac{1}{2}} \tag{12.20}$$

where v_{total} is the overall rate of polymerization

$\quad$ [M] $\quad$ is the concentration of monomer

$\quad$ [I] $\quad$ is the concentration of initiator

$\quad$ k_i $\quad$ is the rate constant of the decomposition of the initiator into radicals

$\quad$ k_p $\quad$ is the rate constant of chain propagation

$\quad$ k_t $\quad$ is the sum of rate constants of the chain termination reactions, and

$\quad$ f $\quad$ denotes initiator efficiency.

The formation of the radicals from the initiator is followed by addition to a molecule of monomer, but, because of the cage effect (see § 12.1), some of the radicals are lost through recombination. Hence not all the molecules of the initiator take part in the polymerization and by initiator efficiency is designated that fraction which successfully reacts with the monomer.

As illustration may be cited the values for $f k_i$ obtained by Baysal and Tobolsky (*213*) for the polymerization of styrene at 60° in the presence of various initiators:

azodi-isobutyronitrile	$f k_i = 128 \quad \times 10^{-7}$ l. mol.$^{-1}$ sec^{-1}
benzoyl peroxide	$29{\cdot}6 \ \times 10^{-7}$
cumene hydroperoxide	$6{\cdot}12 \times 10^{-7}$
t-butyl hydroperoxide	$1{\cdot}00 \times 10^{-7}$

With methyl methacrylate the values are about 10 to 20% smaller, probably because of lower initiator efficiency. By comparing the reaction products and by physicochemical means, it has been shown repeatedly [e.g. (*316, 2221*)] that the mechanism of polymerization when azo compounds are used corresponds to that with other initiators. Under some circumstances it may happen that only one of the two radicals formed from unsymmetrical azo compounds is sufficiently reactive to set off a chain. Schulz's observation (*1851*) that in the polymerization of styrene with phenylazotriphenylmethane one and not two molecules of polystyrene are produced by each molecule of the azo derivative is presumably in the first place not due to recombination, but to the inability of the relatively stable triphenylmethyl radical to initiate formation of polymer. Similar results were obtained by Chadra and Misra (*418*).

The dependence of the rate of polymerization on the square root of the concentration of the initiator, expressed by equation (12.20), has been confirmed several times for azodi-isobutyronitrile, 1,1'-azodicyclohexanecarbonitrile, and similar azo compounds, for example, by Schulz (*1853*), Overberger (*1569*), and others (*9, 213, 1091, 1176*).

The elucidation of the mechanism of the chain termination reactions represents an important problem for fundamental technological research into polymerization. In starting a chain, *one* initiator radical is built into it. The final chain molecule will therefore contain two such residues if termination occurred through the combination of two chains, but only one if termination were due to disproportionation, i.e. transfer of a hydrogen atom. The number of particles derived from the initiator and present in each fibrous molecule can be elegantly determined by means of radioactive initiators. For this purpose azodi-isobutyronitrile is well suited, as the synthesis of the C^{14}-analogue is straightforward. Bevington, Melville, and their co-workers (*238, 239, 241, 264*) have explored the method in detail and have shown, for example, that in the polymerization of methyl methacrylate the ratio of combination to disproportionation is 1:6. Walling (*2101*) was able to demonstrate kinetically that in copolymerizations of styrene–methyl acrylate and of styrene–methyl methacrylate, initiated by azodi-isobutyronitrile, the combination of two different radicals occurs 13 and 50 times more frequently than the geometric mean of the two symmetric termination reactions.

Bickel and Waters (*246*) as well as Japanese workers (*1895*) were able to isolate dimers and oligomers from reactions initiated by azo compounds.

Aliphatic azo derivatives are very suitable for the photo-initiation of chain reactions, since they absorb light in the relatively long wave ultra-violet region [cf. (*119, 862, 1339, 1378, 1423, 1453*)]. Apart from investigations of the quantum yield (*119, 1339*), Miyama's researches (*1453*) are especially noteworthy. For the photosensitization of the polymerization of styrene by 1,1'-dimethylazoethane, he experimentally confirmed equation (12.20) not only as regards the concentration of the sensitizer, but also as regards the amount of light (which enters into k_i).

In connection with the uses of azo compounds as initiators it is worth mentioning that substances, which are here dealt with in other chapters, are employed as polymerization additives. Examples are diazoamino compounds, particularly 3,3-dimethyl-1-phenyltriazene (*619*), and aryldiazothioethers (*1695, 1696, 2505*). Reynolds's observation (*1695*) that the rate of polymerization in the presence of aryldiazothioethers is directly proportional to the concentration of the initiator can be explained by supposing that only one of the two radicals (presumably the phenyl radical) formed on azo decomposition possesses sufficient energy to start a chain.

12.4 Reactions of Azodiformic Acid and its Esters

Azodicarbonyl compounds $(R \cdot CO \cdot N : N \cdot CO \cdot R)$ and the esters of azodiformic acid constitute as regards their reaction behaviour a link between the purely aliphatic and the purely aromatic azo derivatives. Although the photolysis and thermolysis of diaroyldi-imides (azodiaroyls) (§ 12.1) still resembles strongly the homolytic decomposition of the azoalkanes, some characteristic differences are already apparent. Typical of esters of azodiformic acid is the hetero- and homolytic reactivity of the azo bridge itself and especially its participation as dienophile in Diels–Alder reactions.

The parent compound, azodiformic acid itself, was obtained by Thiele (*2028*) in attempting to prepare di-imide. It is considerably less stable than its esters and the decomposition was the subject of a detailed kinetic study by King (*1215*, *1216*). According to mechanism (12.21), the final products are nitrogen, hydrazine, and carbon dioxide.

$$2 \, N_2(COO)_2^{\ominus\ominus} + 2 \, H^{\oplus} \underset{\text{slow}}{\rightleftharpoons} 2 \, HN_2(COO)_2^{\ominus} \xrightarrow[+\,H_2O]{\text{rapid}} N_2 + N_2H_4 + 3 \, CO_2 + CO_3^{\ominus\ominus} \quad (12.21)$$

The rate-determining step here is the addition of a proton to one of the azo nitrogen atoms and it has significance also for electrophilic substitution by esters of azodiformic acid. Such reactions were investigated systematically in the 'twenties by the schools of Diels and Stollé, after they had shown (*584*, *587*, *1959*) that interaction between an ester and dimethylaniline leads to the arylhydrazinedicarboxylic acid derivatives (**XXXX**) (12.22). Diels observed that

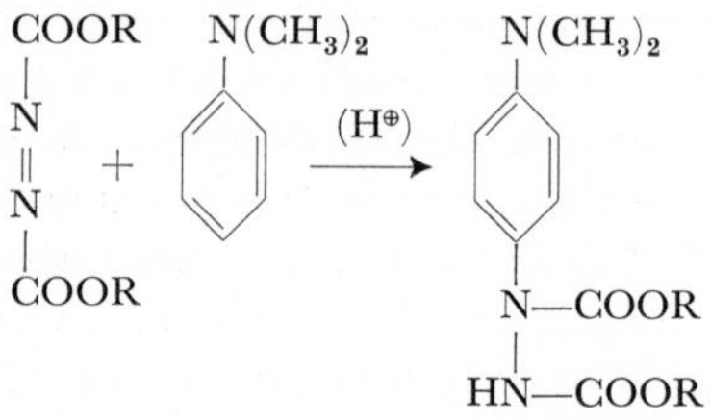

$$(12.22)$$

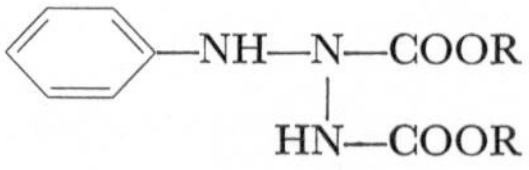

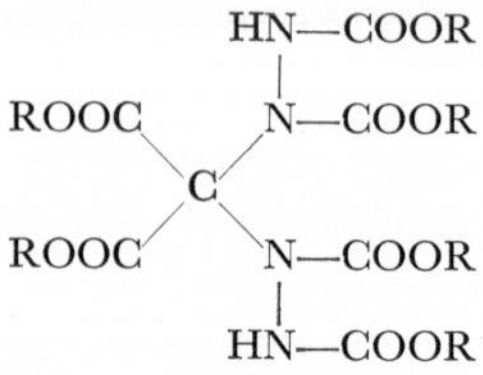

2-naphthylamine reacts in the 1-position to give the analogous naphthylhydrazine (*578*, *581*). On the other hand, in the case of aniline it is not the aromatic ring, but the amino group which is attacked, the triazane (**XXXXI**) resulting. Similarly, alcohols and mercaptans are substituted at the oxygen and sulphur atom, respectively (*589*). *C*-Substitution occurs, however, with enols, phenols, phenol ethers, and compounds containing reactive methylene groups (*578, 582, 1963*), malonic ester, for instance, readily yielding the disubstituted derivative (**XXXXII**). From these reactions it can be seen that the esters of azodiformic acid behave as electrophilic reagents and that there is a striking parallel to azo coupling, because in both types of reaction aniline undergoes *N*- and not *C*-attack.

In fact, these esters are more reactive than most diazonium ions, since benzene (*1962*), naphthalene, biphenyl (*1961*), etc. are smoothly substituted in the nucleus.

Important is the observation that the reactions are catalysed by sulphuric acid and hydrogen chloride. In consequence, mechanism (12.23) probably applies. As the hydrazine residue introduced facilitates substitution in the nucleus, there frequently follows reaction with a second equivalent of azodiformic ester to give a disubstituted derivative, for example, in the case of benzene (*1962*) and of malonic ester (**XXXXII**) (*582*).

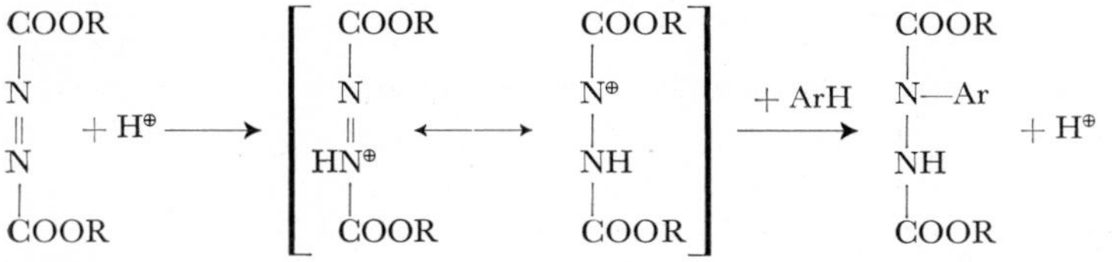

$$
\begin{array}{c}
\text{COOR} \\
| \\
\text{N} \\
\| \quad +\text{H}^{\oplus} \\
\text{N} \\
| \\
\text{COOR}
\end{array}
\longrightarrow
\left[
\begin{array}{ccc}
\text{COOR} & & \text{COOR} \\
| & & | \\
\text{N} & & \text{N}^{\oplus} \\
\| & \longleftrightarrow & | \\
\text{HN}^{\oplus} & & \text{NH} \\
| & & | \\
\text{COOR} & & \text{COOR}
\end{array}
\right]
\xrightarrow{+\,\text{ArH}}
\begin{array}{c}
\text{COOR} \\
| \\
\text{N—Ar} \\
| \quad +\text{H}^{\oplus} \\
\text{NH} \\
| \\
\text{COOR}
\end{array}
\qquad (12.23)
$$

Recently, Huisgen and his co-workers (*1118*) showed that the ready availability of the products of the interaction of azodiformic acid esters and aromatic hydrocarbons has provided a general method of preparation for unsymmetric arylmethylhydrazines, otherwise only made with difficulty. The esters of arylhydrazinedicarboxylic acids obtained in the first stage are smoothly reduced with aluminium lithium hydride, only the COOR group attached to the tertiary nitrogen being affected. Thus the nuclear monosubstituted *p*-xylene is converted into pure monoester in more than 60% yield (12.24).

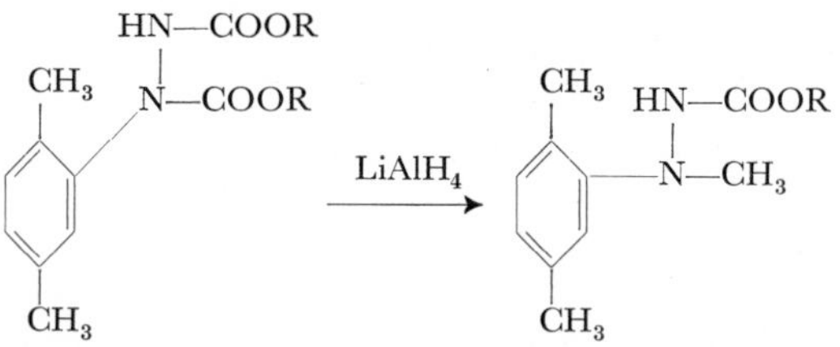

$$(12.24)$$

The reaction of diazoalkanes with azodiformic acid esters, discussed in § 5.4, is of the same type.

Apart from these electrophilic substitutions, the esters of azodiformic acid can also enter into homolytic ones. For example, Alder *et al.* (*13, 14, 16*) found that

1,2,3,4-tetrahydronaphthalene is attacked by the ester in the hydrogenated ring with formation of the hydrazine (**XXXXIII**). Experiments with initiators,

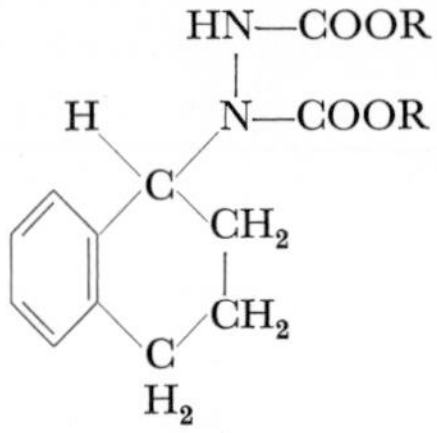

XXXXIII

such as azodi-isobutyronitrile among others, and inhibitors led Huisgen (*1118*) and Horner (*1078*) to postulate the chain mechanism (12.25) for the reaction with fluorene.

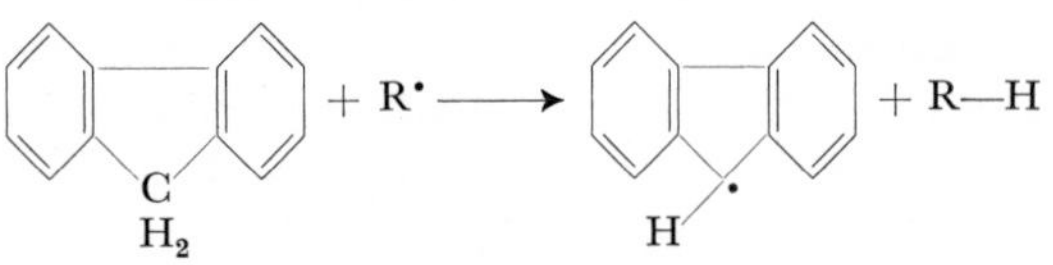

(12.25 a)

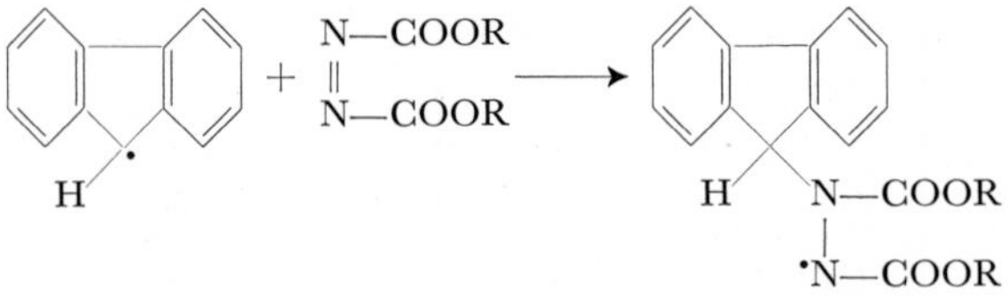

(12.25 b)

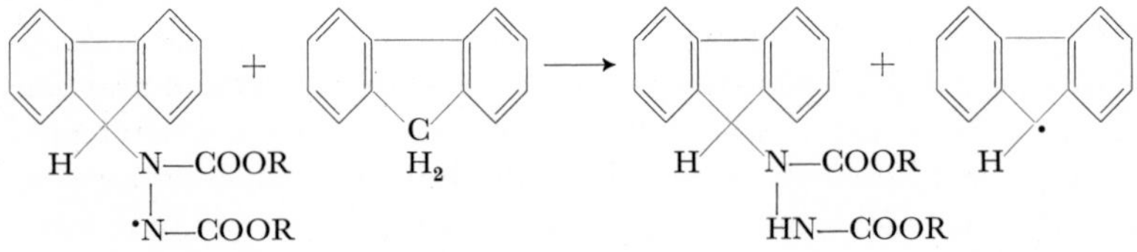

(12.25 c)

The reaction with aldehydes (12.26) (*15*) and ketones (*1119*) and the substitution of olefins in the 'allyl position' (*16*) also proceed by homolysis. Huisgen's

$$(12.26)$$

$$RCHO \xrightarrow{-H^{\bullet}} RCO^{\bullet} \xrightarrow{(ROOC-N=)_2} R-CO-N-COOR \xrightarrow{+H^{\bullet}} R-CO-N-COOR$$
$$\quad\quad\quad\quad\quad\quad\quad\quad\quad\quad\quad\quad ^{\bullet}N-COOR \quad\quad\quad\quad HN-COOR$$

investigation of the substitution of cyclohexanone is of interest, because it has been proved unequivocally that, apart from a radical process resulting in the ester of 2-oxocyclohexylbicarbamic acid, a heterolytic route exists which is catalysed by bases. Mechanism (12.27) has been suggested for it. Recently, Huisgen (*2394*) submitted the reaction of azodiformic acid esters with the allyl position of olefins to detailed study. Here also two mechanisms, a homolytic and a heterolytic one, are operative.

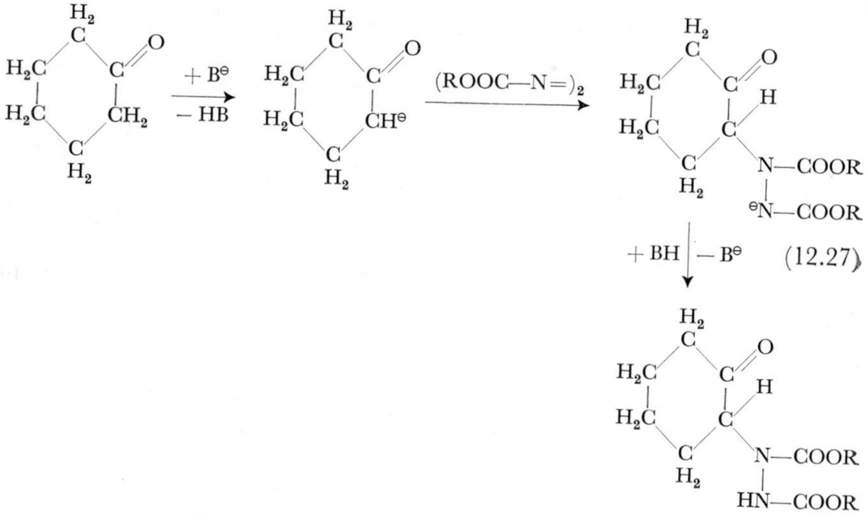

$$+ B^\ominus \atop - HB \quad (ROOC—N=)_2 \quad + BH \Big| - B^\ominus \quad (12.27)$$

Further evidence for the radical reactivity of azodiformic acid esters comes from their ready acceptance of hydrogen, capable as they are of dehydrogenating, for example, hydriodic acid (*1118*), hydroquinone (*584*), and substituted hydrazines (*579*). Schenck and Formanek (*1791*) have found that under the influence of light the esters become particularly powerful dehydrogenating agents, which can attack alcohols, ether, and even hydrocarbons.

In the history of chemistry pride of place is given to the reaction of azodicarboxylic acid esters with dienes, since the Diels–Alder synthesis was discovered not with ethylene derivatives, but with these esters (*580, 583*). Butadienes, such as isoprene (*580*), yield tetrahydropyridazines (**XXXXIV**), cyclopentadiene (*583*) 2,3-diazabicyclo[2.2.1]-hept-5-ene-2,3-dicarboxylic acid ester (**XXXXV**), anthracene (*588*) the 9,10-addition product (**XXXXVI**), and so on [see e.g.

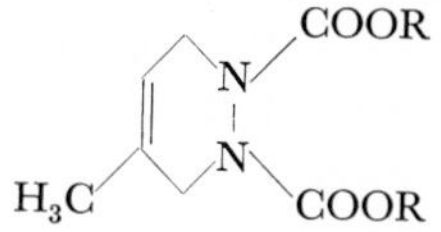

XXXXIV

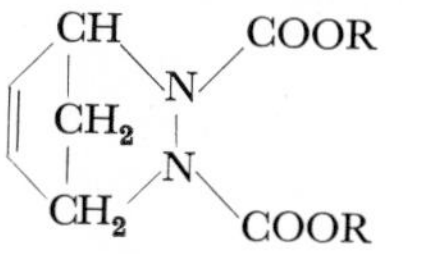

XXXXV

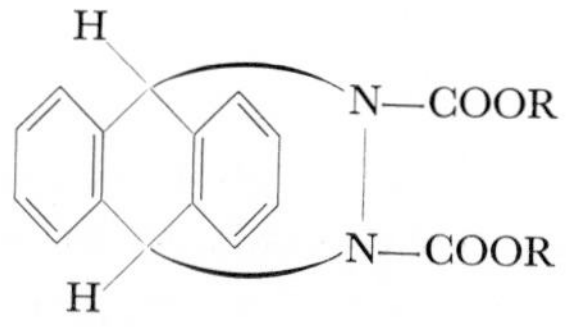

XXXXVI

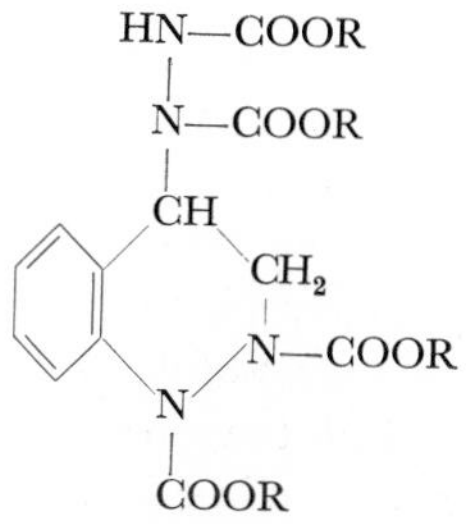

XXXXVII

(13, 14, 189, 1328, 1388)]. The reaction with styrene, which adds one equivalent of azodiformic acid ester as a diene and one as a nucleophilic substrate to give (**XXXXVII**) *(580)*, is interesting.

In connection with these N,N'-additions it is worth mentioning briefly the reactions of ketenes with esters of azodiformic acid and with azobenzene. Photolysis of azibenzil in the presence of the esters has been shown to produce the hexahydropyridazinedione (**XXXXVIII**) by Horner and Spietschka *(1084)*. The same compound is also obtained in a dark reaction with diphenylketene *(1156)* and this indicates that in the photolysis the primary process is formation of the ketene. Azibenzil or diphenylketene attacks azobenzene with or without irradiation to yield the diazacyclobutanone derivative (**XXXXIX**) *(464, 1082, 1084)*.

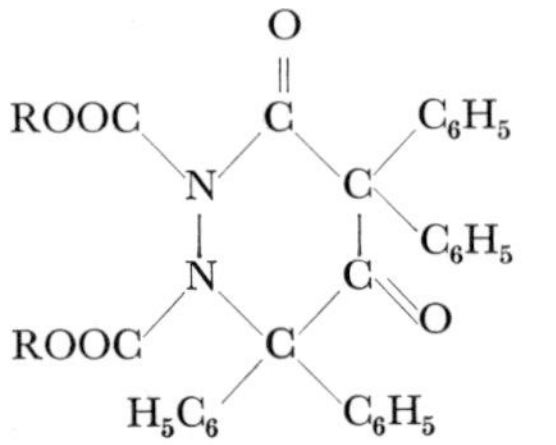

XXXXVIII 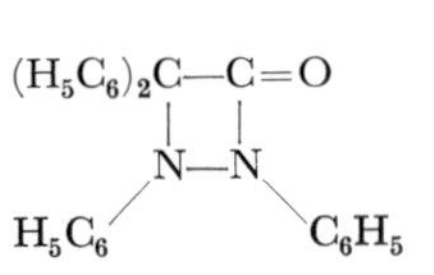   XXXXIX

12.5 Reactions of Aromatic Azo Compounds

Although aromatic azo compounds have been prominent as dyestuffs for some ninety years, their chemical reactions have not been investigated widely or systematically. This can be attributed to two factors.

The first is that dyestuffs technologists see little incentive for trying to obtain deeper insight into the behaviour of azo compounds. On the face of it, this seems justified, since azo dyes are the *end* products of the manufacturing processes and their application lies in fields, such as that of textile chemistry, which are outside the realm of synthetic organic chemistry. For this reason a discovery of fundamental importance for the understanding of aromatic azo derivatives, namely, the *trans–cis* isomerization of azobenzene on irradiation, was made only relatively recently, in 1938, and not in the context of research into azo dyestuffs. However, in connection with fastness to light it is very desirable that much more attention should be paid by dyestuffs technologists to the chemical behaviour of azo compounds in this respect. As will become apparent in § 12.7, very little is known to date.

The second factor is purely chemical. In many reactions of aromatic azo compounds mixtures of products are formed, for example, by disproportionation through simultaneous oxidation and reduction. This frequently detracts from the usefulness of azo derivatives for synthetic purposes. Indeed it is for this reason that very few reactions, particularly of azo *dyestuffs*, have been reported.

Thus, until recently only rarely have attempts been successful to convert sulphonic and carboxylic acids of azo dyes into their acid chlorides. Schroeter (*1844*) tried in vain to obtain sulphonyl chlorides by means of phosphorus pentachloride, but Goldireff and Postowskij (*821*) were able to prepare the acid chloride of Orange II [see formula (**XXV**) of § 13.3] using chlorosulphonic acid. The systematic investigation carried out by M. Schmid and his co-workers (*1814, 2519, 2572*) showed later that azo dyes bearing carboxylic or sulphonic groups smoothly yield acid chlorides under mild conditions when treated with phosphorus pentachloride or thionyl chloride in organic solvents. Thionyl chloride in the presence of dimethylformamide proved particularly suitable (*2579*), even though thionyl chloride alone is incapable of converting sulphonic acids into their chlorides. The mechanism of this catalysis by dimethylformamide has been clarified (*293*) and shown to be closely connected with the formation of α,α-dichloroamines (RR′N—CCl$_2$R″) (*294*). The reaction is not restricted to azo compounds and constitutes the general method of preparing carbonyl and sulphonyl chlorides which gives the highest yields under very mild conditions.

Azo compounds with a hydroxy or amino group in *o*-position to the azo bridge do not need to have these protected before conversion into acid chlorides by this method. The hydrogen bond between the *o*-substituent and the β-azo nitrogen suffices for these groups to withstand the action of thionyl chloride or even phosphorus pentachloride under the mild conditions employed. However, in the technically important *o,o′*-dihydroxyazo dyes only one of the two hydroxy groups is chelated strongly enough to resist attack and so these compounds have to be submitted to a preliminary acetylation or benzoylation.

Carbonyl chlorides of azo dyes have lately achieved considerable importance in the preparation of pigments (*2572*). The range of Cromophtal pigments (Ciba) is selected from compounds made from such chlorides and diamines [e.g. (**L**)]. It would appear possible to synthesize (**L**) from two equivalents of

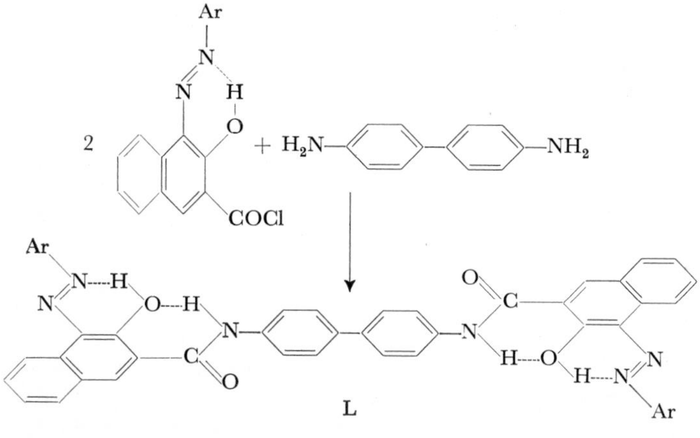

(12.28)

ArN$_2$Cl and bis(3-hydroxy-2-naphthoyl)benzidine, but, in fact, the product obtained by this route is insufficiently pure, since the monoazo compound formed first is very difficultly soluble and therefore only reacts partially with the second molecule of the diazonium salt.

Azobenzene undergoes electrophilic substitution, the incoming groups being generally directed into the *p*- and *p'*-positions. Thus cold fuming nitric acid gives 4-nitroazobenzene, together with some 4-nitroazoxybenzene as well as 4,4'-dinitroazobenzene (*2135*). Among the products of nitration at higher temperatures 2,4,4'-, 2,3',4-, and 2,2',4-trinitroazoxybenzene have been found (*1231, 2135*). In the nitration of 4,4'-dichloroazobenzene the azo group is also oxidized, 4,4'-dichloro-2-nitroazoxybenzene being formed (*2428*).

Sulphonation with oleum at 130° yields, as expected, the 4-mono- and the 4,4'-di-sulphonic acids (*879*), but at higher temperatures (150° to 170°) the 3,4'-disulphonic acid is obtained in addition (*1288*).

Bromination in the absence of solvent produces 4,4'-dibromoazobenzene (*2126, 2127*), but in glacial acetic acid all the three monosubstituted derivatives are formed simultaneously (*1166, 1167*). The substituents already present in azobenzene do not always exert the directing effect anticipated. Whilst, for example, the failure to obtain 2,4-dinitroazobenzene or the bromination of 3-monomethylazobenzene in the 4-position (*395*) are comprehensible, it is surprising that according to Burns, McCombie, and Scarborough (*395*) under conditions effective for the bromination of azobenzene or 3-monomethylazobenzene, the 4-isomer of the latter remains unattacked.

P. W. Robertson, Hitchings, and Will (*1722*) were able to provide an explanation by means of a kinetic study. The bromination of azobenzene is catalysed by hydrogen bromide and the reaction only occurs at a measurable rate when hydrogen bromide is present. Water retards bromination in glacial acetic acid. It may be concluded that the first step consists of the addition of HBr to the azo bridge (12.29). One benzene ring of the intermediate (LI) formed carries a

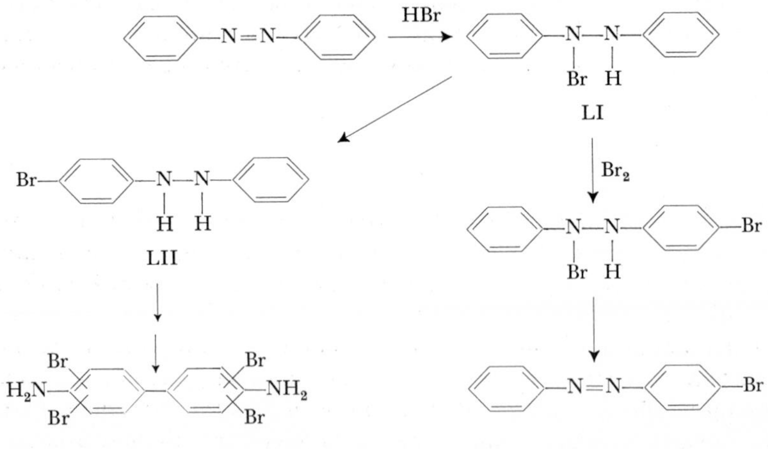

(12.29)

substituted amino group and so readily undergoes electrophilic substitution. In addition, a kind of Orton rearrangement can convert (LI) into 4-bromohydra-

zobenzene (LII), which by further bromination and a benzidine rearrangement
is able to give rise to tetrabromobenzidine, already found as a by-product of the
bromination of azobenzene a long time ago by Mills (*1446*).

According to Robertson *et al.* in the case of 4-methylazobenzene, (LIII) is the
intermediate formed. The reactivity of the 4′-position is lowered by the NBr-

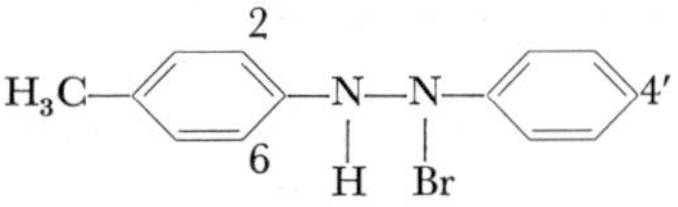

LIII

group and the 2- and the 6-positions are sterically hindered, the consequence
being that the compound is brominated with more difficulty than azobenzene.

Analogously, the chlorination of azobenzene proved to be dependent on the
concentration of hydrogen chloride.

Although mechanism (12.29) explains the experimental results, it remains
desirable that azobenzene substitution should be submitted to an even more
detailed examination.

P. W. Robertson, de la Mare, and Swedlund (*1721*) have compared the rate of
halogenation of azobenzene with that of benzene and found that each phenyl
group of azobenzene is brominated 4·6 times as rapidly as benzene. In view of
mechanism (12.29) the significance of this ratio is questionable, since the kinetic
investigations (*1722*) were not pursued to the stage where one can deduce from
the rate constants determined whether they refer to the rate of the substitution
proper or whether they contain the rate of formation of (LII) or the equilibrium
azobenzene ⇌ (LII).

It also seems uncertain whether the phenylazo group should be classified as a
$+M, -I$ substituent. It is a striking fact that Hampson and J. M. Robertson
(*920*) found the C—N and N:N bonds of *trans*-azobenzene to have practically
the same lengths as those of azomethane. It is therefore doubtful whether limiting structures such as (LIV) play a large part in unsubstituted azobenzene.

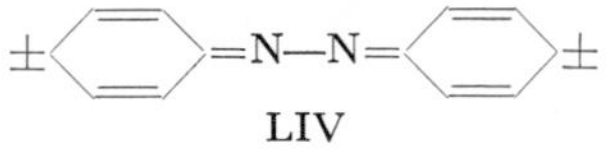

LIV

However, LCAO–MO treatment of azobenzene, using the frontier electron concept and carried out by Fukui *et al.* (*773*), pointed to considerable conjugation
between the azo bridge and the phenyl residues as well as to a high electron
density at the *p*-positions.

Determinations of dipole moments of 4-amino- and 4-nitro-azobenzene due
to Campbell, McAllister, and Rogers (*407*) show that substituents able to exert
large mesomeric effects ($+M$ or $-M$) alter the *whole* double bond system of azobenzene. Table 12.2 contains some of these data, together with those from earlier determinations and the dipole moments of compounds without the phenylazo group for comparison. It can be seen that the dipole moments of azobenze-

Table 12.2

Dipole Moments of Derivatives of trans-*Azobenzene*

Substituent	Dipole moment of derivative of		ΔD	Reference
	Azobenzene	Benzene		
4-NH$_2$	2·48 D	1·54 D	0·94	(407)
4-N(CH$_3$)$_2$	3·22 D	1·58 D	1·64	(408)
4-NO$_2$	4·45 D	3·95 D	0·50	(407)
4-Cl	1·55 D	1·57 D	$\sim$0	(2139)

nes bearing strongly electron-releasing substituents (NH$_2$, NR$_2$) in the 4-position are considerably larger than those of the corresponding benzene derivatives. In nitrobenzene also the dipole moment increases on introducing a *p*-phenylazo residue, but the change is less marked than in compounds with electron-releasing substituents. There is no evidence for interaction between a chlorine atom and the phenylazo group.

Arylazo residues facilitate nucleophilic substitution. Thus, Stepanov (*1951, 2301, 2302*) was able to replace the chlorine of 1-(2'-chlorophenylazo)-2-naphthol by methoxy, ethoxy, phenoxy, and other groups by heating the azo compound for several hours with sodium alcoholate or phenolate in the corresponding alcohol or phenol and an inert solvent and with the addition of copper salts. However, it may be that the intermediate formation of a copper complex is more important in bringing about this substitution than the electronic effects of the phenylazo group.

The presence of phenylazo residues facilitates other reactions which otherwise occur hardly or not at all: Poskočil and Allan (*2403*) recently observed that the CH$_3$CO group in azo dyes made by coupling *o*- or *p*-diazophenols to acetoacetanilide can be split off easily. The same school (*2357*) also reported that in the preparation of polyazo dyes by several consecutive diazotizations and couplings dimerization occurs often.

There are relatively few investigations on the hydrolysis of azo dyes [cf. (*83*)], probably because in most cases mixtures are formed. Chmátal and Allan (*2380*) made a kinetic study of the hydrolysis of aminoazo compounds, in which attention was paid to the influence of the acidity of the solvent and the effect of substituents. The hydrolysis is catalysed by ethanol.

The oxidation and the reduction of azobenzene and its derivatives have been explored relatively intensively. The oxidation is preparatively important as a route to *azoxy compounds*. Azoxybenzene was discovered by Zinin (*2225*) more than a hundred years ago. It is obtained as a by-product in the reduction of nitrobenzene to hydrazobenzene in an alkaline medium, being formed from the nitrosobenzene and phenylhydroxylamine which appear as intermediates. The yield of azoxybenzene is improved when nitrobenzene is treated with boiling methanolic potassium hydroxide, the methanol being oxidized to formaldehyde. However, the most reliable method of preparation is the oxidation of azobenzene. The oxidizing agents of choice are hydrogen peroxide (*38, 48*), peroxyacetic acid (*2323*), and peroxybenzoic acid (*121, 127, 128, 2349*). Electrochemical oxidation (*703*) does indeed give azoxybenzene (LV) primarily, but the reaction proceeds further to yield a mixture of products, consisting essentially of *p*-phenylazophenol (LVI, through rearrangement of azoxybenzene), *p,p′*-azodiphenol (LVII), and 4,4′-di(*p*-hydroxyphenylazo)biphenyl (LVIII).

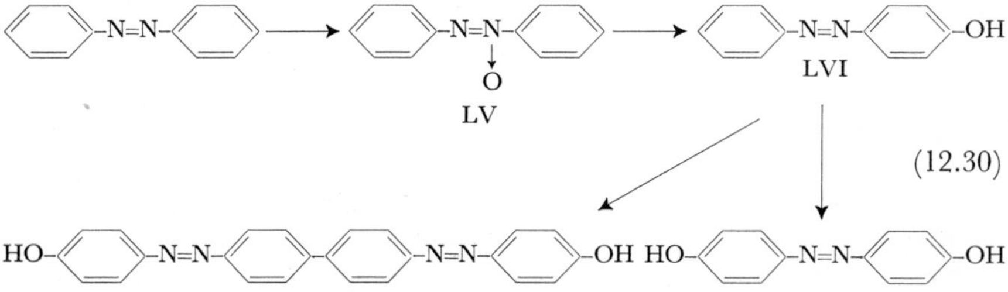

(12.30)

Angeli (*36, 38, 40, 41, 46, 48, 49*) showed in 1906 that the oxidation of monosubstituted azobenzenes gives two isomeric azoxy compounds. This disproved Kekulé's three-membered ring formulation of the azoxy bridge (—N——N—)
                                                                                         \O/
(*1202*) and led to the realization of its *N*-oxide structure (LV). Angeli's formula received further support from the resolution of racemates of the type of (LIX) by Marvel (*422*) and E. Müller (*1488*).

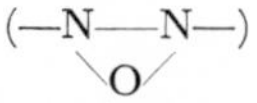

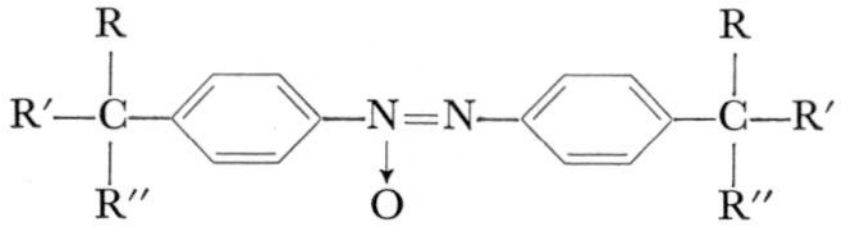

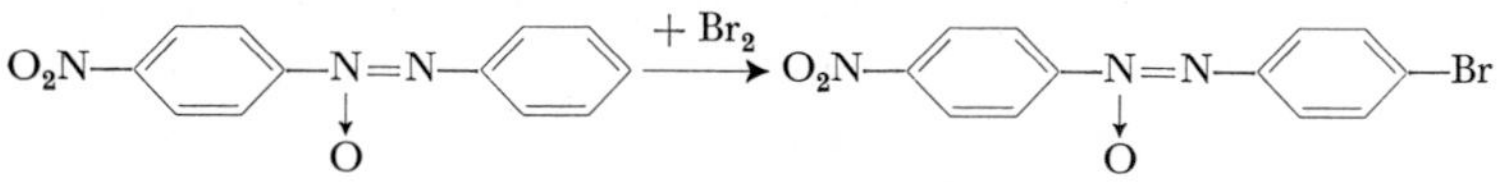

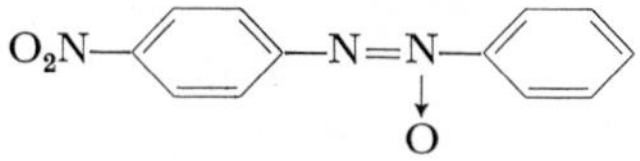

In order to assign structures to the two position isomers in the case of monosubstituted azoxybenzenes it is relevant to consider some experiments carried out by Angeli and Valori (*48*) on the further substitution of nitroazoxybenzenes. They observed that the so-called β-isomer (LX) can be brominated (12.31), but that the α-isomer (**LXI**) remains unchanged under the identical conditions. Hence the compounds must possess the structures shown.

Some years ago, L. C. Behr (*219*) synthesized the two isomers both of *p*-bromo- and of *p*-ethoxy-azoxybenzene unambiguously by route (12.32) via the corresponding indazole oxides (**LXII**), thus providing the final proof for Angeli's formulas.

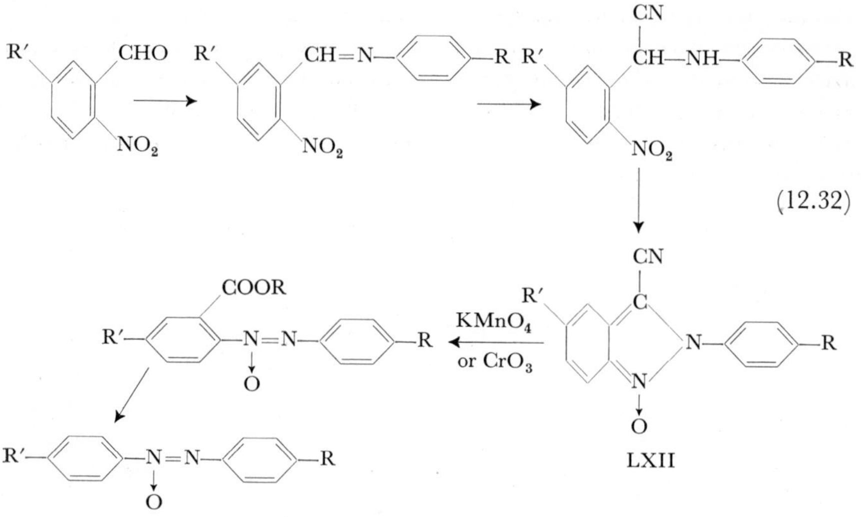

(12.32)

(a) R=Br, R′=H
(b) R=H, R′=Br
(c) R=OC$_2$H$_5$, R′=H
(d) R=H, R′=OC$_2$H$_5$

Quite apart from this position isomerism, azoxybenzene itself and its derivatives can occur both in *cis*- and in *trans*-forms. In fact, azoxybenzene was the first compound in which geometrical isomerism about the N:N bond could be demonstrated unequivocally by experiment. Eugen Müller and his school (*785, 1480, 1485, 1486, 1489*) as well as von Auwers (*98*) were able to differentiate between the *cis*- and the *trans*-isomer (**LXIII** and **LXIV**, respectively) by means of ultra-violet spectra and dipole moments. The spectra exhibit the same characteristic differences as other stereoisomeric pairs and the dipole moments (*cis*: 4·67 D; *trans*: 1·70 D) can only be explained by stereoisomerism. The *cis–trans* rearrangement is catalysed by light, heat, and halogens.

LXIII   LXIV
(*cis*)   (*trans*)

Badger and his co-workers (*121, 127, 128*) have studied in detail the formation of azoxy compounds by oxidation of the corresponding azo derivatives with peroxybenzoic acid. An almost quantitative yield of *trans*-azoxybenzene is obtained in this way from *trans*-azobenzene and *cis*-azobenzene gives *cis*-azoxybenzene, but the latter compound can only be isolated under mild conditions and in the dark as it readily rearranges into the *trans*-isomer. Unless these precautions are taken, solely *trans*-azoxybenzene is obtained (*463*).

Through reduction *trans*-azobenzene is easily obtained back again from *trans*-azoxybenzene (*1546*), but under all conditions *cis*-azoxybenzene gives *trans*-azobenzene with aluminium lithium hydride. Badger, Buttery, and Lewis (*121*) attribute this to mechanism (12.33), in which the N:N bond becomes single, thus allowing free rotation.

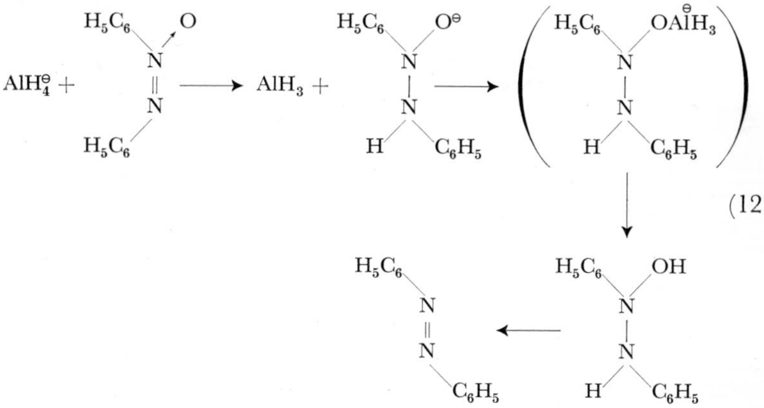

$$(12.33)$$

Peroxyacids are electrophilic reagents (*549, 1994, 1995*) and this is confirmed by the kinetics of the oxidation of substituted azobenzenes with peroxybenzoic acid (*127*). Electron-releasing substituents increase the rate of the reaction, electron-attracting ones decrease it. The effects of *m*- and *p*-substituents follow Hammett's free energy relation (*914b*). At 20° *cis*-azobenzene is attacked 58 times more rapidly than its *trans*-isomer. The origin of the difference lies in the fact that limiting structures of the type of (LXV) contribute much less to the ground state of *cis*-azobenzene than (LXVI) to that of the *trans*-compound, *cis*-azobenzene not being planar. (LXVI) causes the electron density and hence the ease of reaction at the N:N bridge of the *trans*-isomer to be less than in the *cis*-compound. The rates of oxidation of phenylazonaphthalenes and azonaphthalenes, as well as the constitution of the azoxy compounds formed in the case

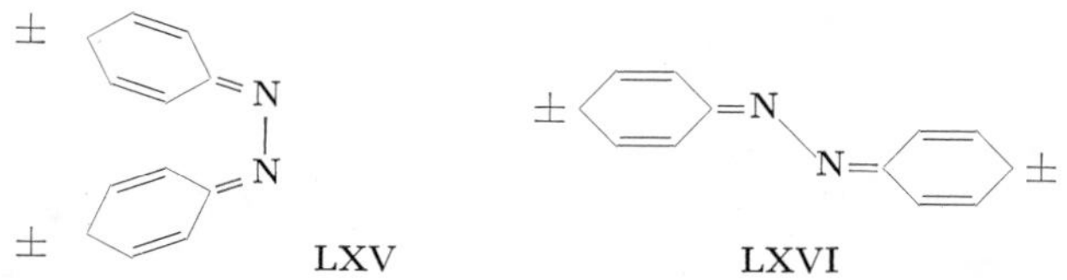

LXV   LXVI

of unsymmetric azo derivatives, can also be interpreted by means of electronic
and steric factors (*128*). Thus 1,2′-azonaphthalene and 1-phenylazonaphtha-
lene give azoxy compounds (**LXVII**) and (**LXVIII**), respectively, whilst 2-phe-
nylazonaphthalene yields the two isomers (**LXIX**) and (**LXX**) in a ratio of
59:41.

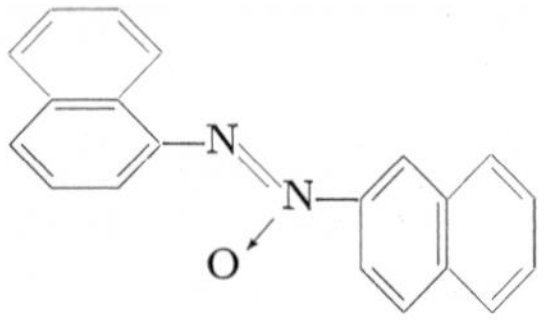

LXVII 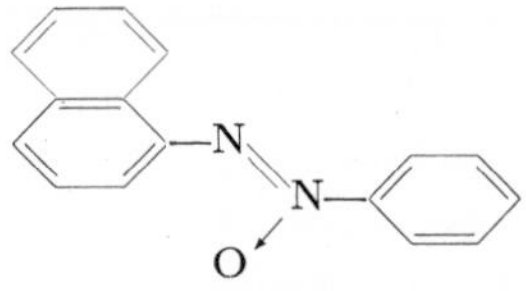   LXVIII

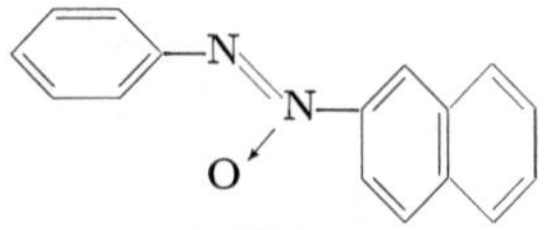

LXIX 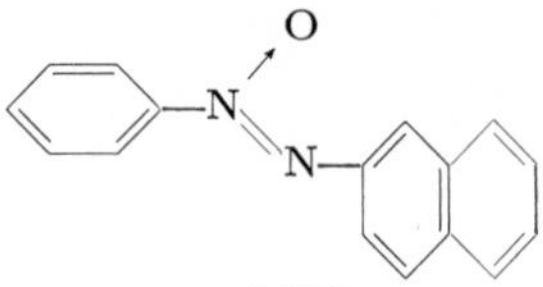   LXX

Mono-oxidation of *N*,*N*-dimethyl-*p*-phenylazoaniline (4-dimethylaminoazo-
benzene) leads to oxide formation at the amino group (*2349*) (see § 13.3). Similarly, the heterocyclic nitrogen is attacked in reactions with 4-phenylazopyri-
dine and 4-phenylazoquinoline (*2315*). A second oxygen atom can be added to
one of the azo nitrogens in all these cases.

Some aliphatic azoxy derivatives are known. For example, Lythgoe *et al.* (*339*)
were able to isolate and identify three of the four possible position and stereoisomers of the azoxy structures (**LXXI**, **LXXII**).

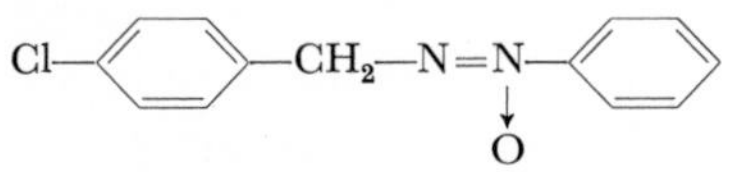

LXXI 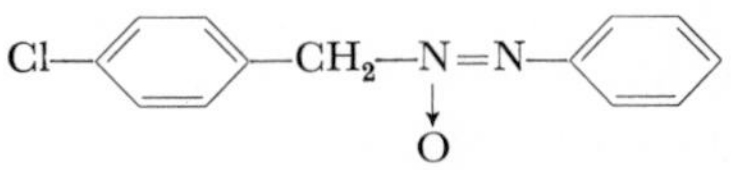   LXXII

Azo compounds have not so far been encountered in nature and only two
diazo derivatives, azaserine (*O*-diazoacetyl-L-serine) (*774, 775, 1461, 1527*) and
6-diazo-5-oxo-L-norleucine (DON) (*2313*), have been found to occur naturally. Both have been investigated intensively with respect to their tumor-inhi-
bitory activity. Several azoxy compounds have been isolated from antibiotics.
These are macrozamin (**LXXIII**) (*1294, 1295*) and elaiomycin (**LXXIV**)
(*1955*), and hydroscopin A presumably also contains an azoxy group (*1505*).

$$CH_3-N=N-CH_2O-Pr$$

(Pr = β-Primeveroside;
$C_6H_{10}O_4 \cdot 0 \cdot C_5H_9O_4$)

LXXIII

$$n\text{-}C_6H_{13}-CH=CH-N=N-CH \overset{CH_2OCH_3}{\underset{CHOH}{|}}$$

CH₃

LXXIV

The oxidation of actual azo dyestuffs is particularly important in connection with fastness to light (see § 12.7). In the case of hydroxyazo compounds, quinones are formed predominantly (550, 1880), but other reactions have been reported [e.g. (909, 1349); for a summary see Desai and Giles (550)].

Of interest to dyestuffs technology is also the introduction of hydroxy groups in o-position to azo residues by means of the so-called oxidative coppering, developed by Pfitzner (1627, 2562, 2566–2568). o,o'-Dihydroxyazo derivatives, important for metal–complex dyes, can be prepared in this way from the more readily accessible o-hydroxyazo compounds. As illustrated by equation (12.34), the starting material is smoothly converted by cupric acetate and hydrogen peroxide into the copper complex of the dihydroxyazo compound, from which copper may be removed with acid. Related to oxidative coppering is the intro-

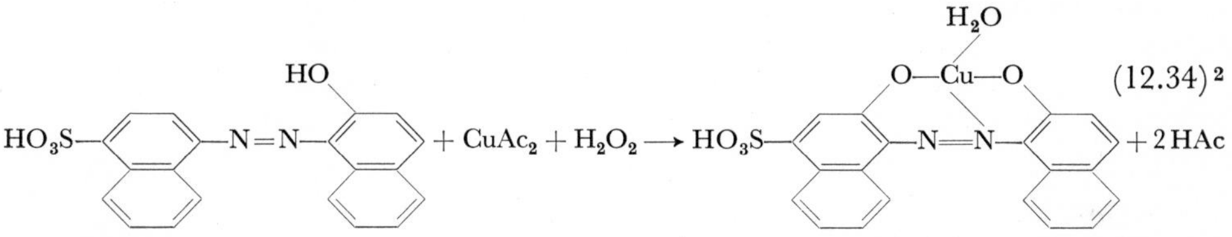

$$\text{HO}_3S-\langle\rangle-N{=}N-\langle\rangle + \text{CuAc}_2 + \text{H}_2\text{O}_2 \longrightarrow \text{HO}_3S-\langle\rangle-N{=}N-\langle\rangle + 2\,\text{HAc} \qquad (12.34)\,[2]$$

duction of o-hydroxy groups into dyestuffs of the type of (LXXV) when dyeings of them are chromed on the fibre. The chemistry of the process was clarified by

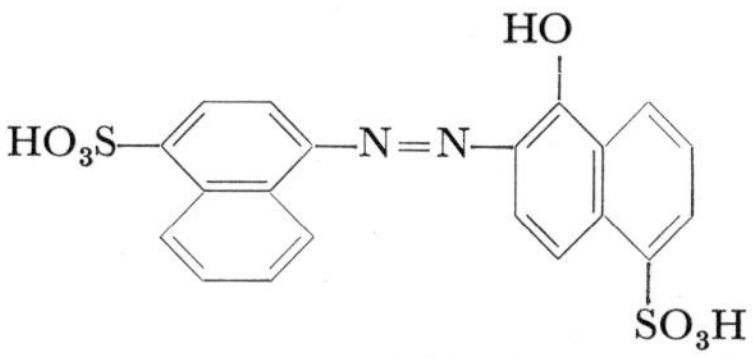

LXXV

Fierz-David and Mannhart (711). As in (12.34), the metal complex is formed, the dichromate employed for chroming acting as oxidizing agent and being itself reduced to the chromic state.

2H-1,2,3-Triazoles are important as intermediates for the manufacture of direct dyes and they are obtained by oxidation of o-aminoazo compounds. The topic is covered by a voluminous patent literature [see also (1820)].

A different kind of oxidation process is represented by the dehydrogenation of azobenzene in an aluminium chloride–sodium chloride melt. According to a patent (2552) at 60° to 120° with or without oxidizing agents benzo[c]cinnoline results (12.35). The same ring closure takes place on irradiation of azobenzene [(2429, 2436), see § 12.7].

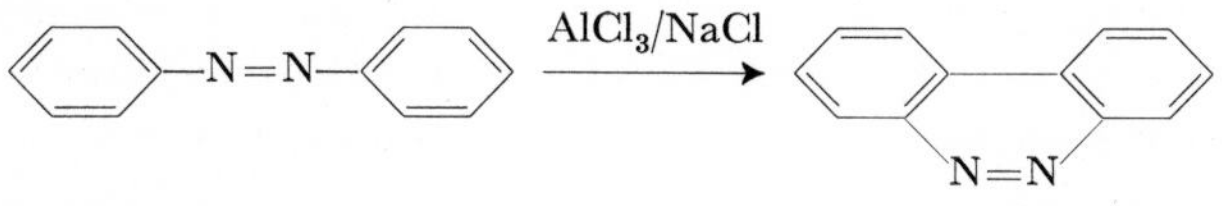

$$\text{(12.35)}$$

___

[2] The method of representing metal complexes is discussed in § 14.1.

Azobenzene is converted by benzene and other aromatic hydrocarbons in the presence of aluminium chloride into a mixture of dehydrogenation and hydrogenation products, mainly hydrazobenzene, 4-phenylazobiphenyl, 4-biphenylazo-4′-biphenyl, and benzidine (*1664, 1665*).

12.6 Addition at the Aromatic Azo Bridge

The *reduction* of aromatic azo compounds is important both preparatively and analytically. It proceeds via the hydrazo derivative to the amine or a mixture of two amines when the original azo compound is unsymmetric. Analytically total reduction to the amines is usually employed, but preparatively the formation of hydrazines plays a greater role, although the amino group of some compounds is best introduced even on the large scale by the detour over an azo derivative. Thus, 5-aminosalicylic acid (LXXVI), a dyestuffs intermediate, is made by coupling diazobenzene to salicylic acid and reducing the azobenzene derivative formed (12.36) (*709b*). Sodium dithionite is used as the reducing agent.

$$(12.36)$$

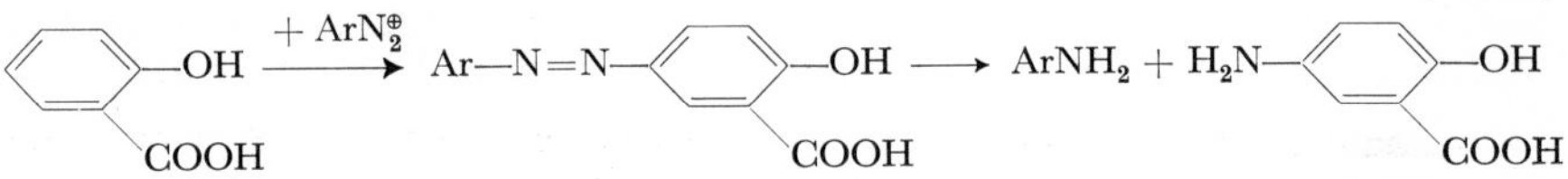

LXXVI

The reduction of azo dyestuffs is exploited technologically in the discharge style of printing, in which textiles dyed with azo dyes are printed with a paste containing sodium formaldehydesulphoxylate, a reducing agent stable to steaming. During steaming the dye is reduced in the printed parts, that is, converted into colourless compounds, a white pattern on a coloured ground being obtained. If vat dyes are present in the printing paste, they are reduced into their leuco compounds, which, on steaming, penetrate into the textile and are fixed in a subsequent oxidation by air or oxidizing agents. A coloured, vat dyed pattern now results on a differently coloured ground.

Hydrazo compounds always appear as intermediates in the reduction of azo dyes (12.37). Their isolation is not easy when powerful reducing agents are

$$Ar\!-\!N\!=\!N\!-\!Ar' \xrightarrow{+2\,H} Ar\!-\!NH\!-\!NH\!-\!Ar' \xrightarrow{+2\,H} ArNH_2 + Ar'NH_2 \qquad (12.37)$$

used, although the preparation of hydrazobenzene by means of sodium dithionite or amalgams, for example, has been described (*858, 1359, 2172*).

Milder reducing agents, such as hydrogen sulphide, already introduced for this purpose a long time ago by A. W. Hofmann (*1064*) and others (*1817*), are to be preferred. However, *o*-hydroxy- and *o*-amino-azo derivatives in general are not converted into hydrazo compounds by hydrogen sulphide. Advantage is taken of their inertness in the selective reduction of nitro substituents in azo dyes. Even so, the best method of preparing hydrazobenzene does not start from azobenzene, but from nitrobenzene, which is treated with zinc and aqueous sodium hydroxide in the presence of *o*-dichlorobenzene at 115° to 125° (*709a*).

Khalifa (*2398, 2430*) studied the influence of substituents on the reduction of azobenzene derivatives, using zinc and acetic acid as well as ammonium sulphide as reagent.

A series of other reducing agents, sodium in liquid ammonia (*2145*), aluminium lithium hydride in ether (*280*), aluminium lithium hydride activated by metal chlorides (*1551*), and catalytic hydrogenation (*628, 1203, 1903, 1975, 2067*), permits the reduction of azobenzene to be stopped at the hydrazo stage.

In recent years the reduction of azobenzene derivatives has been investigated in connection with the biological activity of sulphanilamides. Such studies are based on Domagk's observations on Prontosil (LXXVII) (*620*): this azo compound has itself no chemotherapeutic effect, but is reduced in the body to sulphanilamide (LXXVIII) which is active against micro-organisms. In ad-

$$H_2N\!-\!\langle\rangle\!-\!\overset{\displaystyle NH_2}{\underset{\displaystyle}{\langle\rangle}}\!-\!N\!=\!N\!-\!\langle\rangle\!-\!SO_2NH_2 \xrightarrow[\text{reduction}]{\text{enzymatic}} H_2N\!-\!\langle\rangle\!-\!SO_2NH_2 \quad (12.38)$$

LXXVII   LXXVIII

dition, azobenzene derivatives, particularly Butter Yellow (*N,N*-dimethyl-*p*-phenylazoaniline) are biologically of interest because of their carcinogenic action. It is possible that this too is connected with enzymatic reduction. In consequence, Warwick (*2109*) has concerned himself with the kinetics of the reduction of *N,N*-bis(*β*-chloroethyl)-*p*-phenylazoanilines with various reagents which can be used under biological conditions. The *β*-chloroethyl groups enable nucleophilic substitution to occur with basic residues present in biological systems and so to cause retention of the azobenzene derivative in the tissues. Surprisingly, these compounds did not exhibit a carcinogenic action; on the contrary, they actually retarded tumour formation. Their activity on Walker rat carcinoma 256 was inversely related to their reduction with a xanthine–xanthine oxidase system. It follows that in these compounds the azo group in fact exerts a specific effect.

Under acid conditions hydrazobenzene readily rearranges to benzidine. If therefore azobenzene is reduced in acid solution, normally only benzidine is obtained. This applies especially in the reduction of azobenzene by electrolysis (*1353, 1993, 2534, 2538*), with sulphur dioxide (*2537*), with tin (*1817*), and with stannous chloride (*1816, 2109*). With hydrogen iodide, bromide, and even chloride azobenzene can also be converted into benzidine (*2036, 2226*).

The reduction of aromatic azo compounds with titanous salts has achieved great analytical importance for the determination of the purity of dyestuffs. The method was devised by E. Knecht (*1236*), an aqueous acid solution of the dye being boiled for a short period with an excess of titanous sulphate or chloride in the absence of oxygen. The trivalent titanous ion becomes oxidized to the tetravalent state, whilst the azo compound is decomposed into two amines as in equation (12.37). Some substituents, such as nitro residues, are reduced at the same time. The excess of titanous salt is back-titrated with a ferric salt. The method is very widely used, but fails occasionally, when the hydrazo inter-mediate undergoes a benzidine, semidine, or diphenyline rearrangement (2075). Thus o,o'- and m,m'-dichloroazobenzene require not four, but only two equivalents of the reducing agent and benzidine derivatives can be found among the products (695). In such cases, titration with sodium dithionite may be used, even though the results obtained are less reproducible. Jucker (2331) investigated the potentiometric titration of azo compounds with chromous sulphate. Noteworthy are the different potentials for o- and p-isomers of hydroxyazo dyes. Lohrscheid (2400) recently investigated the electrometric titration of azo dyes.

The kinetics and mechanism of the reduction of azobenzene, 2- and 4-amino-, 2,4-diamino-, 2,4,4'-triamino-, 4-hydroxy-, and other azobenzene derivatives by means of titanous chloride in dilute hydrochloric acid have been subjected to a detailed study by Hinshelwood and his co-workers (1299, 1300). The reaction is of first order with respect to the azo compound and to the titanous salt. If the reaction is carried out in the presence of an excess of azo compound, however, more of it is used up than would be expected stoichiometrically. The explanation lies in the fact that the excess of the azo compound successfully competes with the hydrazobenzene intermediate for the titanous chloride available. The treatment of several cases as a system of consecutive reactions of second order shows that indeed hydrazobenzene may accumulate to a considerable extent. For example, in the reduction of 4-(o-hydroxyphenylazo)resor-cinol in 0·257 N hydrochloric acid at 25·0° it was found that the ratio between the rate constants of the rate-determining steps of the reductions of azo and hydrazo compounds was 1:1·42. The dependence of the rate on the concentration of acid is very complex: the concentration of the reactive species from titanous chloride is inversely proportional to the square of the acid concentration. The azo component also does not enter into the rate-determining step as such, but as singly and doubly protonated cations ($Ar \cdot \overset{\oplus}{N}H : N \cdot Ar'$ and $Ar \cdot \overset{\oplus}{N}H : \overset{\oplus}{N}H \cdot Ar'$).

The polarographic reduction of azobenzene has been investigated frequently and likewise gives involved results in respect of the dependence on the acid concentration. After earlier disagreements (1756, 1757, 1885–1887, 2086, 2169), the connection between half-wave potential and pH has been studied systematically and interpreted by Hillson and Birnbaum (1031) as well as by Castor and Saylor (416). In the presence of a buffer system $HA \rightleftarrows H^{\oplus} + A^{\ominus}$, the following reactions play a part at the mercury surface (R = azobenzene):

$$R + 2 e \rightleftarrows R^{\ominus\ominus} \tag{12.39a}$$

$$R^{\ominus\ominus} + 2 H_3O^{\oplus} \rightleftarrows RH_2 + 2 H_2O \tag{12.39b}$$

and/or

$$R^{\ominus\ominus} + 2 HA \rightleftarrows RH_2 + 2 A^{\ominus} \tag{12.39c}$$

$$HA + H_2O \rightleftarrows H_3O^{\oplus} + A^{\ominus} \tag{12.39d}$$

Depending on whether the dissociation of the buffer component is slower or more rapid than the electron transfer (12.39a), different, yet complex relations follow between the half-wave potential and the acidity and nature of the buffer used. The various half-wave potentials determined for *cis*- and *trans*-azobenzene at pH values greater than 8 can also be understood on the basis of the system (12.39a–d). Even so, this work has not yet exhaustively explained the polarography of aromatic azo compounds.

Zuman (*2244*) investigated the effect of substituents on the half-wave potential of azobenzene and has established a free energy relationship of the Hammett type (*914b*). The polarographic behaviour of azoxy and hydrazo compounds has been compared with that of azo derivatives (*467, 468*).

In addition, a series of azo dyes has been submitted to polarographic study (*792, 1037, 1634, 1886, 2081*). Cabral and Turner (*400*) evaluated polarography for the identification of various kinds of azo dyes, but the half-wave potentials were found not to bear a simple relation to structure. Hence the method can be employed for quantitative estimations, but not for identification.

In several other reactions azobenzene is also reduced. Whilst the reductions considered so far have involved hydrogenation or transfer of hydrogen from the solvent, in those that follow transfer of hydrogen takes place from other organic compounds present.

According to Walther (*2104, 2105*) phenylhydrazine produces hydrazobenzene, being itself decomposed into benzene and nitrogen. Geller (*2385*) studied the mechanism of the reaction, using phenylhydrazine labelled with N^{15}. Hantzsch (*966*) found that sulphinic acids add across the N:N double bond with formation of N-arylsulphonylhydrazobenzenes (12.40), but Bradley and Hannon (*2304*) obtained 4-arylsulphonylazobenzene by working in alcoholic solution. In further work (*2305, 2327*) it was shown that whilst 4-arylsulphonyl-, 4-chloro-, and 3, 3'dibromo-azobenzene remain inert, 4-methylazobenzene yields the addition compound and the 4'-arylsulphone and m, m'azotoluene the addition compound as well as a mono- and a di-sulphone. Fission of the azo link may occur, 1-phenylazo-2-naphthol giving 1-amino-O,4-bis(arylsulphonyl)-2-

$$H_5C_6\!-\!N\!=\!N\!-\!C_6H_5 + Ar\!-\!SO_2H \longrightarrow \quad \overset{H_5C_6}{\underset{H}{>}}N\!-\!N\overset{C_6H_5}{\underset{SO_2Ar}{<}} \qquad (12.40)$$

naphthol, 1-phenylazo-2-naphthylamine, N,4-bis(arylsulphonyl)-1,2-naphthalenediamine, and p-phenylazophenol-4-amino-N,6-bis(arylsulphonyl)phenol.

Bradley and Robinson (*2306*) investigated the reaction of hydroxyazo compounds, especially 1-phenylazo-2-naphthol, with potassium cyanide. The cyanide ion probably adds to the quinonehydrazone tautomer, but the subsequent steps are complex. Apart from 1-amino-4-cyano-2-naphthol, the products include aniline and unidentified phenolic substances.

A series of hydroxy compounds is converted into the corresponding ketones by azobenzene, for example, 2, 7-dibromo-9-fluorenol yielding 2, 7-dibromo-9-fluorenone (12.41) (*1632*) and 10, 10'-bi-9-anthrol $\Delta^{10,10'}$-bianthrone (12.42)

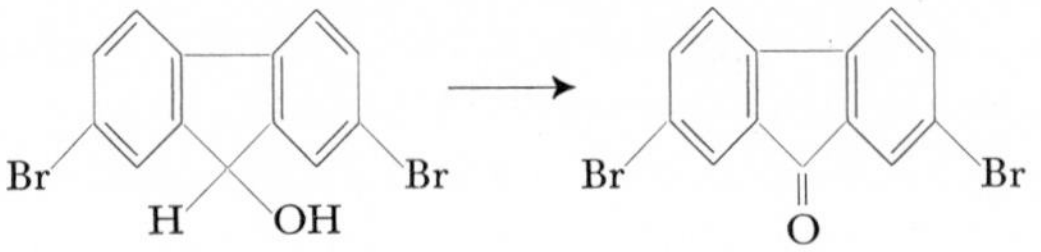

(12.41)

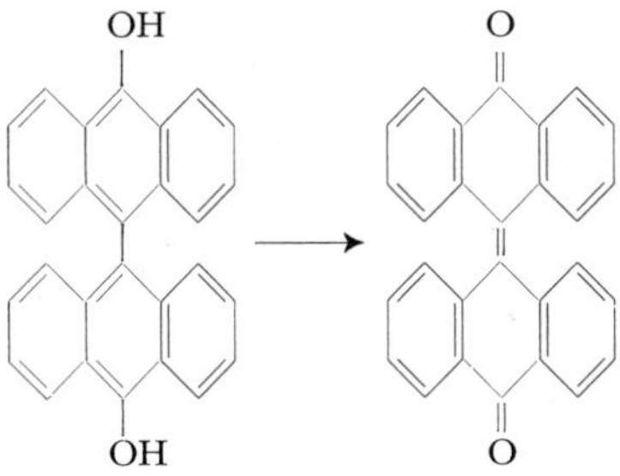

(12.42)

(*303*). Analogous reactions with esters of azodiformic acid have also been described, for instance, the oxidation of hydroquinone to benzoquinone (*584*).

The oxidative coupling of enols brought about by azobenzene is also interesting; this has been studied by Passerini and Losco (*1589*) as well as by Bradley and Watkinson (*303*). Azobenzene converts 3-methyl-1-phenyl-5-pyrazolone at 180° into bi(3-methyl-1-phenylpyrazol-5-on-4-yl) (LXXIX), anthrone into 10,10'-bianthrone (LXXX), and 2-methyl-1-naphthol into 3,3'-

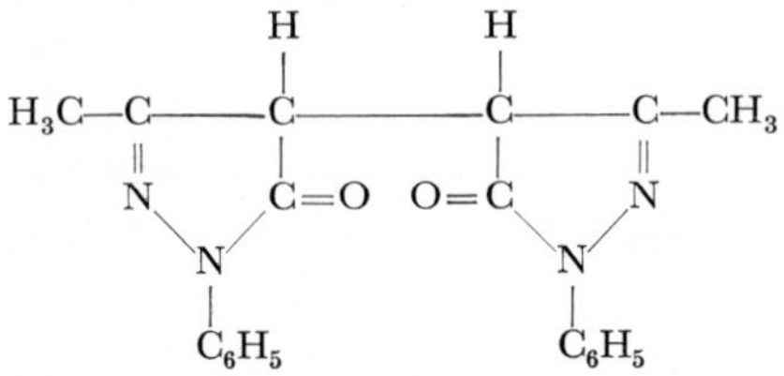

LXXIX

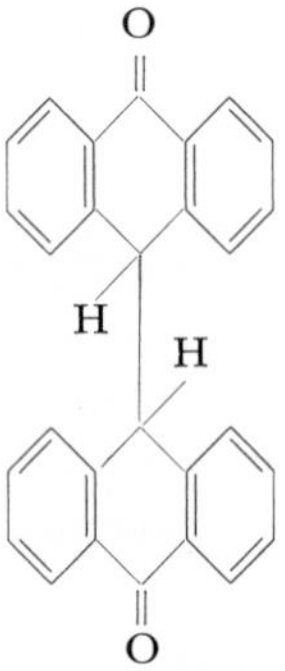

LXXX

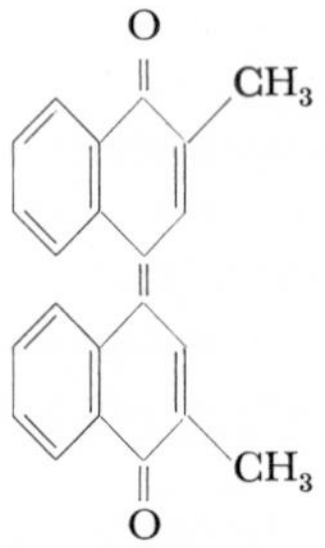

LXXXI

dimethyl [$\Delta^{1,1'(4H,4'H)}$-binaphthalene]-4,4'-dione (LXXXI). However, the reaction takes a different course in the case of 1-naphthol itself. Here azobenzene acts as the electrophilic reagent, rather like esters of azodiformic acid (see § 12.4), adding both at the 2- and the 4-position to form the hydrazines (LXXXII) and LXXXIII). The attack does not stop there, but leads to 2-anilino-*N*-phenyl-1,4-naphthoquinone imine (LXXXIV), presumably via the intermediates given, azobenzene now serving as dehydrogenating agent again (12.43).

Bradley and Watkinson (*302*) have pointed out that similar reactions probably take part in the formation of azines of the type of Safranine. The first

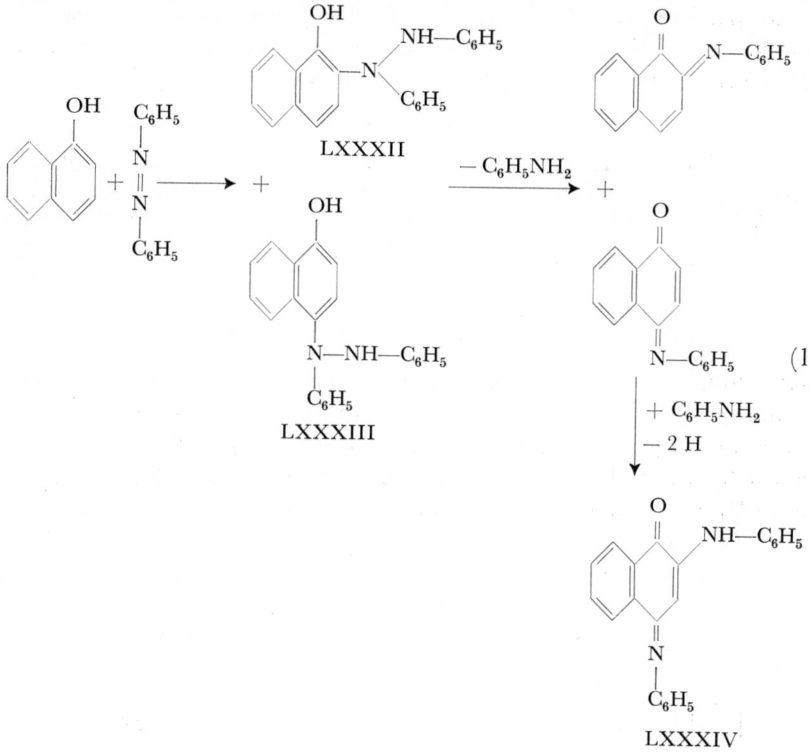

$$(12.43)$$

step could be the addition of the amine to the azo bridge as in equation (12.44).
The conversion of aromatic azo compounds into azines had been investigated

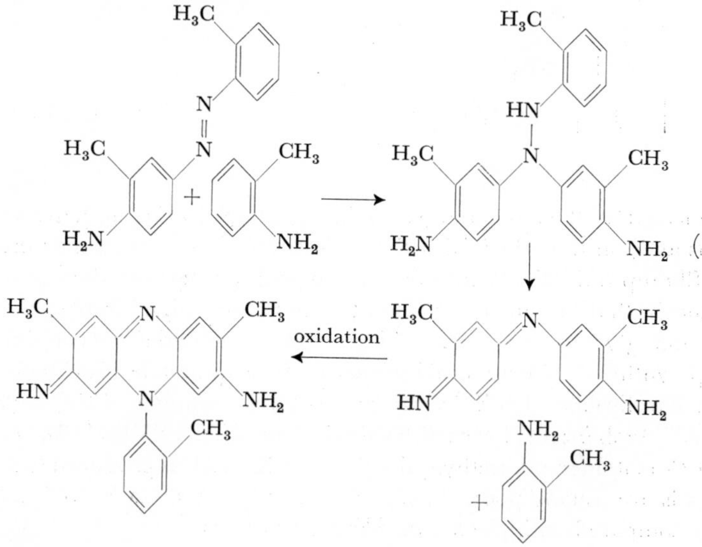

$$(12.44)$$

previously particularly by Witt (*2175*). Tishler (*2040, 2583*) employed the reaction for the synthesis of riboflavin from an *o*-phenylazoaniline derivative and barbituric acid (12.45).

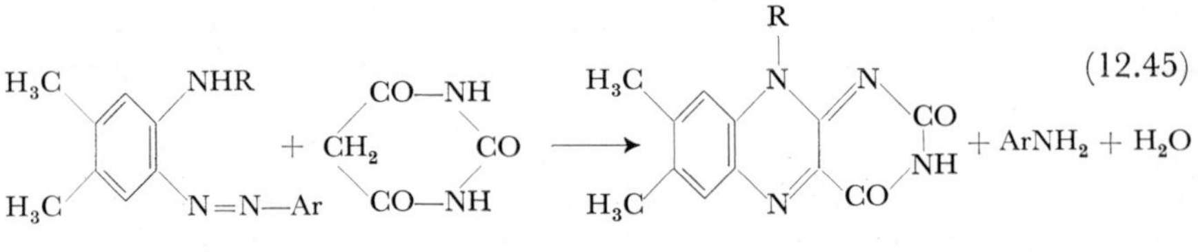

$$R = \text{ribityl residue}$$

Related to these reactions are probably also the formation of imidazole and quinoxaline rings from *o*-aminoazo compounds and aldehydes or ketones, which have been investigated mainly by Crippa (*489–495*). As illustrations may be mentioned the interaction of 1-phenylazo-2-naphthylamine with pyruvic acid (12.46) (*491*) and with acetophenone (12.47) (*489*).

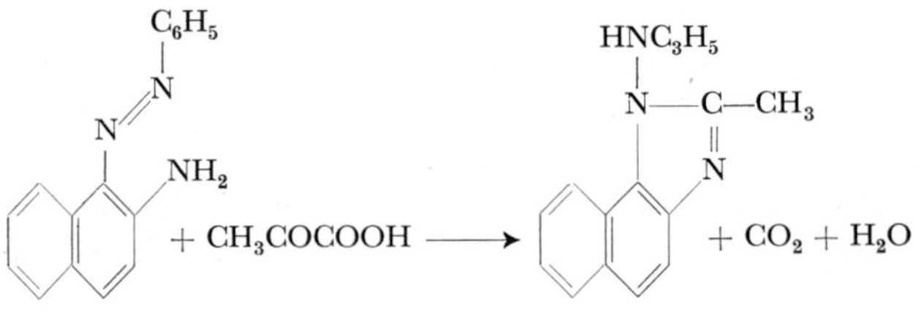

Connected on the one hand with these reactions leading to heterocyclic ring systems and, on the other, with the conversion of azo compounds into amines is the Skraup quinoline synthesis starting with azobenzene derivatives. It has been shown that in some cases when the aromatic amine is replaced by an azo compound, glycerol or acrolein still give quinolines under the conditions of the Skraup synthesis. Matsumura's preparation of quinoline itself together with 4,7-phenanthroline (LXXXV) from *p*-phenylazoaniline (*1379*) serves as an example. Azobenzene forms 6,6′-biquinoline (LXXXVI) (*430, 1379*), but from *p,p′*-azotoluene 6-methylquinoline (LXXXVII) is produced (*1324*). Since the yields are usually poor, these ring closures have not achieved much significance compared with the actual Skraup synthesis.

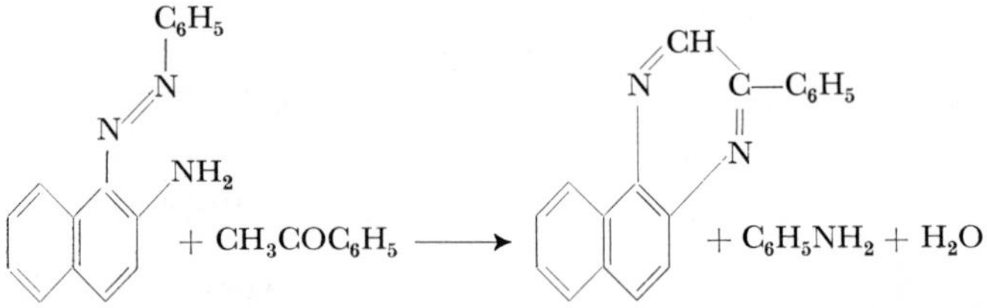

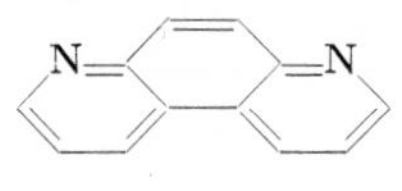

LXXXV 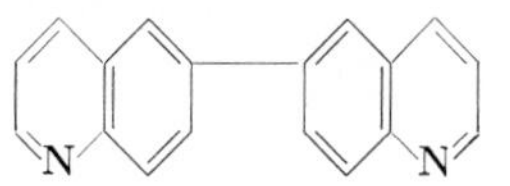 LXXXVI 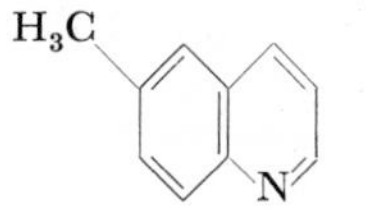 LXXXVII

The addition of organo-metallic compounds at the aromatic azo bridge usually leads to hydrazo derivatives after hydrolysis, but occasionally also to amines. Azobenzene with two equivalents of ethylmagnesium bromide gives hydrazobenzene, ethane, and ethylene (12.48) (*1697*). With alkylzinc and aryl-

$$H_5C_6-N=N-C_6H_5 + 2 C_2H_5MgBr \longrightarrow H_5C_6-NH-NH-C_6H_5 + C_2H_4 + C_2H_6 \quad (12.48)$$

zinc compounds the amine is frequently formed (*800*). Whilst with arylmetal derivatives diaryls are obtained as by-products, alkyl residues disproportionate as in (12.48) to alkane and olefin; the appearance of dialkyls, such as n-butane in (12.48), previously postulated (*754, 802*), could not be confirmed experimentally. The reaction of azobenzene with phenylpotassium takes a different course, hydrolysis resulting in triphenylhydrazine (*800*), and 2-phenylazothiazoles combine with phenylmagnesium bromide in an analogous manner (*242*).

It is appropriate here just to touch on the interaction between triazenes and Grignard reagents. Contrary to Gilman (*802*), who reported that 1,3-diphenyltriazene (diazoaminobenzene) on treatment with ethylmagnesium bromide and subsequent benzoylation undergoes addition at the azo double bond to give

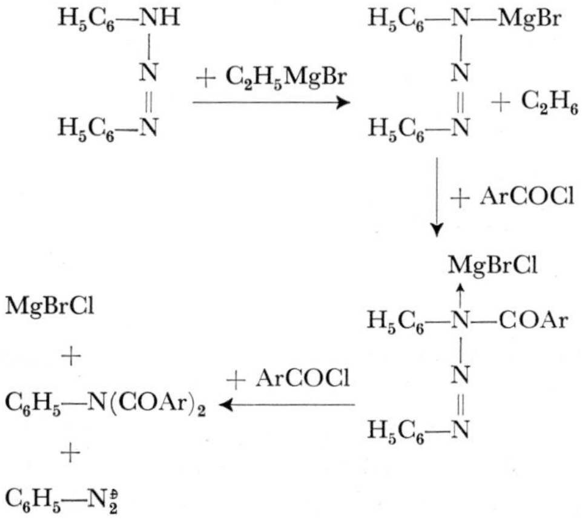

$$(12.49)$$

1,3-diphenyl-1,2,3-tribenzoyltriazane, Klages (*1228*) proved that it is dibenzoylaniline which results (12.49). Cleavage of the nitrogen chain therefore occurs. With phenyl-lithium addition to the azo bridge does not take place either: in the case of 3,3-dimethyl-1-phenyltriazene one of the *N*-methyl groups is metallated, the process being formulated by Klages (*1228*) as (12.50).

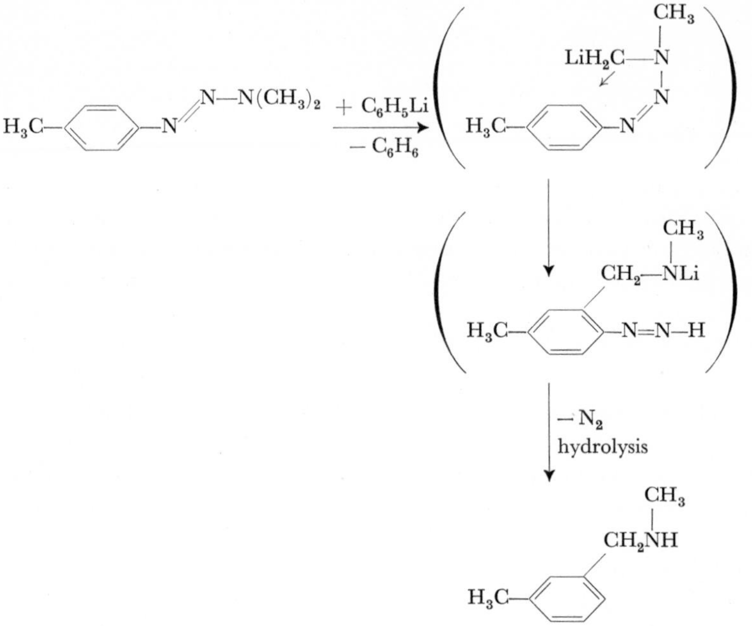

$$(12.50)$$

Some work due to Kharasch *et al.* (*1208*) has shown that azobenzene is also capable of adding radicals at the azo bridge. Reaction (12.51) proceeds at 140° and is catalysed by di-t-butyl peroxide.

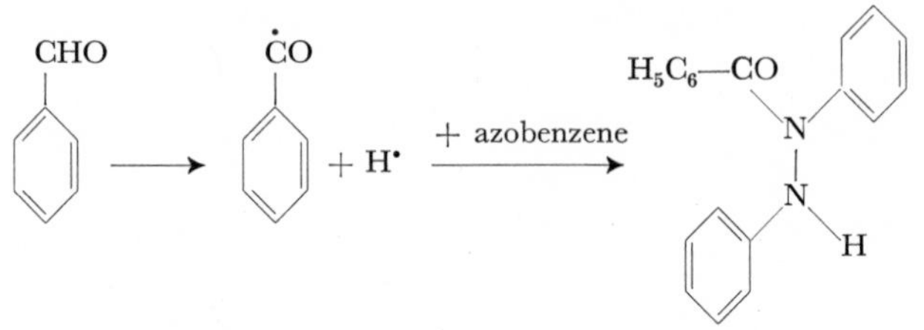

$$(12.51)$$

12.7 The Photochemistry of Aromatic Azo Compounds

The action of light on aromatic azo compounds is important particularly as regards the rearrangement of the *trans-* into the *cis*-isomer of azobenzene and related compounds and also for the problems connected with the fastness to light of dyeings, surface coatings, etc. The *trans–cis* rearrangement has already been discussed in § 4.1. It was mentioned there that it is of significance also technologically, since phototropy is exhibited by certain azo dyes, particularly on cellulose acetate.

The process is a reversible one, but more powerful irradiation leads to decomposition of the azo dyes. The reactions which occur then are of quite a different type to those operating in the photolyses of azoalkanes (§ 12.2). Blais-dell (265) has studied the effects of strong illumination on solutions of azo-benzene and the simple, closely related dye, *p*-(*p*-nitrophenylazo)aniline, in iso-propanol and iso-octane. He found the primary reaction to be reduction to the corresponding hydrazine, but under further irradiation the N—N bond of the hydrazine underwent reductive fission. The solvent served as the reducing agent, isopropanol being converted into acetone. If oxygen is present, it reacts with the solvent before azobenzene is attacked. Hugelshofer, Kalvoda, and Schaffner (2429) and, at the same time, G. E. Lewis (2436) found that the photolysis of azobenzene yields appreciable amounts of benzo[*c*]cinnoline. As mentioned in § 12.5, the same reaction takes place in an aluminium chloridesodium chloride melt [see equation (12.35)].

Because of the importance of light fastness, a tremendous amount of experi-ence has accumulated about the fading of dyestuffs, whether within fibres or other substrates such as paints or plastics. Yet the number of investigations into the constitution of the products of the action of light and the physicochemical principles of such photolyses is very small. It will be appreciated, of course, that the study of colouring matters in most of these substrates is exceedingly difficult for several reasons. Frequently illumination not only decomposes the dye, but also the substrate and, in some cases, for instance, with many yellow vat dyes on cellulosic fibres, the dye acts as photosensitizer for the tendering process. Model experiments using the dye in solution in order to circumvent the substrate give results which often cannot be applied to dyeings, that is, systems in which the substrate is present.

Giles and his co-workers (420, 498) have investigated systematically the in-fluence of the substrate on the light fastness of azo dyes. They determined the rates of fading of dyes of the type of (LXXXVIII) and similar compounds on fifteen different substrates and evaluated the effect of substituents in the *m*- or *p*-position of the phenyl residue according to Hammett's $\sigma\varrho$-relation (914 b). It

LXXXVIII

became apparent that ϱ has a negative value for dyeings on various cellulosic materials, on cellulose acetate, collodion, ethyl methyl cellulose, anodically oxidized aluminium, asbestos, nylon, and polyglycine, but positive ones on gelatin, silk, and wool. In other words, acidifying substituents increase the light fastness of dyes on substrates of the first kind, but decrease it on proteins. These results agree with the earlier experiments of Kienle et al. (1212) and of Atherton and R. H. Peters (77,80). Giles supposes that proteins take part in the fading reaction, in which the dyes undergo reductive fission, but that during the irra-diation of the other materials oxidation processes are occurring.

This interpretation is contrary to Schaeffer's experience (*1788*), who was able to prove the presence of benzidine, that is, of a product of reductive fission, shortly after the illumination of a direct dyeing of a dye made from tetrazotized benzidine. The other fragment of the decomposition of such direct dyes would be derived from the coupling component and therefore would probably be either an *o*-diamine or an *o*-aminophenol. Such compounds oxidize very readily. Indeed, Ziersch and Haller (*909, 910*) proved the presence of 1,2-naphthoquinones and Couper (*471*), who studied the fading of cellulose acetate dyed with 1,4-bismethylaminoanthraquinone, obtained evidence of the formation of 1,4-anthraquinonedi-imine and of its *N*-methyl derivative. Although it seems certain that the end products of the irradiation are due to oxidation, a primary photolytic reaction consisting of a reductive fission of the dye is not excluded. Systematic investigation of the decomposition products of dyeings after different periods of illumination is most desirable.

Hillson and Rideal (*1032*) studied the photochemistry of azo and triphenyl-methane dyes by means of the Becquerel effect: when a platinum electrode, on which dye is adsorbed, was illuminated, a current was produced. Depending on the conditions, either oxidation or reduction of the dye could be observed. It was supposed that oxidation took place when an excited dye molecule reacts with a hydroxy radical formed from the water, but that the reductive process was due to the direct transfer of an electron from the electrode to the excited dye molecule.

Investigations by Bean and Rowe (*215*) of dyeings with azoic dyes showed that treatments which increased the particle size exert a favourable effect on the fastness to light. Giles *et al.* (*210*) in systematically extending this work to a series of substrates were able to confirm that the light fastness improves as the particles become larger, the rate of fading being a function of the surface area of the particles. Indeed, Giles and MacEwan (*793*) have suggested that the consistently high resistance to light of 1:2 metal–complex dyes in a great variety of media is due to their presence as micelles.

According to Krollpfeiffer and his co-workers (*1275*), the irradiation of *o*-aminoazo compounds in solution leads to products which correspond in part to the azine formation described in § 12.6, but the triazolium ion (XC) is obtained as well as the azine (LXXXIX). Hungarian chemists (*2352*) compared the photodecomposition of *o*- and *p*-aminoazobenzene. Their experiments confirmed the assumption that the reaction is an oxidation process, the decomposition of the *o*-isomer being slower due to steric protection of the azo group by the *o*-substituent.

$$\text{LXXXIX} \qquad \text{XC} \qquad\qquad (12.52)$$

13. The Relation of Properties to the Constitution of Azo Compounds

13.1 The Light Absorption of Azo Compounds

Colour, the most important property of dyestuffs, is due to the partial absorption of incident light. Human eyes are sensitive only to the visible portion of the spectrum, that is, to light of wavelengths between 400 and 750 mμ. It is now known that the absorption of light occurs through the acceptance of radiant energy by certain *electrons* of the molecules. This process is responsible not only for absorption in the visible spectrum, but also for that of infra-red radiation up to about 1000 mμ (occasionally even up to 1500 mμ) and especially for that in the ultra-violet region, 100 to 400 mμ. The real infra-red absorption, that is, 2 to 20 μ, depends, on the contrary, on the changes in the vibrations of *atomic nuclei* or *groups of atoms* brought about by the radiant energy.

Here the connections between electronic spectra and chemical constitution will be reviewed briefly in order to recall the principles on which these are based.

By accepting the energy of the incident light, certain electrons of the molecules are raised into what is termed an excited state. The increase in energy obeys the Einstein–Bohr law (13.1), according to which the difference in energy between the excited and ground states (ΔE) is directly proportional to the frequency (ν), or inversely proportional to the wavelength (λ), of the light absorbed, h being Planck's constant of action and c the velocity of light. The electrons affected do not remain in the excited state, but lose the energy acquired

$$\Delta E = h\nu = \frac{hc}{\lambda} \tag{13.1}$$

through collisions with other molecules, emission of radiation of longer wavelength, or photochemical reaction.

The spectra of simple molecules in the gaseous state exhibit distinct, sharp lines, which can be assigned to certain well defined transitions. With larger molecules, the number of possible transitions of roughly the same energy becomes so large that the individual absoption lines fuse into broad bands. This broadening is increased further by intermolecular effects, such as solvation, when liquids or solutions are examined.

The longer the wavelength of the light absorbed, the smaller the amount of energy involved and, according to equation (13.1), the transitions are reduced in energy content from 300 to 30 kcal/mole as the light absorbed varies from the ultra-violet to the near infra-red. Thus visible light of longer wavelength is only capable of raising readily excited, 'mobile' electrons to a higher energy state.

It is very difficult to excite σ-electrons, which are responsible for the homopolar bonds of saturated hydrocarbons, and therefore such compounds absorb only high energy radiation in the far ultra-violet, < 120 mμ. The pairs of lone electrons of hetero atoms (N, O, Cl, etc.) of saturated organic compounds require somewhat less energy (110 to 130 mμ) and the π-electrons of isolated double or triple bonds are still more easily excited (150 to 180 mμ). Compounds with isolated p- and π-electrons exhibit in addition weak bands at 180 to 400 mμ, the origin of which is generally not clear.

Strong absorption in the near ultra-violet (> 210 mμ) and visible region appears when the interaction called *conjugation* becomes possible between two or more pairs of π-electrons. This phenomenon had already been recognized a very long time ago and now it is known that even π-σ-interaction (hyperconjugation) affects absorption, though to a less degree.

Before enlarging on this topic, it is best to describe the development of the quantum theoretical ideas of colour from the older, purely chemical ones. As early as 1868, Graebe and Liebermann (*853*) realized that dyestuffs are unsaturated compounds and a little later Witt (*2174, 2176*) propounded his theory of colour. According to him, dyes consist of chromophores and auxochromes, that is, on the one hand, of an unsaturated group, such as an aromatic, carbonyl, azo, azomethine, ethylene, nitroso, or nitro residue, and, on the other, of substituents, such as hydroxy, amino, methoxy, and dimethylamino groups. He appreciated that an accumulation of chromophores, especially in conjugated systems, brought about a shift of the absorption band to longer wavelengths.

Dilthey and Wizinger (*591, 594, 2179, 2180*) were able to expand Witt's ideas by means of the relations between colour and constitution discovered by Hantzsch (*950, 953, 954*), von Baeyer (*132*), Watson (*2113, 2114*), Pfeiffer (*1615*), and others. According to Dilthey and Wizinger, a dye consists of an electron-releasing, relatively basic group, the auxochrome, which is connected to an electron-attracting, acid residue by a system of conjugated double bonds, i.e. by coordinatively unsaturated atoms, an atom being coordinatively unsaturated when its coordination number is greater than its number of covalent bonds (see § 14.1). The greater the respective electrophilic and nucleophilic character of the two groups and the longer the unsaturated chain joining them, the further is the absorption shifted to longer wavelengths.

The concepts regarding mesomerism or resonance in systems of conjugated double bonds developed by Arndt, Ingold, and Pauling led Bury (*399*) as well as Arndt and Eistert (*661*) to deduce connections between mesomerism and colour. Subsequently, the researches of Schwarzenbach (*1459, 1857, 1866, 1867, 1869, 1871, 1872*), Brooker (*335–338*), and others showed that a dye absorbs at longer wavelengths the more extended the mesomeric system and the greater the similarity in energy content of its mesomeric limiting structures. According to Braude (*309, 312*) auxochromes and chromophores are now best regarded as p- and π-electron-bearing groups, respectively.

The empirically found relations between absorption spectra and electronic states made it possible to tackle the problem of colour and constitution by means of physical methods. When this was realized, the topic became one of chemical physics rather than of organic chemistry and the main contributions in the last twenty years have been made by physical chemists and physicists.

Thus, W. Kuhn (*1285*) and G. N. Lewis and Calvin (*1340*) have used a model for light absorption in which the electrons are regarded as linear oscillators coupled with one another and interacting with the electric field of the light.

In principle the wave number of the absorption of a molecule can be calculated when the energy content of the ground and excited states are known. Quantum mechanics enables this to be done, but the exact application of Schrödinger's wave mechanics to groups of atoms and molecules soon leads to mathematically insoluble difficulties. The three methods of approximation available, namely, the valence bond (*2143*), the molecular orbital (*469, 569*), and the free electron method (*211, 212, 1279–1281*), achieved considerable success in the interpretation and calculation of light absorption, particularly because as already mentioned the easily excited π-electrons are responsible for the spectra and their interaction with the remaining electrons can indeed be neglected without great loss in accuracy.

Of the three methods the second and especially the last has been applied recently to actual dyestuffs. Exceptionally suitable for treatment are the polymethine dyes, in which a polyene chain of variable length joins an amino to an ammonium nitrogen atom. They were discussed by Dewar (*569*), for example, and also provided the most important set of data for H. Kuhn's electron gas model (*1279–1281*). Up to the present, only the MO method has been applied to azo compounds. Maier and co-workers (*1366*), Jaffé (*1164*), and Heilbronner (*788, 789*) interpreted the spectra of azobenzene and arylazoazulene derivatives with its help (see below).

Direct computation of the wavelengths and intensities of the absorption bands of azo compounds is still not possible, but on the basis of the empirically found connections the various bands can be assigned to appropriate energy transitions in conjugated systems.

In order to characterize a band accurately its form is of importance and so its graphical representation is advisable. Unfortunately this is carried out in many different ways, although the acceptance of agreed procedures has been advocated (*1613*). However, in every case not only the wavelength or frequency of the absorption maximum must be given, but also its intensity, that is, the molar extinction coefficient (ε). The older theories of colour concerned themselves almost exclusively with the shifts in the visible absorption bands to shorter or longer wavelengths (*hypsochromic* or *bathochromic* effects, respectively) brought about by changes in constitution. Recent developments have shown that in addition in many instances the extinction is altered in a characteristic manner in the sense of either increasing or decreasing the intensity of absorption (*hyper-* or *hypo-chromic* effects, respectively).

In order to classify the various bands of an absorption spectrum some special terms have come to be used. Burawoy (*386*) realized that certain bands exhibited by conjugated molecules can be assigned to energy transitions of the *whole* π-electron system and they were therefore termed K-bands (from the German: Konjugationsbanden). They are accompanied by much weaker R-bands ('radical' bands) due to the excitation of the *individual* chromophoric groups. Braude (*310*) applied this classification to cyclic π-electron systems. A newer method of designation brings out the character of the process which is occurring even more clearly. Bands caused by π-electrons jumping from the highest occupied to a vacant π-orbital are described as $\pi \rightarrow \pi^*$-transitions. If the absorption is due to the transfer of electrons from atomic orbitals of atoms with lone pairs of electrons to excited σ- or π-molecular orbitals, they are termed $n \rightarrow \sigma^*$- and $n \rightarrow \pi^*$-transitions, respectively. In the case of aromatic compounds interaction of the radiation with the individual rings plays an additional role (sometimes called $\varphi \rightarrow \varphi^*$-transitions).

Whilst the difference in energy between the excited and the ground states determines the frequency of a band, the intensity of absorption (extinction or optical density) is a measure of the probability with which the particular transition occurs. It can be shown that molar extinction coefficients cannot exceed about 10^6 [cf. (*311*)].

The interpretation of the distribution of absorption intensity within bands cannot be dealt with here, but a variety of causes can convert fine structure, often characteristic for the type of compound under consideration, into a diffuse, broad band. This happens, for example, on raising the temperature or, because of increased molecular interaction, in polar solvents.

The general disappearance of fine structure brought about by the introduction of the N:N-group is typical for azo compounds. Whilst the band of longest wavelength of substances, such as *trans*-stilbene, exhibits in ethanol distinct fine structure, *trans*-azobenzene in the same solvent possesses only broad bands without structure. In cyclic compounds also, the azo group destroys fine structure, as can be seen from the spectrum of benzotriazole (I). The very similar benzimidazole (II), on the contrary, clearly shows fine structure (*1922*). G. N.

I   II

Lewis and Calvin (*1340*) have thought the disappearance of fine structure to be connected with energy-consuming, intramolecular processes, which, on analogy with mechanical machines, they called 'loose-bolt' effects. Nothing certain is yet known about the origin of this effect in the case of azo compounds. However, its significance seems to be questionable in the case of azobenzene since Heilbronner (*1001*) recently demonstrated that the spectra of this and related compounds without auxochromic groups do possess fine structure in suitable solvents such as cyclohexene.

The spectrum of azomethane exhibits two bands [see e.g. (*1267*)], namely at 29200 cm^{-1} ($\lambda_{max.}$ = 342 mμ; log ε = 1·16) and at 45000 cm^{-1} ($\lambda_{max.}$ = 222 mμ; log ε = 1·3). Because of the parallel with other compounds containing doubly bonded hetero atoms, such as carbonyl derivatives, the spectra of which have been studied in greater detail, it can be assumed that these bands can be assigned to n$\longrightarrow$$\pi$*-transition. The bathochromic shift of the bands for azomethane compared with those for carbonyl compounds may be attributed to greater ease of excitation due to the lower effective nuclear charge of nitrogen.

Of particular interest are the spectra of those azo compounds which are able to absorb visible radiation and are therefore dyes. As mentioned above, the connection between colour and mesomerism was recognized empirically in the 'thirties and it is appropriate to preface the discussion of the electronic spectra of aromatic azo compounds with a few general remarks on the relation of mesomerism to light absorption.

The band of longest wavelength of benzene, the example *par excellence* of a mesomeric compound, coincides almost exactly with that of cyclohexadiene, a substance with only two double bonds and much less mesomeric character. This fact shows that extending a system of conjugated double bonds bears no direct relation with the position of the absorption band. Indeed mesomerism lowers the energy of the ground *and* the excited states. If the stabilization of the ground state exceeds that for the excited state, the difference in energy becomes greater and, in consequence, further conjugation as in going from cyclohexadiene to benzene does not produce a bathochromic shift. This is due to the especially well marked stabilization of the *ground* state of benzene by mesomerism [the spectrum of benzene has been the subject of a great number of researches: see reviews by Staab (*1923*) and Bayliss (*212*), as well as Platt's papers (*1635–1637*) in particular]. However, in general as the possibilities for mesomerism become greater the stabilization of the excited state is increased relative to that of the ground state and a bathochromic shift of the absorption bands follows. One way of explaining this result is by means of the MO theory (*1094*), which shows that the energy terms of the molecular orbitals become more closely spaced as the size of the conjugated system increases. Therefore with every additional conjugated double bond the energy difference between the highest occupied and the lowest vacant π-electron level becomes smaller and the wavelength of the first absorption band which corresponds to this transition is increased.

The spectra of mesomeric compounds are distinguished not only by bands of long wavelength, but also by great intensity of absorption. Mulliken (*1500*) has ascribed the high extinction to the ready polarization of π-electrons.

Naturally, of the mesomeric azo compounds the spectrum of azobenzene has special interest. Burawoy (*385*) apparently was the first to study azobenzene and a few related compounds systematically and in a series of subsequent

Azo and Diazo Compounds

Table 13.1

Conjugation of the Ethylene, Azomethine, and Azo Chromophores with Phenyl Groups[1]

Group	n → π*		π → π*		Other bands		References
	λ	ε	λ	ε	λ	ε	
C_6H_6			258	230			*(1635–1637)*
			201	6900[2]			
C_6H_5—CH=CH$_2$			282	450			*(310)*
			244	12000			
C_6H_5—C_6H_5			246	20000			*(310)*
trans			307	28300			*(214)*
C_6H_5—CH=CH—C_6H_5 {			295	29000			
cis			280	10450			*(214)*
			224	24400			
C_6H_5—CH=N—C_6H_5	(366)	3,4	314	10000	255	9800	*(1013, 1164)*
			266	14600	<220	>25000	
C_6H_5—N=N—CH$_3$	403	87	260	7800			*(256)*
C_6H_5—N=N—C_6H_5 { *trans*	443	510	319	22000	228	14000	*(256, 1001)*
cis	432	1518	280	5260	242	10480	*(256)*
C_6H_5—$\overset{\oplus}{N}H$=N—C_6H_5 *trans*	300	2400[4]	418	29000	235	8000	*(1164)*
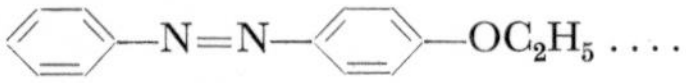 ⟨⟩—N=N—⟨⟩—OC$_2$H$_5$	432	2400	349	22600	236	10300	*(1164)*
					224	13700	
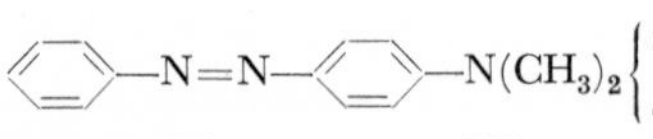 ⟨⟩—N=N—⟨⟩—N(CH$_3$)$_2$ { *trans*	3	3	410	30400	260	10500	*(1649, 2434)*
cis	460	4300	362	12000	<290		*(326)*
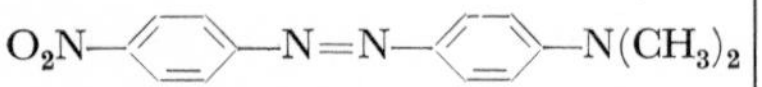 O$_2$N—⟨⟩—N=N—⟨⟩—N(CH$_3$)$_2$	3	3	480	33000	280	12600	*(1649)*

[1] Wherever available, spectra in ethanol are quoted.
[2] A further π ⟶ π*-transition occurs at 181 mμ.
[3] Overlain by π ⟶ π*-band.
[4] Assignment not certain.

papers *(122, 462, 857, 1649)* the spectra of azobenzenes were compared with those of the analogous stilbenes. Apart from the original contribution by Burawoy *(385)*, others *(256, 1164, 1366)* have also concerned themselves with assigning bands to particular transitions.

In Table 13.1 are listed the bands corresponding to π ⟶ π*- and n ⟶ π*-transitions for benzene derivatives, ranging from the parent hydrocarbon to azobenzene and actual azo dyes (*N,N*-dimethyl-*p*-phenylazoaniline = Butter Yellow). The batho- and hyper-chromic effect of additional chromophores is clearly illustrated by the series benzene, styrene and biphenyl, and stilbene. *N*-Benzylideneaniline can be regarded as an azastilbene and it is apparent that the replacement of —CH= by —N= acts batho- and hypo-chromically. The origin of this effect lies probably in the greater electron affinity of the nitrogen, as in the case of the aza analogues of the polymethine dyes discussed by H. Kuhn (*1279–1281*). The introduction of the second nitrogen to give azobenzene acts in the same direction with respect to the wavelength of the $\pi \rightarrow \pi^*$-band; the intensity, however, is increased again, but does not regain that of stilbene. Detailed comparison of azobenzene with its CH-analogues (*1001*) shows that the spectra of azobenzene and *N*-benzylideneaniline cannot be correlated in a simple manner.

Platt (*1637*) has compared the spectrum of (phenylazo)methane with that of the 'isoconjugate' styrene.

The pairs of *p*-electrons of the nitrogen atoms in *N*-benzylideneaniline, (phenylazo)methane, and azobenzene bring about the appearance of a further, weaker band between 360 and 450 mμ, assigned to n $\rightarrow \pi^*$-transitions.

In azobenzene derivatives, which bear an auxochrome in *p*-position, the n $\rightarrow \pi^*$-band is partially or wholly overlain by the batho- and hyper-chromically displaced $\pi \rightarrow \pi^*$-band. The latter has been shifted into the visible region in the case of Butter Yellow and *N,N*-dimethyl-*p*-(*p*-nitrophenylazo)aniline and, because of its high extinction coefficient, it is responsible for the dyestuff

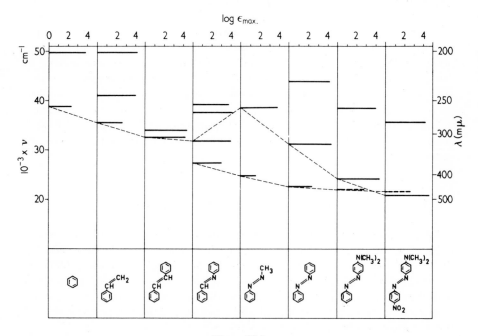

Figure 13.1

Graphical representation of the spectra of some compounds related to azobenzene.

character of these compounds, but the colour of azobenzene itself is due to the
n$\rightarrow$$\pi$*-transition. The contrast between azobenzene and Butter Yellow clearly
illustrates the fundamental tenet of Witt's theory, namely, that chromophores
become actual dyestuffs only through interaction with auxochromes. The
spectra of p-phenylazoaniline and its N,N-dimethyl derivative are to be discussed in § 13.3 in connection with the acid–base equilibria of azo compounds.

Table 13.1 also lists additional bands for the azo and azomethine derivatives.
Different authors, such as Birnbaum (256), Maier (1366), and Jaffé (1164)
and their respective co-workers, have attributed these not to the same transi-
tions, choosing either $\varphi \rightarrow \pi$*- or $\varphi \rightarrow \varphi$*-processes. Further, Jaffé has analysed
the n $\rightarrow$ π*- and $\pi \rightarrow$ π*-bands of azobenzene and assigned the resultant
individual bands to various transitions, but as this was done on the basis of the
most elementary LCAO–MO theory, the assignments are not too convincing.
The simplifications and approximations inherent in the elementary LCAO–
MO method do not yet permit the reliable interpretation in detail of the
spectra of such relatively complex molecules.

In Figure 13.1 the bands of some of the compounds mentioned are given
graphically, the regularities in the position and intensity of the bands being
shown much more clearly than by Table 13.1.

Interesting is the comparison of the spectrum of azobenzene with that of
compounds in which both nitrogens have been replaced by elements of greater
atomic number, but belonging to the same group of the periodic table. The
spectrum of arsenobenzene (III) (659) is similar to that of azobenzene, but the
two bands of longer wavelength have undergone a hypso- and hypo-chromic
shift (340 mμ, $\varepsilon = 200$; 258 mμ, $\varepsilon = 2250$). On the contrary, the spectrum of
phosphorobenzene (IV) (2118) is totally different: one broad, strong band at
244 mμ ($\varepsilon = 25000$) has a shoulder at 320 to 340 mμ, the extinction coefficient
of which is about 1000 to 3000. It is easy to suggest that these correspond to
$\pi \rightarrow \pi$*- and n $\rightarrow \pi$*-transitions, but little certainty attaches to such assignments as so few data are available for compounds of this type. Le Fèvre's
attempts to convert arsenobenzene into the cis-form by irradiation were un-
successful (1312).

III   IV

Steric factors strongly influence conjugation and therefore spectra. The maximum effect of π- and p-electrons can only be exercised in planar molecules,
since only then is the overlap between the individual π-orbitals, which are
perpendicular to the plane of the atomic nuclei, at its optimum. By analogy
with the case of cis- and trans-stilbene, the differences in the spectra of cis- and
trans-azobenzene may be attributed to the inability of the two benzene rings of
the cis-form to come into the same plane (V).

Formally, benzo[c]cinnoline (VI) can be regarded as a derivative of cis-azo-
benzene, but here both benzene rings would be expected to be co-planar.

V   VI   VII

Hence the spectrum of benzo[c]cinnoline (*129*) cannot be directly compared with those of *cis*- or *trans*-azobenzene or even that of biphenyl. It possesses a band at 354 mμ ($\varepsilon = 1\,800$) with a well marked shoulder at about 373 mμ; two n $\rightarrow \pi^*$-transitions are probably responsible. Two further bands, one at 308 mμ ($\varepsilon = 9\,100$) with a shoulder at 296 mμ and the other of extraordinary intensity at 252 mμ ($\varepsilon = 44\,700$), may be assigned to $\pi \rightarrow \pi^*$-transitions. Pyridazine (VII), the parent heterocycle of benzo[c]cinnoline, exhibits in alcohol a weak band at 311 mμ ($\varepsilon = 300$) and a double band at 243 to 248 mμ ($\varepsilon = 1\,650$–$1\,590$) (*654*) and these have been attributed to n$\rightarrow\pi^*$- and $\pi\rightarrow\pi^*$-transitions, respectively (*1087*). A number of authors, such as Maccoll (*1364*), Platt (*1637*), Hirt (*911, 1036*), and Badger (*129*), have evaluated the spectra of aromatic hydrocarbons in which two CH-groups have been replaced by nitrogen.

The effects of the nature of the solvent on the colour are notable both for pyridazine and for azobenzene derivatives. The n$\rightarrow\pi^*$-band of pyridazine in cyclohexane lies at 338 mμ, as, in contrast to alcohol or water, this solvent is unable to make demands on the lone pairs of electrons on the nitrogens through hydrogen atoms (*911, 1036*). The hypsochromic effect of changing to solvents which can donate protons might correspond to the displacement of the n$\rightarrow\pi^*$-band of azobenzene from 443 mμ to 300 mμ on converting it into its conjugate acid. This phenomenon is probably also responsible for the appearance of a band of long wavelength in aqueous solutions of the basic equilibrium forms of the *p*-phenylazo derivatives of phenol, aniline, and dimethylaniline, a band not exhibited by other derivatives of azobenzene. According to Brode (*330*) it is due to solvation of water at the β-nitrogen (VIII). Perhaps a corresponding

VIII

shift of the n$\rightarrow\pi^*$-band of azomethane is involved in the brown-red colour of the complex of this compound with cuprous chloride (see § 14.4) (*585*).

In the case of compounds of the type of *N,N*-dimethyl-*p*-(*p*-nitrophenylazo)-aniline the solvent plays a different role (*595*). As the polar character of the medium becomes more marked, the $\pi \rightarrow \pi^*$-band is displaced bathochromically; thus the absorption maximum is at 442 mμ in ligroine, 467 mμ in benzene, 475 mμ in methanol, 485 mμ in benzonitrile, and 505 mμ in formamide. This might be due to the increasing participation of zwitterionic structures of the kind of $^{\ominus}O_2N:C_6H_4:N\cdot N:C_6H_4:NR_2^{\oplus}$ in the excited state. The exceptionally high dipole moments (about 8 D) of such compounds indicate this (*2125*).

In the spectrum of the conjugate acid of azobenzene the $\pi \rightarrow \pi^*$-band has undergone a strong batho- and hyper-chromic shift, whilst, as mentioned, the weak band at 300 mμ has been assigned by Jaffé (*1164*) to an n$\rightarrow\pi^*$-transition. The unusual structure proposed for the conjugate acid of azobenzene by Jaffé and Gardner (*1162*) will be discussed in § 13.3.

A great deal of information has accumulated over the years about the colour, though less about the absorption spectra, of technical azo dyes and many authors have been engaged in studying the effect of systematic changes in constitution. For example, Brode (*321–324*) investigated the action of one or two methyl, nitro, or halogeno substituents in all the nine positions of *p*-phenylazophenol as well as that of the sulphonic group in over forty *o*- and *p*-phenylazonaphthylamine dyes. Stamm (*1925*) and also Blumberger (*271, 272*) studied the influence of substituents in the phenyl nucleus of several series of *o*- and *p*-phenylazonaphthols in a systematic manner and compared the spectra. The results proved to be disappointing in so far as that the classic rules about auxochromes and chromophores can only be recognized clearly in the case of simple model compounds, such as the *p′*-substituted *p*-phenylazo derivatives of dimethylaniline and phenol, but not where more complex substances, like *o*- and *p*-phenylazonaphthols, are concerned. Presumably the reasons for these complications are to be found in the hydroxyazo–quinonehydrazone tautomerism and the tendency to associate (see §§ 13.2 and 13.3). A comprehensive review of empirical relations between colour and the constitution of the components of azo dyes has been given by Venkataraman (*2077b*).

Much better understood are the effects of substituents in the phenyl ring on the spectra of phenylazoazulenes, recently determined and evaluated in detail by Heilbronner and his co-workers (*787–790*). 1-Phenylazoazulene exhibits five bands in the region >210 mμ and these possess the following values in alcoholic solution:

Band	I	581 mμ	$\varepsilon \simeq$ 590
Band	II	422 mμ	$\varepsilon =$ 29400
Band	III	333 mμ	$\varepsilon =$ 14100
Band	IV	281 mμ	$\varepsilon =$ 19300
Band	V	235 mμ	$\varepsilon =$ 22600

Band I is partly superimposed on band II and exhibits distinct fine structure, which is almost identical as regards position with that of azulene. Band II probably corresponds to the $\pi \rightarrow \pi^*$-transition of azobenzene. Substitution in the phenyl residue causes bands II, III, and IV to undergo a bathochromic shift. The displacement of band II is directly related to the absolute values of Hammett's σ-constants (*913, 1162*), whilst the maxima of the fine structure of the long wavelength band I of substituted phenylazoazulenes, expressed as the difference in wave number between it and the spectrum of the parent unsubstituted phenylazoazulene, run parallel to the σ-values themselves, being bathochromic with negative σ-values and hypsochromic with positive ones.

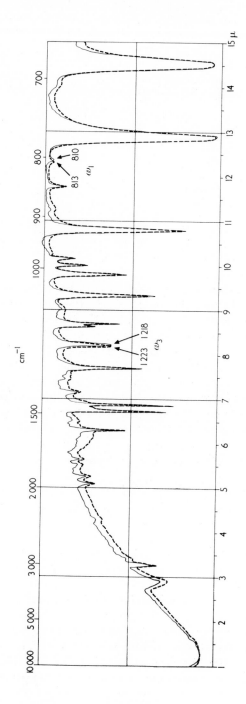

Figure 13.2

Infra-red spectra of azobenzene and mono-N[15]-azobenzene (1362).

If the phenyl group is replaced by a 1- or a 2-naphthyl or a 1- or a 2-anthryl residue, band II shifts by roughly 15 to 20 or 40 to 50 mμ, respectively. In the cases of 2-naphthyl- and 2-anthryl-azoazulene, especially in non-polar media, this band begins to exhibit fine structure.

Just as with azobenzene, the $\pi \rightarrow \pi^*$-band of arylazoazulenes undergoes a strongly batho- and hyper-chromic shift on conversion to the conjugate acid; for example, band II of phenylazoazulene is changed to 522 mμ, $\varepsilon = 34\,800$.

The comparison of azo with azoxy compounds and the dimeric form of nitroso compounds is of interest. Gowenlock and Lüttke [(849) and references cited there] in particular were able to clarify the constitution of the dimeric nitroso compounds and to prove the occurrence of cis–trans-isomerism from the spectra. The close relationship between the three compounds is readily seen from the following structures of the trans-series[5]:

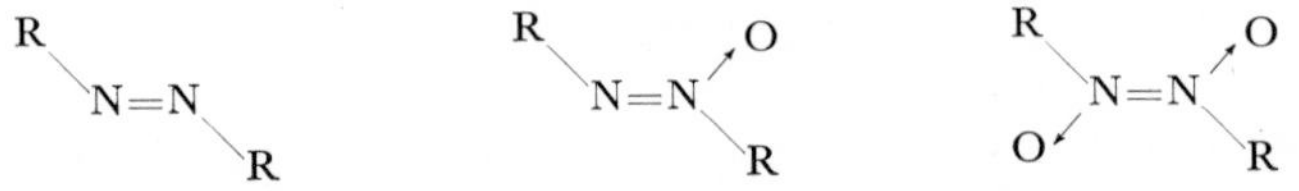

$$\begin{array}{ccc} R\diagdown & R\diagdown \diagup O & R\diagdown \diagup O \\ N{=}N & N{=}N & N{=}N \\ \diagdown R & \diagdown R & O\diagup \ \diagdown R \end{array}$$

The evaluation of the infra-red spectra of azo compounds has so far proved difficult as regards the assigning of characteristic bands for the $>$C—N= and —N:N— vibrations. Hadži (900) as well as Le Fèvre et al. (1311) in spite of comprehensive investigations were unable to do so. Ueno's claim (2058) to have observed a weak —N:N— band at 1395 cm^{-1} seems insufficiently well established, but the study of azobenzene, containing one N^{15} atom, by Lüttke and Kübler (1361, 1362) is relevant. As can be seen from Figure 13.2, the sole difference between the spectra of azobenzene with and without N^{15} lies in the position of the bands at 1223 cm^{-1} and 813 cm^{-1}, which appear in the N^{15} compound at 1218 cm^{-1} and 810 cm^{-1}, respectively. Lüttke and Kübler assign these bands to $>$C—N= vibrations. There is no evidence of an —N:N— band. In addition, a further band (not shown in Figure 13.2) is shifted from 521 cm^{-1} to 516 cm^{-1}.

Stammreich (1929) and Kanda et al. (1194) have examined the Raman spectrum of azobenzene. Stammreich attributes the band at 1442 cm^{-1} to the —N:N— vibration of trans-azobenzene and that at 1487 cm^{-1} to the cis-isomer. The Raman spectrum of azomethane has been studied intensively (1190, 1191, 2141) and it also exhibits a characteristic band at 1442 cm^{-1}.

13.2 Tautomerism of Azo Dyes

Shortly after the discovery of the coupling reaction of phenols (1202), Zincke (2224) showed that the identical hydroxyazo compounds are also obtained by the reaction of quinones with arylhydrazines. Thus, for example, the product from diazobenzene and 1-naphthol or from phenylhydrazine and 1,4-naph-

---

[5] R = alkyl or aryl. The trans-dimeric nitroso isomers are known only in the alkyl series.

thoquinone can be formulated either as the true hydroxyazo derivative (IX) or as the hydrazone (X). Analogous considerations apply to the o-hydroxyazo dyes, though 1,2-naphthoquinone does not give the azo compound obtainable from 2-naphthol, but 2-arylazo-1-naphthols.

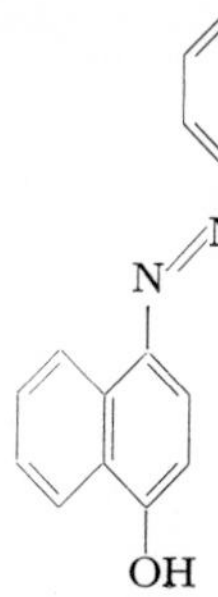

It can be seen that the method of preparation does not permit conclusions to be drawn about the constitution of the product. In the years that followed a great number of research workers tried to clarify the structure of o- and p-hydroxyazo dyes by means of characteristic chemical reactions. In fact, proof was obtained of the presence of hydroxy as well as of carbonyl groups. Dimethyl sulphate and diazomethane yield methyl ethers; acetic anhydride esterifies; on the other hand, 2,4-dinitrophenylhydrazine or semicarbazide give derivatives typical of ketones; cyclopentadiene adds in a Diels-Alder reaction just as to a quinone; and so on.

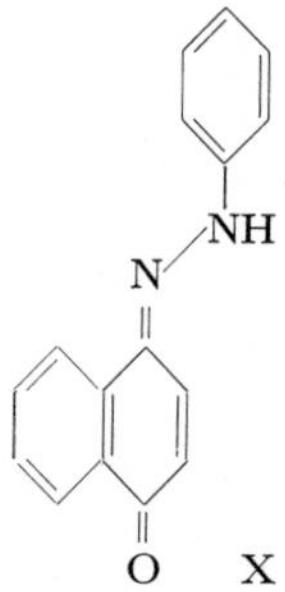

What Pascal (*1588*) already presumed, Hantzsch and Burawoy (*952, 957, 967*) and R. Kuhn and Bär (*1282*) later stated explicitly, namely, that hydroxyazo compounds (and analogously the conjugate acids of aminoazo compounds) are a mixture of (IX) and (X), but equilibrium between the tautomers is reached so quickly that with reactions which proceed quantitatively the exclusive existence of one form or the other can apparently be proved. Hence the occasionally very heated discussion of this problem (*99, 102, 106, 2165, 2166*) has largely lost substance.

It is interesting to ask which side of the azo–hydrazone equilibrium is favoured under given conditions. In principle physicochemical methods can give the answer, but to date no *exact* determination of the position of such an equilibrium has been possible.

A method particularly suitable for tackling this problem is the evaluation of the spectra and it will now be considered, taking p-hydroxyazo dyes as example. Kuhn and Bär (*1282*) compared the spectra between 280 and 550 mμ of 4-phenylazo-1-naphthol (IX $\rightleftharpoons$ X), 4-phenylazo-1-methoxynaphthalene (XI), and 1,4-naphthoquinone α-methylphenylhydrazone (XII) in a variety of solvents. The spectra of the compounds (XI) and (XII), which cannot tautomerize, are largely independent of the nature of the medium, just as those of azobenzene and phenylazonaphthalene. (XI) exhibits an absorption maximum at 400 mμ, (XII) one at 470 mμ. The p-hydroxyazo dye on the contrary possesses two maxima in benzene (410 and 460 mμ), though their extinctions are lower than those of (XI) and (XII). In pyridine and alcohol the maximum

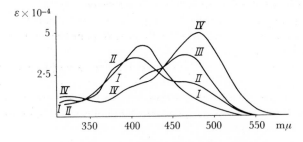

at shorter wavelengths is reinforced, but the other is weakened. In nitrobenzene and glacial acetic acid the relationship is completely reversed. The graphic representation of the spectra in the various solvents (Figure 13.3) shows great similarity to that of an acid–base equilibrium at a series of hydrogen ion

Figure 13.3

Spectra of 4-phenylazo-1-naphthol in different solvents (*1282*)[6]

I: pyridine   III: nitrobenzene
II: alcohol   IV: glacial acetic acid

concentrations. That the isosbestic point at 430 mμ is not completely developed must be expected because of the great differences in solvating power of the media used. This investigation makes it very probable that 4-phenylazo-1-naphthol consists of a mixture of tautomers; in pyridine the azo form (IX) preponderates, in glacial acetic acid and nitrobenzene the hydrazone (X), whilst in benzene the two isomers are present in about equal amounts.

In an analogous manner, other authors have compared the spectra of further p-hydroxyazo compounds with the corresponding O- and N-methyl derivatives as well as with O- and N-acylated products (*1671, 1672*). Thus,

---

[6] According to E. Heilbronner (*1001*) the extinction coefficients given by Kuhn and Bär (*1282*) are too high by a factor of three.

according to Brode (*329*) and Ospenson (*1560, 1561*), the tautomeric equilibrium increasingly favours the hydrazone as the number of rings becomes greater in going from derivatives of phenol, to those of 1-naphthol, to those of 1-anthrol. The spectrum of Orange I, 4-(4′-sulphophenylazo)-1-naphthol (XXIV, see § 13.3), simulates that of its *N*-methyl derivative, and hence the dye consists largely of the hydrazone (*83, 1499*). Substituents in the diazo component influence the equilibrium greatly, the participation of the hydrazone form increasing in the series p-OCH$_3$ < p-CH$_3$ < H < Cl < p-NO$_2$ (*1889*) and therefore being favoured by acidifying groups. However, from the well established effects of substituents on acid–base equilibria of benzene derivatives the reverse sequence would have been expected (*1001*).

The aza analogue of 4-phenylazo-1-naphthol, 5-phenylazo-8-quinolinol, exists preponderantly in the azo form, presumably because of the hydrogen bond between the oxygen and the cyclic nitrogen atom (*125*).

Confirmation of these results comes from Hadži's evaluation of the infra-red spectra of p-hydroxy- and p-deuteroxyazo compounds, in the solid state 4-phenylazophenol exhibiting an OH-band, but 4-phenylazo-1-naphthol C:O- and NH-bands (*900*).

Giles (*794*) has attacked the problem of tautomerism in hydroxyazo compounds by determining the compressibility of the monomolecular films formed by suitably substituted derivatives in a water surface.

m-*Hydroxyazo compounds* can only be prepared indirectly, but they have been investigated for comparison because for them rearrangement into a quinonoid form is impossible (*329, 358*).

In alkaline solution *o*-, *m*-, and *p*-hydroxyazo derivatives lose a proton. The anions corresponding to the azo and hydrazone forms, such as (XIII a) and (XIII b), respectively, differ in the cases of the *o*- and *p*-series only in the electron distribution. Hence they represent mesomeric limiting structures of a *single* compound (*64, 399, 660*).

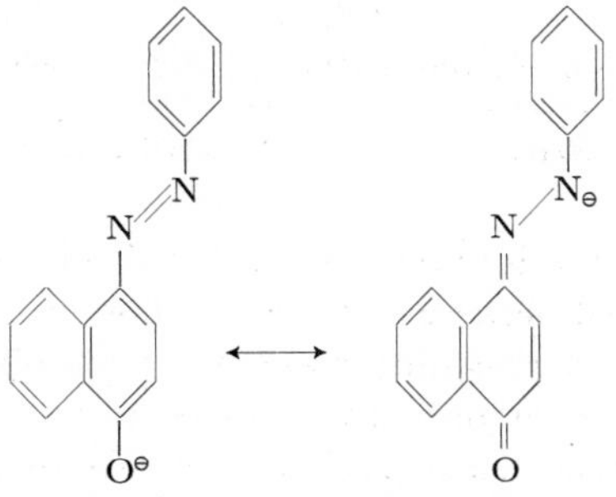

XIII a   XIII b

The structure of the *o-hydroxyazo compounds* was solved only some twenty years after that of the *p*-isomers. The cause of the delay was the hydrogen bond between the phenolic oxygen and the β-nitrogen of the azo bridge. This hydrogen bond has its place in the history of chemistry because it was the first to be clearly recognized and discussed as a new phenomenon by Oddo and Puxeddu in 1906 (*1548*). The question of whether, for instance, in the *o*-coupled products of 1-naphthol, azo and hydrazone forms are present in tautomeric equilibrium (XIV ⇌ XV) was considered in the 'thirties by Burawoy and Markowitsch (*387, 388*) as well as by R. Kuhn and Bär (*1282*). Here also it was assumed because of the similarity of the spectrum with that of the diphenylhydrazone (XVI) that the structure of 2-phenylazo-1-naphthol is quinonoid, but such a conclusion is somewhat doubtful since the hydrogen bond present in (XIV) and (XV) might influence the spectrum considerably.

XIV   XV   XVI

Unfortunately at that time it was not yet possible to demonstrate the conversion of the hydrazone into the azo form to be a function of the nature of the solvent, as had been the case with the *p*-hydroxyazo compounds. This appears to have been one of the reasons why it was postulated that (XIV) and (XV) are not a tautomeric pair of discrete molecules, but limiting structures of one and the same compound (*64, 660, 1011*).

In the meantime, the studies of the character of hydrogen bonding, which have shown the hydrogen bond to be hardly a mesomeric phenomenon, have made it probable that this hypothesis is incorrect. In addition, Burawoy (*389, 390*) was able to demonstrate the occurrence of tautomerism in the special case of the *o*-hydroxyazo compounds through finding that the spectra of the products of coupling to 2-naphthol are dependent on the solvent and on the substituents in the diazo component. Thus, 1-phenylazo-2-naphthol exhibits in hexane a maximum at 420 mμ, corresponding to the hydroxyazo form, but in 50% aqueous alcohol the hydrazone maximum at 480 mμ appears. The spectra in chloroform and in alcohol can be represented in good approximation as mixtures of the spectra in the two previous solvents. Certain deviations in behaviour, as regards the sequence of media and *o*-substituents, compared with the *p*-isomers can be interpreted as effects of solvation.

From investigations of the spectra of 2-phenylazophenols (*329, 900, 1560, 1561, 2058*) and of sulphonated *o*-phenylazonaphthols (*83, 900, 1499*), such as Orange II, it follows that the former are essentially true azo compounds, whereas the latter exist largely as the hydrazones.

The complete evaluation of these spectra with respect to hydroxyazo–hydrazone tautomerism is made difficult and uncertain because such azo compounds frequently are not monomolecularly dispersed in solution, but they form aggregates, that is, dimers or oligomers, the spectra of which differ clearly from those of the monomers. Thus, Stamm and Zollinger (*1928*) showed that dyes

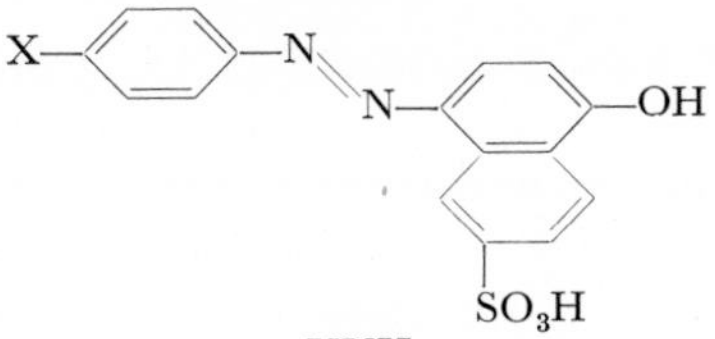

XVII

of the type of (XVII) exist in aqueous solution more and more in the associated, presumably dimeric form as the —M effect of the substituent X is increased. For example, the dye (XVII, X = NO_2) in 5×10^{-6} M solution possesses a maximum at 479 mμ, but as the concentration is increased (up to 4×10^{-4} mole/l.) another at 451 mμ supersedes it.

The difficulty of analysing the infra-red spectra (900, 1011, 2058) is aggravated by the presence of the intramolecular hydrogen bond. So far, bands characteristic for the azo bridge (—N:N—) have not yet been demonstrated with certainty (see § 13.1), but all the same the similarity of the spectra with those of p-azonaphthols in the region 6·5 to 7 μ led Hadži (900) to suppose the hydrazone form to be present. Determinations of dipole moments (230, 984) do not allow any conclusions to be drawn about the tautomeric equilibrium.

Ospenson (1560, 1561) compared the positions of the o- and p-azo–hydrazone equilibria with the reduction potentials of the corresponding 1,2- and 1,4-quinones. As the reduction potentials decrease in the series benzoquinone > naphthoquinone > anthraquinone, that is, as the quinone increases in stability, so the hydrazone form tends to assume greater importance. However, the preponderance of the hydrazone in the o-series as compared with the p-isomers apparently contradicts the lower stability of o-quinones.

Aminoazo compounds probably always exist in the azo form (1375). The structure of the products obtained on the addition of a proton will be discussed in the next section.

The cis–trans-isomerism of azo dyes has already been dealt with in connection with the isomeric diazo compounds and the spectra (§§ 4.1 and 13.1).

In aliphatic azo compounds bearing at least one hydrogen atom at one of the α-carbon atoms the possibility of azo–hydrazone tautomerism also exists (13.2),

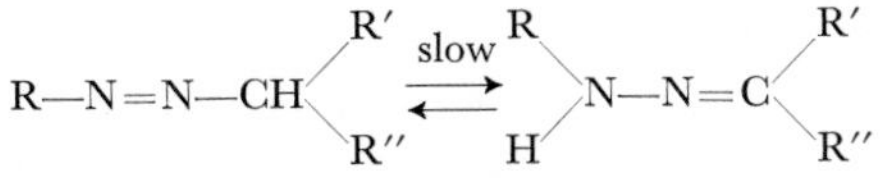

$$\text{(13.2)}$$

XVIII   XIX

but it has always been found that the hydrazone is the more stable species. Since the rate of rearrangement of the azo into the hydrazone form is in general very low, azo compounds of the type of (XVIII) can readily be isolated in spite of this (see § 9.2). The reaction (XVIII) → (XIX) is favoured by solvents able to provide protons and is catalysed by acids and bases [see e.g. (1355)], but no exact investigations have yet been undertaken.

13.3 Acid–Base Equilibria of Azo Compounds

It seems appropriate to follow the discussion of the spectra and the tautomerism of hydroxyazo compounds with a consideration of the closely connected acid–base equilibria and to defer some remarks about the basic character of azo-benzene and related substances to the end of this section.

Protolytic equilibria play an important part in azo dyes. On the one hand, some azo compounds are much used as indicators, for example, Congo Red (XX), Methyl Orange (XXI), Methyl Red (XXII), and Alizarin Yellow 2G (XXIII), but, on the other, these very indicator properties provide ob-

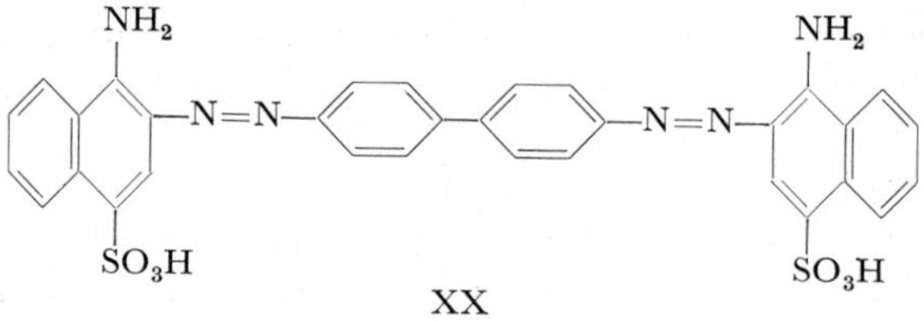

XX

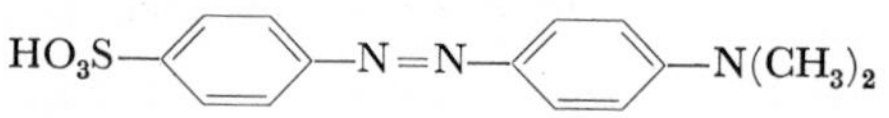

XXI

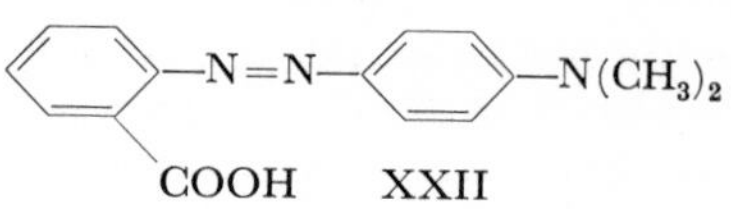

XXII

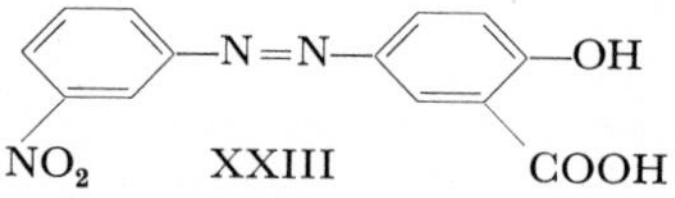

XXIII

stacles to their universal application as dyestuffs. Dyes for wool must not exhibit a change in colour roughly in the range of pH between 2 and 9, dyes for cellulosic fibres not between pH 4 and 11.

This aspect is clearly demonstrated by the isomeric dyes Orange I (XXIV) and Orange II (XXV), the former being almost obsolete because its hue is

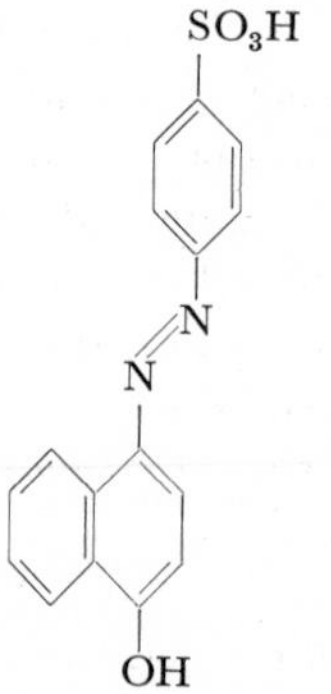

$pK_2 = 8·2$ (83, 1499, 1904)

XXIV

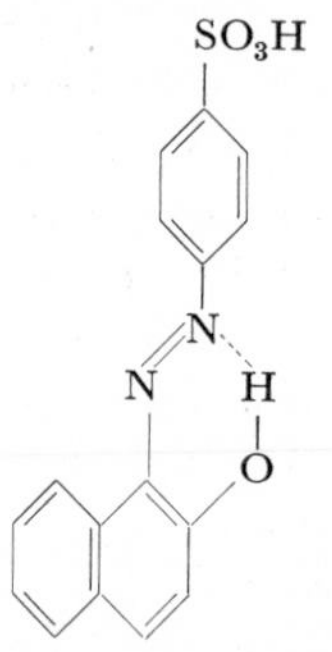

$pK_2 = 11·4$ (83, 1499)

XXV

affected both by sodium carbonate and by soap. Already above pH 8·2, it is present mainly as the dibasic anion, whilst Orange II does not lose its phenolic proton until the alkalinity is raised much higher. The constants K_2 which correspond to the acid dissociation of the phenolic groups differ by more than 10^3, the cause being the intramolecular hydrogen bond of Orange II.

Compared with 1- and 2-naphthol (pK = 9·8 and 9·9, respectively), the introduction of an arylazo residue distinctly increases the acidity, as Orange I illustrates. The acidifying nature of this group is also apparent from the fact that its Hammett substituent constant (*913, 914*c) is positive (σ_{para} = 0·64). In Orange II this effect is quite outweighed by the hydrogen bond. If it is assumed that Orange II should have an acid dissociation constant of magnitude similar to that of Orange I, it can be seen that a thousandfold reduction in the dissociation constant corresponds to a hydrogen bond energy of about 5 kcal/mole.

Through a series of systematic experiments, Stamm (*1925*) found that the strength of the hydrogen bond of *o*-hydroxyazo dyes depends on the nature of the substituents present in the coupling component apart from the arylazo group. From sequence (13.3) it can be seen that the bond is stronger when the neighbouring residue is voluminous.

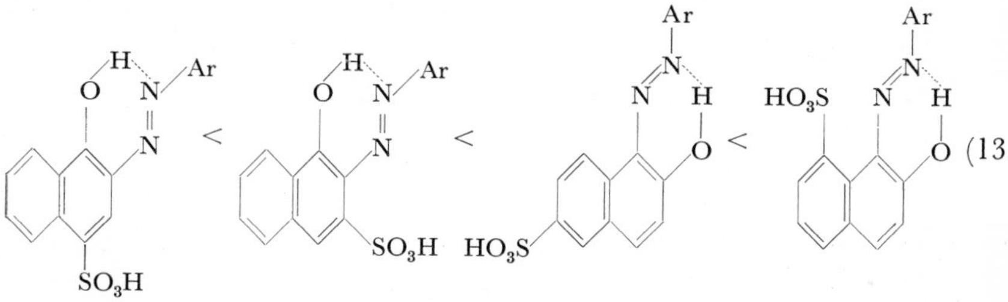

increasing strength of hydrogen bond

Substituents in the diazo component have either no or an unexpected effect on the acid dissociation constants of both *o*- and *p*-hydroxyazo dyes. In Table 13.2 are listed two typical series from the publications of Stamm and Zollinger (*1732, 1925, 2237*). That the pK$_2$ values do not decrease as anticipated from *p*-OCH$_3$ to *p*-NO$_2$ is presumably due to two factors, namely, the position of the azo–hydrazone equilibrium and the influence of the substituent on the formation of aggregates. As in the last decade conclusions about the position of the tautomeric equilibria of azo compounds have frequently been drawn from determinations of the acid dissociation constants, the connection between the protolytic and the prototropic equilibria of azonaphthols must be considered briefly. It is relevant also to the subsequent discussion of the structure of the products obtained by the addition of acid to aminoazobenzene derivatives. Although the connection has been appreciated in the case of analogous systems, such as β-diketones (*1868*), this has only rarely been the case with azo compounds (*304, 1163, 2237, 2366*).

Table 13.2

Acid Dissociation Constants (pK_2) *of Substituted Phenylazonaphtholsulphonic Acids* (2237)

(Water, 20°, ionic strength $I = 0.25$, pK measured
spectrophotometrically in 4×10^{-5} molar solutions.)

X	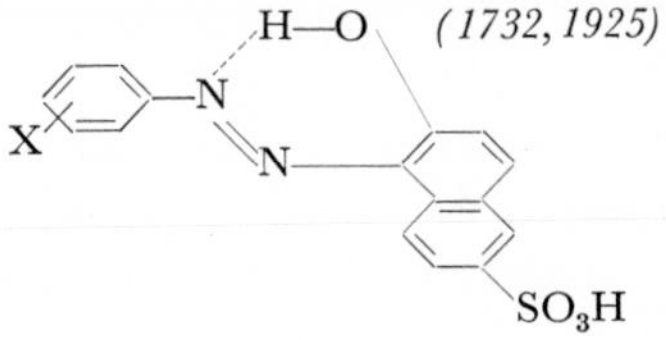 (1732, 1925)	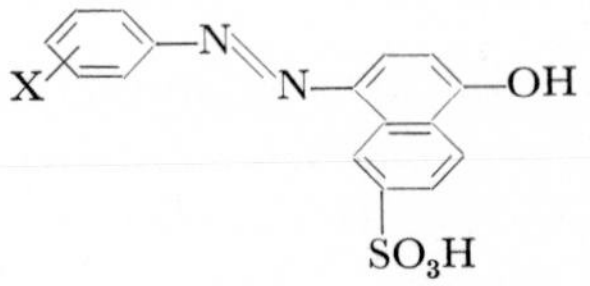 (1732, 2237)
p-OCH$_3$	10·44	7·30
p-CH$_3$	10·62	7·30
H	10·57	7·30
m-OCH$_3$	10·66	7·45
p-Cl	10·29	7·40
m-Cl	10·40	7·49
p-NO$_2$	10·48	8·08

Scheme (13.4) includes both these equilibria with Orange I (Ar = p-C$_6$H$_4$·SO$_3^{\ominus}$) as example. The following abbreviations will now be used for the particles of this system: E for enol, K for ketone, A for anion, and H for hydrogen ion. The effective acid dissociation constant, which is directly determinable ($K_{\text{eff.}}$),

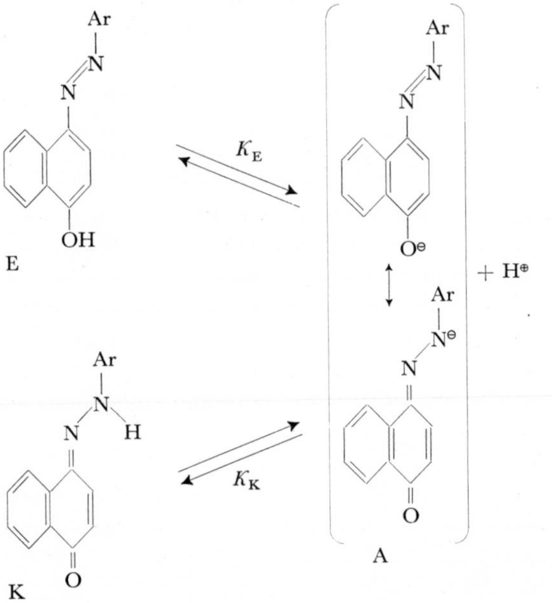

(13.4)

is connected with those of the separate equilibria (K_E and K_K) and the ratio between the enol and keto tautomers (K_T) as follows:

$$K_{eff.} = \frac{A \times H}{K + E} \qquad \left[\text{or } A \times H = K_{eff.} \, (K + E) \right] \tag{13.5}$$

$$K_K = \frac{A \times H}{K} \qquad K_E = \frac{A \times H}{E} \qquad \left[\text{or } A \times H = K_E \times E \right] \tag{13.6}$$

$$K_T = \frac{E}{K} = \frac{K_K}{K_E} \tag{13.7}$$

From (13.5) and (13.6): $\quad K_E \times E = K_{eff.} \, (K + E) \tag{13.8}$

By substituting for K in (13.8) by means of (13.7), K_E is obtained as a function of $K_{eff.}$ and K_T (13.9). From equation (13.9) it can be seen that $K_{eff.}$ is a measure

$$K_E = K_{eff.} \, \frac{1 + K_T}{K_T} \tag{13.9}$$

of the phenol producing protolytic equilibrium (K_E) only when the tautomerism greatly favours the azo form ($K_T \gg 1$).

As described in the preceding section, acidifying substituents in the diazo component shift the equilibrium to the advantage of the hydrazone ($K_T < 1$) and in this way the influence of the substituent concerned on $K_{eff.}$ is reduced. As K_T becomes smaller, $K_{eff.}$ decreases relatively to K_E as can be seen from equation (13.9). Substituents which increase K_E have, therefore, their acidifying effect on $K_{eff.}$ *damped*.

However, on these grounds it still cannot be explained how the effect of the substituent can disappear altogether or even be exerted in the opposite sense, as happens with 1-(4'-nitrophenylazo)-4-naphthol-7-sulphonic acid. Responsibility rests on the formation of aggregates by the conjugate acids, which can be demonstrated spectrophotometrically. Substituents in the 4'-position with a —M effect, such as nitro, acetyl, or cyano groups, cause the acids in aqueous solution already at a concentration of 5×10^{-6} M to be present mainly as aggregates, probably preponderantly dimeric, whilst, for instance, the corresponding 4'-methoxy compound exists wholly as the monomer in this range of concentration. In the dimers the dissociation of the second hydroxy group is hindered electrostatically, thus reducing the acidity. It seems reasonable to suppose that —M substituents favour co-planarity through the limiting structures (XXVIb) or (XXVIIb), respectively, in *both* azo and hydrazone forms and that thus the van der Waals forces responsible for association are able to assert themselves. Nothing definite is known with respect to the structure of these aggregates.

In contrast to these phenylazonaphthols, the acid dissociation constants of phenylazophenols obey the Hammett equation as shown by Yeh and Jaffé (2367). Based on the investigations in the phenylazonaphthol series this result may be explained by the lower tendency of phenylazophenols to aggregate.

The discussion of the equilibria has special interest in connection with the until recently disputed constitution of the conjugate acids of N,N-dimethyl-p-phenylazoaniline (Butter Yellow) and similar compounds. As with the o- and

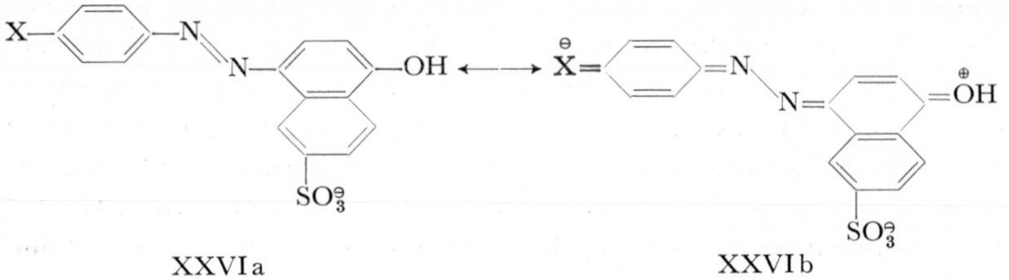

XXVIa   XXVIb

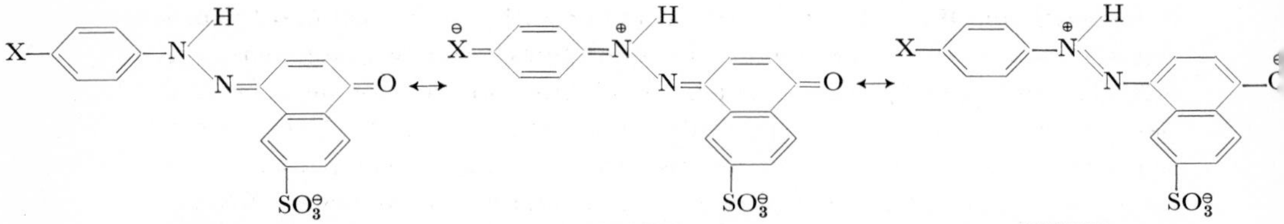

XXVIIa   XXVIIb   XXVIIc

p-hydroxyazo dyes, here also two acids (**XXVIII** and **XXIX**) are in equilibrium with a common base (**XXX**). The third acid in which the proton is bound to the α-nitrogen of the azo bridge is very unstable for several reasons. From equation (13.9) it is apparent that conclusions drawn from the effective equilibrium constant of system (13.10) about the constitution of the conjugate acid (i.e. whether **XXVIII** or **XXIX** is favoured) (*1233, 1382*) must not be regarded as proof. More reliable information comes from the comparison of the spectra of p-phenylazoanilines in acid solution with those of the two isomeric N-alkyl derivatives. Already Hantzsch and Hilscher (*952, 957, 967*) pointed out that, although the spectrum of N,N,N-trimethyl-p-phenylazoanilinium is roughly the same as that of azobenzene, that of the conjugate acid of N,N-

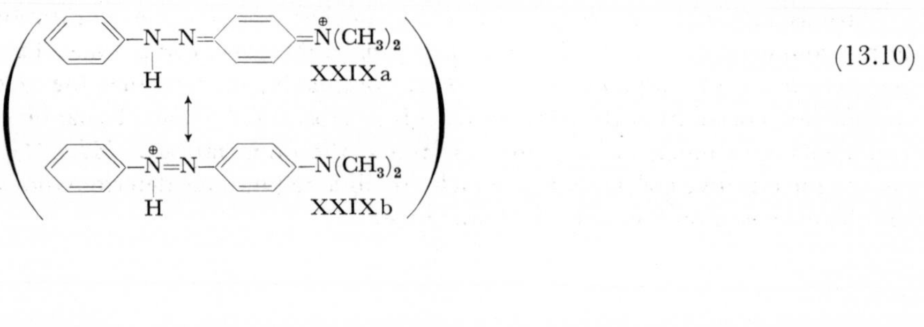

XXVIII

XXXa

XXXb

XXIXa

XXIXb

(13.10)

dimethyl-*p*-phenylazoaniline is quite different. This suggests structure (XXIX). The surprising consequence that the β-nitrogen of the azo link is more basic than that of the amino group can be interpreted at least in part through the mesomerism (XXIX a–b), which increases the electron density at the β-nitrogen as well as the stability of the cation. As soon as the co-planarity between the dimethylamino group and the benzene ring is hindered, these effects are ruled out. Thus Sawicki (*1778, 1780*) has shown, for example, that the cation of *N,N*-dimethyl-*p*-phenylazo-*o*-toluidine possesses a spectrum like that of azobenzene with a $\pi \longrightarrow \pi^*$-band at 319 m$\mu$, whilst the conjugate acid of *N,N*-dimethyl-*p*-phenylazoaniline absorbs strongly in the region 512 to 520 mμ (see Table 13.3).

Hantzsch and Burawoy (*957*) drew attention earlier to the fact that the products of such a proton addition consist of mixtures of the two tautomers (e.g. XXVIII and XXIX). This is apparent from the spectra, for instance. The band at 310 to 350 mμ, assigned to the azoanilinium form (XXVIII), is present also, though it is much less intense, in the spectra of compounds which possess a strong band at 480 to 520 mμ and therefore exist mainly as (XXIX). On the other hand, substances with a prominent azoammonium band absorb to some extent at longer wavelengths, as can be seen from Table 13.3. Cilento, Miller, and Miller (*425*) have demonstrated on about twenty derivatives of *p*-phenylazoaniline (4-aminoazobenzene) that the intensities of the two bands are inversely proportional to one another, in full agreement with their interpretation on the basis of the presence of mixtures of tautomers. From the spectra, Sawicki (*1778, 1780*) has determined the ratio between the tautomers XXVIII/XXIX, i.e. K_T, for about a hundred *p*-phenylazoanilines and their *N*-alkylated derivatives. Later, he found that in disazo dyes such as (XXXI) the first proton probably adds to the β-, the second to the δ-nitrogen atom (*1783*).

$$\langle\!\!\!\bigcirc\!\!\!\rangle\!-\!N\!=\!N\!-\!\langle\!\!\!\bigcirc\!\!\!\rangle\!-\!N\!=\!N\!-\!\langle\!\!\!\bigcirc\!\!\!\rangle\!-\!N(CH_3)_2 \qquad \text{XXXI}$$

$$\qquad\quad \delta \;\; \gamma \qquad\qquad\qquad \beta \;\; \alpha$$

Apart from the papers already mentioned, the products of the addition of protons to *p*-phenylazoanilines have been investigated by Sawicki (*1779, 1781, 1782, 1784, 1785*), Badger (*123*), Rogers (*1728*), Miller (*1444*), Horner (*1077*), Jaffé (*2366*), G. E. Lewis (*2435*), and their co-workers. Sawicki's determinations of K_T in Butter Yellow derivatives (Table 13.3) have been confirmed by Gränacher, Suhr, Zenhäusern, and Zollinger (*2444*) with the help of nuclear magnetic resonance.

Various authors have attempted to draw conclusions about the constitution of the conjugate acids from the basic strengths of these azo compounds. Thus Klotz *et al.* (*1233*), as well as Jaffé (*1161*) originally, thought that the acid dissociation constants of the conjugate acids of substituted *p*-phenylazoanilines could only be reconciled with proton addition at the amino nitrogen (XXVIII). As it is the effective constants K_{eff} which are obtained in these determinations, arguments based on them are not conclusive.

Table 13.3

$\pi \longrightarrow \pi^*$-Bands of the Conjugate Acids of Azobenzene Derivatives

Conjugate acid of	Azonium band		Azoanilinium band		$K_T = \dfrac{[XXVIII]}{[XXIX]}$
	$\lambda_{max.}$	ε	$\lambda_{max.}$	ε	
⬡—N=N—⬡ [7]	—	—	319	22 000	—
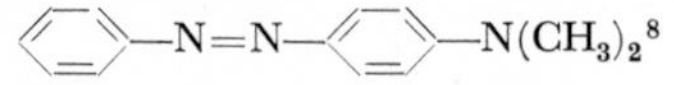 ⬡—N=N—⬡—N(CH$_3$)$_2$ [8]	512–520	35 500	320	9 800	0·31
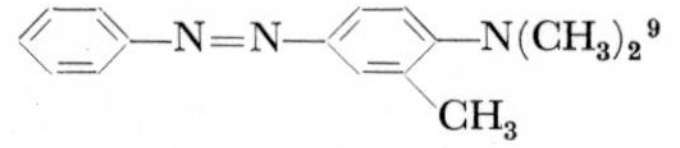 ⬡—N=N—⬡(CH$_3$)—N(CH$_3$)$_2$ [9]	500	500	319	19 800	40·0

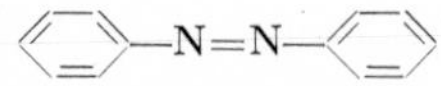

[7] In 95% alcohol (spectrum of azobenzene, not of its conjugate acid).
[8] In 50% alcohol, 1·2 N hydrochloric acid, from (1780)
[9] In 50% alcohol, 1·0 N hydrochloric acid, from (1780)

Using Sawicki's data (1778, 1780, 1784, 1785), Zollinger (1732) has calculated the acid dissociation constants K_E and K_K belonging to (XXVIII) and (XXIX), respectively, and these are listed in Table 13.4. Comparison of the parent compound with its 2-methyl derivative indicates that the non-planarity occasioned by the substituent in o-position to the dimethylamino group decreases the acidity by more than ten times. However, substituents in the other phenyl ring have only minor influence on the effective acid dissociation constant. The pK$_{eff}$.-value of the 4'-nitro compound deviates in a manner similar to that observed in the phenylazonaphthol series (see Table 13.2), as, surprisingly, its conjugate acid is weaker than the isomeric 3'-nitro derivative. The calculated pK$_E$- and pK$_K$-values show the azonium form (XXIX) to be responsible. Here also the explanation lies in the greater co-planarity due to the presence of a —M substituent in the 4'-position, which increases the tendency to associate. That this effect of the 4'-nitro group appears only in the azonium tautomer (pK$_K$) follows from the fact that only forms of the type of (XXIXa) and (XXIXb), but not (XXVIII), possess limiting structures in which the mesomeric participation of the nitro group is energetically favourable.

That aggregation is superimposed on the keto–enol–anion equilibria is probably the reason why the action of substituents in the second phenyl nucleus of p-phenylazoaniline derivatives, as well as in phenylazonaphthols, cannot be represented by a Hammett $\sigma\varrho$-relation (913, 914c) [cf., however, (304)].

Heilbronner's discussion of the spectrum of 4'-dimethylaminophenylazo-1-azulene and his MO calculations show that the tautomeric equilibrium of the conjugate acid corresponding to XXVIII ⇌ XXIX is practically completely on the side of the azonium compound.

In 2- and 4-phenylazopyridine the proton seems to add to the heterocyclic nitrogen (425, 1233) and from Hünig's work (1134) it also appears that in the

Table 13.4

The Ratios between the Tautomers and the Acid–Base Equilibrium Constants of Substituted
N,N-Dimethyl-p-phenylazoanilines

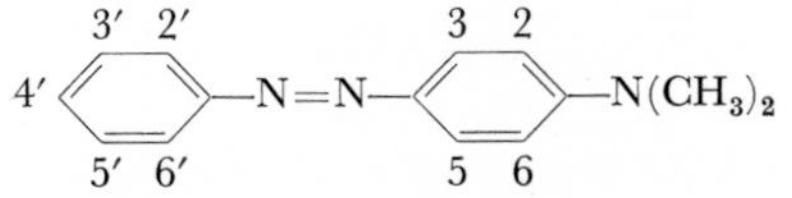

Substituent	$K_T{}^{10}$	$pK_{eff.}{}^{11}$	pK_E	pK_K
4'-OCH$_3$	1·00	2·40	2·10	2·10
4'-CH$_3$	0·38	2·36	1·80	2·22
H	0·29	2·28	1·64	2·17
3'-Cl	0·28	2·01	1·35	1·90
3'-NO$_2$	0·28	1·67	1·01	1·56
4'-NO$_2$	0·12	1·81	0·82	1·76
3-CH$_3$	40·0	3·48	3·47	1·87

[10] $K_T = \dfrac{[XXVIII]}{[XXIX]}$, calculated from Sawicki's values for $C_\mathcal{E}/A_\mathcal{E}$ (*1780*).
[11] From Sawicki (*1780*).

products of oxidative azo coupling the proton is bound preferentially to the amino group, as for example in (XXXII). However, the addition of a proton to (*o*- or *p*-dimethylaminophenylazo)pyridine shifts the absorption maximum from ~470 to ~555 mμ and Cilento *et al.* (*425*) have sought to explain this through resonance or intermolecular hydrogen bonding.

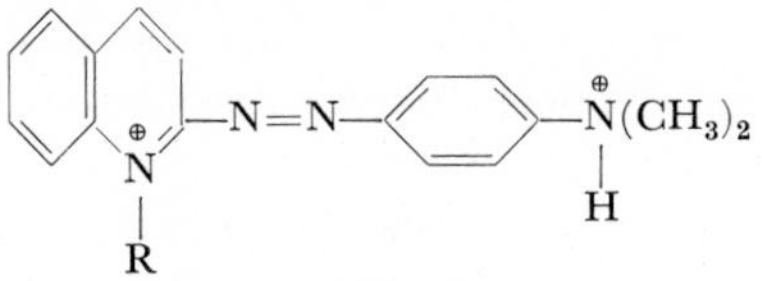

XXXII

Pentimalli and co-workers (*2315, 2349*) approached the problem of the relative basicity of the nitrogen atoms in *N*-heterocyclic azo and aminoazo compounds on the basis of some analogies between *N*-oxidation and *N*-protonation. Mono-oxidation of *N*,*N*-dimethyl-*p*-phenylazoaniline leads to the amine (XXXIII) and a second oxygen atom adds to the azo nitrogen remote from the substituted phenyl group. Pentimalli concludes that, therefore, the amino nitrogen is more basic. As already discussed in connection with the structural problem of diazo-amino compounds (§ 8.2), it is doubtful if such a conclusion is correct. Competitive oxidation at two nitrogen atoms of a molecule is probably a rate-determining reaction whereas *N*-protonation is so fast a process as to be definitely dependent on the position of the equilibrium.

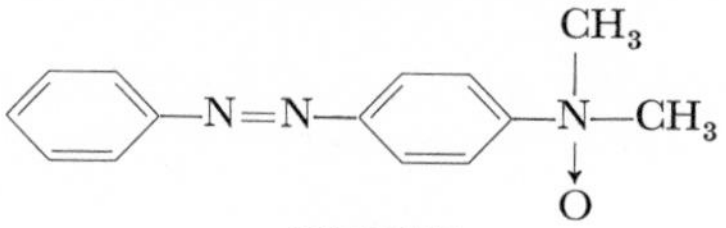

CH$_3$

⟨benzene⟩—N=N—⟨benzene⟩—N—CH$_3$

O

XXXIII

Not yet understood is the observation repeatedly made by Sawicki [(*1782, 1783*) and especially (*1778, 1780*)] and confirmed by Jaffé (*1163*), namely, that the tautomeric equilibrium is easily altered in favour of the azonium ion (XXVIII) as the concentration of acid is increased. Perhaps this is due to the superimposed association equilibria.

In even more strongly acid media the *p*-phenylazoanilines take up a second proton (*1199*) to give an ion such as (XXXIV). The equilibrium constants corresponding to this step (K_2) have been determined by Rogers (*1728*) amongst others.

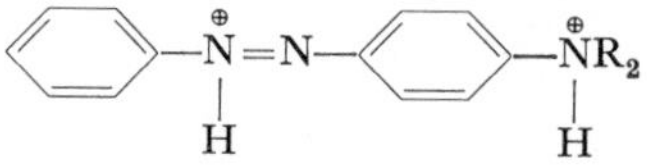

⟨benzene⟩—$\overset{\oplus}{N}$=N—⟨benzene⟩—$\overset{\oplus}{N}R_2$

H   H

XXXIV

Azobenzene itself is also able to act as a base, monofunctionally only, of course. The dissociation constant of the conjugate acid has been obtained by Klotz and co-workers (*1233*) for water and by Jaffé et al. (*1162, 2433*) for 20% v/v ethanol (pK_a = −2·48 and −2·90, respectively). Astonishing is the comparison with benzo[*c*]cinnoline, which can be regarded as azobenzene ring-closed in the 2,2′-position [§ 13.1, formula (VI)]. Benzo[*c*]cinnoline is nearly 100000 times more basic (pK_a = 2·2) (*845*), corresponding well with pyridazine (pK_a = 2·33) (*11*). Interaction between the two benzene nuclei therefore occurs mainly through the direct biphenyl link and not through the azo bridge. Hence analogies between pyridazines and azo compounds are justified only to a limited extent.

From their determinations of the acid dissociation constants of substituted azobenzenes, Jaffé and Gardner (*1162, 2205, 2433*) infer that the proton of the conjugate acids is not bound to one, but to both the nitrogen atoms of the azo bridge and that in consequence the phenyl rings take up the *cis*-configuration. This in itself rather improbable conclusion is not convincing because it is based on modified σ-values [the σ$^+$-constants of H. C. Brown and Okamoto (*345*)] which exhibit sufficient scatter for Jaffé's measurements to be reconcilable also with the classic azonium formulation. Still another constitution, namely that of a π-complex, has been proposed by Cilento (*2432*) for the conjugate acid of 4,4′-bisdimethylaminoazobenzene.

Based on Jaffé's hypothesis, the conjugate acids of *cis*- and *trans*-azobenzene should be identical. Heilbronner, Wepster, and their co-workers (*2425*) recently characterized these compounds carefully: they are definitely different species (appearance of crystals, spectra, acidity; pK-values, measured in 20% v/v ethanol, were —2·25 and —2·95, respectively). In consequence, Jaffé's hypothesis cannot be correct. The spectra of *cis*-azobenzene and its conjugate acid are very similar to those of 11,12-dihydrodibenzo[*c*,*g*][1,2]diazocine (*o*,*o*'-azodibenzyl,

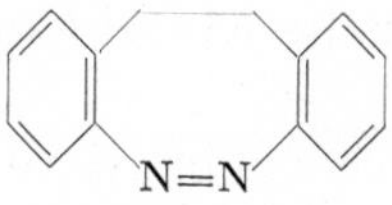

XXXV

XXXV) and its protonated derivative, compounds which are forced into the *cis*-azo configuration by the —CH$_2$·CH$_2$— linkage between the benzene rings.

A comparison of the pK-values of these azobenzene derivatives with those of substituted azomethines, recently obtained (*2122*), should be of interest in view of the differences in spectra between these two classes of compounds which were discussed in § 13.1.

The pK-values of arylazoazulenes, in which aryl can be a phenyl, naphthyl, or anthryl residue, have lately been determined and evaluated by Heilbronner and his co-workers (*787, 790, 2348*). The acid dissociation constants of the phenylazoazulenes substituted in the phenyl group obey Hammett's $\sigma\varrho$-relation (*913, 914c*).

14. The Chemistry of the Metal Complexes of Azo Dyes

14.1 The Nature of the Chemical Bonds holding the Metal Ions in Complex Compounds

Alfred Werner studied complex compounds in general and, in 1891, he advanced his theory of coordination, which explained how stable molecules can combine to form molecular complexes (*1197, 2129, 2132*). Werner developed his ideas above all from the coordination compounds of metal ions, the metal complexes. In addition, the present knowledge of the structure and nature of the bonds in other complexes, such as in simple inorganic ions (e.g. $NH_4^\oplus$ and $SO_4^{\ominus\ominus}$) and in hydrated salts, can be traced back to him. Werner's theories were propagated and extended particularly by his pupil Paul Pfeiffer (*1616, 1618*), to whom are due fundamental investigations of importance for the more limited field of the metal–complex dyes. Recent years have been characterized by the systematic application of physical and physicochemical methods, of which the quantitative study of the equilibria of the complexes in the last decade has been specially significant. The work of Schwarzenbach, which springs first to mind, is outstanding not only because of its manifold applications in analytical chemistry, but also because of the general progress in the whole of chemistry that followed from it.

Metal complexes play a considerable role in the field of azo compounds and have achieved prominence particularly as azo dyestuffs. Since the chemistry of metal complexes is not too widely known, a brief review of its principles will now be given, before the problems most closely connected with the complex azo dyes are dealt with in § 14.4.

A metal complex is a compound formed from a metal ion and a *ligand*, the latter being a particle (ion or molecule), which possesses a free pair of electrons. So-called bi- and poly-functional ligands, in which two or more such pairs of electrons are available, can give rise to the presence of rings in the complexes; these are termed *chelates*. Although all known ligands have free pairs of electrons, it appears that in those cases in which the complex is held together purely electrostatically the pair of electrons is not donated to take part in the bonding.

According to G. N. Lewis's definition, a base is an electron donor and an acid an electron acceptor. Complex formation therefore corresponds formally to an acid–base reaction. This follows readily from a comparison of the combination of ammonia, on the one hand, with a proton (14.1) and, on the other, with a cuprous ion (14.2). Both are complexing reactions.

$$NH_3 \qquad OS = -III \quad CV = 3 \quad CN = 3$$
$$NH_4^{\oplus} \qquad OS = -III \quad CV = 4 \quad CN = 4$$
$$[O-N=O]^{\ominus} \quad OS = +III \quad CV = 3 \quad CN = 2$$

Independently of the origin of the electrons concerned two extreme types of bond exist: either the lone pair of electrons remains on the ligand, when the metal ion and the ligand are held together purely electrostatically because of their respective electropositive and electronegative characters, a so-called *normal complex* with *ionic bonding* being formed, or both of the electrons are used to constitute a *covalent bond*, giving a *penetration complex*. The latter expression was coined because the electronic orbitals of metal ion and ligand overlap or penetrate one another.

The newer theories of chemical bonding and the current knowledge of the electronic structure of the elements permit insight to be gained into the types of bonding present in complexes. They provide the standpoint from which the coordination compounds of the metal ions Cr^{III}, Co^{III}, Cu^{II}, and Ni^{II}, important for azo dyes, will be considered below. Recent, general accounts of coordination chemistry are given in several monographs (*133a, 203, 469a, 1003, 1095, 1371, 1591a*).

All these ions belong to the transition elements of the first long period of the periodic system. They are therefore characterized by the fact that in them the $3d$-region of the M-shell is being filled with electrons. In the two preceding elements of this long period, potassium and calcium, the $4s$-orbital of the N-shell already contains one and two electrons, respectively, so that the elements under consideration possess the following arrangements of electrons in the metallic state:

$$Cr \text{ (atomic number 24)}: \ 3d^5 \ 4s^1$$
$$Co \text{ (atomic number 27)}: \ 3d^7 \ 4s^2$$
$$Ni \text{ (atomic number 28)}: \ 3d^8 \ 4s^2$$
$$Cu \text{ (atomic number 29)}: \ 3d^{10} \ 4s^1$$

In copper the ten electrons have completely filled the $3d$-region. The irregularities in the occupation of the $4s$-orbitals are due to the small differences in energy between $3d$- and $4s$-orbitals (*469b*). In the corresponding, *non*-coordinatively bound *ions*, the $4s$- and a part of the $3d$-electrons have been lost and the remaining ones distribute themselves between the five $3d$-orbitals (see Table 14.1).

When these metal ions take part in purely ionic complexes, the distribution of electrons among the orbitals remains that of the ion, but in penetration complexes the lone pairs of electrons fill individual or all $3d$-, the $4s$-, and, in addition, also individual or all $4p$-orbitals. As the energies of all three types of orbital are very similar, groups of energetically equal, so-called hybrid orbitals, are formed. The number of pairs of electrons in these groups corresponds to the coordination number. From the nickel complexes in Table 14.1 it can be seen that there is a connection between the stereochemistry of complexes and the type of hybridization.

Table 14.1

Electronic Orbitals Occupied in Some Compounds of Chromium, Cobalt, Nickel, and Copper

Compound	Electronic orbitals[1] $3d$ $4s$ $4p$	CN	Stereochemistry of the complex	Magnetic moment[2]
Metallic Cr	[•][•][•][•][•] [•][ ][ ][ ]			
Cr^{III}-ion	[•][•][•][ ][ ] [ ][ ][ ][ ]			3·85–3·9
Cr^{III}-penetration complex	[•][•][•][XX][XX] [XX][ ] [XXX][XXX] — d^2sp^3 —	6	octahedral	3·8
Normal Cr^{III}-complex	[•][•][•][ ][ ] [ ][ ][ ][ ]	6	octahedral	3·8
Co^{III}-ion and normal Co^{III}-complex	[•][•][•][•][•] [•][ ][ ][ ]	6	octahedral	5·0–5·6
Co^{III}-penetration complex	[•][•][•][XX][XX] [XX][ ] [XXX][XXX] — d^2sp^3 —	6	octahedral	dia-magnetic
Nickel glyoxime	[•][•][•][•][X] [X][ ] [XX][XX] — dsp^2 —	4	planar	dia-magnetic
Ni(salicylalde-hyde)$_2$	[•][•][•][•][•] [X][ ] [XXX][XXX] — sp^3 —	4	tetrahedral	~ 3 (?)
Cu^{II}-penetration complex	[•][•][•][•][X] [X][ ] [XXX][XXX] — sp^3 — or [•][•][•][•][X] [X][ ] [XX][XX •] — dsp^2 —	4 4	tetrahedral planar	1·9 1·9

[1] The dots and the crosses indicate electrons originating from the metal and ligand, respectively. The hybridized orbitals of penetration complexes are bracketed.
[2] In Bohr magnetons, data from Nyholm (*1544*).

The schematic representation used in Table 14.1 is based on valency bond theory (*1545*). The treatment of coordinative bonding by means of the molecular orbital method (*2073*), in which the interactions between the different bonds present in a molecule or ion are taken into account, has led not only to an understanding of previously inexplicable phenomena encountered in individual complexes, but has hastened the recognition of the fact that it is hardly correct to draw a sharp distinction between covalent and ionic bonding in complexes. Coulson (469c) has pointed out that purely covalent bonding would give improbably high charges on the central atom. It is therefore better to talk of 'preponderantly covalent' and 'preponderantly ionic'. An entirely electrostatic interpretation of coordinative bonding is equally possible and has been developed by Garrick (777) in particular. All these topics have been discussed critically by Basolo and Pearson (203a) and by Orgel (2427).

To differentiate between the two types of bonding several methods are available, but they do not always lead to concordant results. Especially important is the investigation of the behaviour of the compound studied in a magnetic field (1230, 1591a, 1876). Apart from the induced diamagnetic polarization, that is, the induction of a weak, opposed magnetic field, observed in all substances, certain compounds exhibit paramagnetism, i.e. a great increase in the strength of the field by induction. The main, but not exclusive, cause of paramagnetic polarization lies in the presence of electrons of unpaired spin. The ratio of the induced to the applied field is termed magnetic susceptibility and from it can be calculated the magnetic moment of a substance (μ, the unit of which is a Bohr magneton, symbol β). If the effect of spin is considered alone, μ is related in a simple manner to the number of unpaired electrons (n):

$$\mu = \left\{ n(n+2) \right\}^{\frac{1}{2}} \tag{14.3}$$

For instance, the ferrifluoride ion, $[FeF_6]^{-3}$, possesses a magnetic moment of 5·9 β, corresponding to five unpaired d-electrons. It is therefore a complex held together by predominantly electrostatic (ionic) forces. Ferric salts, such as $FeCl_3$, have similar moments, but the ferricyanide ion, $[Fe(CN)_6]^{-3}$, exhibits a moment of only 2·3 β. This is in agreement with the occupation of three $3d$-orbitals by five electrons, leaving one unpaired, and a $3d^2 4s 4p^3$-hybrid, which is filled by the lone pairs of electrons of the cyanide residues and which leads to a mainly covalent, octahedral structure. Further examples are to be found in Table 14.1.

This physical criterion frequently supports chemical observations. In general, substitutions or rearrangements in which the bond of a complex takes part occur substantially more slowly with penetration complexes than with normal ones (2140). However, in this way certain proof of the type of bond present cannot be obtained, as has been found in some instances (133b, 2006).

Determinations of conductivity were carried out by Werner (2133, 2134), but even complexes with predominantly ionic bonds are not ionized and so cannot be distinguished conductometrically from penetration complexes.

The question of whether double bonds can exist between the metal ion and the ligands of complexes has been discussed often. X-ray analysis has in several cases yielded atomic distances which are shorter than those of single bonds and hence a certain degree of double bond character can be deduced. Pauling

(*1591c*) considered the ferricyanide ion in this light and MO calculations have led to the conclusion that double bonds can be formed by the overlap of $d\pi$- and $p\pi$-orbitals (*476, 887*).

Infra-red spectra can be helpful and Duval's work (*631–633*) on chromium and cobalt complexes must be mentioned.

14.2 Equilibria and Stability of Complexes

In the preceding section, an analogy was drawn between the reaction of ammonia with a proton and that with a cuprous ion. Just as the addition of the proton is in equilibrium with its back-reaction and just as the acid and basic dissociation constants are a measure of the stability of, for example, the NH_3 molecule and the ammonium ion, so the formation and the dissociation of a complex constitute an equilibrium which can be treated by the same methods. In recent years the fundamental work particularly of J. Bjerrum (*257, 258*) and of Schwarzenbach (*1862*) has made great headway in the field of complex equilibria both as regards methods and applications. Bjerrum, Schwarzenbach, and Sillén published recently a compilation of all the available stability constants of complexes with organic ligands (*261*).

According to Brönsted's definition, ligands are bases. The reaction in aqueous solution of a metal ion with a ligand occurs simultaneously or in competition with the addition of a proton to the ligand. The solution becomes acid because basic components are being removed. The process can therefore be followed potentiometrically (titrimetrically) like a neutralization and in this manner the equilibrium can be determined. Equations (14.4) and (14.5) for the protolytic and the complex equilibrium of a metal ammine can be united to give (14.6). Strictly speaking, in the aqueous solutions exclusively considered here, it is not complex formation by a free metal ion M^{+n} which is occurring, but substitution of a water molecule of an aquo complex $[M(H_2O)]^{+n}$ by another ligand. Since in the case of the hydroxonium ion $H_3\overset{\oplus}{O}$ usually only $H^{\oplus}$ is written, so for the sake of simplicity the solvated metal ion is frequently represented by M^{+n}, as in (14.5) and (14.6).

$$\overset{\oplus}{N}H_4 \underset{\longleftarrow}{\overset{K_a}{\longrightarrow}} NH_3 + H^{\oplus} \tag{14.4}$$

$$M^{+n} + NH_3 \underset{\longleftarrow}{\overset{K_{kI}}{\longrightarrow}} M(NH_3)^{+n} \tag{14.5}$$

$$\overset{\oplus}{N}H_4 + M^{+n} \underset{\longleftarrow}{\overset{K_{ka}}{\longrightarrow}} M(NH_3)^{+n} + H^{\oplus} \tag{14.6}$$

The formation constant K_{kI} is a measure of the stability of the complex $[M(NH_3)]^{+n}$. It is defined in the usual way (14.7) and can be determined from K_a and K_{ka} (14.8).

$$K_{kI} = \frac{[M(NH_3)^{+n}]}{[M^{+n}] \cdot [NH_3]} \tag{14.7}$$

$$K_{kI} = \frac{K_{ka}}{K_a} = \frac{[M(NH_3)^{+n}] \cdot [H^\oplus]}{[\overset{\oplus}{N}H_4] \cdot [M^{+n}] \cdot K_a} \tag{14.8}$$

Depending on the coordination number of the metal ion usually several monofunctional ligands are bound. Further complex reactions therefore follow the system of equilibria (14.4) to (14.6) and these can be formulated analogously, for example, for a diammine as (14.9) or (14.10).

$$M(NH_3)^{+n} + NH_3 \xrightleftharpoons{K_{kII}} M(NH_3)_2^{+n} \tag{14.9}$$

$$\overset{\oplus}{N}H_4 + M(NH_3)^{+n} \rightleftharpoons M(NH_3)_2^{+n} + H^\oplus \tag{14.10}$$

Diammine formation thus corresponds to the second step in the neutralization of a dibasic acid. In practice it is found that the formation constants of successive steps differ only little and in consequence it is not possible to distinguish the appropriate point in the titration or to isolate intermediates through partial neutralization. The situation bears a resemblance to the titration curve of the diazonium ion as a dibasic acid (Figure 3.1, § 3.5).

Conditions become very greatly simplified by the use of polyfunctional ligands, which circumvents the stepwise reaction (1860). In addition the chelates obtained are characterized by much higher stability. This can be seen from the following comparison of the overall constant of nickel complex formation from ammonia (i.e. the product of the constants K_{kI}, K_{kII} ... K_{kN} of a complex formation with N steps) with that of the hexamine (V), the so-called 'penten' (1870).

$$\begin{matrix} H_2N—CH_2—CH_2 \diagdown & & \diagup CH_2—CH_2—NH_2 \\ & N—CH_2—CH_2—N & \\ H_2N—CH_2—CH_2 \diagup & & \diagdown CH_2—CH_2—NH_2 \end{matrix}$$

'penten'

V

$$Ni^{\oplus\oplus} + 6\,NH_3 \rightleftharpoons Ni(NH_3)_6^{\oplus\oplus} \qquad K_k = 3{\cdot}1 \times 10^8 \tag{14.11}$$

$$Ni^{\oplus\oplus} + penten \rightleftharpoons Ni(penten)^{\oplus\oplus} \qquad K_k' = 2 \times 10^{19} \tag{14.12}$$

Although an aliphatic hexamine such as (V) behaves otherwise very much like ammonia, for example as regards its basic strength, its nickel complex is almost 10^{11} times more stable. This enormous effect has been termed the *chelate effect* by Schwarzenbach (1861, 1873). It is defined as the difference between the logarithms of the two formation constants and in this case equals 10·8.

As complex dyes must be very stable, it follows that for them only chelating agents, but not monofunctional ligands, can be considered. Organic polyamines do not fully meet the demands made in this direction, because the chelates formed with basic nitrogens as the sole ligands are insufficiently stable. Oxygen atoms are more favourable, not least because they undergo complex reactions with large free energies with a much wider range of metal ions. For the same reason polyamines are practically of no importance for complexometric titrations, in which predominant roles are played by ethylenediaminetetra-acetic acid (EDTA, VI, $n = 2$) and by nitrilotriacetic acid (NTA).

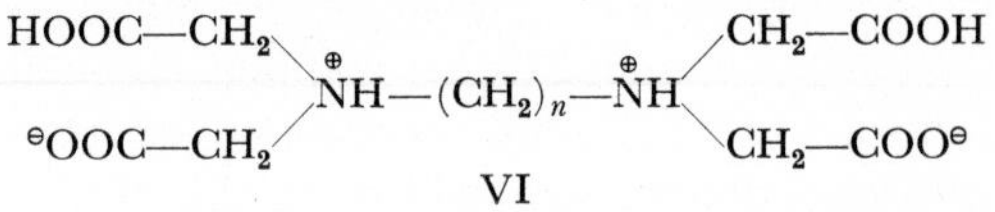

VI

Many data have been accumulated about the relationship between stability and the size of the chelate ring, particularly for aliphatic di- and poly-functional ligands. For instance, Schwarzenbach (*1861*, *1863*) was able to show that in the series of EDTA homologues (VI, $n = 2$ to 5) the stability of the complexes with five-membered chelate rings ($n = 2$) was the highest and that it decreased greatly as the ring size was increased. On the contrary, in unsaturated chelates six-membered rings are often more stable, as in alizarin (VII), in which complex formation takes place between the 1-hydroxy and the 9-carbonyl groups and not in the 1,2-position. According to Heller and Schwarzenbach (*1010*), the ferric complex of catechol-3,5-disulphonic acid (VIII) is

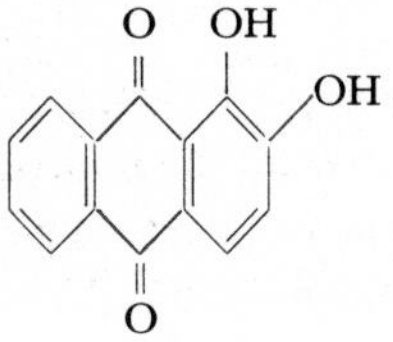

VII 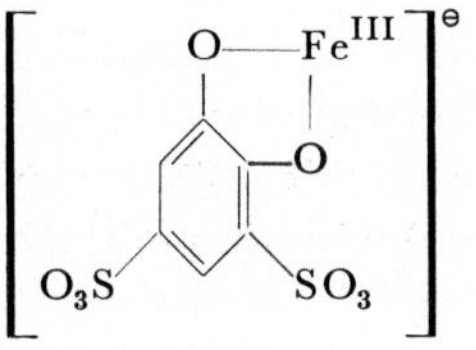   VIII 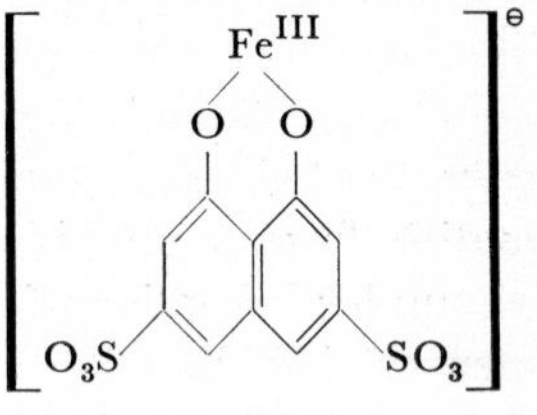   IX

less stable than that of chromotropic acid (IX). In contrast the well-known nickel dimethylglyoxime is a chelate with a five-membered ring. Formula (X) was advanced by Hieber, Leutert, and Pfeiffer (*1028*, *1617*, *1619*, *1620*) on a stereochemical basis, but has since been confirmed by X-ray analysis of the crystals (*810*).

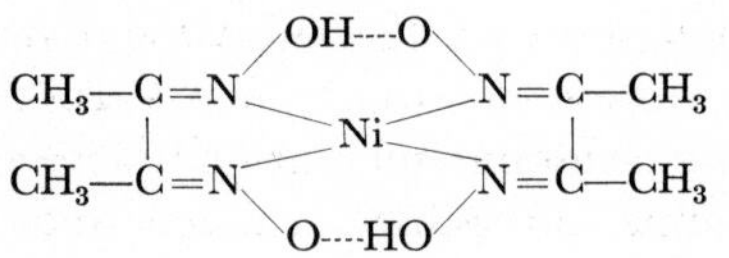

X

Four-membered chelate rings have only rarely been encountered, but one type occurs in azo chemistry, namely, the complexes of diazoamino compounds, for example the nickel complex (XI) (*637*).

The analogy between acid–base and complex equilibria suggests that the stability of complexes might increase with the basic strength of the ligand. Calvin and Wilson (*404*) looked for such a relationship in the cupric complexes of substituted salicylaldehydes and enolizable β-diketones. They compared the

$$
\begin{array}{c}
\text{C}_6\text{H}_5 \quad \text{C}_6\text{H}_5 \\
| \qquad | \\
\text{N} \qquad \text{N} \\
\diagup \diagdown \quad \diagup \diagdown \\
\text{N} \qquad \text{Ni} \qquad \text{N} \\
\diagdown \diagup \quad \diagdown \diagup \\
\text{N} \qquad \text{N} \\
| \qquad | \\
\text{C}_6\text{H}_5 \quad \text{C}_6\text{H}_5
\end{array}
$$

XI

product of the formation constants of each step, $K_k = K_1 \times K_2$, the overall process being represented by equation (14.13), with the acid dissociation constant K_a of the enol (14.14). The expected, inverse proportionality between the cons-

$$
2 -\text{C} \underset{\text{C=O}}{\overset{\text{C—O}^\ominus}{\diagup}} + \text{Cu}^{\oplus\oplus} \overset{K_k}{\rightleftarrows} -\text{C} \underset{\text{C=O}}{\overset{\text{C—O}}{\diagup}} \text{Cu} \underset{\text{O—C}}{\overset{\text{O=C}}{\diagup}} \text{C—} \tag{14.13}
$$

$$
-\text{C} \underset{\text{C=O}}{\overset{\text{C—O}}{\diagup}} \text{H} \overset{K_a}{\rightleftarrows} -\text{C} \underset{\text{C=O}}{\overset{\text{C—O}^\ominus}{\diagup}} + \text{H}^{\oplus} \tag{14.14}
$$

tants K_k and K_a was confirmed experimentally. When log K_k was plotted against the pK_a values of the complexing agents, it was found that all the points for substituted salicylaldehydes lie on a straight line and those for substituted naphthaldehydes and 2,4-pentanedione derivatives on parallel ones. This shows that, apart from the effect of the basic strength of the ligand, other influences of a steric and electronic nature enter into the complex formation constants and that these are different in the various series. The importance of mesomerism could be demonstrated in the case of the anils of salicylaldehyde (2-hydroxyazomethines) substituted in the aniline nucleus (403). Holm and Cotton (1066) reinvestigated 2,4-pentanedione complexes recently and interpreted their results differently in part.

In addition to the potentiometric determination of the stability of complexes other methods can be used for quantitative investigations of the structure and equilibria of complexes in solution and these have been briefly summarized in the tables compiled by Bjerrum, Schwarzenbach, and Sillén (261).

Job's method (1172, 1173) is particularly important for the determination of the stoichiometric composition of complexes in solution. It can be applied when in a complex equilibrium $M + nB \rightleftarrows MB_n$ one of the three species possesses a spectrum which is clearly differentiated from those of the others. A series of solutions is then prepared for which the sum of the equivalents of M and B is constant, but their proportion varies. The extinction is next determined at a wavelength characteristic of the complex MB_n and plotted against the molecular proportion of M or B. If a complex MB_n is formed, the extinction is not a linear function of the ratio of the components, but it exhibits a maximum at the point corresponding to its composition. Extensions to Job's method for the investigation of the stoichiometry when several complexes are produced simultaneously have been developed (108–110, 848, 2088).

Because of the technical importance of azo dyes derived from salicylic acid the study of the interaction of 5-sulphosalicylic acid and cupric ions is of interest. Turner and Anderson (2054) applied Job's method, using buffers of pH 5 and 9. In the acid solution the absorption maximum was at 700 mμ, in alkali at 660 mμ. By continuously varying the relative concentrations in the two buffers it was found that the stoichiometric ratio $Cu^{\oplus\oplus}$: sulphosalicylic acid was 1:1 in acid and 1:2 in alkali (Figure 14.1). The complexes therefore have the structures (XII) and (XIII), respectively. The system cupric ion–salicylic acid has been treated similarly by Babko (108–110).

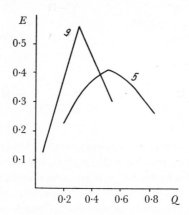

Figure 14.1

Job's method applied to the cupric complexes of sulphosalicylic acid (2054).

E = extinction at 700 mμ for curve 5, at 660 mμ for curve 9
$Q = [Cu^{\oplus\oplus}] / ([Cu^{\oplus\oplus}] + [\text{sulphosalicylic acid}])$
Buffer: pH 5 for curve 5, pH 9 for curve 9

XII   XIII

The spectrophotometric method can also be employed for the determination of stability constants (1462). Equilibrium (14.15) can be expressed as equation (14.16), from which it can be seen that, if the concentration of the metal ion M is kept constant, whilst the concentration of the ligand B is varied, log $[M_mB_n]$ becomes a linear function of log $[B]$. If the logarithm of the extinction which is proportional to $\log [M_m B_n]$, is plotted against $\log [B]$, the slope of the straight line corresponds to the number n. After obtaining m analogously, the constant K can then be calculated from (14.15).

$$mM + nB \overset{K}{\underset{}{\rightleftarrows}} M_m B_n \tag{14.15}$$

$$\log [M_m B_n] = m \log [M] + n \log [B] - \log K \tag{14.16}$$

14.3 The Stereochemistry of Metal Complexes

The classic investigations into the steric arrangement of ligands were based on the separation into optical and geometrical isomers. Since in the context of dyestuffs chemistry interest is limited, on the one hand, only to metal ions with a coordination number (CN) of 4 or 6, and, on the other, predominantly to chelated complexes, the following discussion is restricted to these. The full treatment of the field can be found in the appropriate textbooks (*133, 1003, 1095, 1371*).

In metal ions of coordination number 4 the ligands can take up tetrahedral or planar positions (*1422*). With two identical or different, symmetric bifunctional ligands (A—A + A—A or A—A + B—B) the tetrahedral arrangement gives rise to only *one* compound, whilst with two identical, but unsymmetric ligands (A—B + A—B) a pair of isomers is formed. These are mirror images of one another and hence optical antipodes (Figure 14.2 and 14.3). If a complex of this type derived from a metal of coordination number 4 can be resolved into optically active compounds, not only is the tetrahedral configuration proved, but also the chelate nature of the linking of each pair of coordination sites. Of course, two pairs of *mono*functional ligands A and B would not give rise to any optical isomerism.

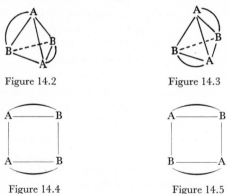

Figure 14.2   Figure 14.3

Figure 14.4   Figure 14.5

A planar arrangement normally gives rise not to optical, but to geometrical isomers. A chelating agent A—B yields the *cis-* and the *trans-*compound, depicted respectively by Figure 14.4 and 14.5. These correspond to Werner's classic

example of geometrical isomers, namely, the two forms of diamminodichloro-
platinum compounds, the isolation of which proved the planar structure of
Pt^{II} complexes (*2130*).

Stereochemical considerations do not exclude pyramidal or rectangular
structures for these complexes, but the determination of dipole moments, e.g.
(*1169, 1170*), and X-ray analyses, e.g. (*475*), have confirmed the planar,
square arrangement.

Salicylic acid derivatives and other types of substances important in the
dyestuffs field always appear to form planar cupric complexes. On the contrary, Ni^{II} ions are able to give planar, predominantly covalent, diamagnetic
derivatives, as well as tetrahedral, predominantly ionic, paramagnetic complexes, such as nickel di(2,4-pentanedione) and nickel disalicylaldehyde (see
Table 14.1). Unsymmetrically substituted nickel diglyoximes could be isolated
in *cis*- and *trans*-forms (*1978*), but the corresponding copper complexes are so
far only known in the *trans*-configuration. From Lifschitz and his co-workers'
investigations (*1343*) it is apparent that planar, predominantly covalent nickel
complexes of coordination number 4 are relatively readily converted into octahedral, predominantly ionic compounds. A great change in the absorption spectrum accompanies the process and it seems probable that this peculiarity of
nickel is responsible for its lack of suitability for complex dyes. Copper does have
some slight tendency to assume a coordination number of 5 (*257, 258, 260*) or
possibly even 6 (*1290*) and it may be the cause of the disadvantages, such as
lack of fastness to potting, exhibited by copper-complex dyes on the relatively
strongly basic wool fibre.

Metal ions of coordination number 6 are particularly interesting for dyes in
combination with bi- and tri-functional, unsymmetric ligands. Three particles
of a bidentate compound A—B, for example, salicylic acid, can occupy all six
coordination sites to yield so-called 1:3-complexes. Here the *cis*- and the *trans*-
isomers can each exist in enantiomorphous forms. More important as dyes are
the 1:2-complexes of bifunctional, unsymmetric chelating agents, in which the
fifth and sixth coordination sites are filled by water molecules or hydroxyl ions.
If the two monodentate ligands (C) are identical and in *trans*-position to one
another, the complex possesses a plane of symmetry and thus is optically inac-
tive, but the way the two particles of A—B are held gives rise to *cis–trans*-iso-
merism. Presumably the configuration of the chrome complexes of azosalicylic
acid dyes is of this type. If the two ligands C are in *cis*-position to each other,
six optical isomers are possible.

Complexes containing two tridentate chelating agents A—B—C can exist in
an all-*trans*-form, which has a centre of symmetry, or in one of five pairs of
enantiomeric structures. However, such a large number of isomers is excluded
in the case of the most important class of trifunctional dyes, the o,o'-disubsti-
tuted azo compounds, as here A, B, and C are part of a mesomeric system and
therefore must lie in the plane of the aromatic rings. The all-*trans*- and eight of
the ten optically active forms do not allow this, but demand that the two halves
of each azo dyestuff particle shall be at 90° to one another. In consequence,

only two isomers are to be expected for complexes of unsymmetric o,o'-disubstituted azo compounds.

Indeed, Pfeiffer (*1622*) was only able to demonstrate the existence of one pair of optical antipodes for the $1:2$-Cr^{III}-complexes of the azomethine (XIV) and the azo compound (XV). The planes of the two dyestuff particles in each complex are at right angles to one another.

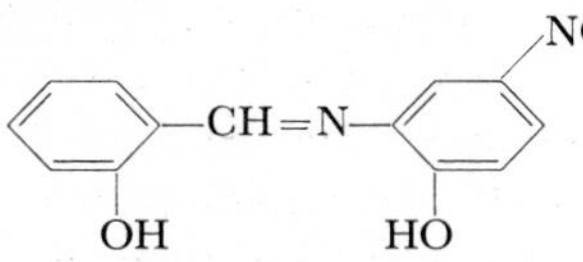

XIV 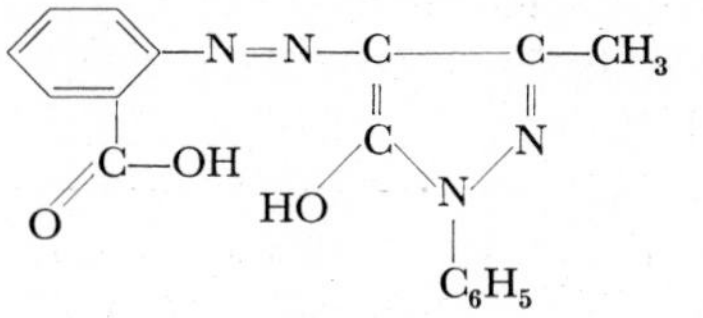   XV

14.4 Aspects of Special Importance in the Chemistry of Metal-Complex Azo Dyes

Previously in this chapter only those investigations of azo complexes were mentioned which had significance for complex chemistry *in general*. Now it is appropriate to turn to three problems associated with azo complexes in particular, namely, the consideration of the *ligand groups* of practical importance, the *stability of complex dyes* with special reference to stepwise complex formation, and, lastly, the effect of coordination with the metal ion on the *absorption spectra* of the dyes.

In colouring matters the phenolic hydroxy group is the predominant ligand group, followed by the carboxy residue in azosalicylic acid derivatives. Occasionally amino groups are also encountered, as, for example, in Benzo Fast Copper Red GGL (FBy; XVI) [cf. (*2557, 2559, 2561*)], in which all four coordination sites of the cupric ion are occupied by the ligands of the disazo compound. In some dyes the oxygen of a carbonyl residue acts as ligand, as in the lake from alizarin. The mercapto group has not achieved any importance (*391, 1920*). Indispensable for complex formation by compounds of the o,o'-disubstituted azo type is one of the nitrogen atoms. Kharasch (*1207*) investigated the tendency to give complexes with salts of platinum of olefinic and azo double bonds in the absence of other ligands.

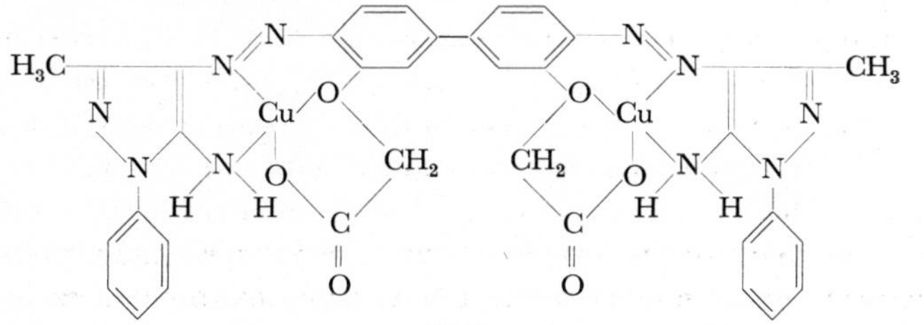

XVI 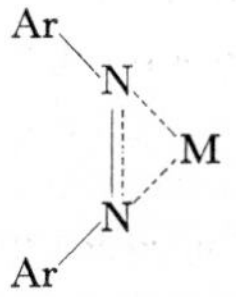   XVII

A. E. A. Werner (*2136*) has supposed that in the azobenzene complex the pair of π-electrons is responsible for coordinatively binding the metal ion (XVII). I. D. Brown and J. D. Dunitz (*349*) analysed the structure of the complex from azomethane and cuprous chloride by means of X-rays and derived the configuration illustrated by Figure 14.6. The N—Cu bond, which is about 2·03 Å long, lies 15° outside the plane of the azomethane molecule. It is remarkable that each nitrogen of azomethane is able to provide its lone pair of electrons to one molecule of cuprous chloride.

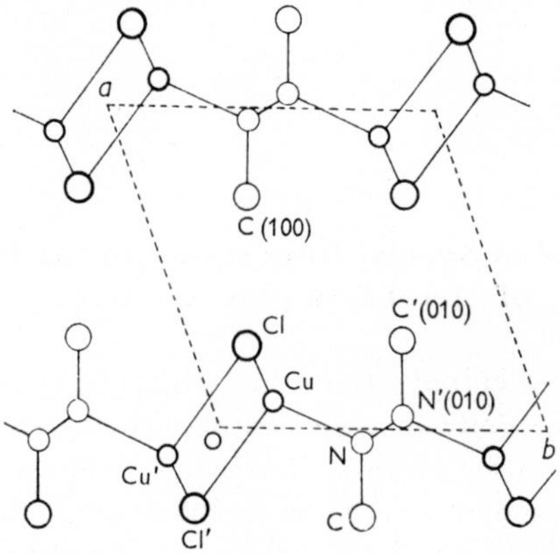

Figure 14.6

Structure of the cuprous chloride azomethane complex, after I. D. Brown and J. D. Dunitz (*349*)

(Reproduced by kind permission of *Acta Crystallographica*)

It is very improbable that *o,o'*-disubstituted azobenzene derivatives on complexing should yield symmetric *cis*-compounds such as (XVII). On the other hand, molecular models show clearly that in the *trans*-configuration of the azo bridge only *one* nitrogen atom can link to the metal ion. It follows that unsymmetric azo compounds should give rise to two isomers (XVIII–XIX), but their separation has not so far been attempted.

XVIII   XIX

Some support for this view comes from observations by Eistert (*606*) and by Menzi (*1425*) on copper complexes of sulphonated *o,o'*-dihydroxyazo dyes, the low solubility of which is possibly due to the formation of the sheet-like aggregates (XX). If an energetic ligand, such as an aliphatic amine, is added, the latter displaces the second azo nitrogen atom from the fourth coordination site of the copper and the dye becomes readily soluble. Such a process cannot be visualized on the basis of a π-complex of the type of (XVII).

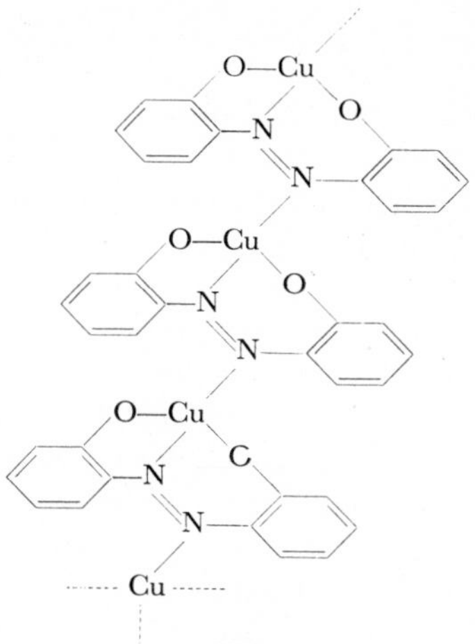

XX

Beech and Drew (*217*) isolated a complex, containing three cupric ions and two 2,2'-dihydroxy-5'-sulphophenylazonaphthalene residues, to which they assigned formula (XXI). Such a constitution does not seem to be excluded for Eistert's sheet-like complex and a thorough investigation of this structural problem is desirable.

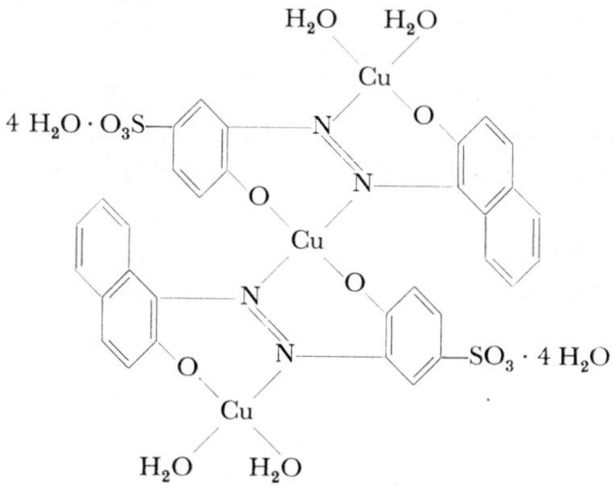

XXI

Complexes in which not all the coordination sites of the metal are occupied by ligand atoms belonging to the dye raise the question of whether the remaining positions are taken up in aqueous solution by H_2O molecules or by

hydroxyl ions. Jonassen *et al.* (*1179, 1180*) showed that addition of caustic
alkali to alcoholic solutions of metallized *o,o′*-dihydroxy- and *o*-carboxy-*o′*-
hydroxy-azo compounds produced monohydroxo complexes, but dihydroxo
ones in the case of *o*-amino-*o′*-carboxyazo derivatives. The latter fact is a sign
of the presence of cupric ions of coordination number 5, for which Bjerrum
obtained some evidence from other sources (*257, 258, 260*).

The equilibria between hydroxo and aquo complexes of chromium have
been much studied. For example, Schwarzenbach and Biedermann (*1864*)
found that the remaining coordination sites of the chromium complex of the
tetradentate nitrilotriacetic acid were occupied by two water molecules below
pH 7, by one water molecule and a hydroxyl ion between pH 7 and 9, and by
two hydroxyl ions in still more strongly alkaline solution. In consequence, one
can assume that in the 1:1 chromium complexes of the Neolan type of dye
(Ciba) three molecules of water serve as the ligands in neutral or acid media.

Complexing dyes with more than three ligand groups are rare. Apart from
the *o*-azophenoxyacetic acid derivatives, which supply some of the members
of the Benzo Fast Copper dyestuff range (FBy; e.g. XVI), Schetty [(*1798,
2576, 2577*), see also (*2521*)] has recently described tetra- and hexa-functional
ligands, such as (XXII), with which can be prepared 1:1 chromium complexes
applicable from neutral solution, i.e. stable to heat.

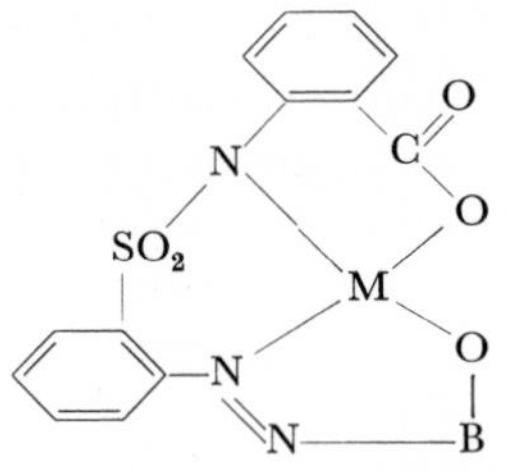

B = coupling component
giving rise to
o-hydroxyazo grouping

XXII

In view of the great number of *complex equilibria* investigated in the last
fifteen years, it is astonishing how few involving dyestuffs have been studied.
Hence special significance attaches to Schwarzenbach's determination of the
stability constants of the magnesium and calcium complexes of azo compounds
of the type of Eriochrome Black T (Gy) (*1865*). The spectrophotometric

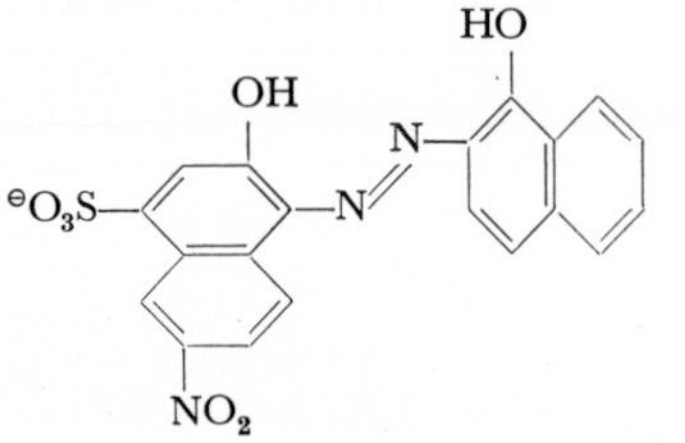

XXIII

$(= H_2F^{\ominus})$

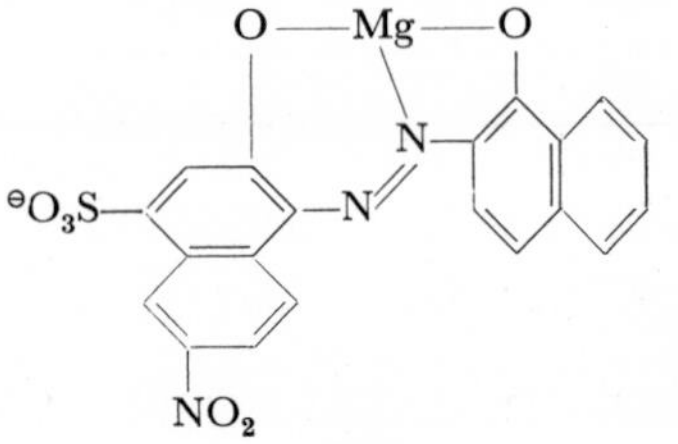

XXIV

$(= MgF^{\ominus})$

method applied in this instance is eminently suitable for the examination of the complex equilibria of other dyes.

In aqueous acid solution Eriochrome Black T exists as the wine-red anion (XXIII), which will be designated by $H_2F^\ominus$. In weakly alkaline media the blue anion $HF^{\ominus\ominus}$ is formed and, finally, the orange ion $F^{\ominus\ominus\ominus}$ (14.17).

$$H_2F^\ominus \underset{+\ H^\oplus}{\xrightarrow{\quad pK_2 = 6\cdot3 \quad}} HF^{\ominus\ominus} \underset{+\ H^\oplus}{\xrightarrow{\quad pK_3 = 11\cdot5 \quad}} F^{\ominus\ominus\ominus} \tag{14.17}$$

In the presence of magnesium salts the wine-red complex ion $MgF^\ominus$ (XXIV) results. For the determination of the complex equilibrium advantage is taken of the fact that this ion exhibits practically no absorption at 610 mμ, in contrast to the blue ion $HF^{\ominus\ominus}$. In the range of acidity in which $HF^{\ominus\ominus}$ predominates (pH 8–10), the position of the equilibrium can readily be obtained by measuring the extinction and the pH.

Equations (14.18) and (14.19) represent complex formation by the tribasic ($F^{\ominus\ominus\ominus}$) and by the dibasic dyestuff anion ($HF^{\ominus\ominus}$), respectively. The substantially higher stability constant of the tribasic anion clearly shows that complex formation is a function of the basicity of the ligand.

$$Mg^{\oplus\oplus} + F^{\ominus\ominus\ominus} \rightleftharpoons MgF^\ominus \qquad \log K\ = 7 \tag{14.18}$$

$$Mg^{\oplus\oplus} + HF^{\ominus\ominus} \rightleftharpoons MgF^\ominus + H^\oplus \qquad \log K' = -4\cdot5 \tag{14.19}\ [3]$$

For the investigation of the equilibria of the complexes of 2-(4'-dimethyl-aminophenylazo)pyridine (XXV) Klotz and Ming (*1234*) also chose the spectrophotometric method.

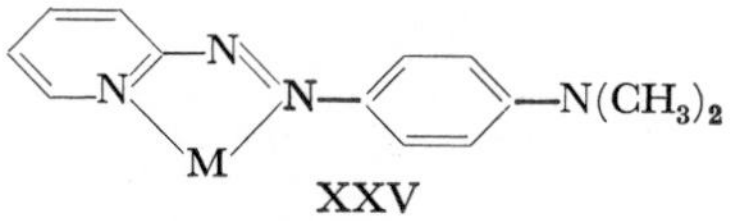

XXV

Of great interest is Snavely's comprehensive study (*1914–1917*) of the complexes formed between one of up to twelve dibasic metal ions and one of nine different o-hydroxy-, o-carboxy- and o,o'-dihydroxy-azo compounds. His determinations enable a whole series of empirical conclusions drawn from practical experience to be traced back to their physicochemical causes, namely, the stability constants of the complexes. Thus, as with the phenylazo–pyridine complexes mentioned above, cupric ions throughout yield the most stable complexes (Table 14.2). From Table 14.3 the chelate effect due to introducing an o'-carboxy group into an o-hydroxyazo complex and the lowering of stability produced by acidifying substituents (Cl, NO_2) are clearly evident.

In comparing complexes of 3-methyl-1-phenyl-4-phenylazo-5-pyrazolone derivatives which carry a methoxy or a methylthio group in o-position in the

---

[3] $\log K' = \log K - pK_3$.

Table 14.2

Stability Constants of Azo Complexes with Divalent Cations (261, 1914, 1916)

Azo compounds	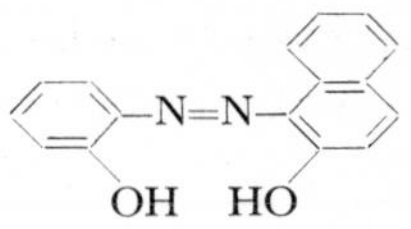 —N=N— ... OH HO	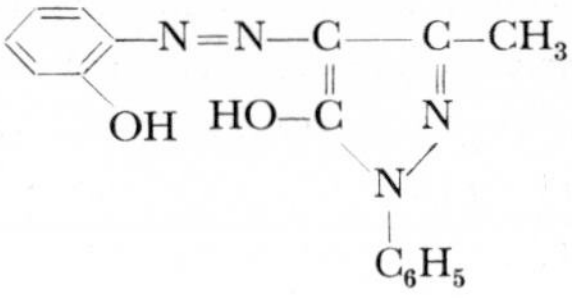 —N=N—C—C—CH₃ ... OH HO—C N ... N ... C₆H₅
pK values of the two hydroxy groups	11·00 13·75	10·66 13·12
Metal ion	log K_I in 75% dioxane at 30° [4]	
Ba	5·74	6·12
Sr	6·81	7·05
Ca	8·61	8·72
Mg	10·93	10·94
Mn	—	13·16
Cd	13·03	13·76
Pb	14·65	15·26
Zn	16·35	16·09
Co	—	16·62
Ni	19·62	17·05
		(log K_{II}: 8·15)
Cu	23·30	22·33

[4] $K_I = \dfrac{ML}{M \times L}$; $K_{II} = \dfrac{ML_2}{ML \times L}$ (L being the dibasic anion of the o, o'-dihydroxyazo compound).

Table 14.3

The Effects of Substituents on the Stability Constants of Nickel and Copper Complexes of o-Hydroxyazo Compounds (261, 1914, 1916)

o-Hydroxyazo residue	Substituent X	Metal ion	pK₁	pK₂	log K_I [5]	log K_{II} [5]
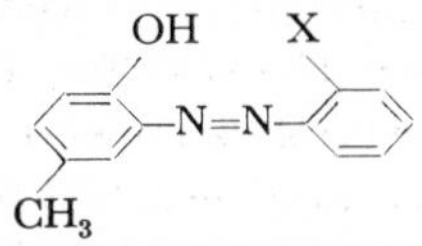 OH X ... —N=N— ... CH₃	H	Ni	11·70	—	6·54	5·98
	COOH	Ni	7·19	13·17	14·00	8·45
	H	Cu	11·70	—	9·67	8·91
	COOH	Cu	7·19	13·17	> 17·00	
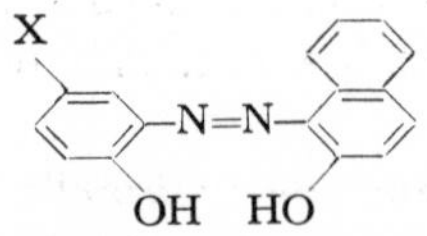 X ... —N=N— ... OH HO	H	Cu	11·00	13·75	23·30	
	Cl	Cu	10·55	13·61	22·95	
	NO₂	Cu	7·67	13·67	20·50	

[5] Definition of the constants and reaction conditions as in Table 14.2.

phenylazo residue, Snavely (*1917*) showed that the thio complexes possess the greater stability constants. The sulphur atom of the methylthio group is evidently a more powerful electron donor than the methoxy oxygen, but this result should not be used as an analogy for the relative effects of OH and SH groups.

The systematic investigation of the complex equilibria between chromic ions and *o,o'*-dihydroxyazo dyes is desirable particularly because in practice *different* steps of the equilibria are utilized. Bentley and Elder's work (*225*), in which the equilibrium with Solochrome Violet RS (ICI; 2-aminophenol-5-sulphonic acid → 2-naphthol) was determined, provides a noteworthy beginning in this field.

Two types of metal–complex monoazo dyes are of commercial importance. The kind first marketed (Neolan and Palatine Fast dyes, Ciba and BASF, respectively) contained one chromium atom for every *o,o'*-dihydroxyazo particle, together with at least one sulphonic group, whereas the much more recent 1:2-complexes are free from sulphonic and carboxyl groups, being solubilized by residues such as alkylsulphonyl (*2565*), sulphamoyl, and acetamido substituents (*1796, 1797, 2243*). The Irgalan range (Gy) was the first of the latter type, Irgalan Brown Violet DL (**XXVI**) serving as an example. As a

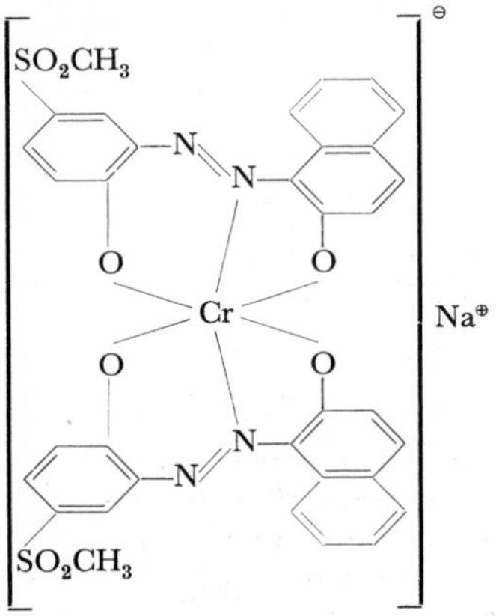

XXVI

general rule 1:1-complexes are prepared in an acid medium (pH < 4), whereas 1:2-complexes require weakly acid to alkaline solutions. The stability of the resulting dyes runs parallel: 1:1-complexes must be dyed from a mineral acid bath (pH 1·9–2·0) (*417*), but 1:2-complexes are applied from weakly acid or neutral solution, disproportionation occurring in other regions of acidity. From the overall equations (14.20) and (14.21) it is apparent that this phenomenon is a consequence of the fact that the complex equilibria are a function of the hydrogen ion concentration.

1:2-Complexes can be prepared from those azo compounds normally employed for the manufacture of the Neolan type of dye, but because of the presence of the ionized sulphonic group they cannot be applied to wool with an

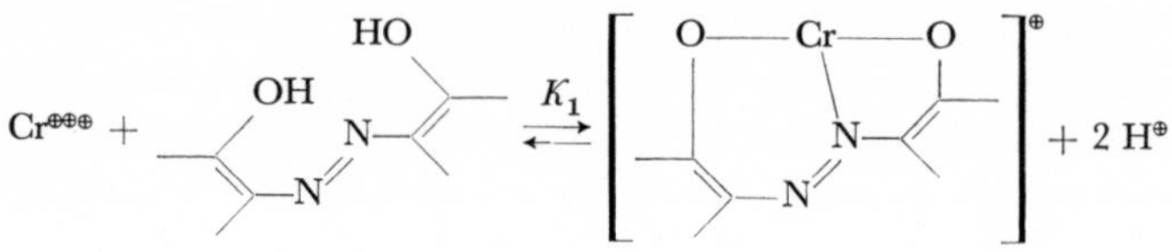

$$+ 2\,H^{\oplus} \qquad (14.20)$$

$$+ 2\,H^{\oplus} \qquad (14.21)$$

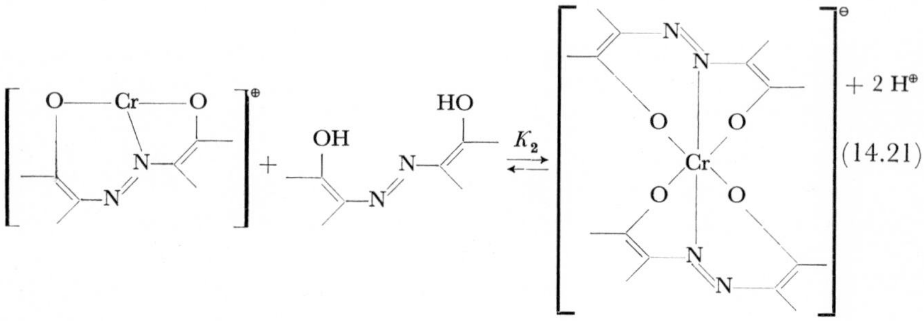

acceptable degree of levelness. However, in spite of the absence of sulphonic residues, the commercial 1:2-complexes of dihydroxyazo derivatives are relatively strong acids, as shown by Schetty (*1796, 1797*) and by Back (*118*) (pK $\simeq$ —1). It is not known to which atom of the complex acid (XXVII) the proton is bound.

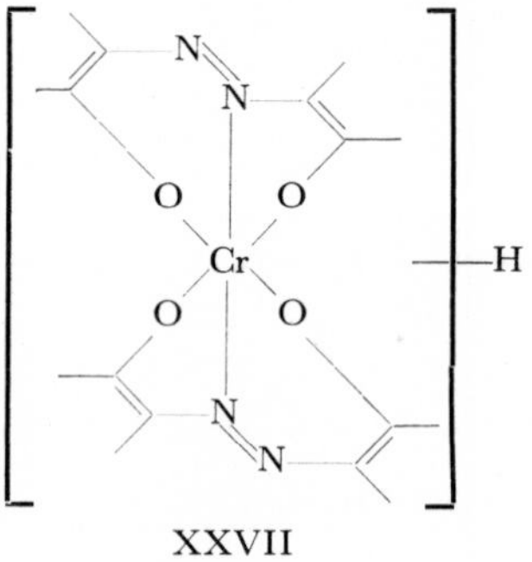

XXVII

2:3-Chromium complexes have also been described (*1470, 1795*). Probably they are salt-like compounds of a 1:1-complex cation with a 1:2-complex anion in the ratio of 1:1. For a few of the dyes on the market the chromium: dye ratio is 2:3 [e.g. Neolan Black WA (Ciba), derived from 6-nitro-1-diazo-2-naphthol-4-sulphonic acid → 2-naphthol].

Extensive studies of the composition of chromium and copper complexes of hydroxy- and dihydroxy-azo compounds were carried out by Pfeiffer (*1621*), by Drew (*217, 218, 625–627*), and by Hunter (*674*). Azo derivatives possessing *one* o-hydroxy group yield 1:2-copper complexes (XXVIII), but those with o,o'-dihydroxy substituents produce 1:1-complexes (XXIX) in which the fourth coordination site of the copper is taken up by a monofunctional ligand (B), such as pyridine.

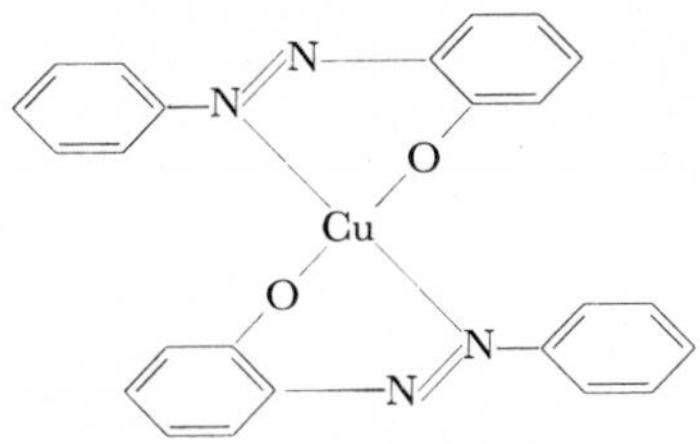

XXVIII 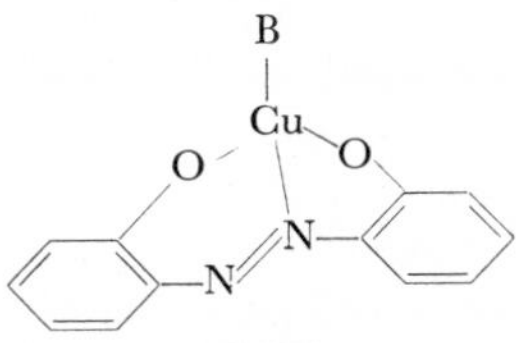   XXIX

Azosalicylic acid dyes are bidentate and hence with chromic ions 1:3-, 1:2-, and 1:1-complexes, for instance (XXX) and (XXXI), can be isolated (*225, 1470, 1795*). In the 1:2-compound (XXXI) ammonia can take the place of the water molecules. Cupric ions similarly give 1:1- and 1:2-complexes (see XII and XIII).

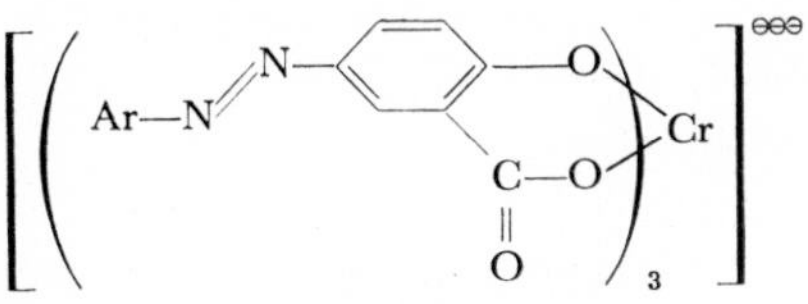

XXX 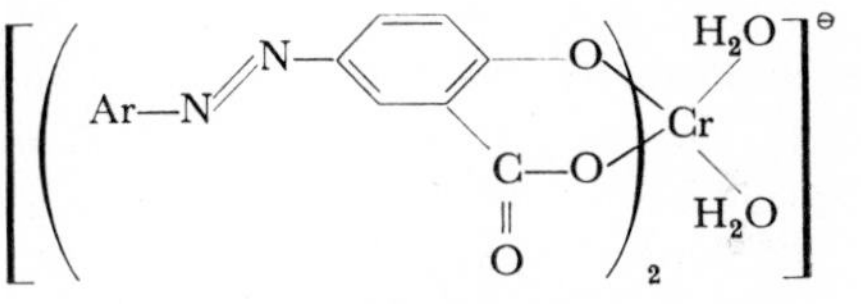   XXXI

Interesting also are the more recent investigations of Bailar *et al.* (*134, 402*) into the state of oxidation of the metal and the composition of cobalt complexes. It became apparent that the cobalt ion accepts the state of oxidation characteristic of the particular chelating agent independently of whether the complex is prepared starting from Co^{II} or Co^{III} salts.

Chromium complexes of dyestuffs often simulate very high stability, because chromic compounds equilibrate only very slowly. It is now supposed that the reason for this special property lies in the fact that such reactions proceed via a transition state in which the metal ion exhibits a coordination number of 7 (*133c, 2006*). This is most fortunate, as in consequence the time taken by processes, such as those to which dyed textiles are subjected during washing, is relatively not long enough to bring about changes in the chromium complex.

Metal-complex dyes are more resistant to chemical agents of all kinds than their metal-free counterparts. It is noteworthy, for example, that the fastness to light of *o,o'*-disubstituted azo compounds is greatly increased by complex formation, but azosalicylic acid derivatives possess roughly the same light fastness whether complexed or not. Hence complex formation must have a favourable effect on the stability of the azo bridge. Polarographically, Willard and Dean (*2162*) have shown that the azo group of *o,o'*-dihydroxyazo dyes becomes more difficult to reduce in the aluminium complex.

The *colour* of azo compounds is greatly affected on complex formation if one of the azo nitrogens serves as a ligand. Through its strongly electropositive character the metal ion alters the π-electron distribution in the dye and thus the absorption spectrum. Hence, complex formation brings about a marked bathochromic shift of the colour of o,o'-dihydroxyazo compounds. The effects of substituents in the phenyl group of 1-phenylazo-2-naphthol derivatives on the visible part of the absorption spectrum have been described by Händler and Smith (*921*). On the other hand, the hue of azosalicylic acid dyes is altered only little by complex formation, since the azo bridge is not involved.

Chromium complexes are always coloured more deeply than the corresponding copper and particularly cobalt compounds and this is exploited technically for the ranges of neutral dyeing 1:2-complexes. McKenzie (*1385*) has investigated the differences in the spectra of normal and penetration complexes of nickel and found that the spectra of the ionic complexes were very similar to those of the chelating agents, but that in the covalent types new characteristic bands appeared (*203b*).

Since the parent azo compound of azo–metal complexes always absorbs light more strongly and at longer wavelengths than the metal ion solvated by water, it would be expected that it is far easier to compare the spectrum of the complex with that of the azo compound than with that of the unchelated metal ion. However, in a series of recent studies the changes brought about in the spectrum of a metal ion by complex formation have been discussed (*133d, 137, 202, 203b, 259, 985, 1066, 1182–1188, 1554, 1555*), but consideration is limited to coordination compounds with ligands which, unlike azo compounds, absorb more weakly and at shorter wavelengths than the metal ion. It is possible that the ligand-field theory of transition metal complexes [see e.g. (*2427*)] will be able to give more information on azo coordination compounds in the future.

REFERENCES

1 Abel, E., *Monatsh.*, **81,** 539 (1950).
2 Abel, E., *Monatsh.*, **83,** 1103 (1952).
3 Abel, E., *Monatsh.*, **85,** 1169 (1954).
4 Abel, E., *Monatsh.*, **85,** 1312 (1954).
5 Adamson, D. W., and J. Kenner, *J. Chem. Soc.*, **1934,** 838.
6 Adamson, D. W., and J. Kenner, *J. Chem. Soc.*, **1935,** 286.
7 Adamson, D. W., and J. Kenner, *J. Chem. Soc.*, **1937,** 1551.
8 Adamson, D. W., and J. Kenner, *J. Chem. Soc.*, **1939,** 181.
9 Aggarwal, S. L., and O. J. Sweeting, *Chem. Revs.*, **57,** 665 (1957).
10 Ainley, A. D., and R. Robinson, *J. Chem. Soc.*, **1937,** 369.
11 Albert, A., R. Goldacre, and J. Phillips, *J. Chem. Soc.*, **1948,** 2240.
12 Alder, K., H. Jungen, and K. Rust, *Ann.*, **602,** 94 (1957).
13 Alder, K., and H. Niklas, *Ann.*, **585,** 81 (1954).
14 Alder, K., and H. Niklas, *Ann.*, **585,** 97 (1954).
15 Alder, K., and T. Noble, *Ber.*, **76,** 54 (1943).
16 Alder, K., F. Pascher, and A. Schmitz, *Ber.*, **76,** 27 (1943).
17 Alder, K., H. K. Schaefer, H. Esser, H. Krieger, and R. Reubke, *Ann.*, **593,** 23 (1955).
18 Alder, K., and P. Schmitz, *Ber.*, **86,** 1539 (1953).
19 Alder, K., and G. Stein, *Ann.*, **485,** 211 (1931).
20 Alder, K., and G. Stein, *Ann.*, **501,** 1 (1933).
21 Alder, M. G., and J. E. Leffler, *J. Am. Chem. Soc.*, **76,** 1425 (1954).
22 Alexander, E. R., and R. E. Burge, *J. Am. Chem. Soc.*, **72,** 3100 (1950).
23 Allan, Z. J., *Coll. Czech. Chem. Com.*, **15,** 904 (1950).
24 Allan, Z. J., *Coll. Czech. Chem. Com.*, **16–17,** 620 (1952).
25 Allan, Z. J., and J. I. Dobáš, *Chem. Listy*, **44,** 227 (1950); through *Chem. Abstracts*, **45,** 7992f (1951).
26 Alphen van, J., *Rec. trav. chim.*, **62,** 210 (1943).
27 Anderson, A. G., J. A. Nelson, and J. J. Tazuma, *J. Am. Chem. Soc.*, **75,** 4980 (1953).
28 Anderson, D., M. E. Bedwell, and R. J. W. Le Fèvre, *J. Chem. Soc.*, **1947,** 457.
29 Anderson, D., R. J. W. Le Fèvre, and J. Savage, *J. Chem. Soc.*, **1947,** 445.
30 Anderson, J. D. C., R. J. W. Le Fèvre, and I. R. Wilson, *J. Chem. Soc.*, **1949,** 2082.
31 Anderson, L. C., and M. J. Roedel, *J. Am. Chem. Soc.*, **67,** 955 (1945).
32 Anderson, L. C., and J. W. Steedly, *J. Am. Chem. Soc.*, **76,** 5144 (1954).
33 Andrews, L. J., and R. M. Keefer, *J. Am. Chem. Soc.*, **71,** 2379 (1949).
34 Andrews, L. J., and R. M. Keefer, *J. Am. Chem. Soc.*, **71,** 2381 (1949).
35 Angeli, A., *Ber.*, **26,** 1715 (1893).
36 Angeli, A., *Atti R. Accad. Lincei*, **15,** 480 (1906).
37 Angeli, A., *Atti R. Accad. Lincei*, **16 II,** 790 (1907).
38 Angeli, A., *Atti R. Accad. Lincei*, **19 I,** 793 (1910).
39 Angeli, A., *Atti R. Accad. Lincei*, **20 I,** 626 (1911).
40 Angeli, A., *Ahrens Sammlung*, Verlag Enke, Stuttgart, **19,** 447 (1913).
41 Angeli, A., *Atti R. Accad. Lincei*, **23 I,** 557 (1914).
42 Angeli, A., *Gazz. chim. ital.*, **51,** 35 (1921).
43 Angeli, A., *Ber.*, **59,** 1400 (1926).
44 Angeli, A., *Ber.*, **62,** 1924 (1929).
45 Angeli, A., *Ber.*, **63,** 1977 (1930).
46 Angeli, A., and L. Alessandri, *Atti R. Accad. Lincei*, **20 II,** 170 (1911).
47 Angeli, A., and Z. Jolles, *Ber.*, **62,** 2099 (1929).
48 Angeli, A., and B. Valori, *Atti R. Accad. Lincei*, **21 I,** 155 (1912).
49 Angeli, A., and B. Valori, *Atti R. Accad. Lincei*, **21 I,** 729 (1912).
50 Anschütz, R., *Ann.*, **294,** 238 (1897).
51 Anziani, P., and R. Cornubert, *Bull. soc. chim. France*, **15,** 857 (1948).
52 Appel, W. D., W. R. Brode, and I. M. Welche, *Ind. Eng. Chem.*, **18,** 627 (1926).
53 Applequist, D. E., and J. D. Roberts, *Chem. Revs.*, **54,** 1065 (1954).
54 Arndt, F., *Ber.*, **63,** 1180 (1930).
55 Arndt, F., *Org. Syntheses*, *Coll. Vol. II*, 165, 461 (1941).
56 Arndt, F., *Organic Analysis*, Interscience Publishers, New York, 1953, Vol. I, p. 197.

57 Arndt, F., and J. Amende, *Ber.*, **61,** 1122 (1928).
58 Arndt, F., J. Amende, and W. Ender, *Monatsh.*, **59,** 202 (1932).
59 Arndt, F., B. Eistert, and W. Partale, *Ber.*, **60,** 1364 (1927).
60 Arndt, F., B. Eistert, and J. Amende, *Ber.*, **61,** 1949 (1928).
61 Arndt, F., B. Eistert, and W. Ender, *Ber.*, **62,** 44 (1929).
62 Arndt, F., and B. Eistert, *Ber.*, **68,** 200 (1935).
63 Arndt, F., and B. Eistert, *Ber.*. **69,** 1805 (1936).
64 Arndt, F., and B. Eistert, *Ber.*, **71,** 2040 (1938).
65 Arndt, F., L. Loewe, R. Un, and E. Ayca, *Ber.*, **84,** 327 (1951).
66 Arndt, F., and C. Martius, *Ann.*, **499,** 228, 247, 268, 274 (1932).
67 Arndt, F., and H. Scholz, *Ber.*, **66,** 1012 (1933).
68 Arndt, F., H. Scholz, and E. Frobel, *Ann.*, **521,** 95 (1936).
69 Arnett, L. M., *J. Am. Chem. Soc.*, **74,** 2027 (1952).
70 Arnett, L. M., and J. H. Peterson, *J. Am. Chem. Soc.*, **74,** 2031 (1952).
71 Arnold, H., *Ber.*, **76,** 777 (1943).
72 Arnold, H., *Ber.*, **80,** 123 (1947).
73 Arnold, H., *Ber.*, **80,** 172 (1947).
74 Aroney, M., R. J. W. Le Fèvre, and R. L. Werner, *J. Chem. Soc.*, **1955,** 276.
75 Aroney, M., and R. J. W. Le Fèvre, *J. Chem. Soc.*, **1955,** 2138.
76 Asahina, Y., and K. Yamaguti, *Ber.*, **71,** 318 (1938).
77 Atherton, E., and R. H. Peters, *J. Soc. Dyers Col.*, **68,** 64 (1952).
78 Atherton, E., and R. H. Peters, *Hexagon Digest*, **23,** 3 (1956).
79 Atherton, E., and R. H. Peters, *Chem. Soc. Spec. Publ.*, **4,** 17 (1956).
80 Atherton, E., and I. Seltzer, *J. Soc. Dyers Col.*, **65,** 629 (1949).
81 Atkinson, E. R., C. E. Garland, and A. F. Butler, *J. Am. Chem. Soc.*, **75,** 983 (1953).
82 Atkinson, E. R., H. H. Warren, P. I. Abell, and R. E. Wing, *J. Am. Chem. Soc.*, **72,** 915 (1950).
83 Auer, E., Thesis, ETH, Zurich, 1943, p. 26.
84 Augood, D. R., J. I. G. Cadogan, D. H. Hey, and G. H. Williams, *J. Chem. Soc.*, **1953,** 3412.
85 Augood, D. R., D. H. Hey, and G. H. Williams, *J. Chem. Soc.*, **1952,** 2094.
86 Augood, D. R., D. H. Hey, and G. H. Williams, *J. Chem. Soc.*, **1953,** 44.
87 Augood, D. R., and G. H. Williams, *Chem. Revs.*, **57,** 123 (1957).
88 Ausloos, P., and E. W. R. Steacie, *Bull. soc. chim. Belges*, **63,** 87 (1954).
89 Ausloos, P., and E. W. R. Steacie, *Can. J. Chem.*, **33,** 31 (1955).
90 Ausloos, P., and E. W. R. Steacie, *Can. J. Chem.*, **33,** 39 (1955).
91 Ausloos, P., and E. W. R. Steacie, *Can. J. Chem.*, **33,** 47 (1955).
92 Ausloos, P., and E. W. R. Steacie, *Can. J. Chem.*, **33,** 1062 (1955).
93 Austin, A. T., Thesis, University College, London, 1950; *Nature*, **188,** 1086 (1960).
94 Austin, A. T., *J. Chem. Soc.*, **1950,** 149.
95 Austin, A. T., and J. Howard, *Chemistry and Industry*, **1960,** 625.
96 Austin, A. T., E. D. Hughes, and C. K. Ingold, *Nature*, **160,** 406 (1947).
97 Austin, A. T., E. D. Hughes, C. K. Ingold, and J. H. Ridd, *J. Am. Chem. Soc.*, **74,** 555 (1952).
98 Auwers von, K., *Ann.*, **499,** 123 (1932).
99 Auwers von, K., *Ann.*, **505,** 283 (1933).
100 Auwers von, K., and E. Borsche, *Ber.*, **48,** 1716 (1915).
101 Auwers von, K., and E. Cauer, *Ann.*, **470,** 284 (1929).
102 Auwers von, K., and F. Eisenloher, *Ber.*, **41,** 415 (1908).
103 Auwers von, K., and F. König, *Ann.*, **496,** 27, 252 (1932).
104 Auwers von, K., and F. Michaelis, *Ber.*, **47,** 1275 (1914).
105 Auwers von, K., and H. Roehrig, *Ber.*, **30,** 988 (1897).
106 Auwers von, K., and E. Wolter, *Ann.*, **487,** 79 (1931).
107 Ayling, E. E., J. H. Gorvin, and L. E. Hinkel, *J. Chem. Soc.*, **1941,** 613.

108 Babko, A. K., *J. Gen. Chem. U.S.S.R.*, **15,** 758, 874 (1945); through *Chem. Abstracts*, **40,** 6359, 6943 (1946).
109 Babko, A. K., *J. Gen. Chem. U.S.S.R.*, **16,** 33 (1946); through *Chem. Abstracts*, **40,** 7042 (1946).
110 Babko, A. K., *J. Gen. Chem. U.S.S.R.*, **17,** 443, 642 (1947); through *Chem. Abstracts*, **42,** 475, 476 (1948).
111 Bachmann, W. E., and J. W. Ferguson, *J. Am. Chem. Soc.*, **56,** 2081 (1934).
112 Bachmann, W. E., and R. A. Hoffman, *Organic Reactions*, J. Wiley & Sons, New York, 1944, Vol. II, 224.
113 Bachmann, W. E., and D. W. Holmes, *J. Am. Chem. Soc.*, **62,** 2750 (1940).

114 Bachmann, W. E., and F. H. Moser, *J. Am. Chem. Soc.*, **54,** 1124 (1932).
115 Bachmann, W. E., and J. C. Sheehan, unpublished.
116 Bachmann, W. E., and J. C. Sheehan, *J. Am. Chem. Soc.*, **62,** 2687 (1940).
117 Bachmann, W. E., and W. S. Struve, *Organic Reactions*, J. Wiley & Sons, New York, 1942, Vol. I, 38.
118 Back, G., and H. Zollinger, *Chimia*, **11,** 103 (1957).
119 Back, R., and C. Sivertz, *Can. J. Chem.*, **32,** 1061 (1954).
120 Badger, G. M., *Rec. trav. chim.*, **71,** 468 (1952).
121 Badger, G. M., R. G. Buttery, and G. E. Lewis, *J. Chem. Soc.*, **1953,** 2143.
122 Badger, G. M., and R. G. Buttery, *J. Chem. Soc.*, **1953,** 2156.
123 Badger, G. M., R. G. Buttery, and G. E. Lewis, *J. Chem. Soc.*, **1954,** 1888.
124 Badger, G. M., and R. G. Buttery, *J. Chem. Soc.*, **1954,** 2243.
125 Badger, G. M., and R. G. Buttery, *J. Chem. Soc.*, **1956,** 614.
126 Badger, G. M., J. W. Cook, and A. R. M. Gibb, *J. Chem. Soc.*, **1951,** 3456.
127 Badger, G. M., and G. E. Lewis, *J. Chem. Soc.*, **1953,** 2147.
128 Badger, G. M., and G. E. Lewis, *J. Chem. Soc.*, **1953,** 2151.
129 Badger, G. M., R. S. Pearce, and R. Pettit, *J. Chem. Soc.*, **1951,** 3199.
130 Baer, D. R., *J. Org. Chem.*, **23,** 1560 (1958).
131 Baeyer von, A., *Ber.*, **7,** 1638 (1874).
132 Baeyer von, A., *Ann.*, **354,** 152 (1907).
133 Bailar, J. C., *The Chemistry of the Coordination Compounds*, Reinhold Publ., New York, 1956. a) chap. 3, 4, and 18; b) p. 212-213; c) p. 214; d) p. 563–569.
134 Bailar, J. C., and C. F. Callis, *J. Am. Chem. Soc.*, **74,** 6018 (1952).
135 Bailey, P. S., and J. G. Burr, *J. Am. Chem. Soc.*, **75,** 2951 (1953).
136 Baker, J. W., *Hyperconjugation*, Clarendon Press, Oxford, 1952.
137 Ballhausen, C. J., *Acta Chem. Scand.*, **9,** 821 (1955).
138 Balli, H., *Angew. Chem.*, **71,** 374 (1959).
139 Balz, G., and G. Schiemann, *Ber.*, **60,** 1186 (1927).
140 Balz, G., and G. Schiemann, *Ber.*, **60,** 1187 (1927).
141 Bamberger, E., *Ber.*, **27,** 359 (1894).
142 Bamberger, E., *Ber.*, **27,** 584 (1894).
143 Bamberger, E., *Ber.*, **27,** 679 (1894).
144 Bamberger, E., *Ber.*, **27,** 680 (1894).
145 Bamberger, E., *Ber.*, **27,** 914 (1894).
146 Bamberger, E., *Ber.*, **27,** 915 (1894).
147 Bamberger, E., *Ber.*, **27,** 917, 3412 (1894).
148 Bamberger, E., *Ber.*, **27,** 1273 (1894).
149 Bamberger, E., *Ber.*, **27,** 1948 (1894).
150 Bamberger, E., *Ber.*, **27,** 2582 (1894).
151 Bamberger, E., *Ber.*, **27,** 2596 (1894).
152 Bamberger, E., *Ber.*, **27,** 2601 (1894).
153 Bamberger, E., *Ber.*, **27,** 2930 (1894).
154 Bamberger, E., *Ber.*, **28,** 406 (1895).
155 Bamberger, E., *Ber.*, **28,** 444 (1895).
156 Bamberger, E., *Ber.*, **28,** 538 (1895).
157 Bamberger, E., *Ber.*, **28,** 837 (1895).
158 Bamberger, E., *Ber.*, **29,** 102 (1896).
159 Bamberger, E., *Ber.*, **29,** 446 (1896).
160 Bamberger, E., *Ber.*, **29,** 473 (1896).
161 Bamberger, E., *Ber.*, **29,** 564 (1896).
162 Bamberger, E., *Ber.*, **30,** 211 (1897).
163 Bamberger, E., *Ber.*, **30,** 366 (1897).
164 Bamberger, E., *Ber.*, **30,** 506 (1897).
165 Bamberger, E., *Ber.*, **30,** 1248 (1897).
166 Bamberger, E., *Ber.*, **33,** 3188 (1900).
167 Bamberger, E., *Ber.*, **33,** 3192 (1900).
168 Bamberger, E., *Ber.*, **53,** 2313 (1920).
169 Bamberger, E., *Ber.*, **53,** 2314 (1920).
170 Bamberger, E., *Ber.*, **53,** 2321 (1920).
171 Bamberger, E., *Ber.*, **55,** 3383 (1922).
172 Bamberger, E., and O. Baudisch, *Ber.*, **42,** 3568 (1909).
173 Bamberger, E., and O. Baudisch, *Ber.*, **42,** 3582 (1909).

174 Bamberger, E., and O. Baudisch, *Ber.*, **45,** 2055 (1912).
175 Bamberger, E., and R. Hübner, *Ber.*, **36,** 3818 (1903).
176 Bamberger, E., and E. Kraus, *Ber.*, **29,** 1829 (1896).
177 Bamberger, E., and K. Landsteiner, *Ber.*, **26,** 471 (1893).
178 Bamberger, E., and F. Meimberg, *Ber.*, **28,** 1887 (1895).
179 Bamberger, E., and F. Meimberg, *Ber.*, **28,** 1893 (1895).
180 Bamberger, E., and J. Müller, *Ann.*, **313,** 126 (1900).
181 Bamberger, E., and L. Storch, *Ber.*, **26,** 471 (1893).
182 Bamberger, E., and F. Tschirner, *Ber.*, **33,** 955 (1900).
183 Bamberger, E., and E. Wheelwright, *Ber.*, **25,** 3201 (1892).
184 Bamberger, E., and E. Wheelwright, *J. prakt. Chem.*, **65,** 133 (1902).
185 Bamberger, E., and H. Witter, *Ber.*, **26,** 2788 (1893).
186 Bamberger, E., and P. Wulz, *Ber.*, **24,** 2079 (1891).
187 Bamford, C. H., W. G. Barb, A. D. Jenkins, and P. F. Onyon, *The Kinetics of Vinyl Polymerisation by Radical Mechanisms*, Academic Press, New York, 1958.
188 Bamford, W. R., and T. S. Stevens, *J. Chem. Soc.*, **1952,** 4675.
189 Baranger, P., J. Levisalles, and M. Vuidart, *Compt. rend.*, **236,** 1365 (1953).
190 Barger, G., and G. Weitnauer, *Helv. Chim. Acta*, **22,** 1036 (1939).
191 Bart, H., *Ann.*, **429,** 55 (1922).
192 Bartlett, P. D., *Bull. soc. chim. France*, **18,** 100 (1951).
193 Bartlett, P. D., in *Organic Chemistry*, H. Gilman, ed., John Wiley & Sons, New York, 1953, Vol. III, p. 8.
194 Bartlett, P. D., *Experientia Supplementum VII*, Birkhäuser Verlag, Basel, 1957, p. 275.
195 Bartlett, P. D., and S. G. Cohen, *J. Am. Chem. Soc.*, **62,** 1183 (1940).
196 Bartlett, P. D., and L. H. Knox, *J. Am. Chem. Soc.*, **61,** 3184 (1939).
197 Bartlett, P. D., and E. S. Lewis, *J. Am. Chem. Soc.*, **72,** 1005 (1950).
198 Barton, D. H. R., *Experientia*, **6,** 316 (1950).
199 Barton, D. H. R., *Experientia Supplementum II*, 121 (1955).
200 Barton, D. H. R., in *Perspectives in Organic Chemistry*, A. R. Todd, ed., Interscience Publishers, New York, 1956, p. 68.
201 Barton, N., J. W. Cook, J. D. Loudon, and J. MacMillan, *J. Chem. Soc.*, **1949,** 1079.
202 Basolo, F., C. J. Ballhausen, and J. Bjerrum, *Acta Chem. Scand.*, **9,** 810 (1955).
203 Basolo, F., and R. G. Pearson, *Mechanism of Inorganic Reactions*, J. Wiley & Sons, New York, 1958. a) chap. 2; b) chap. 9.
204 Bassett, I. M., and R. D. Brown, *J. Chem. Soc.*, **1954,** 2701.
205 Battegay, M., and J. Béha, *Bull. soc. chim. France*, **33,** 1089 (1923).
206 Battegay, M., and J. Béha, *Bull. Soc. Mulhouse*, **89,** 241 (1923).
207 Bavin, P. M. G., and M. J. S. Dewar, *J. Chem. Soc.*, **1956,** 164.
208 Bawn, C. E. H., and A. Ledwith, *Chemistry and Industry*, **1958,** 1329.
209 Bawn, C. E. H., and S. F. Mellish, *Trans. Faraday Soc.*, **47,** 1216 (1951).
210 Baxter, G., C. H. Giles, M. N. McKee, and N. Macaulay, *J. Soc. Dyers Col.*, **71,** 218 (1955).
211 Bayliss, N. S., *J. Chem. Phys.*, **16,** 287 (1948).
212 Bayliss, N. S., *Quart. Revs.*, **6,** 319 (1952).
213 Baysal, B., and A. V. Tobolsky, *J. Polymer Sci.*, **8,** 529 (1952).
214 Beale, R. N., and E. M. F. Roe, *J. Chem. Soc.*, **1953,** 2755.
215 Bean, P., and F. M. Rowe, *J. Soc. Dyers Col.*, **45,** 67 (1929).
216 Becker, F., *Angew. Chem.*, **65,** 97 (1953).
217 Beech, W. F., and H. D. K. Drew, *J. Chem. Soc.*, **1940,** 603.
218 Beech, W. F., and H. D. K. Drew, *J. Chem. Soc.*, **1940,** 608.
219 Behr, L. C., *J. Am. Chem. Soc.*, **76,** 3672 (1954).
220 Bell, R. P., *Acid-Base Catalysis*, Clarendon Press, Oxford, 1941, chap. IV.
221 Bell, R. P., unpublished.
222 Benjamin, B. M., and C. J. Collins, *J. Am. Chem. Soc.*, **78,** 4952 (1956).
223 Benjamin, B. M., and C. J. Collins, *J. Am. Chem. Soc.*, **78,** 4954 (1956).
224 Bent, R. L., J. C. Dessloch, F. C. Duennebier, D. W. Fassett, D. B. Glass, T. H. James, D. B. Julian, W. R. Ruby, J. M. Suell, J. H. Sterner, J. R. Thirtle, P. W. Vittum, and A. Weissberger, *J. Am. Chem. Soc.*, **73,** 3100 (1951).
225 Bentley, R. B., and J. P. Elder, *J. Soc. Dyers Col.*, **72,** 332 (1956).
226 Benzing, E., *Chimia*, **13,** 89 (1959).
227 Berglund-Larsson, U., and L. Melander, *Arkiv Kemi*, **6,** 219 (1953).
228 Berglund-Larsson, U., *Arkiv Kemi*, **10,** 549 (1957).
229 Bergmann, E., and F. Bergmann, *J. Org. Chem.*, **3,** 125 (1938).

230 Bergmann, E., and A. Weizmann, *Trans. Faraday Soc.*, **32,** 1318 (1936).
231 Bergmann, F., and D. Schapiro, *J. Org. Chem.*, **12,** 57 (1947).
232 Bernthsen, A., and A. Goske, *Ber.*, **20,** 925 (1887).
233 Berson, J. A., and D. A. Ben Efraim, *J. Am. Chem. Soc.*, **81,** 4094 (1959).
234 Best, A. P., and C. L. Wilson, *J. Chem. Soc.*, **1938,** 28.
235 Betterton, A. J., and W. A. Waters, *J. Chem. Soc.*, **1953,** 329.
236 Bevington, J. C., *J. Chem. Soc.*, **1954,** 3707.
237 Bevington, J. C., *Nature*, **175,** 477 (1955).
238 Bevington, J. C., J. H. Bradbury, and G. M. Bunnett, *J. Polymer Sci.*, **12,** 469 (1954).
239 Bevington, J. C., N. A. Ghanem, and H. W. Melville, *Trans. Faraday Soc.*, **51,** 946 (1955).
240 Bevington, J. C., H. W. Melville, and R. P. Taylor, *J. Polymer Sci.*, **12,** 449 (1954).
241 Bevington, J. C., H. W. Melville, and R. P. Taylor, *J. Polymer Sci.*, **12,** 463 (1954).
242 Beyer, H., C. F. Kröger, and M. Zander, *Ber.*, **88,** 1233 (1955).
243 Bickel, A. F., and E. C. Kooyman, *Nature*, **170,** 211 (1952).
244 Bickel, A. F., and E. C. Kooyman, *Rec. trav. chim.*, **71,** 1137 (1952).
245 Bickel, A. F., and W. A. Waters, *J. Chem. Soc.*, **1950,** 1764.
246 Bickel, A. F., and W. A. Waters, *Rec. trav. chim.*, **69,** 312 (1950).
247 Bickel, A. F., and W. A. Waters, *Rec. trav. chim.*, **69,** 1490 (1950).
248 Bigeleisen, J., *Science*, **110,** 14 (1949).
249 Bigeleisen, J., *J. Chem. Phys.*, **17,** 425 (1949) and subsequent papers (see *250*).
250 Bigeleisen, J. and M. Wolfsberg, *Advances in Chemical Physics*, Vol. I, 1958, Interscience, New York, p. 15.
251 Bigelow, H. E., and D. B. Robinson, *Org. Syntheses, Coll. Vol. III*, 103 (1955).
252 Biltz, H., and H. Paetzold, *Ber.*, **55,** 1069 (1922).
253 Biltz, H., and H. Paetzold, *Ann.*, **433,** 64 (1923).
254 Binks, J. H., and J. H. Ridd, *J. Chem. Soc.*, **1957,** 2398.
255 Birkhofer, L., *Ber.*, **75 B,** 429 (1942).
256 Birnbaum, P. P., J. H. Linford, and D. W. G. Style, *Trans. Faraday Soc.*, **49,** 735 (1953).
257 Bjerrum, J., *Metal Ammine Formation in Aqueous Solution*, P. Haase & Son, Copenhagen, 1941.
258 Bjerrum, J., *Chem. Revs.*, **46,** 381 (1950).
259 Bjerrum, J., C. J. Ballhausen, and C. K. Jorgensen, *Acta Chem. Scand.*, **8,** 1275 (1954).
260 Bjerrum, J., and E. J. Nielsen, *Acta Chem. Scand.*, **2,** 297 (1948).
261 Bjerrum, J., G. Schwarzenbach, and L. G. Sillén, *Stability Constants of Metal-ion Complexes*, Part I, The Chemical Society, London, 1957.
262 Blacet, F. F., and A. Taurog, *J. Am. Chem. Soc.*, **61,** 3024 (1939).
263 Blackall, E. L., E. D. Hughes, and C. K. Ingold, *J. Chem. Soc.*, **1952,** 28.
264 Blackley, D. C., and H. W. Melville, *Die makromol. Chem.*, **18/19,** 16 (1956).
265 Blaisdell, B. E., *J. Soc. Dyers Col.*, **65,** 618 (1949).
266 Blangey, L., *Helv. Chim. Acta*, **8,** 780 (1925).
267 Blangey, L., *Helv. Chim. Acta*, **21,** 1579 (1938).
268 Blomstrand, C. W., *Chemie der Jetztzeit*, **4,** 272 (1869).
269 Blomstrand, C. W., *Ber.*, **8,** 51 (1875).
270 Blumberger, J. S. P., *Rec. trav. chim.*, **49,** 259 (1930).
271 Blumberger, J. S. P., *Rec. trav. chim.*, **59,** 665 (1940).
272 Blumberger, J. S. P., *Rec. trav. chim.*, **63,** 127 (1944).
273 Bodenstein, M., *Z. physik. Chem.*, **85,** 329 (1913).
274 Boer de, T. J., and H. J. Backer, *Org. Syntheses*, **36,** 16 (1956).
275 Boersch, H., *Monatsh.*, **65,** 331 (1935).
276 Boeseken, J., W. F. Brandma, and H. A. J. Schoutissen, *Koninkl. Akad. Wetensch. Amsterdam*, **28,** 936 (1920); through *Chem. Zentr.*, **1920 III,** 617.
277 Boeseken, J., and H. Schoutissen, *Rec. trav. chim.*, **54,** 956 (1935).
278 Bogoslovskii, B. M., *J. Gen. Chem. U.S.S.R.*, **16,** 193 (1946).
279 Bogoslovskii, B. M., and Z. S. Kazakova, *J. Appl. Chem. U.S.S.R.*, **24,** 556 (1951); through *Chem. Abstracts*, **46,** 2003f (1952).
280 Bohlmann, F., *Ber.*, **85,** 390 (1952).
281 Böhme, H., and R. Marx, *Ber.*, **74,** 1667 (1941).
282 Bolto, B. A., M. Liveris, and J. Miller, *J. Chem. Soc.*, **1956,** 750.
283 Bonner, W. A., and C. J. Collins, *J. Am. Chem. Soc.*, **75,** 5372 (1953).
284 Bonner, W. A., and C. J. Collins, *J. Am. Chem. Soc.*, **75,** 5379 (1953).
285 Bonner, W. A., and C. J. Collins, *J. Am. Chem. Soc.*, **77,** 99 (1955).
286 Bonner, W. A., and C. J. Collins, *J. Am. Chem. Soc.*, **78,** 5587 (1956).
287 Bonner, W. A., and D. D. Tanner, *J. Am. Chem. Soc.*, **80,** 1447 (1958).

288 Boozer, C. E., G. S. Hammond, C. E. Hamilton, and J. N. Sen, *J. Am. Chem. Soc.*, **77,** 3233 (1955).

289 Boozer, C. E., G. S. Hammond, C. E. Hamilton, and J. N. Sen, *J. Am. Chem. Soc.*, **77,** 3238 (1955).

290 Boozer, C. E., G. S. Hammond, C. E. Hamilton, and C. Peterson, *J. Am. Chem. Soc.*, **77,** 3380 (1955).

291 Bose, A. K., *Experientia*, **9,** 256 (1953).

292 Bose, A. K., and P. Yates, *J. Am. Chem. Soc.*, **74,** 4703 (1952).

293 Bosshard, H. H., R. Mory, M. Schmid, and H. Zollinger, *Helv. Chim. Acta*, **42,** 1653 (1959).

294 Bosshard, H. H., and H. Zollinger, *Helv. Chim. Acta*, **42,** 1659 (1959).

295 Boudreaux, E. A., and E. Boulet, *J. Am. Chem. Soc.*, **80,** 1588 (1958).

296 Boyland, E., and P. Sims, *J. Chem. Soc.*, **1958,** 4198.

297 Bradfield, A. E., and K. J. P. Orton, *J. Chem. Soc.*, **1929,** 915.

298 Bradley, W., and R. Robinson, *J. Chem. Soc.*, **1928,** 1310.

299 Bradley, W., and R. Robinson, *J. Am. Chem. Soc.*, **52,** 1558 (1930).

300 Bradley, W., and G. Schwarzenbach, *J. Chem. Soc.*, **1928,** 2904.

301 Bradley, W., and J. D. Thompson, *Nature*, **178,** 1069 (1956).

302 Bradley, W., and L. J. Watkinson, *Chemistry and Industry*, **1954,** 1482.

303 Bradley, W., and L. J. Watkinson, *J. Chem. Soc.*, **1956,** 319.

304 Branch, G. E. K., and M. Calvin, *The Theory of Organic Chemistry*, Prentice-Hall, New York, 1941, p. 301.

305 Braren, W., and E. Buchner, *Ber.*, **33,** 684 (1900).

306 Braren, W., and E. Buchner, *Ber.*, **34,** 982 (1901).

307 Brass, K., and P. Sommer, *Ber.*, **61,** 996 (1928).

308 Brassard, P., and P. L'Écuyer, *Can. J. Chem.*, **36,** 1346 (1958).

309 Braude, E. A., *J. Chem. Soc.*, **1949,** 1902.

310 Braude, E. A., *Ann. Repts. on Progr. Chem.*, **42,** 105 (1945).

311 Braude, E. A., *J. Chem. Soc.*, **1950,** 379.

312 Braude, E. A., *Determination of Organic Structures by Physical Methods*, Academic Press, New York, 1955, p. 154.

313 Bredig, G., and W. Fraenkel, *Z. Elektrochem.*, **11,** 525 (1905).

314 Bredig, G., and P. F. Ripley, *Ber.*, **40,** 4015 (1907).

315 Bredt, J., and W. Holz, *J. prakt. Chem.*, **95,** 133 (1917).

316 Breitenbach, J. W., and A. Schindler, *Monatsh.*, **83,** 271 (1952).

317 Breitenbach, J. W., and A. Schindler, *Monatsh.*, **83,** 724 (1952).

318 Brewster, P., F. Hiron, E. D. Hughes, C. K. Ingold, and P. A. D. S. Rao, *Nature*, **166,** 179 (1950).

319 Broadhead, G. D., and P. L. Pauson, *J. Chem. Soc.*, **1955,** 367.

320 Brode, W. R., *Ind. Eng. Chem.*, **18,** 708 (1926).

321 Brode, W. R., *Ber.*, **61,** 1722 (1928).

322 Brode, W. R., *J. Am. Chem. Soc.*, **51,** 1204 (1929).

323 Brode, W. R., *J. Org. Chem.*, **5,** 162 (1940).

324 Brode, W. R., *J. Org. Chem.*, **6,** 341 (1941).

325 Brode, W. R., *Chem. Soc., Spec. Publ.*, **4,** 1 (1956).

326 Brode, W. R., J. H. Gould, and G. M. Wyman, *J. Am. Chem. Soc.*, **74,** 4641 (1952).

327 Brode, W. R., J. H. Gould, and G. M. Wyman, *J. Am. Chem. Soc.*, **75,** 1856 (1953).

328 Brode, W. R., J. H. Gould, and M. N. Inscoe, *J. Am. Chem. Soc.*, **81,** 5634 (1959).

329 Brode, W. R., and L. E. Herdle, *J. Org. Chem.*, **6,** 713 (1941).

330 Brode, W. R., I. L. Seldin, P. E. Spoerri, and G. M. Wyman, *J. Am. Chem. Soc.*, **77,** 2762 (1955).

331 Brönsted, J. N., *Z. physik. Chem.*, **102,** 169 (1922).

332 Brönsted, J. N., *Z. physik. Chem.*, **115,** 337 (1925).

333 Brönsted, J. N., *Chem. Revs.*, **5,** 265 (1928).

334 Brönsted, J. N., and R. P. Bell, *J. Am. Chem. Soc.*, **53,** 2478 (1931).

335 Brooker, L. G. S., *Chem. Revs.*, **41,** 325 (1947).

336 Brooker, L. G. S., G. H. Keyes, and W. W. Williams, *J. Am. Chem. Soc.*, **64,** 199 (1942).

337 Brooker, L. G. S., G. H. Keyes, R. H. Sprague, R. H. Van Dyke, E. Van Lare, G. Van Zandt, F. L. White, H. W. J. Cressman, and S. G. Dent, *J. Am. Chem. Soc.*, **73,** 5332 (1951).

338 Brooker, L. G. S., R. H. Sprague, C. P. Smyth, and G. L. Lewis, *J. Am. Chem. Soc.*, **62,** 1116 (1940).

339 Brough, J. N., B. Lythgoe, and P. Waterhouse, *J. Chem. Soc.*, **1954,** 4069.

340 Brown, D. J., *J. Soc. Dyers Col.*, **60,** 186 (1944).

341 Brown, H. C., and J. D. Brady, *J. Am. Chem. Soc.*, **71,** 3573 (1949).
342 Brown, H. C., and J. D. Brady, *J. Am. Chem. Soc.*, **74,** 3570 (1952).
343 Brown, H. C., and I. Moritani, *J. Am. Chem. Soc.*, **77,** 3607 (1956).
344 Brown, H. C., and K. L. Nelson, in *The Chemistry of Petroleum Hydrocarbons*, B. T. Brooks
     et al., eds., Reinhold Publ., New York, 1955, Vol. III, p. 465.
345 Brown, H. C., and Y. Okamoto, *J. Am. Chem. Soc.*, **79,** 1913 (1957).
346 Brown, H. C., and H. W. Pearsall, *J. Am. Chem. Soc.*, **74,** 192 (1952).
347 Brown, H. C., and W. J. Wallace, *J. Am. Chem. Soc.*, **75,** 6265 (1953).
348 Brown, H. C., and W. J. Wallace, *J. Am. Chem. Soc.*, **75,** 6268 (1953).
349 Brown, I. D., and J. D. Dunitz, *Acta Cryst.*, **13,** 28 (1960).
350 Brown, R. D., B. A. W. Coller, and M. L. Heffernan, *J. Chem. Soc.*, **1958,** 1776.
351 Brown, R. D., H. C. Duffin, J. C. Maynard, and J. H. Ridd, *J. Chem. Soc.*, **1953,** 3937.
352 Brown, W. G., A. H. Widiger, and N. J. Letang, *J. Am. Chem. Soc.*, **61,** 2597 (1939).
353 Bruin, P., A. F. Bickel, and E. C. Kooyman, *Rec. trav. chim.*, **61,** 1115 (1952).
354 Brütsch, H., Thesis, ETH, Zurich, 1921.
355 Buchanan, J., and S. D. Hamann, *Trans. Faraday Soc.*, **49,** 1425 (1953).
356 Bucherer, H. T., *Ber.*, **42,** 47 (1909).
357 Bucherer, H. T., and A. Fröhlich, *J. prakt. Chem.*, **132,** 72 (1931).
358 Bucherer, H. T., and E. Hoffmann, *J. prakt. Chem.*, **121,** 113 (1929).
359 Bucherer, H. T., and M. Rauch, *J. prakt. Chem.*, **132,** 232 (1931).
360 Bucherer, H. T., and G. von der Recke, *J. prakt. Chem.*, **132,** 123 (1931).
361 Buchner, E., *Ber.*, **21,** 2637 (1888).
362 Buchner, E., *Ber.*, **22,** 842 (1889).
363 Buchner, E., *Ber.*, **29,** 106 (1896).
364 Buchner, E., *Ber.*, **30,** 632 (1897).
365 Buchner, E., *Ber.*, **31,** 2241 (1898).
366 Buchner, E., and T. Curtius, *Ber.*, **18,** 2377 (1885).
367 Buchner, E., and K. Delbrück, *Ann.*, **358,** 1 (1908).
368 Buchner, E., and L. Feldmann, *Ber.*, **36,** 3509 (1903).
369 Buchner, E., and S. Hediger, *Ber.*, **36,** 3502 (1903).
370 Buchner, E., and A. Jacobi, *Ber.*, **31,** 2004 (1898).
371 Buchner, E., and F. Lingg, *Ber.*, **31,** 402 (1898).
372 Buchner, E., and F. Lingg, *Ber.*, **31,** 2247 (1898).
373 Buchner, E., and A. Papendieck, *Ann.*, **273,** 232 (1893).
374 Buchner, E., and A. Papendieck, *Ber.*, **28,** 221 (1895).
375 Buchner, E., and H. Schroeder, *Ber.*, **35,** 782 (1902).
376 Buchner, E., and P. Schulze, *Ann.*, **377,** 259 (1910).
377 Buchner, E., H. Witter, and H. Dessauer, *Ber.*, **27,** 868, 877, 879 (1894).
378 Buckley, G. D., L. H. Cross, and N. H. Ray, *J. Chem. Soc.*, **1950,** 2714.
379 Buckley, G. D., L. H. Cross, and N. H. Ray, *J. Chem. Soc.*, **1952,** 3701.
380 Bull, W. E., J. A. Seaton, and L. F. Audrieth, *J. Am. Chem. Soc.*, **80,** 2516 (1958).
381 Bunnett, J. F., and G. B. Hoey, *J. Am. Chem. Soc.*, **80,** 3142 (1958).
382 Bunnett, J. F., and R. E. Zahler, *Chem. Revs.*, **49,** 273 (1951).
383 Bunton, C. A., D. R. Llewellyn, and G. Stedman, *J. Chem. Soc.*, **1959,** 568.
384 Bunton, C. A., and G. Stedman, *J. Chem. Soc.*, **1958,** 2440.
385 Burawoy, A., *J. Chem. Soc.*, **1937,** 1865.
386 Burawoy, A., *J. Chem. Soc.*, **1939,** 1177.
387 Burawoy, A., and I. Markowitsch, *Ann.*, **503,** 180 (1933).
388 Burawoy, A., and I. Markowitsch, *Ann.*, **504,** 71 (1933).
389 Burawoy, A., A. G. Salem, and A. R. Thompson, *J. Chem. Soc.*, **1952,** 4793.
390 Burawoy, A., and A. R. Thompson, *J. Chem. Soc.*, **1953,** 1443.
391 Burawoy, A., and C. Turner, *J. Chem. Soc.*, **1952,** 1286.
392 Burger, A., and W. L. Yost, *J. Am. Chem. Soc.*, **70,** 2198 (1948).
393 Burmistrov, S. I., *J. Gen. Chem. U.S.S.R.*, **19,** 906 (1949); through *Chem. Abstracts*, **44,**
     1048e (1950).
394 Burmistrov, S. I., *J. Gen. Chem. U.S.S.R.*, **20,** 277 (1950); through *Chem. Abstracts*, **44,**
     6131c (1950).
395 Burns, J., H. McCombie, and H. A. Scarborough, *J. Chem. Soc.*, **1928,** 2928.
396 Burr, J. C., *J. Am. Chem. Soc.*, **75,** 5008 (1953).
397 Burton, M., T. W. Davis, and H. A. Taylor, *J. Am. Chem. Soc.*, **59,** 1038 (1937).
398 Burton, M., T. W. Davis, and H. A. Taylor, *J. Am. Chem. Soc.*, **59,** 1989 (1937).
399 Bury, C. R., *J. Am. Chem. Soc.*, **57,** 2116 (1935).

400 Cabral, de, O. J., and H. A. Turner, *J. Soc. Dyers Col.*, **72**, 158 (1956).
401 Cain, J. C., *Ber.*, **38**, 2511 (1905).
402 Callis, C. F., N. C. Nielsen, and J. C. Bailar, *J. Am. Chem. Soc.*, **74**, 3461 (1952).
403 Calvin, M., and R. H. Bailes, *J. Am. Chem. Soc.*, **68**, 949 (1946).
404 Calvin, M., and K. W. Wilson, *J. Am. Chem. Soc.*, **67**, 2003 (1945).
405 Campbell, N., and J. A. R. MacLean, *J. Chem. Soc.*, **1942**, 504.
406 Campbell, T. W., and B. F. Day, *Chem. Revs.*, **48**, 299 (1951).
407 Campbell, T. W., W. A. McAllister, and M. T. Rogers, *J. Am. Chem. Soc.*, **75**, 864 (1953).
408 Campbell, T. W., D. A. Young, and M. T. Rogers, *J. Am. Chem. Soc.*, **73**, 5789 (1951).
409 Cannell, L. G., *J. Am. Chem. Soc.*, **79**, 2927 (1957).
410 Cannell, L. G., *J. Am. Chem. Soc.*, **79**, 2932 (1957).
411 Cannell, L. G., and R. W. Taft, *J. Am. Chem. Soc.*, **78**, 5812 (1956).
412 Cannell, L. G., and R. W. Taft, *Abstr. 129th Meeting Am. Chem. Soc.*, *Dallas*, 1956, p. 46 N.
413 Cannon, C. V., and O. K. Rice, *J. Am. Chem. Soc.*, **63**, 2900 (1941).
414 Carlisle, P. J., *Chem. Eng. News.* **27**, 150 (1949).
415 Caserio, M. C., J. D. Roberts, M. Neeman, and W. S. Johnson, *J. Am. Chem. Soc.*, **80**, 2584 (1958).
416 Castor, C. R., and J. H. Saylor, *J. Am. Chem. Soc.*, **75**, 1427 (1953).
417 Casty, R., *Melliand Textilber.*, **33**, 950 (1952).
418 Chadra, R. N., and G. S. Misra, *Die makromol. Chem.*, **14**, 97 (1954).
419 Chattaway, F. D., F. L. Garton, and G. D. Parkes, *J. Chem. Soc.*, **125**, 1980 (1924).
420 Chipalkatti, H. R., N. F. Desai, C. H. Giles, and N. Macauly, *J. Soc. Dyers Col.*, **70**, 487 (1954).
421 Chopard-dit-Jean, L. H., and E. Heilbronner, *Helv. Chim. Acta*, **35**, 2170 (1952).
422 Chu, T., and C. S. Marvel, *J. Am. Chem. Soc.*, **55**, 2841 (1933).
423 Ciereszko, L. S., and J. G. Burr, *J. Am. Chem. Soc.*, **74**, 145 (1952).
424 Ciereszko, L. S., and J. G. Burr, *J. Am. Chem. Soc.*, **74**, 5431 (1952).
425 Cilento, G., E. C. Miller, and J. A. Miller, *J. Am. Chem. Soc.*, **78**, 1718 (1956).
426 Claasz, M., *Ber.*, **44**, 1415 (1911).
427 Clark, D., and H. O. Pritchard, *J. Chem. Soc.*, **1956**, 2136.
428 Claudon, M. M., P. Anziani, and R. Cornubert, *Bull. soc. chim. France*, **23**, 150 (1956).
429 Claus, A., *Ber.*, **8**, 37 (1875).
430 Claus, A., and P. Stegelitz, *Ber.*, **17**, 2380 (1884).
431 Clibbens, D. A., and M. Nierenstein, *J. Chem. Soc.*, **107**, 1491 (1916).
432 Cliffe, W. H., *J. Soc. Dyers Col.*, **75**, 278 (1959).
433 Clusius, K., and M. Hoch, *Helv. Chim. Acta*, **33**, 2122 (1950).
434 Clusius, K., H. Hürzeler, R. Huisgen, and H. J. Koch, *Naturwissenschaften*, **41**, 213 (1954).
435 Clusius, K., and H. Hürzeler, *Helv. Chim. Acta*, **37**, 383 (1954).
436 Clusius, K., and H. Hürzeler, *Helv. Chim. Acta*, **37**, 798 (1954).
437 Clusius, K., and H. Hürzeler, *Helv. Chim. Acta*, **38**, 1831 (1955).
438 Clusius, K., and U. Lüthi, *Helv. Chim. Acta*, **40**, 445 (1957).
439 Clusius, K., and K. Schwarzenbach, *Helv. Chim. Acta*, **41**, 1413 (1958).
440 Clusius, K., and M. Vecchi, *Helv. Chim. Acta*, **39**, 1469 (1956).
441 Clusius, K., and H. R. Weisser, *Helv. Chim. Acta*, **35**, 400 (1952).
442 Clusius, K., and H. R. Weisser, *Helv. Chim. Acta*, **35**, 1548 (1952).
443 Cohen, M. D., J. E. Leffler, and L. M. Barbato, *J. Am. Chem. Soc.*, **76**, 4169 (1954).
444 Cohen, S. G., *J. Polymer Sci.*, **2**, 511 (1947).
445 Cohen, S. G., S. J. Groszos, and D. B. Sparrow, *J. Am. Chem. Soc.*, **72**, 3947 (1950).
446 Cohen, S. G., and C. H. Wang, *J. Am. Chem. Soc.*, **75**, 5504 (1953).
447 Cohen, S. G., and C. H. Wang, *J. Am. Chem. Soc.*, **77**, 2417 (1955).
448 Cohen, S. G., and C. H. Wang, *J. Am. Chem. Soc.*, **77**, 2457 (1955).
449 Cohen, S. G., and C. H. Wang, *J. Am. Chem. Soc.*, **77**, 2458 (1955).
450 Cohen, S. G., and C. H. Wang, *J. Am. Chem. Soc.*, **77**, 3628 (1955).
451 Cohen, S. G., and C. H. Wang, *J. Am. Chem. Soc.*, **77**, 4435 (1955).
452 Cohn, G., *Die Pyrazolfarbstoffe*, F. Enke, Stuttgart, 1910.
453 Coleman, G. H., *Org. Syntheses*, *Coll. Vol. I*, 432 (1932).
454 Coleman, G. H., H. Gilman, C. E. Adams, and P. E. Pratt, *J. Org. Chem.*, **3**, 99 (1938).
455 Collins, C. J., and W. A. Bonner, *J. Am. Chem. Soc.*, **77**, 92 (1955).
456 Collins, C. J., and W. A. Bonner, *J. Am. Chem. Soc.*, **77**, 6725 (1955).
457 Collins, C. J., W. A. Bonner, and C. T. Lester, *J. Am. Chem. Soc.*, **81**, 466 (1959).
458 Colour Index, edited by Soc. Dyers Col. and Am. Ass. Text. Chem. Col., 2nd ed., Bradford and Lowell, 1956–58, 4 volumes.
459 Conant, J. B., and W. D. Peterson, *J. Am. Chem. Soc.*, **52**, 1220 (1930).

460 Cook, A. H., *J. Chem. Soc.*, **1938,** 876.
461 Cook, A. H., and D. G. Jones, *J. Chem. Soc.*, **1939,** 1309.
462 Cook, A. H., D. G. Jones, and J. B. Polya, *J. Chem. Soc.*, **1939,** 1315.
463 Cook, A. H., and D. G. Jones, *J. Chem. Soc.*, **1941,** 184.
464 Cook, A. H., and D. G. Jones, *J. Chem. Soc.*, **1941,** 189.
465 Cook, J. W., and R. Schoental, *J. Chem. Soc.*, **1945,** 288.
466 Corey, E. J., H. J. Burke, and W. A. Remers, *J. Am. Chem. Soc.*, **77,** 4941 (1955).
467 Costa, G., *Gazz. chim. ital.*, **83,** 875 (1953).
468 Costa, G., *Ann. triestini univ. Trieste*, Sez. 2, **2223,** 115, 127, 151, 167 (1953); through *Chem. Abstracts*, **48,** 4331 (1954).
469 Coulson, C. A., *Valence*, Clarendon Press, Oxford, 1952. a) sect. 8.12; b) p. 35; c) pp. 213–217; d) pp. 255–257.
470 Coulson, C. A., and H. C. Longuet-Higgins, *Proc. Roy. Soc.*, **A 192,** 16 (1947).
471 Couper, M., *Text. Res. J.*, **21,** 720 (1951).
472 Cowdrey, W. A., and D. S. Davies, *J. Chem. Soc. Suppl.*, **1949,** 48.
473 Cowdrey, W. A., and D. S. Davies, *Quart. Revs.*, **6,** 358 (1952).
474 Cox, A. P., C. F. Thomas, and J. Sheridan, *Nature*, **181,** 1000 (1958).
475 Cox, E. G., and K. C. Webster, *J. Chem. Soc.*, **1935,** 731.
476 Craig, D. P., A. Maccoll, R. S. Nyholm, L. E. Orgel, and L. E. Sutton, *J. Chem. Soc.*, **1954,** 332.
477 Cram, D. J., *J. Am. Chem. Soc.*, **71,** 3863 (1949).
478 Cram, D. J., *J. Am. Chem. Soc.*, **71,** 3875 (1949).
479 Cram, D. J., *J. Am. Chem. Soc.*, **74,** 2129 (1952).
480 Cram, D. J., *J. Am. Chem. Soc.*, **74,** 2137 (1952).
481 Cram, D. J., *J. Am. Chem. Soc.*, **74,** 2159 (1952).
482 Cram, D. J., in *Steric Effects in Organic Chemistry*, M. S. Newman, ed., J. Wiley & Sons, New York, 1956, p. 272.
483 Cram, D. J., and R. Davis, *J. Am. Chem. Soc.*, **71,** 3871 (1949).
484 Cram, D. J., and F. A. A. Elhafez, *J. Am. Chem. Soc.*, **75,** 3189 (1953).
485 Cram, D. J., and J. E. McCarty, *J. Am. Chem. Soc.*, **79,** 2866 (1957).
486 Crary, J. W., O. R. Quayle, and C. T. Lester, *J. Am. Chem. Soc.*, **78,** 5584 (1956).
487 Crawford, B. L., W. H. Fletcher, and D. A. Ramsay, *J. Chem. Phys.*, **19,** 406 (1951).
488 Cremlyn, R. J. W., D. L. Garmaise, and C. W. Shoppee, *J. Chem. Soc.*, **1953,** 1847.
489 Crippa, G. B., *Gazz. chim. ital.*, **59,** 330 (1929).
490 Crippa, G. B., *Gazz. chim. ital.*, **60,** 301 (1930).
491 Crippa, G. B., *Gazz. chim. ital.*, **63,** 251 (1933).
492 Crippa, G. B., *Gazz. chim. ital.*, **66,** 649 (1936).
493 Crippa, G. B., and M. Long, *Gazz. chim. ital.*, **62,** 394 (1932).
494 Crippa, G. B., and G. Perroncito, *Gazz. chim. ital.*, **65,** 678 (1935).
495 Crippa, G. B., and G. Perroncito, *Ann. Chim. applicata*, **25,** 618 (1935).
496 Crossley, M. L., R. H. Kienle, and C. H. Benbrook, *J. Am. Chem. Soc.*, **62,** 1400 (1940).
497 Cullinane, N. M., A. G. Rees, and C. A. J. Plummer, *J. Chem. Soc.*, **1939,** 151.
498 Cumming, J. W., C. H. Giles, and A. E. McEachran, *J. Soc. Dyers Col.*, **72,** 373 (1956).
499 Curtin, D. Y., and M. C. Crew, *J. Am. Chem. Soc.*, **76,** 3719 (1954).
500 Curtin, D. Y., and M. C. Crew, *J. Am. Chem. Soc.*, **77,** 354 (1955).
501 Curtin, D. Y., and S. M. Gerber, *J. Am. Chem. Soc.*, **74,** 4052 (1952).
502 Curtin, D. Y., and S. Schmukler, *J. Am. Chem. Soc.*, **77,** 1105 (1955).
503 Curtin, D. Y., and J. A. Ursprung, *J. Org. Chem.*, **21,** 1221 (1956).
504 Curtius, T., *Ber.*, **16,** 2230 (1883).
505 Curtius, T., *Ber.*, **17,** 953 (1884).
506 Curtius, T., *J. prakt. Chem.*, **38,** 396 (1888).
507 Curtius, T., *J. prakt. Chem.*, **38,** 409 (1888).
508 Curtius, T., *J. prakt. Chem.*, **39,** 107 (1889).
509 Curtius, T., *Ber.*, **23,** 3023 (1890).
510 Curtius, T., *Ber.*, **23,** 3033 (1890).
511 Curtius, T., *Ber.*, **26,** 1263 (1893).
512 Curtius, T., and E. Buchner, *Ber.*, **18,** 2371 (1885).
513 Curtius, T., A. Darapsky, and E. Müller, *Ber.*, **41,** 3140 (1908).
514 Curtius, T., A. Darapsky, and E. Müller, *Ber.*, **41,** 3161 (1908).
515 Curtius, T., and K. Heidenreich, *Ber.*, **27,** 773 (1894).
516 Curtius, T., and K. Heidenreich, *J. prakt. Chem.*, **52,** 476 (1894).
517 Curtius, T., and H. Lang, *J. prakt. Chem.*, **44,** 544 (1891).

518 Curtius, T., and F. Rauterberg, *J. prakt. Chem.*, **44,** 192 (1891).
519 Curtius, T., and K. Thun, *J. prakt. Chem.*, **44,** 161 (1891).
520 Cyriax, B., Thesis, Bonn University, 1936.

521 Dacey, J. R., and D. M. Young, *J. Chem. Phys.*, **23,** 1302 (1955).
522 Dahn, H., and H. v. Castelmur, *Helv. Chim. Acta*, **36,** 638 (1953).
523 Dale, W. J., and H. E. Hennis, *J. Am. Chem. Soc.*, **81,** 2143 (1959).
524 Darzens, G., and M. Meyer, *Compt. rend.*, **233,** 749 (1951).
525 Dauben, W. G., and E. Hoerger, *J. Am. Chem. Soc.*, **73,** 1504 (1951).
526 Dauben, W. G., and J. Jiu, *J. Am. Chem. Soc.*, **76,** 4426 (1954).
527 Dauben, W. G., and K. S. Pitzer, in *Steric Effects in Organic Chemistry*, M. S. Newman, ed., J. Wiley & Sons, New York, 1956, p. 13.
528 Dauben, W. G., R. C. Tweit, and C. Mannerskantz, *J. Am. Chem. Soc.*, **76,** 4420 (1954).
529 Dauben, W. G., R. C. Tweit, and R. L. MacLean, *J. Am. Chem. Soc.*, **77,** 48 (1955).
530 Davidson, H. R., *J. Chem. Education*, **27,** 598 (1950).
531 Davidson, W. B., and A. Hantzsch, *Ber.*, **31,** 1612 (1898).
532 Davies, W., *J. Chem. Soc.*, **121,** 715 (1922).
533 Davis, T. W., F. P. Jahn, and M. Burton, *J. Am. Chem. Soc.*, **60,** 10 (1938).
534 Day, B. F., T. W. Campbell, and G. M. Coppinger, *J. Am. Chem. Soc.*, **73,** 4687 (1951).
535 De Jong, A. W. K., *Rec. trav. chim.*, **56,** 198 (1937).
536 De Jong, J. I., and J. de Jonge, *Rec. trav. chim.*, **72,** 497 (1953).
537 De Jonge, J., R. J. H. Alink, and R. Dijkstra, *Rec. trav. chim.*, **69,** 1448 (1950).
538 De Jonge, J., and R. Dijkstra, *Rec. trav. chim.*, **67,** 328 (1948).
539 De la Mare, P. B. D., E. D. Hughes, and C. A. Vernon, *Research*, **3,** 192 (1950).
540 De la Mare, P. B. D., A. D. Ketley, and C. A. Vernon, *J. Chem. Soc.*, **1954,** 1290.
541 De la Mare, P. B. D., and J. H. Ridd, *Aromatic Substitution, Nitration and Halogenation*, Butterworth, London, 1959.
542 Demjanow, N., *J. Russ. Phys. Chem. Soc.*, **36,** 166 (1904); through *Chem. Zentr.*, **1904 I,** 1214.
543 Demjanow, N., *Ber.*, **40,** 4393 (1907).
544 Demjanow, N., *J. Russ. Phys. Chem. Soc.*, **39,** 1077 (1907); through *Chem. Zentr.*, **1908 I,** 818.
545 Demjanow, N., and M. Luschnikow, *J. Russ. Phys. Chem. Soc.*, **33,** 279 (1901); through *Chem. Zentr.*, **1901 II,** 335.
546 Demjanow, N., and M. Luschnikow, *J. Russ. Phys. Chem. Soc.*, **35,** 26 (1903); through *Chem. Zentr.*, **1903 I,** 828.
547 Denney, D. B., and P. P. Klemchuk, *J. Am. Chem. Soc.*, **80,** 3289 (1958).
548 Deno, N. C., J. J. Jaruzelski, and A. Schriesheim, *J. Am. Chem. Soc.*, **77,** 3044 (1955).
549 Derbyshire, D. H., and W. A. Waters, *Nature*, **165,** 401 (1950).
550 Desai, N. F., and C. H. Giles, *J. Soc. Dyers Col.*, **65,** 639 (1949).
551 DeTar, D. F., *J. Am. Chem. Soc.*, **73,** 1446 (1951).
552 DeTar, D. F., *J. Am. Chem. Soc.*, **78,** 3911 (1956).
553 DeTar, D. F., *Organic Reactions*, J. Wiley & Sons, New York, 1957, Vol. IX, p. 409.
554 DeTar, D. F., and A. R. Ballentine, *J. Am. Chem. Soc.*, **78,** 3916 (1956).
555 DeTar, D. F., and Y. W. Chu, *J. Am. Chem. Soc.*, **76,** 1686 (1954).
556 DeTar, D. F., and J. C. Howard, *J. Am. Chem. Soc.*, **77,** 4393 (1955).
557 DeTar, D. F., and T. Kosuge, *J. Am. Chem. Soc.*, **80,** 6072 (1958).
558 DeTar, D. F., and S. Kwong, *J. Am. Chem. Soc.*, **78,** 3921 (1956).
559 DeTar, D. F., and D. I. Relyea, *J. Am. Chem. Soc.*, **76,** 1680 (1954).
560 DeTar, D. F., and D. I. Relyea, *J. Am. Chem. Soc.*, **78,** 4302 (1956).
561 DeTar, D. F., and S. V. Sagmanli, *J. Am. Chem. Soc.*, **72,** 965 (1950).
562 DeTar, D. F., and H. J. Scheifele, *J. Am. Chem. Soc.*, **73,** 1442 (1951).
563 DeTar, D. F., and M. N. Turetzky, *J. Am. Chem. Soc.*, **77,** 1745 (1955).
564 DeTar, D. F., and M. N. Turetzky, *J. Am. Chem. Soc.*, **78,** 3925 (1956).
565 DeTar, D. F., and M. N. Turetzky, *J. Am. Chem. Soc.*, **78,** 3928 (1956).
566 Dev, S., *J. Indian Chem. Soc.*, **30,** 729 (1953).
567 Dewar, M. J. S., *Electronic Theory of Organic Chemistry*, Oxford University Press, London, 1949, p. 181.
568 Dewar, M. J. S., reviewed by M. Szwarc, *Chem. Revs.*, **47,** 151 (1950).
569 Dewar, M. J. S., *Chem. Soc. Spec. Publ.*, **4,** 64 (1956).
570 Dewar, M. J. S., and A. N. James, *J. Chem. Soc.*, **1958,** 917.
571 Dewar, M. J. S., and A. N. James, *J. Chem. Soc.*, **1958,** 4265.
572 Dias, A., A. N. Kothare and V. V. Nadkarny, *Current Sci.* (India), **18,** 261 (1949); through *Chem. Abstracts*, **44,** 1435 (1950).

573 Dickerman, S. C., L. B. Levy, and A. W. Schwartz, *Chemistry and Industry*, **1958,** 360.
574 Dickerman, S. C., K. Weiss, and A. K. Ingberman, *J. Org. Chem.*, **21,** 380 (1956).
575 Dickerman, S. C., and K. Weiss, *J. Org. Chem.*, **22,** 1070 (1957).
576 Dickerman, S. C., K. Weiss, and A. K. Ingberman, *J. Am. Chem. Soc.*, **80,** 1904 (1958).
577 Dieckmann, W., *Ann.*, **317,** 44 (1901).
578 Diels, O., *Ann.*, **429,** 1 (1922).
579 Diels, O., *Ber.*, **56,** 1933 (1923).
580 Diels, O., and K. Alder, *Ann.*, **450,** 237 (1926).
581 Diels, O., and J. Back, *Ber.*, **54,** 213 (1921).
582 Diels, O., and H. Behncke, *Ber.*, **57,** 653 (1924).
583 Diels, O., J. H. Blom, and W. Koll, *Ann.*, **443,** 242 (1925).
584 Diels, O., and P. Fritzsche, *Ber.*, **44,** 3018 (1911).
585 Diels, O., and W. Koll, *Ann.*, **443,** 262 (1925).
586 Diels, O., and H. König, *Ber.*, **71,** 1179 (1938).
587 Diels, O., and M. Paquin, *Ber.*, **46,** 2000 (1913).
588 Diels, O., S. Schmidt, and W. Witte, *Ber.*, **71,** 1186 (1938).
589 Diels, O., and C. Wulff, *Ann.*, **437,** 309 (1924).
590 Dijkstra, R., and J. de Jonge, *Rec. trav. chim.*, **77,** 538 (1958).
591 Dilthey, W., *J. prakt. Chem.*, **109,** 273 (1925).
592 Dilthey, W., C. Blankenburg, W. Brandt, and W. Huthwelker, *J. prakt. Chem.*, **135,** 36 (1932).
593 Dilthey, W., and C. Blankenburg, *J. prakt. Chem.*, **142,** 177 (1935).
594 Dilthey, W., and R. Wizinger, *J. prakt. Chem.*, **118,** 321 (1928).
595 Dimroth, K., *Marburger Sitzungsberichte*, **76,** 1 (1953).
596 Dimroth, O., *Ber.*, **36,** 909 (1903).
597 Dimroth, O., *Ber.*, **38,** 670 (1905).
598 Dimroth, O., *Ber.*, **39,** 3905 (1906).
599 Dimroth, O., *Ber.*, **40,** 2376 (1907).
600 Dimroth, O., *Ber.*, **40,** 2404 (1907).
601 Dimroth, O., M. Eble, and W. Gruhl, *Ber.*, **40,** 2390 (1907).
602 Dimroth, O., and M. Hartmann, *Ber.*, **40,** 4460 (1907).
603 Dimroth, O., and M. Hartmann, *Ber.*, **41,** 4012 (1908).
604 Dimroth, O., and M. Hartmann, *Ber.*, **41,** 4013, footnote 1 (1908).
605 Dimroth, O., H. Leichtlin, and O. Friedmann, *Ber.*, **50,** 1534 (1917).
606 Dimroth, O., and G. de Montmollin, *Ber.*, **43,** 2904 (1910).
607 Dittmar, G., Thesis, Marburg, 1949.
608 Doering, W. von E., R. G. Buttery, R. G. Laughlin, and N. Chaudhuri, *J. Am. Chem. Soc.*, **78,** 3224 (1956).
609 Doering, W. von E., and W. A. Henderson, *J. Am. Chem. Soc.*, **80,** 5274 (1958).
610 Doering, W. von E., and A. K. Hoffmann, *J. Am. Chem. Soc.*, **76,** 6162 (1954).
611 Doering, W. von E., and L. H. Knox, *J. Am. Chem. Soc.*, **72,** 2305 (1950).
612 Doering, W. von E., and L. H. Knox, *J. Am. Chem. Soc.*, **78,** 4947 (1956).
613 Doering, W. von E., L. H. Knox, and M. Jones, *J. Org. Chem.*, **24,** 136 (1959).
614 Doering, W. von E., G. Laber, R. Vonderwahl, N. F. Chamberlain, and R. B. Williams, *J. Am. Chem. Soc.*, **78,** 5448 (1956).
615 Doering, W. von E., M. Levitz, A. Sayigh, M. Sprecher, and W. P. Whelan, *J. Am. Chem. Soc.*, **75,** 1008 (1953).
616 Doering, W. von E., J. R. Mayer, and C. H. De Puy, *J. Am. Chem. Soc.*, **75,** 2386 (1953).
617 Doering, W. von E., and H. Prinzbach, *Tetrahedron*, **6,** 24 (1959).
618 Doering, W. von E., and C. H. De Puy, *J. Am. Chem. Soc.*, **75,** 5955 (1953).
619 Dolgoplosk, B. A., P. G. Ugrymuov, and V. A. Krol, *Doklady Akad. Nauk S.S.S.R.*, **96,** 757 (1954).
620 Domagk, G., *Deutsche med. Wochenschrift*, **61,** 250 (1935).
621 Dostrovsky, I., and E. D. Hughes, *J. Chem. Soc.*, **1946,** 157, 161, 164, 166, 169, 171.
622 Dostrovsky, I., E. D. Hughes, and C. K. Ingold, *J. Chem. Soc.*, **1946,** 173.
623 Dows, D. A., G. C. Primentel, and E. Whittle, *J. Chem. Phys.*, **23,** 1606 (1955).
624 Drake, N. L., and T. R. Sweeney, *J. Org. Chem.*, **11,** 67 (1946).
625 Drew, H. D. K., and F. G. Dunton, *J. Chem. Soc.*, **1940,** 1064.
626 Drew, H. D. K., and R. E. Fairbairn, *J. Chem. Soc.*, **1939,** 823.
627 Drew, H. D. K., and J. K. Landquist, *J. Chem. Soc.*, **1938,** 292.
628 Dunworth, W. P., and F. F. Nord, *J. Am. Chem. Soc.*, **74,** 1459 (1952).
629 Durham, R. W., and E. W. R. Steacie, *Can. J. Chem.*, **31,** 377 (1953).

372   References

630 Dusenbury, J. H., and R. E. Powell, *J. Am. Chem. Soc.*, **73**, 3266 (1951).
631 Duval, C., R. Freymann, and J. Lecomte, *Bull. soc. chim. France*, **1952,** 106.
632 Duval, R., C. Duval, and J. Lecomte, *Bull. soc. chim. France*, **1947,** 1048.
633 Duval, R., C. Duval, and J. Lecomte, *Compt. rend.*, **224,** 1632 (1947).
634 Dwyer, F. P., *Austral. Chem. Inst. J. and Proc.*, **6,** 348 (1939); through *Chem. Abstracts*, **34,** 733 (1940).
635 Dwyer, F. P., *Austral. Chem. Inst. J. and Proc.*, **6,** 362 (1939); through *Chem. Abstracts*, **34,** 734 (1940).
636 Dwyer, F. P., *J. Am. Chem. Soc.*, **63,** 78 (1941).
637 Dwyer, F. P., and D. P. Mellor, *J. Am. Chem. Soc.*, **63,** 81 (1941).
638 Dyakonov, I. A., *J. Gen. Chem. U.S.S.R.*, **21,** 1986 (1951); through *Chem. Abstracts*, **46,** 6591 b (1952).
639 Dyakonov, I. A., and O. V. Guseva, *J. Gen. Chem. U.S.S.R.*, **22,** 1355 (1952); through *Chem. Abstracts*, **47,** 4293 e (1953).
640 Dyakonov, I. A., and N. A. Lugovtsova, *J. Gen. Chem. U.S.S.R.*, **21,** 839 (1951); through *Chem. Abstracts*, **46,** 439 h (1952).
641 Dyakonov, I. A., and N. D. Pirogova, *J. Gen. Chem. U.S.S.R.*, **21,** 1979 (1951); through *Chem. Abstracts*, **46,** 6590 c (1952).
642 Dyakonov, I. A., and N. B. Vinogradova, *J. Gen. Chem. U.S.S.R.*, **21,** 851 (1951); through *Chem. Abstracts*, **46,** 440 c (1952).
643 Dyakonov, I. A., and N. B. Vinogradova, *J. Gen. Chem. U.S.S.R.*, **22,** 1349 (1952); through *Chem. Abstracts*, **47,** 4293 c (1953).
644 Dyakonov, I. A., and N. B. Vinogradova, *J. Gen. Chem. U.S.S.R.*, **23,** 66 (1953); through *Chem. Abstracts*, **48,** 1256 f (1954).
645 Dziewonski, K., and A. Loewenhof, *Bull. Int. Acad. Pol.*, **A 1927,** 521.

646 Earl, J. C., *Chemistry and Industry*, **55,** 192 (1936).
647 Earl, J. C., and N. G. Hills, *J. Chem. Soc.*, **1938,** 1954.
648 Earl, J. C., and N. G. Hills, *J. Chem. Soc.*, **1939,** 1089.
649 Earl, J. C., and N. G. Hills, *Chemistry and Industry*, **60,** 834 (1941).
650 Earl, J. C., and C. H. Laurence, *J. Chem. Soc.*, **1939,** 419.
651 Earl, J. C., and C. S. Ralph, *J. Chem. Soc.*, **1939,** 401.
652 Eggers, J., *Z. Elektrochem.*, **60,** 987 (1956).
653 Eggers, J., and H. Frieser, *Z. Elektrochem.*, **60,** 372 (1956).
654 Eichenberger, K., R. Rometsch, and J. Druey, *Helv. Chim. Acta*, **37,** 1298 (1954).
655 Eigenmann, G. W., Thesis, Missouri University, 1957.
656 Einhorn, A., and Y. Tahara, *Ber.*, **26,** 324 (1893).
657 Einhorn, A., and R. Willstätter, *Ber.*, **27,** 2823 (1894).
658 Einhorn, A., and R. Willstätter, *Ann.*, **280,** 96 (1895).
659 Eisenbrand, J., *Archiv. f. Pharmazie,* **269,** 683 (1931); through *Chem. Zentr.*, **1932 I,** 2166.
660 Eistert, B., *Angew. Chem.*, **49,** 33 (1936).
661 Eistert, B., *Tautomerie und Mesomerie*, F. Enke Verlag, Stuttgart, 1938.
662 Eistert, B., *Angew. Chem.*, **54,** 99 (1941).
663 Eistert, B., *Angew. Chem.*, **54,** 124 (1941).
664 Eistert, B., *Angew. Chem.*, **54,** 308 (1941).
665 Eistert, B., *Angew. Chem.*, **55,** 118 (1942).
666 Eistert, B., in *Die aromatischen Diazoverbindungen*, K. Holzach, ed., F. Enke Verlag, Stuttgart, 1947, p. 191.
667 Eistert, B., *Angew. Chem.*, **61,** 185 (1949).
668 Eistert, B., and G. Bock, *Ber.*, **92,** 1239 (1959).
669 Eistert, B., and G. Bock, *Ber.,* **92,** 1247 (1959).
670 Eistert, B., H. Elias, E. Kosch, and R. Wollheim, *Ber.*, **92,** 130 (1959).
671 Eistert, B., G. Fink, and R. Wollheim, *Ber.*, **91,** 2710 (1958).
672 Eistert, B., F. Weygand, and E. Csendes, *Ber.*, **84,** 745 (1951).
673 Eiszner, J. R., and W. H. Urry, *J. Am. Chem. Soc.*, **74,** 5822 (1952).
674 Elkins, M., and L. Hunter, *J. Chem. Soc.*, **1935,** 1598.
675 Elks, J., J. W. Haworth, and D. H. Hey, *J. Chem. Soc.*, **1940,** 1284.
676 Elofson, R. M., R. L. Edsberg, and P. A. Mecherly, *J. Electrochem. Soc.*, **97,** 166 (1950).
677 Elphimoff-Felkin, I., and B. Tchoubar, *Compt. rend.*, **233,** 964 (1951).
678 Elphimoff-Felkin, I., and B. Tchoubar, *Compt. rend.*, **237,** 726 (1953).
679 Engelsma, J. W., E. Farenhorst, and E. C. Kooyman, *Rec. trav. chim.*, **73,** 878 (1954).
680 Engler, A., *Ber.*, **33,** 2188 (1900).

681 Engler, A., and A. Hantzsch, *Ber.*, **33,** 2147 (1900).

682 Erlenmeyer, E., *Ber.*, **7,** 1110 (1874).

683 Ernest, I., and Z. Linhartová, *Coll. Czech. Chem. Com.*, **24,** 1022 (1959).

684 Ernest, I., and J. Stanek, *Chem. Listy*, **52,** 302, 348, 350 (1958); through *Chem. Abstracts*, **52,** 11896a (1958).

685 Ernst, R., O. A. Stamm, and H. Zollinger, *Helv. Chim. Acta*, **41,** 2274 (1958).

686 Ershov, A. P., and I. S. Joffe, *J. Gen. Chem. U.S.S.R.*, **9,** 2211 (1939); through *Chem. Abstracts*, **34,** 5420 (1940).

687 Etter, R. M., H. S. Skovronek, and P. S. Skell, *J. Am. Chem. Soc.*, **81,** 1008 (1959).

688 Euler von, H., *Ann.*, **325,** 292 (1902).

689 Euler von, H., *Ber.*, **36,** 2503 (1903).

690 Euler von, H., *Ber.*, **36,** 3835 (1903).

691 Euler von, H., *Ann.*, **330,** 280 (1904).

692 Euler von, H., and A. Hantzsch, *Ber.*, **34,** 4166 (1901).

693 Ewald, A. H., *Disc. Faraday Soc.*, **22,** 138 (1956).

694 Fahr, E., *Ann.*, **617,** 11 (1958).

695 Fainer, P., J. L. Myers, and K. F. Keirstead, *Can. J. Chem.*, **30,** 498 (1952).

696 Farenhorst, E., and E. C. Kooyman, *Rec. trav. chim.*, **72,** 993 (1953).

697 Farenhorst, E., and E. C. Kooyman, *Nature*, **175,** 598 (1955).

698 Favrel, G., *Bull. soc. chim. France*, (4), **41,** 1494 (1927).

699 Feer, A., *Bull. Soc. Mulhouse*, **61,** 220 (1891).

700 Felkin, H., *Compt. rend.*, **226,** 819 (1948).

701 Felkin, H., *Compt. rend.*, **234,** 2203 (1952).

702 Feltzin, J., A. J. Restaino, and R. B. Mesrobian, *J. Am. Chem. Soc.*, **77,** 206 (1955).

703 Fichter, F., and W. Jaeck, *Helv. Chim. Acta*, **4,** 1000 (1921).

704 Fierz-David, H. E., *Künstliche organische Farbstoffe*, J. Springer, Berlin, 1926, p. 105, 106, 134.

705 Fierz-David, H. E., *Z. angew. Chem.*, **49,** 24 (1936).

706 Fierz-David, H. E., L. Blangey, and H. Streiff, *Helv. Chim. Acta*, **29,** 1718 (1946).

707 Fierz-David, H. E., L. Blangey, and H. Kaul, *Helv. Chim. Acta*, **29,** 1765 (1946).

708 Fierz-David, H. E., L. Blangey, and E. Merian, *Helv. Chim. Acta*, **34,** 846 (1951).

709 Fierz-David, H. E., and L. Blangey, *Grundlegende Operationen der Farbenchemie*, 8th ed., Springer-Verlag, Vienna, 1952. a) p.120; b) p.150; c) p. 240; d) p.243; e) p.244; f) p.328.

710 Fierz-David, H. E., and H. Brütsch, *Helv. Chim. Acta*, **4,** 380 (1921).

711 Fierz-David, H. E., and E. Mannhart, *Helv. Chim. Acta*, **20,** 1024 (1937).

712 Fierz-David, H. E., and E. Ziegler, *Helv. Chim. Acta*, **11,** 776 (1928).

713 Fieser, L. F., in *Organic Chemistry*, H. Gilman, ed., J. Wiley & Sons, New York, 1938, Vol. I, p. 128.

714 Fieser, L. F., and W. P. Campbell, *J. Am. Chem. Soc.*, **60,** 1142 (1938).

715 Fieser, L. F., and J. L. Hartwell, *J. Am. Chem. Soc.*, **57,** 1479 (1935).

716 Fieser, L. F., and W. C. Lothrop, *J. Am. Chem. Soc.*, **57,** 1459 (1935).

717 Fieser, L. F., and M. A. Peters, *J. Am. Chem. Soc.*, **53,** 4080 (1931).

718 Filippytschew, S. F., and M. A. Tschekalin, *Anilinokras. Prom.*, **5,** 76 (1935); through *Chem. Abstracts*, **29,** 5087 (1935).

719 Finholt, A. E., E. C. Jacobson, A. E. Ogard, and P. Thompson, *J. Am. Chem. Soc.*, **77,** 4163 (1955).

720 Fischer, B., and H. Wimmer, *Ber.*, **20,** 1579 (1887).

721 Fischer, E., *Ber.*, **8,** 589 (1875).

722 Fischer, E., *Ann.*, **190,** 67 (1878).

723 Fischer, E., *Ann.*, **199,** 319 (1879).

724 Fischer, E., *Ber.*, **17,** 572 (1884).

725 Fischer, E., *Ber.*, **29,** 794 (1896).

726 Fischer, E., and W. Ehrhard, *Ann.*, **199,** 325 (1879).

727 Fischer, H., and H. W. Haberland, *Z. physiol. Chem.*, **232,** 236 (1935).

728 Fischer, O., *Ber.*, **9,** 464 (1876).

729 Fischer, O., *Ber.*, **41,** 397 (1908).

730 Fischer, O., and C. Bauer, *J. prakt. Chem.*, **94,** 13 (1916).

731 Fischer, O., and C. Bauer, *J. prakt. Chem.*, **95,** 261 (1917).

732 Fischer, O., and H. Schmidt, *Ber.*, **27,** 2786 (1894).

733 Fischer, R., and H. Siegrist, *Phot. Korr.*, **51,** 18 (1914).

734 Fletcher, W. H., and T. P. Garrett, *J. Chem. Phys.*, **25,** 50 (1956).

735 Flory, P. J., *Principles of Polymer Chemistry*, Cornell University Press, Ithaca, 1953.

736 Forbes, G. S., L. J. Heidt, and D. V. Sickman, *J. Am. Chem. Soc.*, **57,** 1935 (1935).
737 Ford, M. C., L. J. Hunt, and W. A. Waters, *J. Chem. Soc.*, **1953,** 3529.
738 Ford, M. C., W. A. Waters, and H. T. Young, *J. Chem. Soc.*, **1950,** 833.
739 Ford, M. C., and W. A. Waters, *J. Chem. Soc.*, **1951,** 1851.
740 Ford, M. C., and W. A. Waters, *J. Chem. Soc.*, **1952,** 2240.
741 Forrest, J., and S. H. Tucker, *J. Chem. Soc.*, **1948,** 1137.
742 Forster, M. O., *J. Chem. Soc.*, **107,** 260 (1915).
743 Forster, M. O., and D. Cardwell, *J. Chem. Soc.*, **103,** 861 (1913).
744 Forster, M. O., and H. E. Fierz-David, *J. Chem. Soc.*, **91,** 855 (1907).
745 Forster, M. O., and H. E. Fierz-David, *J. Chem. Soc.*, **91,** 1350 (1907).
746 Forster, M. O., and A. Zimmerli, *J. Chem. Soc.*, **97,** 2156 (1910).
747 Fort, A. W., and J. D. Roberts, *J. Am. Chem. Soc.*, **78,** 584 (1956).
748 Fraenkel, W., *Z. physik. Chem.*, **60,** 202 (1907).
749 France, H., I. M. Heilbron, and D. H. Hey, *J. Chem. Soc.*, **1940,** 369.
750 Franchimont, A. P. N., *Rec. trav. chim.*, **9,** 146 (1890).
751 Francis, F., and F. G. Willson, *J. Chem. Soc.*, **103,** 2238 (1913).
752 Franck, J., and E. Rabinowitch, *Trans. Faraday Soc.*, **30,** 120 (1934).
753 Frankel, M., R. Wolovsky, and E. Fischer, *J. Chem. Soc.*, **1955,** 3441.
754 Franzen, H., and W. Deibel, *Ber.*, **38,** 2716 (1905).
755 Franzen, V., *Ber.*, **88,** 1697 (1955).
756 Franzen, V., *Ann.*, **602,** 199 (1957).
757 Franzen, V., *Reaktionsmechanismen*, 1. Folge, Dr. Alfred Hüthig Verlag, Heidelberg, 1958, p. 55.
758 Franzen, V., and L. Fikentscher, *Ann.*, **617,** 1 (1958).
759 Freeman, H. C., and W. P. Georgans, *Chemistry and Industry*, **1951,** 148.
760 Freeman, H. C., and R. J. W. Le Fèvre, *J. Chem. Soc.*, **1950,** 3128.
761 Freeman, H. C., and R. J. W. Le Fèvre, *J. Chem. Soc.*, **1951,** 415.
762 Freeman, H. C., R. J. W. Le Fèvre, and I. R. Wilson, *J. Chem. Soc.*, **1951,** 1977.
763 Freeman, H. C., and R. J. W. Le Fèvre, *J. Chem. Soc.*, **1952,** 2932.
764 Freeman, H. C., R. J. W. Le Fèvre, J. Northcott, and I. Youhotsky, *J. Chem. Soc.*, **1952,** 3381.
765 Freeman, J. H., and C. E. Scott, *J. Am. Chem. Soc.*, **77,** 3384 (1955).
766 Frey, H. M., *J. Am. Chem. Soc.*, **79,** 1259 (1957).
767 Frey, H. M., *J. Am. Chem. Soc.*, **80,** 5005 (1958).
768 Frey, H. M., and G. B. Kistiakowsky, *J. Am. Chem. Soc.*, **79,** 6373 (1957).
769 Friedländer, P., *Monatsh.*, **19,** 627 (1898).
770 Friedländer, P., and A. Chwala, *Monatsh.*, **28,** 247 (1907).
771 Friswell, R. J., and A. G. Green, *J. Chem. Soc.*, **47,** 917 (1885).
772 Friswell, R. J., and A. G. Green, *J. Chem. Soc.*, **49,** 746 (1886).
773 Fukui, K., T. Yonezawa, C. Nagata, and H. Shingu, *J. Chem. Phys.*, **22,** 1433 (1954).
774 Fusari, S. A., R. P. Frohardt, A. Ryder, T. H. Haskell, D. W. Johannessen, C. C. Elder, and Q. R. Bartz, *J. Am. Chem. Soc.*, **76,** 2878 (1954).
775 Fusari, S. A., T. H. Haskell, R. P. Frohardt, and Q. R. Bartz, *J. Am. Chem. Soc.*, **76,** 2881 (1954).

776 Gabriel, S., *Ber.*, **12,** 1637 (1879).
777 Garrick, F. J., *Phil. Mag.*, **9,** 131 (1930); **10,** 71, 76 (1930); **11,** 741 (1931); **14,** 914 (1932).
778 Garrick, L. D., G. W. Drake, and H. L. Lochte, *J. Am. Chem. Soc.*, **58,** 160 (1936).
779 Gattermann, L., *Ber.*, **23,** 1218 (1890).
780 Gattermann, L., *Ber.*, **32,** 1136 (1899).
781 Gattermann, L., and A. Cantzler, *Ber.*, **23,** 1225 (1890).
782 Gattermann, L., and H. Liebermann, *Ann.*, **393,** 198 (1912).
783 Gattermann, L., and H. Schulze, *Ber.*, **30,** 50 (1897).
784 Gattermann, L., and H. Wieland, *Die Praxis des organischen Chemikers*, 36th ed., W. Gruyter, Berlin, 1954, p. 241.
785 Gehrckens, K. A., and E. Müller, *Ann.*, **500,** 296 (1933).
786 Gerilowski, D., and A. Hantzsch, *Ber.*, **29,** 743 (1896).
787 Gerson, F., and E. Heilbronner, *Helv. Chim. Acta*, **41,** 1444 (1958).
788 Gerson, F., and E. Heilbronner, *Helv. Chim. Acta*, **41,** 2332 (1958).
789 Gerson, F., and E. Heilbronner, *Helv. Chim. Acta*, **42,** 1877 (1959).
790 Gerson, F., J. Schulze, and E. Heilbronner, *Helv. Chim. Acta*, **41,** 1463 (1958).
791 Gies, H., and E. Pfeil, *Ann.*, **578,** 11 (1952).
792 Gilbert, G. A., and E. K. Rideal, *Trans. Faraday Soc.*, **47,** 396 (1951).
793 Giles, C. H., and T. H. MacEwan, *J. Chem. Soc.*, **1959,** 1791.

794 Giles, C. H., and E. L. Neustädter, *J. Chem. Soc.*, **1952,** 1864.
795 Gillespie, R. J., *J. Chem. Soc.*, **1950,** 2537.
796 Gillespie, R. J., J. Graham, E. D. Hughes, C. K. Ingold, and E. R. A. Peeling, *J. Chem. Soc.*, **1950,** 2504.
797 Gillespie, R. J., and R. Graham, *J. Chem. Soc.*, **1950,** 2532.
798 Gillespie, R. J., E. D. Hughes, and C. K. Ingold, *J. Chem. Soc.*, **1950,** 2473.
799 Gillespie, R. J., E. D. Hughes, and C. K. Ingold, *J. Chem. Soc.*, **1950,** 2552.
800 Gilman, H., and J. C. Bailie, *J. Org. Chem.*, **2,** 84 (1937).
801 Gilman, H., and R. G. Jones, *J. Am. Chem. Soc.*, **65,** 1458 (1943).
802 Gilman, H., and R. M. Pickens, *J. Am. Chem. Soc.*, **47,** 2406 (1925).
803 Gingras, B. A., and W. A. Waters, *J. Chem. Soc.*, **1954,** 1920.
804 Giraitis, A. P., and J. L. Bullock, *J. Am. Chem. Soc.*, **59,** 951 (1937).
805 Glaser, C., *Ann.*, **142,** 364 (1867).
806 Glasstone, S., H. Eyring, and K. J. Laidler, *Theory of Rate Processes*, McGraw Hill, New York, 1941, p. 471.
807 Glemser, O., H. Schröder, and H. Haeseler, *Z. anorg. u. allgem. Chem.*, **282,** 80 (1955).
808 Gnehm, R., and L. Benda, *Ann.*, **299,** 124 (1898).
809 Godchot, M., and M. Mousseron, *Bull. soc. chim. France*, **1,** 1625 (1934).
810 Godycki, L. E., and R. E. Rundle, *Acta Cryst.*, **6,** 487 (1953).
811 Gold, M. H., and H. H. Levine, *J. Org. Chem.*, **16,** 1507 (1951).
812 Gold, V., B. W. V. Hawes, and F. L. Tye, *J. Chem. Soc.*, **1952,** 2167.
813 Gold, V., E. D. Hughes, C. K. Ingold, and G. H. Williams, *J. Chem. Soc.*, **1950,** 2452.
814 Gold, V., E. D. Hughes, and C. K. Ingold, *J. Chem. Soc.*, **1950,** 2467.
815 Gold, V., and D. P. N. Satchell, *J. Chem. Soc.*, **1955,** 3609.
816 Gold, V., and D. P. N. Satchell, *J. Chem. Soc.*, **1955,** 3619.
817 Gold, V., and D. P. N. Satchell, *J. Chem. Soc.*, **1955,** 3622.
818 Gold, V., and F. L. Tye, *J. Chem. Soc.*, **1952,** 2172.
819 Gold, V., and F. L. Tye, *J. Chem. Soc.*, **1952,** 2181.
820 Gold, V., and F. L. Tye, *J. Chem. Soc.*, **1952,** 2184.
821 Goldireff, L., and J. Postowskij, *J. Appl. Chem. U.S.S.R., (B)*, **11,** 316 (1938); through *Chem. Zentr.*, **1939 I,** 4934.
822 Goldschmidt, H., *Ber.*, **23,** 3220 (1890).
823 Goldschmidt, H., *Ber.*, **24,** 2317 (1891).
824 Goldschmidt, H., and B. Bardach, *Ber.*, **25,** 1347 (1892).
825 Goldschmidt, H., and E. Bürkle, *Ber.*, **32,** 355 (1899).
826 Goldschmidt, H., and F. Buss, *Ber.*, **30,** 2075 (1897).
827 Goldschmidt, H., and J. Holm, *Ber.*, **21,** 1016 (1888).
828 Goldschmidt, H., S. Johnson, and E. Overwien, *Z. physik. Chem.*, **110,** 251 (1924).
829 Goldschmidt, H., and H. Keller, *Ber.*, **35,** 3534 (1902).
830 Goldschmidt, H., and G. Keppeler, *Ber.*, **33,** 893 (1900).
831 Goldschmidt, H., and A. Merz, *Ber.*, **30,** 670 (1897).
832 Goldschmidt, H., and E. Molinari, *Ber.*, **21,** 2557 (1888).
833 Goldschmidt, H., and R. U. Reinders, *Ber.*, **29,** 1369 (1896).
834 Goldschmidt, H., and R. U. Reinders, *Ber.*, **29,** 1899 (1896).
835 Goldschmidt, H., and M. Salcher, *Z. physik. Chem.*, **29,** 89 (1899).
836 Goldschmidt, S., and B. Acksteiner, *Ann.*, **618,** 173 (1958).
837 Goldschmidt, S., and B. Acksteiner, *Ber.*, **91,** 502 (1958).
838 Goldschmidt, S., and W. Sarnecki, *Ann.*, **595,** 179 (1955).
839 Gomberg, M., *Ber.*, **30,** 2043 (1897).
840 Gomberg, M., *J. Am. Chem. Soc.*, **20,** 773 (1898).
841 Gomberg, M., and W. E. Bachmann, *J. Am. Chem. Soc.*, **46,** 2339 (1924).
842 Gomberg, M., and J. C. Pernert, *J. Am. Chem. Soc.*, **48,** 1372 (1926).
843 Gordon, M., *Chem. Revs.*, **50,** 127 (1952).
844 Gore, P. H., and G. K. Hughes, *Australian J. Sci. Research,* **4 A,** 185 (1951); through *Chem. Abstracts*, **46,** 448 b (1952).
845 Gore, P. H., and J. N. Phillips, *Nature*, **163,** 690 (1949).
846 Gore, T. S., and K. Venkataraman, *Proc. Indian Acad. Sci.*, **34 A,** 368 (1951).
847 Gorvin, J. H., *J. Chem. Soc.*, **1951,** 1693.
848 Gould, R. K., and W. C. Vosburgh, *J. Am. Chem. Soc.*, **64,** 1630 (1942).
849 Gowenlock, B. G., and W. Lüttke, *Quart. Revs.*, **12,** 321 (1958).
850 Grachev, I. V., *J. Gen. Chem. U.S.S.R.*, **17,** 1834, 1843 (1947); through *Chem. Abstracts*, **42,** 5866 d, h (1948).

851 Grachev, I. V., *J. Gen. Chem. U.S.S.R.*, **17,** 2268 (1947); through *Chem. Abstracts*, **43,** 169 h (1949).
852 Grachev, I. V., and N. A. Kirzner, *J. Gen. Chem. U.S.S.R.*, **18,** 1528 (1948); through *Chem. Abstracts*, **43,** 2491 h (1949).
853 Graebe, C., and C. Liebermann, *Ber.*, **1,** 106 (1868).
854 Graebe, C., and F. Ullmann, *Ber.*, **27,** 3483 (1894).
855 Graebe, C., and F. Ullmann, *Ann.*, **291,** 16 (1896).
856 Graebe, C., and F. Ullmann, *Ber.*, **29,** 1876 (1896).
857 Grammaticakis, P., *Bull. soc. chim. France*, **1951,** 951.
858 Grandmougin, E., *Ber.*, **39,** 2494 (1906).
859 Grandmougin, E., and H. Freimann, *Ber.*, **40,** 2662 (1907).
860 Grandmougin, E., and H. Freimann, *Ber.*, **40,** 3453 (1907).
861 Grandmougin, E., and H. Freimann, *J. prakt. Chem.*, **78,** 384 (1908).
862 Grassie, N., and H. W. Melville, *Proc. Roy. Soc.*, **A 207,** 285 (1951).
863 Green, A., *Ber.*, **30,** 3097 (1897).
864 Green, A., *Ber.*, **31,** 1078 (1898).
865 Green, A. G., *J. Soc. Dyers Col.*, **45,** 141 (1929) (discussion).
866 Greuter, F., J. Kalvoda, and O. Jeger, *Proc. Chem. Soc.*, **1958,** 349.
867 Griess, P., *Ann.*, **106,** 123 (1858).
868 Griess, P., *Ann.*, **113,** 207 (1860).
869 Griess, P., *Ann.*, **121,** 258 (1862).
870 Griess, P., *Phil. Trans.*, **154,** 675, 699, 706 (1864).
871 Griess, P., *Phil. Trans.*, **154,** 683 (1864).
872 Griess, P., *J. Chem. Soc.*, **3,** 299 (1865).
873 Griess, P., *Ann.*, **137,** 39 (1866).
874 Griess, P., *Ann.*, **137,** 52 (1866).
875 Griess, P., *Ann.*, **137,** 54 (1866).
876 Griess, P., *Ann.*, **137,** 65 (1866).
877 Griess, P., *Ann.*, **137,** 78 (1866).
878 Griess, P., *Ann.*, **137,** 89 (1866).
879 Griess, P., *Ann.*, **154,** 208 (1870).
880 Griess, P., *Ber.*, **7,** 1618 (1874).
881 Griess, P., *Ber.*, **9,** 132 (1876).
882 Griess, P., *Ber.*, **9,** 1659 (1876).
883 Griess, P., *Ber.*, **15,** 2190 (1882).
884 Griess, P., *Ber.*, **20,** 1528 (1887).
885 Griess, P., and C. A. Martius, *Z. Chem.*, **2,** 132 (1866).
886 Grieve, W. S. M., and D. H. Hey, *J. Chem. Soc.*, **1934,** 1797.
887 Griffith, J. S., and L. E. Orgel, *Quart. Revs.*, **11,** 381 (1957).
888 Grimmel, H. W., and J. F. Morgan, *J. Am. Chem. Soc.*, **70,** 1750 (1948).
889 Grundmann, C., *Ann.*, **536,** 29 (1938).
890 Grundmann, C., and G. Ottmann, *Ann.*, **582,** 163 (1953).
891 Grundmann, C., and G. Ottmann, *Ann.*, **582,** 173 (1953).
892 Günther, P., and F. Gebert, *Z. physik. Chem.*, **B 44,** 203 (1939).
893 Gutsche, C. D., *J. Am. Chem. Soc.*, **70,** 4150 (1948).
894 Gutsche, C. D., *J. Am. Chem. Soc.*, **71,** 3513 (1949).
895 Gutsche, C. D., *Organic Reactions*, J. Wiley & Sons, New York, 1954, Vol. VIII, p. 364.
896 Gutsche, C. D., E. F. Jason, R. S. Coffey, and H. E. Johnson, *J. Am. Chem. Soc.*, **80,** 5756 (1958).
897 Gutsche, C. D., and H. E. Johnson, *J. Am. Chem. Soc.*, **77,** 5933 (1955).
898 Gutsche, C. D., and H. H. Peter, *J. Am. Chem. Soc.*, **77,** 5971 (1955).
899 Gutsche, C. D., H. F. Strohmayer, and J. M. Chang, *J. Org. Chem.*, **23,** 1 (1958).

900 Hadži, D., *J. Chem. Soc.*, **1956,** 2143.
901 Hafner, K., *Ann.*, **606,** 79 (1957).
902 Hafner, K., *Ann.*, **618,** 140 (1958).
903 Hafner, K., *Angew. Chem.*, **70,** 419 (1958).
904 Haginiwa, J., and J. Murakoshi, *J. Pharm. Soc. Japan*, **71,** 1460 (1951); through *Chem. Abstracts*, **46,** 7068 b (1952).
905 Haginiwa, J., and J. Murakoshi, *J. Pharm. Soc. Japan*, **73,** 287 (1953); through *Chem. Abstracts*, **48,** 2017 g (1954).
906 Haginiwa, J., J. Murakoshi, K. Yokota, H. Takayama, and T. Tsuchiya, *J. Pharm. Soc. Japan*, **78,** 232 (1958).

907 Halberstadt, E. S., E. D. Hughes, and C. K. Ingold, *J. Chem. Soc.*, **1950,** 2441.
908 Hall, N. F., and M. R. Sprinkle, *J. Am. Chem. Soc.*, **54,** 3469 (1932).
909 Haller, R., and G. Ziersch, *Melliand Textilber.*, **10,** 951 (1929).
910 Haller, R., and G. Ziersch, *Angew. Chem.*, **43,** 209 (1930).
911 Halverson, F., and R. C. Hirt, *J. Chem. Phys.*, **19,** 711 (1951).
912 Hamer, F. M., R. J. Rathbone, and B. S. Winton, *J. Chem. Soc.*, **1947,** 954.
913 Hammett, L. P., *J. Am. Chem. Soc.*, **59,** 96 (1937).
914 Hammett, L. P., *Physical Organic Chemistry*, McGraw Hill, New York, 1940. a) chap. IX;
   b) p. 184; c) p. 186; d) p. 188; e) p. 288; f) p. 294; g) p. 295; h) p. 314.
915 Hammond, G. S., *J. Am. Chem. Soc.*, **77,** 334 (1955).
916 Hammond, G. S., J. N. Sen, and C. E. Boozer, *J. Am. Chem. Soc.*, **77,** 3244 (1955).
917 Hammond, G. S., and G. B. Lucas, *J. Am. Chem. Soc.*, **77,** 3249 (1955).
918 Hammond, G. S., J. N. Sen, and C. E. Boozer, *J. Am. Chem. Soc.*, **77,** 3244 (1955).
919 Hammond, G. S., and L. M. Soffer, *J. Am. Chem. Soc.*, **72,** 4711 (1950).
920 Hampson, G. C., and J. M. Robertson, *J. Chem. Soc.*, **1941,** 409.
921 Händler, H. M., and G. M. Smith, *J. Am. Chem. Soc.*, **62,** 1669 (1940).
922 Hantzsch, A., *Ber.*, **24,** 13 (1891).
923 Hantzsch, A., *Ber.*, **27,** 1702 (1894).
924 Hantzsch, A., *Ber.*, **27,** 1715 (1894).
925 Hantzsch, A., *Ber.*, **27,** 1860 (1894).
926 Hantzsch, A., *Ber.*, **27,** 2099 (1894).
927 Hantzsch, A., *Ber.*, **27,** 2968 (1894).
928 Hantzsch, A., *Ber.*, **27,** 3527 (1894).
929 Hantzsch, A., *Ber.*, **28,** 444 (1895).
930 Hantzsch, A., *Ber.*, **28,** 741 (1895).
931 Hantzsch, A., *Ber.*, **28,** 1734 (1895).
932 Hantzsch, A., *Ber.*, **28,** 1751 (1895).
933 Hantzsch, A., *Ber.*, **30,** 339 (1897).
934 Hantzsch, A., *Ber.*, **30,** 340 (1897).
935 Hantzsch, A., *Ber.*, **31,** 340 (1898).
936 Hantzsch, A., *Ber.*, **31,** 636 (1898).
937 Hantzsch, A., *Ber.*, **31,** 637 (1898).
938 Hantzsch, A., *Ber.*, **32,** 1717 (1899).
939 Hantzsch, A., *Ber.*, **32,** 1719 (1899).
940 Hantzsch, A., *Ber.*, **33,** 2158 (1900).
941 Hantzsch, A., *Ber.*, **33,** 2163 (1900).
942 Hantzsch, A., *Ber.*, **33,** 2517 (1900).
943 Hantzsch, A., *Ber.*, **33,** 2556 (1900).
944 Hantzsch, A., *Ber.*, **35,** 889 (1902).
945 Hantzsch, A., *Ber.*, **35,** 895 (1902).
946 Hantzsch, A., *Ann.*, **325,** 241 (1902).
947 Hantzsch, A., *Ber.*, **36,** 2056 (1903).
948 Hantzsch, A., *Ber.*, **36,** 2072 (1903).
949 Hantzsch, A., *Ber.*, **36,** 3097 (1903).
950 Hantzsch, A., *Ber.*, **39,** 1073 (1906).
951 Hantzsch, A., *Ber.*, **45,** 3036 (1912).
952 Hantzsch, A., *Ber.*, **52,** 509 (1919).
953 Hantzsch, A., *Ber.*, **54,** 2569 (1921).
954 Hantzsch, A., *Ber.*, **54,** 2573 (1921).
955 Hantzsch, A., *Ber.*, **63,** 1278 (1930).
956 Hantzsch, A., *Ber.*, **63,** 1279 (1930).
957 Hantzsch, A., and A. Burawoy, *Ber.*, **63,** 1760 (1930).
958 Hantzsch, A., and H. Berghaus, *Ber.*, **30,** 89 (1897).
959 Hantzsch, A., and J. W. Blagden, *Ber.*, **33,** 2544 (1900).
960 Hantzsch, A., and E. Czapp, *Ber.*, **63,** 566 (1930).
961 Hantzsch, A., and K. Danziger, *Ber.*, **30,** 2529 (1897).
962 Hantzsch, A., and W. B. Davidson, *Ber.*, **29,** 1522 (1896).
963 Hantzsch, A., and H. Euler, *Ber.*, **34,** 4166 (1901).
964 Hantzsch, A., and H. Freese, *Ber.*, **28,** 3237 (1895).
965 Hantzsch, A., and D. Gerilowski, *Ber.*, **28,** 2002 (1895).
966 Hantzsch, A., and R. Glogauer, *Ber.*, **30,** 2548 (1897).
967 Hantzsch, A., and F. Hilscher, *Ber.*, **41,** 1171 (1908).

968 Hantzsch, A., and E. Jochem, *Ber.*, **34,** 3337 (1901).
969 Hantzsch, A., and M. Lehmann, *Ber.*, **34,** 2506 (1901).
970 Hantzsch, A., and M. Lehmann, *Ber.*, **35,** 897 (1902).
971 Hantzsch, A., and J. Lifschitz, *Ber.*, **45,** 3011 (1912).
972 Hantzsch, A., and F. M. Perkin, *Ber.*, **30,** 1412 (1897).
973 Hantzsch, A., and W. Pohl, *Ber.*, **35,** 2964 (1902).
974 Hantzsch, A., and G. Reddelien, *Die Diazoverbindungen*, J. Springer, Berlin, 1921.
975 Hantzsch, A., and M. Schmiedel, *Ber.*, **30,** 71 (1897).
976 Hantzsch, A., and O. W. Schulze, *Ber.*, **28,** 671 (1895).
977 Hantzsch, A., and M. Schümann, *Ber.*, **32,** 1691 (1899).
978 Hantzsch, A., M. Schümann, and A. Engler, *Ber.*, **32,** 1703 (1899).
979 Hantzsch, A., and K. J. Thompson, *Ber.*, **41,** 3519 (1908).
980 Hantzsch, A., and A. Werner, *Ber.*, **23,** 11 (1890).
981 Harris, E. F. P., and W. A. Waters, *J. Chem. Soc.*, **1952,** 3108.
982 Hartley, G. S., *Nature*, **140,** 281 (1937).
983 Hartley, G. S., *J. Chem. Soc.*, **1938,** 633.
984 Hartley, G. S., and R. J. W. Le Fèvre, *J. Chem. Soc.*, **1939,** 531.
985 Hartmann, H., and H. L. Schläfer, *Angew. Chem.*, **70,** 155 (1958).
986 Hartmann, M., and H. Kägi, *Angew. Chem.*, **41,** 127 (1928).
987 Hass, H. B., and E. F. Riley, *Chem. Revs.*, **32,** 373 (1943).
988 Hatch, L. F., and G. B. Roberts, *J. Am. Chem. Soc.*, **68,** 1196 (1946).
989 Hauser, C. R., and D. S. Breslow, *J. Am. Chem. Soc.*, **63,** 418 (1941).
990 Hausser, J., and P. T. Muller, *Bull. soc. chim. France*, **7,** 721 (1892).
991 Hausser, J., and P. T. Muller, *Compt. rend.*, **114,** 549, 669, 760, 1438 (1892).
992 Hausser, J., and P. T. Muller, *Bull. soc. chim. France*, **9,** 353 (1893).
993 Haworth, W., and D. H. Hey, *J. Chem. Soc.*, **1940,** 361.
994 Haworth, W. N., and C. R. Porter, *J. Chem. Soc.*, **1930,** 649.
995 Heacock, R. A., and D. H. Hey, *J. Chem. Soc.*, **1952,** 1508.
996 Heacock, R. A., and D. H. Hey, *J. Chem. Soc.*, **1952,** 4059.
997 Heacock, R. A., and D. H. Hey, *J. Chem. Soc.*, **1953,** 3.
998 Head, F. S. H., *Shirley Institute Memoirs*, **25,** 209 (1951).
999 Head, F. S. H., *J. Textile Inst.*, **43,** T 1 (1952).
1000 Heidt, L. J., and G. S. Forbes, *J. Am. Chem. Soc.*, **57,** 2331 (1935).
1001 Heilbronner, E., personal communication.
1002 Heilbronner, E., and M. Simonetta, *Helv. Chim. Acta*, **35,** 1049 (1952).
1003 Hein, F., *Chemische Koordinationslehre*, S. Hirzel Verlag, Zurich, 1950.
1004 Heller, G., *J. prakt. Chem.*, **77,** 189 (1908).
1005 Heller, G., *J. prakt. Chem.*, **81,** 184 (1910).
1006 Heller, G., *Ber.*, **52,** 741 (1919).
1007 Heller, G., *Ber.*, **59,** 704 (1926).
1008 Heller, G., and M. Meyer, *Ber.*, **52,** 2287 (1919).
1009 Heller, G., and O. Nötzel, *J. prakt. Chem.*, **76,** 58 (1907).
1010 Heller, J., and G. Schwarzenbach, *Helv. Chim. Acta*, **34,** 1876 (1951).
1011 Hendricks, S. B., O. R. Wulf, G. E. Hilbert, and U. Liddel, *J. Am. Chem. Soc.*, **58,** 1991 (1936).
1012 Henkin, H., and H. A. Taylor, *J. Chem. Phys.*, **8,** 1 (1940).
1013 Hertel, E., and M. Schinzel, *Z. physik. Chem.*, **B 48,** 289 (1941).
1014 Herz, W., *J. Am. Chem. Soc.*, **75,** 73 (1953).
1015 Hesse, G., and E. Reichold, *Ber.*, **90,** 2101 (1957).
1016 Hesse, G., E. Reichold, and S. Majmudar, *Ber.*, **90,** 2106 (1957).
1017 Heumann, K., and L. Oeconomides, *Ber.*, **20,** 372 (1887).
1018 Heusser, H., P. T. Herzig, A. Fürst, and P. A. Plattner, *Helv. Chim. Acta*, **33,** 1093 (1950).
1019 Hey, D. H., *J. Chem. Soc.*, **1952,** 1974.
1020 Hey, D. H., and T. M. Moynehan, *J. Chem. Soc.*, **1959,** 1563.
1021 Hey, D. H., A. Nechvatal, and T. S. Robinson, *J. Chem. Soc.*, **1951,** 2892.
1022 Hey, D. H., C. J. M. Stirling, and G. H. Williams, *J. Chem. Soc.*, **1955,** 3963.
1023 Hey, D. H., J. Stuart-Webb, and G. H. Williams, *Research*, **4,** 385 (1951).
1024 Hey, D. H., J. Stuart-Webb, and G. H. Williams, *J. Chem. Soc.*, **1952,** 4657.
1025 Hey, D. H., and W. A. Waters, *Chem. Revs.*, **21,** 169 (1937).
1026 Hey, D. H., and W. A. Waters, *J. Chem. Soc.*, **1948,** 882.
1027 Heyns, K., and W. von Bebenburg, *Ber.*, **86,** 278 (1953).
1028 Hieber, W., and F. Leutert, *Ber.*, **62,** 1839 (1929).
1029 Higgins, H. G., D. Fraser, and E. J. Williams, *Australian J. Sci. Research*, **5,** 736 (1952).

1030 Higgins, H. G., D. Fraser, and E. J. Williams, *Australian J. Chem.*, **6,** 195 (1953).
1031 Hillson, P. J., and P. P. Birnbaum, *Trans. Faraday Soc.*, **48,** 478 (1952).
1032 Hillson, P. J., and E. K. Rideal, *Proc. Roy. Soc.*, **A 216,** 458 (1953).
1033 Hine, J., *J. Am. Chem. Soc.*, **72,** 2438 (1950).
1034 Hine, J., and A. M. Dowell, *J. Am. Chem. Soc.*, **76,** 2688 (1954).
1035 Hine, J., R. C. Peak, and B. D. Oakes, *J. Am. Chem. Soc.*, **76,** 827 (1954).
1036 Hirt, R. C., F. T. King, and J. C. Cavagnol, *J. Chem. Phys.*, **25,** 574 (1956).
1037 Hoang, T. N., *J. chim. phys.*, **36,** 164 (1939).
1038 Hoberg, H., and K. Ziegler, *Brennstoff-Chemie*, **39,** 302 (1958).
1039 Hodgson, H. H., *J. Soc. Dyers Col.*, **58,** 228 (1942).
1040 Hodgson, H. H., *J. Chem. Soc.*, **1944,** 18.
1041 Hodgson, H. H., *J. Chem. Soc.*, **1948,** 348.
1042 Hodgson, H. H., *J. Soc. Dyers Col.*, **64,** 99 (1948).
1043 Hodgson, H. H., and D. Bailey, *J. Chem. Soc.*, **1948,** 1183.
1044 Hodgson, H. H., S. Birtwell, and J. Walker, *J. Chem. Soc.*, **1941,** 770.
1045 Hodgson, H. H., and S. Birtwell, *J. Chem. Soc.*, **1943,** 321.
1046 Hodgson, H. H., F. Leigh, and G. Turner, *J. Chem. Soc.*, **1942,** 744.
1047 Hodgson, H. H., A. P. Mahadevan, and E. R. Ward, *J. Chem. Soc.*, **1947,** 1392.
1048 Hodgson, H. H., and E. Marsden, *J. Chem. Soc.*, **1943,** 379.
1049 Hodgson, H. H., and E. Marsden, *J. Chem. Soc.*, **1943,** 470.
1050 Hodgson, H. H., and E. Marsden, *J. Soc. Dyers Col.*, **59,** 271 (1943).
1051 Hodgson, H. H., and E. Marsden, *J. Chem. Soc.*, **1944,** 22.
1052 Hodgson, H. H., and E. Marsden, *J. Soc. Dyers Col.*, **60,** 16 (1944).
1053 Hodgson, H. H., and E. Marsden, *J. Soc. Dyers Col.*, **60,** 120 (1944).
1054 Hodgson, H. H., and E. Marsden, *J. Soc. Dyers Col.*, **60,** 122 (1944).
1055 Hodgson, H. H., and E. Marsden, *J. Chem. Soc.*, **1945,** 207.
1056 Hodgson, H. H., and E. Marsden, *J. Chem. Soc.*, **1945,** 274.
1057 Hodgson, H. H., D. Nicholson, and G. Turner, *J. Chem. Soc.*, **1944,** 15.
1058 Hodgson, H. H., and W. H. H. Norris, *J. Soc. Dyers Col.*, **65,** 226 (1949).
1059 Hodgson, H. H., and H. S. Turner, *J. Chem. Soc.*, **1943,** 86.
1060 Hodgson, H. H., and J. Walker, *J. Chem. Soc.*, **1933,** 1620.
1061 Hodgson, H. H., and E. R. Ward, *J. Chem. Soc.*, **1947,** 127.
1062 Hodson, H. F., O. A. Stamm, and H. Zollinger, *Helv. Chim. Acta*, **41,** 1816 (1958).
1063 Hoey, G. R., and K. O. Kutschke, *Can. J. Chem.*, **33,** 496 (1955).
1064 Hofmann, A. W., *Jahresber. Fortsch. Chem.*, **1863,** 424.
1065 Hofmann, K. A., and H. Hock, *Ber.*, **44,** 2946 (1911).
1066 Holm, R. H., and F. A. Cotton, *J. Am. Chem. Soc.*, **80,** 5658 (1958).
1067 Holt, P. F., *J. Chem. Soc.*, **1952,** 4251.
1068 Holt, P. F., and B. I. Bullock, *J. Chem. Soc.*, **1950,** 2310.
1069 Holt, P. F., and B. P. Hughes, *J. Chem. Soc.*, **1953,** 1666.
1070 Holt, P. F., and B. P. Hughes, *J. Chem. Soc.*, **1955,** 98.
1071 Holzach, K., *Die aromatischen Diazoverbindungen*, F. Enke, Stuttgart, 1947. a) pp. 152 to 155; b) p. 246.
1072 Horner, L., and A. Gross, unpublished.
1073 Horner, L., and H. Hoffmann, *Angew. Chem.*, **68,** 473 (1956).
1074 Horner, L., W. Kirmse, and H. Hoffmann, *Ann.*, **614,** 19 (1958).
1075 Horner, L., W. Kirmse, and K. Muth, *Ber.*, **91,** 430 (1958).
1076 Horner, L., and E. Lingnau, *Ann.*, **591,** 21 (1955).
1077 Horner, L., and H. Müller, *Ber.*, **89,** 2756 (1956).
1078 Horner, L., and W. Naumann, *Ann.*, **587,** 81 (1954).
1079 Horner, L., and W. Naumann, *Ann.*, **587,** 93 (1954).
1080 Horner, L., and E. Schwenk, *Ann.*, **566,** 69 (1950).
1081 Horner, L., E. Spietschka, and A. Gross, *Ann.*, **573,** 17 (1951).
1082 Horner, L., E. Spietschka, and A. Gross, *Ann.*, **573,** 26 (1951).
1083 Horner, L., and E. Spietschka, *Ber.*, **85,** 225 (1952).
1083a Horner, L., and E. Spietschka, *Ber.*, **88,** 934 (1955).
1084 Horner, L., and E. Spietschka, *Ber.*, **89,** 2765 (1956).
1085 Horner, L., and H. Stöhr, *Ber.*, **85,** 993 (1952).
1086 Horner, L., and H. Stöhr, *Ber.*, **86,** 1066, 1073 (1953).
1087 Hornig, R. H., and E. D. Amstutz, *J. Org. Chem.*, **20,** 1069 (1955).
1088 Horwitz, J. P., and Y. A. Grakanskas, *J. Am. Chem. Soc.*, **79,** 1249 (1957).
1089 Hough, L., and J. K. N. Jones, *Chemistry and Industry*, **1952,** 380.

380 References

1090 Howard, J., Thesis, Leeds University, 1958.
1091 Howard, R. N., and W. Simpson, *Trans. Faraday Soc.*, **47,** 212 (1951).
1092 Hoyer, H., *Kolloid-Z.*, **121,** 121 (1951).
1093 Hoyer, H., *Ber.*, **86,** 507 (1953).
1094 Hückel, E., *Z. Elektrochem.*, **61,** 866 (1957).
1095 Hückel, W., *Anorganische Strukturchemie*, F. Enke Verlag, Stuttgart, 1948.
1096 Hückel, W., and J. Dathow, *Z. physik. Chem.*, **A 186,** 159 (1940).
1097 Hückel, W., and R. Kupka, *Ber.*, **89,** 1694 (1956).
1098 Hückel, W., and E. Wilip, *J. prakt. Chem.*, **158,** 21 (1941).
1099 Huggett, C., R. T. Arnold, and T. I. Taylor, *J. Am. Chem. Soc.*, **64,** 3043 (1943).
1100 Hughes, E. D., quoted by Bunnett and Zahler (*382*); cf. Ingold (*1153i*).
1101 Hughes, E. D., C. K. Ingold, and G. A. Benford, *J. Chem. Soc.*, **1938,** 929.
1102 Hughes, E. D., C. K. Ingold, and R. I. Reed, *J. Chem. Soc.*, **1950,** 2400.
1103 Hughes, E. D., C. K. Ingold, and J. H. Ridd, *Nature*, **166,** 642 (1950).
1104 Hughes, E. D., and C. K. Ingold, *Quart. Revs.*, **6,** 34 (1952).
1105 Hughes, E. D., C. K. Ingold, and J. H. Ridd, *J. Chem. Soc.*, **1958,** 58.
1106 Hughes, E. D., C. K. Ingold, and J. H. Ridd, *J. Chem. Soc.*, **1958,** 65.
1107 Hughes, E. D., C. K. Ingold, and J. H. Ridd, *J. Chem. Soc.*, **1958,** 77.
1108 Hughes, E. D., C. K. Ingold, and J. H. Ridd, *J. Chem. Soc.*, **1958,** 88.
1109 Hughes, E. D., and J. H. Ridd, *J. Chem. Soc.*, **1958,** 70.
1110 Hughes, E. D., and J. H. Ridd, *J. Chem. Soc.*, **1958,** 82.
1111 Huisgen, R., *Ann.*, **573,** 163 (1951).
1112 Huisgen, R., *Ann.*, **574,** 171 (1951).
1113 Huisgen, R., *Ann.*, **574,** 184 (1951).
1114 Huisgen, R., *Angew. Chem.*, **67,** 439 (1955).
1115 Huisgen, R., and R. Fleischmann, *Ann.*, **623,** 47 (1959).
1116 Huisgen, R., and R. Grashey, *Ann.*, **607,** 46 (1957).
1117 Huisgen, R., and G. Horeld, *Ann.*, **562,** 137 (1949).
1118 Huisgen, R., F. Jakob, W. Siegel, and A. Cadus, *Ann.*, **590,** 1 (1954).
1119 Huisgen, R., and F. Jakob, *Ann.*, **590,** 37 (1954).
1120 Huisgen, R., and H. J. Koch, *Ann.*, **591,** 200 (1955).
1121 Huisgen, R., and L. Krause, *Ann.*, **574,** 157 (1951).
1122 Huisgen, R., and H. Nakaten, *Ann.*, **573,** 181 (1951).
1123 Huisgen, R., and H. Nakaten, *Ann.*, **586,** 70 (1954).
1124 Huisgen, R., and H. Nakaten, *Ann.*, **586,** 84 (1954).
1125 Huisgen, R., and H. Reimlinger, *Ann.*, **599,** 161 (1956).
1126 Huisgen, R., and H. Reimlinger, *Ann.*, **599,** 183 (1956).
1127 Huisgen, R., and J. Reinertshofer, *Ann.*, **575,** 174 (1952).
1128 Huisgen, R., and J. Reinertshofer, *Ann.*, **575,** 197 (1952).
1129 Huisgen, R., and C. Rüchardt, *Ann.*, **601,** 1 (1956).
1130 Huisgen, R., and C. Rüchardt, *Ann.*, **601,** 21 (1956).
1131 Huisgen, R., and I. Ugi, *Ber.*, **90,** 2914 (1957).
1132 Hultsch, K. *Chemie der Phenolharze*, Springer-Verlag, Berlin, 1950, p. 35.
1133 Humphries, J. E., *J. Chem. Soc.*, **1926,** 374.
1134 Hünig, S., *Angew. Chem.*, **70,** 215 (1958).
1135 Hünig, S., and H. Balli, *Ann.*, **609,** 160 (1957).
1136 Hünig, S., and O. Boes, *Ann.*, **579,** 28 (1953).
1137 Hünig, S., and W. Daum, *Ann.*, **595,** 131 (1955).
1138 Hünig, S., and K. H. Fritsch, *Ann.*, **609,** 143 (1957).
1139 Hünig, S., and K. H. Fritsch, *Ann.*, **609,** 172 (1957).
1140 Hünig, S., and G. Köbrich, *Ann.*, **617,** 181 (1958).
1141 Hünig, S., and G. Köbrich, *Ann.*, **617,** 203 (1958).
1142 Hünig, S., and G. Köbrich, *Ann.*, **617,** 210 (1958).
1143 Hünig, S., and G. Köbrich, *Ann.*, **617,** 220 (1958).
1144 Hünig, S., R. D. Rauschenbach, and A. Schütz, *Ann.*, **623,** 191 (1959).
1145 Hunter, L., *J. Chem. Soc.*, **1937,** 320.
1146 Hunter, L., and C. B. Roberts, *J. Chem. Soc.*, **1941,** 820.
1147 Hurd, C. D., and H. M. Priestley, *J. Am. Chem. Soc.*, **69,** 859 (1947).
1148 Hüttig, G. F., *Z. anorg. Chem.*, **142,** 135 (1925).

1149 Illy, H., Ciba Ltd., personal communication.
1150 Impastato, F. J., L. Barash, and H. M. Walborsky, *J. Am. Chem. Soc.*, **81,** 1514 (1959).

1151 Ingham, C. E., and G. C. Hampson, *J. Chem. Soc.*, **1939,** 981.
1152 Ingold, C. K., *Bull. soc. chim. France*, (5), **19,** 667 (1952).
1153 Ingold, C. K., *Structure and Mechanism in Organic Chemistry*, G. Bell & Sons, London, 1953.
       a) chap. II, p. 67; b) chap. VII; c) p. 61; d) p. 279; e) p. 288; f) p. 297; g) p. 583;
       h) p. 610; i) p. 800.
1154 Ingold, C. K., C. G. Raisin, and C. L. Wilson, *J. Chem. Soc.*, **1936,** 915.
1155 Ingold, C. K., C. G. Raisin, and C. L. Wilson, *J. Chem. Soc.*, **1936,** 1637.
1156 Ingold, C. K., and S. S. Weaver, *J. Chem. Soc.*, **1925,** 378.
1157 Inhoffen, H. H., H. Pommer, and F. Bohlmann, *Ber.*, **81,** 507 (1948).

1158 Jackson, R. W., and R. H. Manske, *J. Am. Chem. Soc.*, **52,** 5029 (1930).
1159 Jacobs, T. L., in *Heterocyclic Compounds*, R. C. Elderfield, ed., J. Wiley & Sons, New York,
       1957, Vol. VI, p. 136.
1160 Jaffé, H. H., *Chem. Revs.*, **53,** 191 (1953).
1161 Jaffé, H. H., *J. Chem. Phys.*, **21,** 415 (1953).
1162 Jaffé, H. H., and R. W. Gardner, *J. Am. Chem. Soc.*, **80,** 319 (1958).
1163 Jaffé, H. H., and S. J. Yeh, *J. Org. Chem.*, **22,** 1281 (1957).
1164 Jaffé, H. H., S. J. Yeh, and R. W. Gardner, *J. Mol. Spectr.*, **2,** 120 (1958).
1165 Jambuserwala, G. B., and F. A. Mason, *J. Soc. Dyers Col.*, **46,** 339 (1930).
1166 Janovsky, J. V., and L. Erb, *Ber.*. **19,** 2155 (1886).
1167 Janovsky, J. V., and L. Erb, *Ber.*, **20,** 357 (1887).
1168 Jaquiss, M. T., and M. Szwarc, *Nature*, **170,** 312 (1952).
1169 Jensen, K. A., *Z. anorg. Chem.*, **225,** 97 (1935).
1170 Jensen, K. A., *Z. anorg. Chem.*, **229,** 225 (1936).
1171 Jerchel, D., and H. Fischer, *Ann.*, **563,** 200 (1949).
1172 Job. P., *Ann. Chim.*, (10), **9,** 113 (1928).
1173 Job, P., *Ann. Chim.*, (11), **6,** 97 (1936).
1174 Joffe, I. S., *J. Gen. Chem. U.S.S.R.*, **6,** 1074 (1936); through *Chem. Zentr.*, **1937 I,** 726.
1175 Joffe, I. S., *J. Gen. Chem. U.S.S.R.*, **7,** 2637 (1937); through *Chem. Zentr.*, **1938 I,** 3042.
1176 Johnson, D. H., and A. V. Tobolsky, *J. Am. Chem. Soc.*, **74,** 938 (1952).
1177 Jolles, E., *Gazz. chim. ital.*, **66,** 204 (1936).
1178 Jolles, Z., *Atti R. Accad. Lincei*, (6), **15,** 292 (1932); through *Chem. Zentr.*, **1932 II,** 699.
1179 Jonassen, H. B., M. M. Cook, and J. S. Wilson, *J. Am. Chem. Soc.*, **73,** 4683 (1951).
1180 Jonassen, H. B., and J. S. Wilson, *J. Am. Chem. Soc.*, **75,** 4201 (1953).
1181 Jones, M. H., and E. W. R. Steacie, *J. Chem. Phys.*, **21,** 1018 (1953).
1182 Jorgensen, C. K., *Acta Chem. Scand.*, **9,** 116 (1955).
1183 Jorgensen, C. K., *Acta Chem. Scand.*, **9,** 717 (1955).
1184 Jorgensen, C. K., *Acta Chem. Scand.*, **9,** 1362 (1955).
1185 Jorgensen, C. K., *Acta Chem. Scand.*, **11,** 53 (1957).
1186 Jorgensen, C. K., *Acta Chem. Scand.*, **11,** 73 (1957).
1187 Jorgensen, C. K., *Acta Chem. Scand.*, **11,** 151 (1957).
1188 Jorgensen, C. K., *Acta Chem. Scand.*, **11,** 166 (1957).
1189 Justoni, R., *Gazz. chim. ital.*, **66,** 775 (1936).

1190 Kahovec, L., and K. W. F. Kohlrausch, *Z. physik. Chem.*, **B 38,** 96 (1937).
1191 Kahovec, L., K. W. F. Kohlrausch, A. W. Reitz, and J. Wagner, *Z. physik. Chem.*, **B 39,**
       431 (1938).
1192 Kalb, L., F. Schweizer, and G. Schimpf, *Ber.*, **59,** 1858 (1926).
1193 Kalb, L., F. Schweizer, H. Zellner, and E. Berthold, *Ber.*, **59,** 1860 (1926).
1194 Kanda, Y., and S. Imanishi, *J. Sci. Res. Inst. Tokyo*, **43,** 8885 (1949).
1195 Kantor, S. W., and R. C. Osthoff, *J. Am. Chem. Soc.*, **75,** 931 (1953).
1196 Karrer, P., *Ber.*, **48,** 1398 (1915).
1197 Karrer, P., *Helv. Chim. Acta*, **3,** 196 (1920).
1198 Keefer, R. M., L. J. Andrews, and R. E. Kepner, *J. Am. Chem. Soc.*, **71,** 3906 (1949).
1199 Kehrmann, F., *Ber.*, **48,** 1933 (1915).
1200 Kehrmann, F., and M. Goldenberg, *Ber.*, **30,** 2125 (1897).
1201 Kekulé, A., *Lehrbuch der organischen Chemie*, Erlangen, 1866, Vol. II, p. 716.
1202 Kekulé, A., and C. Hidegh, *Ber.*, **3,** 233 (1870).
1203 Kelber, C., *Ber.*, **57,** 142 (1924).
1204 Kenner, G. W., and R. J. Stedman, *J. Chem. Soc.*, **1952,** 2089.
1205 Kenner, J., *Chemistry and Industry*, **60,** 443 (1941).
1206 Kenner, J., *Chemistry and Industry*, **60,** 899 (1941).

1207 Kharasch, M. S., and T. A. Ashford, *J. Am. Chem. Soc.*, **58,** 1733 (1936).
1208 Kharasch, M. S., M. Zimmermann, W. Zimmt, and W. Nudenberg, *J. Org. Chem.*, **18,** 1045 (1953).
1209 Kharkharov, A. A., *J. Gen. Chem. U.S.S.R.*, **23,** 1175 (1953); through *Chem. Abstracts*, **47,** 12390c (1953).
1210 Kice, J. L., and F. M. Parham, *J. Am. Chem. Soc.*, **80,** 3792 (1958).
1211 Kidd, H. V., *J. Org. Chem.*, **2,** 198 (1938).
1212 Kienle, R. H., E. I. Stearns, and P. van der Meulen, *J. Phys. Chem.*, **50,** 363 (1956).
1213 Kilpatrick, J. E., K. S. Pitzer, and R. Spitzer, *J. Am. Chem. Soc.*, **69,** 2483 (1947).
1214 Kilpatrick, J. E., K. S. Pitzer, and R. Spitzer, *J. Am. Chem. Soc.*, **69,** 2488 (1947).
1215 King, C. V., *J. Am. Chem. Soc.*, **62,** 379 (1940).
1216 King, C. V., and J. J. Josephs, *J. Am. Chem. Soc.*, **66,** 767 (1944).
1217 Kirkpride, F. W., and R. G. W. Norrish, *J. Chem. Soc.*, **1933,** 119.
1218 Kirmse, W., *Naturwissenschaften*, **46,** 379 (1959).
1219 Kirmse, W., and L. Horner, *Ann.*, **614,** 1 (1958).
1220 Kirmse, W., and L. Horner, *Ann.*, **614,** 4 (1958).
1221 Kirmse, W., L. Horner, and H. Hoffmann, *Ann.*, **614,** 19 (1958).
1222 Kistiakowsky, G. B., and P. H. Kydd, *J. Am. Chem. Soc.*, **79,** 4825 (1957).
1223 Kistiakowsky, G. B., and B. H. Mahan, *J. Am. Chem. Soc.*, **79,** 2412 (1957).
1224 Kistiakowsky, G. B., and W. L. Marshall, *J. Am. Chem. Soc.*, **74,** 88 (1952).
1225 Kistiakowsky, G. B., and N. W. Rosenberg, *J. Am. Chem. Soc.*, **72,** 321 (1950).
1226 Kistiakowsky, G. B., and K. Sauer, *J. Am. Chem. Soc.*, **78,** 5699 (1956).
1227 Klages, A., and A. Rönneburg, *Ber.*, **36,** 1128 (1903).
1228 Klages, F., and W. Mesch, *Ber.*, **88,** 388 (1955).
1229 Klemenc, A., *Ber.*, **47,** 1407 (1914).
1230 Klemm, W., *Magnetochemie*, Akadem. Verlagsgesellschaft, Leipzig, 1936.
1231 Klinger, H., and J. Zuurdeeg, *Ann.*, **255,** 310 (1889).
1232 Kloosterziel, H., and H. J. Backer, *Rec. trav. chim.*, **71,** 1235 (1952).
1233 Klotz, I. M., H. A. Fiess, J. Y. Chen Ho, and M. Mellody, *J. Am. Chem. Soc.*, **76,** 5136 (1954).
1234 Klotz, I. M., and W. C. Loh Ming, *J. Am. Chem. Soc.*, **75,** 4159 (1953).
1235 Knecht, E., *J. Chem. Soc.*, **125,** 1537 (1924).
1236 Knecht, E., and E. Hibbert, *New Reduction Methods in Analytical Chemistry*, Longmans, Green & Co., London, 1925.
1237 Knight, A. H., *J. Soc. Dyers Col.*, **66,** 410 (1950).
1238 Knoevenagel, E., *Ber.*, **23,** 2994 (1890).
1239 Knoevenagel, E., *Ber.*, **23,** 2995 (1890).
1240 Knorr, L., and A. Weidel, *Ber.*, **42,** 3523, footnote 4 (1909).
1241 Knott, E. B., *J. Chem. Soc.*, **1951,** 1586.
1242 Knox, G. R., *Proc. Chem. Soc.*, **1959,** 56.
1243 Knox, J. H., and A. F. Trotman-Dickenson, *Chemistry and Industry*, **1957,** 731.
1244 Kobelt, M., P. Barman, V. Prelog, and L. Ruzicka, *Helv. Chim. Acta*, **32,** 256 (1949).
1245 Kochi, J. K., *J. Am. Chem. Soc.*, **77,** 5090 (1955).
1246 Kochi, J. K., *J. Am. Chem. Soc.*, **78,** 1228 (1956).
1247 Kochi, J. K., *J. Am. Chem. Soc.*, **79,** 2942 (1957).
1248 Kodama, S., Y. Takezaki, and J. Yoshida, *J. Chem. Soc. Japan*, **71,** 173 (1950).
1249 Kodama, S., and Y. Takezaki, *J. Chem. Soc. Japan*, **73,** 13 (1952).
1250 Koelsch, C. F., *J. Am. Chem. Soc.*, **65,** 57 (1943).
1251 Koelsch, C. F., and V. Boekelheide, *J. Am. Chem. Soc.*, **66,** 412 (1944).
1252 Koenigs, E., and H. Bueren, *J. prakt. Chem.*, **146,** 121 (1936).
1253 Kohler, E. P., M. Tishler, H. Potter, and H. T. Thompson, *J. Am. Chem. Soc.*, **61,** 1057 (1939).
1254 König, W., and J. Keil, *Ber.*, **55,** 2149 (1922).
1255 König, W., and K. Köhler, *Ber.*, **54,** 981 (1921).
1256 König, W., and K. Köhler, *Ber.*, **55,** 2139 (1922).
1257 König, W., and H. Rösler, *Naturwissenschaften*, **42,** 211 (1955).
1258 Kooyman, E. C., *Rec. trav. chim.*, **74,** 117 (1955).
1259 Kooyman, E. C., personal communication.
1260 Kornblum, N., in *Organic Reactions*, J. Wiley & Sons, New York, 1944, Vol. II, p. 262.
1261 Kornblum, N., G. D. Cooper, and J. E. Taylor, *J. Am. Chem. Soc.*, **72,** 3011 (1950).
1262 Kornblum, N., G. D. Cooper, and J. E. Taylor, *J. Am. Chem. Soc.*, **72,** 3013 (1950).
1263 Kornblum, N., and D. C. Iffland, *J. Am. Chem. Soc.*, **71,** 2137 (1949).

1264 Kornblum, N., A. E. Kelley, and G. D. Cooper, *J. Am. Chem. Soc.*, **74,** 3074 (1952).
1265 Kornblum, N., and A. E. Kelley, *Science*, **117,** 379 (1953).
1266 Korschak, W. W., and W. A. Ssergejew, *Doklady Akad. Nauk S.S.S.R.*, **115,** 308 (1957); cited in (*1038*).
1267 Kortüm, G., and B. Finckh, *Z. physik. Chem.*, **B 48,** 32 (1941).
1268 Kothe, K., Thesis, Leipzig, 1937, cited in K. Holzach, *Die aromatischen Diazoverbindungen*, F. Enke Verlag, Stuttgart, 1947, p. 69.
1269 Kovats, E., P. A. Plattner, and H. H. Günthard, *Helv. Chim. Acta*, **37,** 983, 997 (1954).
1270 Kozlov, V. V., and B. I. Stepanov, *Zhur. Fiz. Khim.*, **26,** 592, 701 (1952); through *Chem. Abstracts*, **47,** 10494e, h (1953).
1271 Krause, M., *Ber.*, **32,** 124 (1899).
1272 Kröhnke, F., and H. Kübler, *Ber.*, **70,** 538 (1937).
1273 Krolik, L. G., and V. O. Lukashevich, *Doklady Akad. Nauk S.S.S.R.*, **87,** 229 (1952); through *Chem. Abstracts*, **48,** 621g (1954).
1274 Krollpfeiffer, F., and E. Braun, *Ber.*, **70,** 89 (1937).
1275 Krollpfeiffer, F., C. Mühlhausen, and G. Wolf, *Ann.*, **508,** 39 (1934).
1276 Kruger, S., *J. Chem. Soc.*, **1953,** 700.
1277 Krzikalla, H., and B. Eistert, *J. prakt. Chem.*, **143,** 50 (1935).
1278 Küchler, L., *Polymerisationskinetik*, Springer-Verlag, Berlin, 1951, p. 105.
1279 Kuhn, H., *Chimia*, **4,** 203 (1950).
1280 Kuhn, H., *Experientia*, **9,** 41 (1953).
1281 Kuhn, H., *Chimia*, **9,** 237 (1955).
1282 Kuhn, R., and F. Bär, *Ann.*, **516,** 143 (1935).
1283 Kuhn, R., and H. H. Baer, *Ber.*, **86,** 724 (1953).
1284 Kuhn, R., and D. Jerchel, *Ber.*, **74,** 948 (1941).
1285 Kuhn, W., *Helv. Chim. Acta*, **31,** 1780 (1948).
1286 Kursanov, D. N., A. S. Kursanova, and A. H. Bloklina, *J. Gen. Chem. U.S.S.R.*, **8,** 1786 (1938); through *Chem. Abstracts*, **33,** 4979 (1939).
1287 Kvalnes, D. E., *J. Am. Chem. Soc.*, **56,** 2478 (1934).

1288 Laar, C., *Ber.*, **14,** 1928 (1881).
1289 Laidler, K. J., and E. J. Casey, *J. Chem. Phys.*, **17,** 213 (1949).
1290 Laitinen, H. A., E. I. Onstott, J. C. Bailar, and S. Swann, *J. Am. Chem. Soc.*, **71,** 1550 (1949).
1291 Lane, J., and E. Wallis, *J. Am. Chem. Soc.*, **63,** 1674 (1941).
1292 Lane, J., and E. Wallis, *J. Org. Chem.*, **6,** 443 (1941).
1293 Lane, J., J. Willenz, A. Weissberger, and E. Wallis, *J. Org. Chem.*, **5,** 276 (1940).
1294 Langley, B. W., B. Lythgoe, and N. V. Riggs, *J. Chem. Soc.*, **1951,** 2309.
1295 Langley, B. W., B. Lythgoe, and L. S. Rayner, *J. Chem. Soc.*, **1952,** 4191.
1296 Langmuir, I., *J. Am. Chem. Soc.*, **41,** 1546 (1919).
1297 Langmuir, I., *J. Am. Chem. Soc.*, **42,** 285 (1920).
1298 Lapworth, A., *J. Chem. Soc.*, **79,** 1265 (1901).
1299 Large, N. R., and C. Hinshelwood, *J. Chem. Soc.*, **1956,** 620.
1300 Large, N. R., F. J. Stubbs, and C. Hinshelwood, *J. Chem. Soc.*, **1954,** 2736.
1301 Lauth, C., *Bull. soc. chim. France*, (3), **6,** 94 (1891).
1302 Leake, P. H., *Chem. Revs.*, **56,** 27 (1956).
1303 Lebris, M. T., and H. Wahl, *Bull. soc. chim. France*, **1954,** 248.
1304 Lee, C. C., and J. W. T. Spinks, *Can. J. Chem.*, **31,** 761 (1953).
1305 Lee, W., J. G. Calvert, and E. Malmberg, unpublished investigations, cited by D. F. DeTar and T. Kosuge (*557*).
1306 Leermakers, J. A., *J. Am. Chem. Soc.*, **55,** 3499 (1933).
1307 Le Fèvre, R. J. W., and G. S. Hartley, *J. Chem. Soc.*, **1939,** 531.
1308 Le Fèvre, R. J. W., and T. H. Liddicoet, *J. Chem. Soc.*, **1951,** 2743.
1309 Le Fèvre, R. J. W., and J. Northcott, *J. Chem. Soc.*, **1949,** 333.
1310 Le Fèvre, R. J. W., and J. Northcott, *J. Chem. Soc.*, **1949,** 944.
1311 Le Fèvre, R. J. W., M. F. O'Dwyer, and R. L. Werner, *Austral. J. Chem.*, **6,** 341 (1953).
1312 Le Fèvre, R. J. W., and C. A. Parker, *J. Chem. Soc.*, **1939,** 677.
1313 Le Fèvre, R. J. W., J. B. Sousa, and R. L. Werner, *J. Chem. Soc.*, **1954,** 4686.
1314 Le Fèvre, R. J. W., and J. B. Sousa, *J. Chem. Soc.*, **1955,** 3154.
1315 Le Fèvre, R. J. W., and J. B. Sousa, *J. Chem. Soc.*, **1957,** 745.
1316 Le Fèvre, R. J. W., and J. B. Sousa, *J. Chem. Soc.*, **1957,** 746.
1317 Le Fèvre, R. J. W., and H. Vine, *J. Chem. Soc.*, **1937,** 1805.

1318 Le Fèvre, R. J. W., and H. Vine, *J. Chem. Soc.*, **1938,** 431.
1319 Le Fèvre, R. J. W., and H. Vine, *J. Chem. Soc.*, **1938,** 1878.
1320 Le Fèvre, R. J. W., and I. R. Wilson, *J. Chem. Soc.*, **1949,** 1106.
1321 Leffler, J. E., *The Reactive Intermediates of Organic Chemistry*, Interscience Publishers, New York, 1956. a) p. 25; b) p. 29; c) p. 45.
1322 Leffler, J. E., and W. B. Bond, *J. Am. Chem. Soc.*, **78,** 335 (1956).
1323 Leffler, J. E., and R. A. Hubbard, *J. Org. Chem.*, **19,** 1089 (1954).
1324 Lellmann, E., and W. Lippert, *Ber.*, **24,** 2623 (1891).
1325 Lennard-Jones, J., and J. A. Pople, *Disc. Faraday Soc.*, **10,** 9 (1951).
1326 Leonard, N. J., *Chem. Revs.*, **37,** 269 (1945).
1327 Lettré, H., and U. Brose, *Naturwissenschaften*, **36,** 57 (1949).
1328 Levisalles, J., and P. Baranger, *Compt. rend.*, **238,** 592 (1954).
1329 Lewis, E. S., *J. Am. Chem. Soc.*, **80,** 1371 (1958).
1330 Lewis, E. S., and W. H. Hinds, *J. Am. Chem. Soc.*, **74,** 304 (1952). a) footnote 16.
1331 Lewis, E. S., and M. D. Johnson, *J. Am. Chem. Soc.*, **81,** 2070 (1959).
1332 Lewis, E. S., J. L. Kinsey, and R. R. Johnson, *J. Am. Chem. Soc.*, **78,** 4294 (1956).
1333 Lewis, E. S., and E. B. Miller, *J. Am. Chem. Soc.*, **75,** 429 (1953).
1334 Lewis, E. S., and H. Suhr, *Ber.*, **91,** 2350 (1958).
1335 Lewis, E. S., and H. Suhr, *J. Am. Chem. Soc.*, **80,** 1367 (1958).
1336 Lewis, E. S., and H. Suhr, *Ber.*, **92,** 3031 (1959).
1337 Lewis, E. S., and H. Suhr, *Ber.*, **92,** 3043 (1959).
1338 Lewis, E. S., and H. Suhr, *J. Am. Chem. Soc.*, **82,** 862 (1960).
1339 Lewis, F. M., and M. S. Matheson, *J. Am. Chem. Soc.*, **71,** 747 (1949).
1340 Lewis, G. N., and M. Calvin, *Chem. Revs.*, **25,** 273 (1939).
1341 Lewis, H. H., M. Nierenstein, and E. M. Rich, *J. Am. Chem. Soc.*, **47,** 1728 (1926).
1342 Lieser, T., and G. Beck, *Ber.*, **83,** 137 (1950).
1343 Lifschitz, J., J. G. Bos, and K. M. Dijkema, *Z. anorg. Chem.*, **242,** 97 (1939).
1344 Lindsay, R. O., and C. F. Allen, *Org. Syntheses*, **22,** 96 (1942).
1345 Linnemann, E., *Ann.*, **144,** 129 (1867).
1346 Linnemann, E., *Ann.*, **150,** 370 (1869).
1347 Linnemann, E., *Ann.*, **161,** 43 (1872).
1348 Linstead, R. P., and A. B. L. Wang, *J. Chem. Soc.*, **1937,** 807.
1349 Linton, E. P., C. H. Holder, and H. E. Bigelow, *Can. J. Research*, **19 B,** 132 (1941).
1350 Lipp, P., J. Buchkremer, and H. Seeles, *Ann.*, **499,** 1 (1932).
1351 Lipp, P., and R. Köster, *Ber.*, **64,** 2823 (1931).
1352 Ljaschenko, W. L., and N. A. Kirzner, *Anilinokrass. Prom.*, **4,** 272 (1934); through *Chem. Zentr.*, **1935 I,** 2261.
1353 Löb, W., *Ber.*, **33,** 2329 (1900).
1354 Locher, M., *Ber.*, **21,** 911 (1888).
1355 Lochte, H. L., W. A. Noyes, and J. R. Bailey, *J. Am. Chem. Soc.*, **44,** 2556 (1922).
1356 Longuet-Higgins, H. C., and C. A. Coulson, *Trans. Faraday Soc.*, **42,** 756 (1946).
1357 Loose, A., *J. prakt. Chem.*, **79,** 507 (1909).
1358 Lopez Aparicio, F. J., and W. A. Waters, *J. Chem. Soc.*, **1952,** 4666.
1359 Lukashevich, V. O., *J. Gen. Chem. U.S.S.R.*, **11,** 1007 (1941); through *Chem. Abstracts,* **40,** 1150 (1946).
1360 Luner, P., and C. A. Winkler, *Can. J. Chem.*, **30,** 679 (1952).
1361 Lüttke, W., *Angew. Chem.*, **70,** 576 (1958).
1362 Lüttke, W., R. Kübler and S. Weckherlin, *Z. Elektrochem.*, **64,** 650 (1960).
1363 Lyalikoff, K. S., *Doklady Akad. Nauk S.S.S.R.*, **75,** 59 (1950).

1364 Maccoll, A., *J. Chem. Soc.*, **1946,** 670.
1365 Mai, J., *Ber.*, **25,** 372 (1892).
1366 Maier, W., A. Saupe, and A. Englert, *Z. physik. Chem.*, **10,** 273 (1957).
1367 Makarova, L. G., and E. A. Gribcenko, *Izv. Akad. Nauk S.S.S.R.*, **1958,** 693.
1368 Malkin, T., and M. Nierenstein, *J. Am. Chem. Soc.*, **52,** 1504 (1930).
1369 Manske, R. H. F., and R. Robinson, *J. Chem. Soc.*, **1927,** 240.
1370 Marriott, G. J., *J. Soc. Dyers Col.*, **52,** 172 (1936).
1371 Martell, A. E., and M. Calvin, *Chemistry of Metal Chelate Compounds*, Prentice-Hall, New York, 1952.
1372 Martius, C. A., *J. prakt. Chem.*, **98,** 94 (1866).
1373 Martynoff, M., *Compt. rend.*, **223,** 747 (1946).
1374 Martynoff, M., *Bull. soc. chim. France*, **1951,** 214.

1375 Martynoff, M., *Compt. rend.*, **235,** 54 (1952).
1376 Maschka, A., *Monatsh.*, **84,** 853 (1953).
1377 Maschka, A., *Monatsh.*, **84,** 872 (1953).
1378 Matheson, M. S., E. E. Auer, E. B. Bevilacqua, and E. J. Hart, *J. Am. Chem. Soc.*, **71,** 497, 2610 (1949).
1379 Matsumura, K., *J. Am. Chem. Soc.*, **52,** 3974 (1930).
1380 Maynard, C. W., in *The Chemistry of Synthetic Dyes and Pigments*, H. A. Lubs, ed., Reinhold Publ., New York, 1955, p. 220.
1381 Mazur, R. H., W. N. White, D. A. Semenow, C. C. Lee, M. S. Silver, and J. D. Roberts, *J. Am. Chem. Soc.*, **81,** 4390 (1959).
1382 McGuire, W. S., T. F. Izzo, and S. Zuffanti, *J. Org. Chem.*, **21,** 632 (1956).
1383 McKay, A. F., *J. Am. Chem. Soc.*, **70,** 1974 (1948).
1384 McKay, A. F., *J. Am. Chem. Soc.*, **71,** 1968 (1949).
1385 McKenzie, J., *J. Proc. Roy. Soc. N. S. Wales*, **78,** 70 (1944).
1386 McKenzie, A., and J. R. Myles, *Ber.*, **65,** 209 (1932).
1387 McKenzie, A., and A. C. Richardson, *J. Chem. Soc.*, **123,** 79 (1923).
1388 McKenzie, J. C. J., A. Rodgman, and G. F. Wright, *J. Org. Chem.*, **17,** 1666 (1952).
1389 McLeod Elofson, R., R. L. Edsberg, and P. A. Meckerly, *J. Electrochem. Soc.*, **97,** 166 (1950).
1390 Mechel von, L., and H. Stauffer, *Helv. Chim. Acta*, **24,** 151 E (1941).
1391 Meerwein, H., *Angew. Chem.*, **60,** 78 (1948).
1392 Meerwein, H., H. Allendörfer, P. Beekman, F. Kundert, H. Morschel, F. Pawellek, and K. Wunderlich, *Angew. Chem.*, **70,** 211 (1958).
1393 Meerwein, H., T. Bersin, and W. Burneleit, *Ber.*, **62,** 999 (1929).
1394 Meerwein, H., and T. Bersin, *Ber.*, **62,** 1006 (1929).
1395 Meerwein, H., E. Büchner, and K. van Emster, *J. prakt. Chem.*, **152,** 237 (1939).
1396 Meerwein, H., and W. Burneleit, *Ber.*, **61,** 1840 (1928).
1397 Meerwein, H., H. Disselnkötter, F. Rappen, H. von Rintelen, and H. van de Vloed, *Ann.*, **604,** 151 (1957).
1398 Meerwein, H., G. Dittmar, R. Göllner, K. Hafner, F. Mensch, and O. Steinfort, *Ber.*, **90,** 841 (1957).
1399 Meerwein, H., G. Dittmar, G. Kaufmann, and R. Raue, *Ber.*, **90,** 853 (1957).
1400 Meerwein, H., and K. van Emster, *Ber.*, **53,** 1815 (1920).
1401 Meerwein, H., and G. Hinz, *Ann.*, **484,** 1 (1930).
1402 Meerwein, H., H. Rathjen, and H. Werner, *Ber.*, **75,** 1610 (1942).
1403 Mehner, H., *J. prakt. Chem.*, **65,** 401 (1902).
1404 Mehta, S. M., and M. V. Vakilwala, *J. Am. Chem. Soc.*, **74,** 563 (1952).
1405 Melander, L., *Arkiv Kemi*, **2,** 213 (1951).
1406 Melander, L., *Arkiv Kemi*, **3,** 525 (1951).
1407 Melander, L., *The Use of Nuclides in the Determination of Organic Reaction Mechanisms*, University of Notre Dame Press, Notre Dame, Ind., 1955, p. 65.
1408 Meldola, R., and L. Eynon, *J. Chem. Soc.*, **87,** 1 (1905).
1409 Meldola, R., and J. V. Eyre, *J. Chem. Soc.*, **79,** 1076 (1901).
1410 Meldola, R., and J. V. Eyre, *J. Chem. Soc.*, **81,** 988 (1902).
1411 Meldola, R., and J. G. Hay, *J. Chem. Soc.*, **91,** 1474 (1907).
1412 Meldola, R., and J. G. Hay, *J. Chem. Soc.*, **95,** 1378 (1909).
1413 Meldola, R., and F. Reverdin, *J. Chem. Soc.*, **97,** 1204 (1910).
1414 Meldola, R., and F. G. Stephens, *J. Chem. Soc.*, **87,** 1199 (1905).
1415 Meldola, R., and F. W. Streatfield, *J. Chem. Soc.*, **49,** 624 (1886).
1416 Meldola, R., and F. W. Streatfield, *J. Chem. Soc.*, **51,** 102, 434 (1887).
1417 Meldola, R., and F. W. Streatfield, *J. Chem. Soc.*, **53,** 664 (1888).
1418 Meldola, R., and F. W. Streatfield, *J. Chem. Soc.*, **55,** 412 (1889).
1419 Meldola, R., and F. W. Streatfield, *J. Chem. Soc.*, **57,** 785 (1890).
1420 Meldola, R., and F. W. Streatfield, *J. Chem. Soc.*, **67,** 907 (1895).
1421 Meldola, R., and E. Wechsler, *J. Chem. Soc.*, **77,** 1172 (1900).
1422 Mellor, D. P., *Chem. Revs.*, **33,** 137 (1943).
1423 Melville, H. W., and T. G. Majury, *Nature*, **165,** 642 (1950).
1424 Mène, C., *Compt. rend.*, **52,** 311 (1861).
1425 Menzi, K., personal communication.
1426 Merian, E., Thesis, ETH, Zurich, 1949, pp. 29–32.
1427 Meyer, H., *Monatsh.*, **26,** 1295 (1905).
1428 Meyer, K. H., *Ber.*, **52,** 1468 (1919).

1429 Meyer, K. H., *Ber.*, **54,** 2265 (1921).
1430 Meyer, K. H., and H. Hopff, *Ber.*, **54,** 2274 (1921).
1431 Meyer, K. H., A. Irschick, and H. Schlösser, *Ber.*, **47,** 1741 (1914).
1432 Meyer, K. H., and S. Lenhardt, *Ann.*, **398,** 66 (1913).
1433 Meyer, K. H., and S. Lenhardt, *Ann.*, **398,** 74 (1913).
1434 Meyer, K. H., and H. Tochtermann, *Ber.*, **54,** 2283 (1921).
1435 Meyer, V., *Ber.*, **10,** 2075 (1877).
1436 Meyer, V., and G. Ambühl, *Ber.*, **8,** 751 (1875).
1437 Meyer, V., and F. Forster, *Ber.*, **9,** 535 (1876).
1438 Michaelis, A., *Ber.*, **24,** 745 (1891).
1439 Michaelis, A., *Ann.*, **274,** 255 (1893).
1440 Michaelis, A., and K. Petou, *Ber.*, **31,** 994 (1898).
1441 Michaelis, A., and J. Ruhl, *Ann.*, **270,** 114 (1892).
1442 Michaelis, L., *Ann. N. Y. Acad. Sci.*, **40,** 37 (1940).
1443 Miklukhin, G. P., and A. F. Rekasheva, *Doklady Akad. Nauk S.S.S.R.*, **85,** 827 (1952);
        through *Chem. Abstracts*, **47,** 1455 (1953).
1444 Miller, J. A., R. W. Sapp, and E. C. Miller, *J. Am. Chem. Soc.*, **70,** 3458 (1958).
1445 Mills, A. K., *J. Chem. Soc.*, **1934,** 1565.
1446 Mills, C., *J. Chem. Soc.*, **65,** 51 (1894).
1447 Mills, I. M., and H. W. Thompson, *Trans. Faraday Soc.*, **50,** 1270 (1954).
1448 Mills, J. A., *J. Chem. Soc.*, **1953,** 260.
1449 Mills, W. H., *J. Chem. Soc.*, **1944,** 340.
1450 Mills, W. H., and J. G. Nixon, *J. Chem. Soc.*, **1930,** 2510.
1451 Misslin, E., *Helv. Chim. Acta*, **3,** 626 (1920).
1452 Mitscherlich, E., *Ann.*, **12,** 311 (1834).
1453 Miyama, H., *J. Chem. Soc. Japan*, **76,** 658 (1955); through *Chem. Abstracts*, **50,** 3093 e (1956).
1454 Moelwyn-Hughes, E. A., and P. Johnson, *Trans. Faraday Soc.*, **36,** 948 (1940).
1455 Möhlau, R., *Ber.*, **16,** 3080 (1883).
1456 Möhlau, R., *Ber.*, **45,** 2233, 2244 (1912).
1457 Möhlau, R., and E. Strohbach, *Ber.*, **33,** 804 (1900).
1458 Möhlau, R., and E. Strohbach, *Ber.*, **34,** 4162 (1901).
1459 Mohler, H., H. Forster, and G. Schwarzenbach, *Helv. Chim. Acta*, **20,** 654 (1937).
1460 Mohr, R., Thesis, ETH, Zurich, 1934.
1461 Moore, J. A., J. R. Dice, E. D. Nicolaides, R. D. Westland, and E. L. Wittle, *J. Am.
        Chem. Soc.*, **76,** 2884 (1954).
1462 Moore, R. L., and R. C. Anderson, *J. Am. Chem. Soc.*, **67,** 167 (1945).
1463 Morgan, G. T., and D. A. Cleage, *J. Chem. Soc.*, **113,** 588 (1918).
1464 Morgan, G. T., and E. G. Couzens, *J. Chem. Soc.*, **97,** 1691 (1910).
1465 Morgan, G. T., and E. D. Evens, *J. Chem. Soc.*, **115,** 1126 (1919).
1466 Morgan, G. T., and W. R. Grist, *J. Chem. Soc.*, **113,** 688 (1918).
1467 Morgan, G. T., and F. M. G. Micklethwait, *J. Chem. Soc.*, **93,** 602 (1908).
1468 Morgan, G. T., and F. M. G. Micklethwait, *J. Chem. Soc.*, **97,** 2557 (1910).
1469 Morgan, G. T., and J. W. Porter, *J. Chem. Soc.*, **107,** 645 (1915).
1470 Morgan, G. T., and J. D. M. Smith, *J. Chem. Soc.*, **1924,** 1731.
1471 Morgan, G. T., and H. P. Tomlins, *J. Chem. Soc.*, **111,** 497 (1917).
1472 Mosettig, E., *Ber.*, **61,** 1391 (1928).
1473 Mosettig, E., and A. Burger, *J. Am. Chem. Soc.*, **52,** 3456 (1930).
1474 Mosettig, E., and K. Czadek, *Monatsh.*, **57,** 291 (1931).
1475 Mousseron, M., *Bull. soc. chim. France*, **1956,** 1008.
1476 Mousseron, M., and R. Jacquier, *Compt. rend.*, **229,** 216 (1949).
1477 Mousseron, M., L. Souche, and R. Granger, *Bull. soc. chim. France*, **4,** 1197 (1937).
1478 Muller, N., L. W. Pickett, and R. S. Mulliken, *J. Am. Chem. Soc.*, **76,** 4770 (1954).
1479 Müller, E., *Ber.*, **47,** 3001 (1914).
1480 Müller, E., *Die Azoxyverbindungen*, F. Enke Verlag, Stuttgart, 1936.
1481 Müller, E., *Angew. Chem.*, **61,** 179 (1949).
1482 Müller, E., *Neuere Anschauungen der organischen Chemie*, 2nd ed., Springer-Verlag, Berlin,
        1957. a) p. 454; b) p. 460; c) p. 462; d) p. 476.
1483 Müller, E., and H. Disselhoff, *Ann.*, **512,** 250 (1934).
1484 Müller, E., E. Hory, W. Krüger, and W. Kreutzmann, *Ann.*, **493,** 166 (1932).
1485 Müller, E., E. Hory, W. Krüger, and W. Kreutzmann, *Ann.*, **493,** 167 (1932).
1486 Müller, E., and E. Hory, *Z. physik. Chem.*, **A 162,** 281 (1932).
1487 Müller, E., H. Huber-Emden, and W. Rundel, *Ann.*, **623,** 34 (1959).

1488 Müller, E., and R. Illgen, *Ann.*, **521,** 72 (1935).
1489 Müller, E., and W. Kreutzmann, *Ann.*, **495,** 133 (1932).
1490 Müller, E., and W. Kreutzmann, *Ann.*, **512,** 264 (1934).
1491 Müller, E., and D. Ludsteck, *Ber.*, **87,** 1887 (1954).
1492 Müller, E., D. Ludsteck, and W. Rundel, *Angew. Chem.*, **67,** 617 (1955).
1493 Müller, E., and D. Ludsteck, *Ber.*, **88,** 921 (1955).
1494 Müller, E., and S. Petersen, *Angew. Chem.*, **63,** 18 (1951).
1495 Müller, E., and E. Roser, *J. prakt. Chem.*, **133,** 291 (1932).
1496 Müller, E., and W. Rundel, *Ber.*, **88,** 917 (1955).
1497 Müller, E., and W. Rundel, *Ber.*, **90,** 2673 (1957).
1498 Müller, E., and W. Rundel, *Angew. Chem.*, **70,** 105 (1958).
1499 Müller, J. B., L. Blangey, and H. E. Fierz-David, *Helv. Chim. Acta,* **35,** 2579 (1952).
1500 Mulliken, R. S., *J. Chem. Phys.*, **7,** 14, 20, 21 (1939).
1501 Mužík, F., and Z. J. Allan, *Coll. Czech. Chem. Com.*, **18,** 388 (1953).
1502 Mužík, F., and Z. J. Allan, *Coll. Czech. Chem. Com.*, **20,** 623 (1955).

1503 Nace, H. C., and M. H. Gollis, *J. Am. Chem. Soc.*, **74,** 5189 (1952).
1504 Nagasaka, A., and R. Oda, *J. Chem. Soc. Japan,* **56,** 42, (1953); through *Chem. Abstracts,* **48,** 7597 a (1954).
1505 Nakazawa, K., *J. Antibiotics (Japan)*, **7,** 329 (1954).
1506 Neeman, M., M. C. Caserio, J. D. Roberts, and W. S. Johnson, *Tetrahedron,* **6,** 36 (1959).
1507 Nef. J. U., *Ann.*, **270,** 267 (1892).
1508 Nef, J. U., *Ann.*, **280,** 291 (1894).
1509 Nef, J. U., *Ann.*, **287,** 265 (1895).
1510 Nef, J. U., *Ann.*, **298,** 202 (1897).
1511 Nelson, K. L., *J. Org. Chem.*, **21,** 145 (1956).
1512 Nelson, K. L., and H. C. Brown in *The Chemistry of Petroleum Hydrocarbons,* B. T. Brooks, C. E. Boord, S. S. Kurtz, and L. Schmerling, eds., Reinhold Publ., New York, 1955, Vol. III.
1513 Nemodruk, A. A., *J. Gen. Chem. U.S.S.R.* **28,** 1082 (1958).
1514 Nenitzescu, C. D., and E. Solomonica, *Org. Syntheses,* *Coll. Vol. II*, 496 (1943).
1515 Neogi, P., *J. Chem. Soc.*, **105,** 1270 (1914).
1516 Nesmeyanov, A. N., *Experientia, Supplementum II*, 49 (1955).
1517 Nesmeyanov, A. N., L. I. Emeljanova, and L. G. Makarova, *Doklady Akad. Nauk S.S.S.R.,* **122,** 403 (1958).
1518 Nesmeyanov, A. N., and E. J. Kahn, *Ber.*, **62,** 1018 (1929).
1519 Nesmeyanov, A. N., K. A. Kocheshkow, and W. A. Klimova, *Ber.*, **68,** 1877 (1935).
1520 Nesmeyanov, A. N., L. G. Makarova, and T. P. Tolstaya, *Tetrahedron,* **1,** 145 (1957).
1521 Nesmeyanov, A. N., and E. G. Perevalova, *Uspekhi Khim.*, **27,** 3 (1958); through *Chem. Abstracts,* **52,** 14579 (1958).
1522 Nesmeyanov, A. N., T. P. Tolstaya, and S. S. Isajera, *Doklady Akad. Nauk S.S.S.R.,* **122,** 614 (1958).
1523 Neunhoeffer, O., and J. Weise, *Ber.*, **71,** 2703 (1938).
1524 Newman, M. S., and A. Arkell, *J. Org. Chem.*, **24,** 385 (1959).
1525 Newman, M. S., and P. Beal, *J. Am. Chem. Soc.*, **71,** 1506 (1949).
1526 Newman, M. S., and P. Beal, *J. Am. Chem. Soc.*, **72,** 5161 (1950).
1527 Nicolaides, E. D., R. D. Westland, and E. L. Wittle, *J. Am. Chem. Soc.*, **76,** 2887 (1954).
1528 Nierenstein, M., D. G. Wang, and J. C. Warr, *J. Am. Chem. Soc.*, **46,** 2551 (1925).
1529 Nietzki, R., *Ber.*, **10,** 662 (1877).
1530 Nietzki, R., and A. L. Guiterman, *Ber.*, **20,** 1274 (1887).
1531 Nightingale, D. V., J. D. Kerr, J. A. Gallagher, and M. Maienthal, *J. Org. Chem.*, **17,** 1017 (1952).
1532 Nightingale, D. V., and M. Maienthal, *J. Am. Chem. Soc.*, **72,** 4823 (1950).
1533 Nineham, A. W., *Chem. Revs.*, **55,** 355 (1955).
1534 Noether, H., Thesis, Marburg University, 1957.
1535 Noether, H., Thesis, Marburg University, 1958.
1536 Nölting, E., and F. Binder, *Ber.*, **20,** 3004 (1887).
1537 Nölting, E., and F. Binder, *Ber.*, **20,** 3014 (1887).
1538 Nölting, E., and E. Grandmougin, *Ber.*, **24,** 1601 (1891).
1539 Nölting, E., and O. Michel, *Ber.*, **26,** 86 (1893).
1540 Norris, J. F., and W. H. Strain, *J. Am. Chem. Soc.*, **57,** 187 (1935).
1541 Norrish, R. G. W., and G. Porter, *Disc. Faraday Soc.*, **2,** 97 (1947).

1542 Nunn, J. R., and W. S. Rapson, *J. Chem. Soc.*, **1949,** 825.
1543 Nursten, H. E., unpublished.
1544 Nyholm, R. S., *Quart. Revs.*, **7,** 377 (1953).
1545 Nyholm, R. S., *Rev. Pure and Appl. Chem.*, **4,** 15 (1954).
1546 Nystrom, R. F., and W. D. Brown, *J. Am. Chem. Soc.*, **70,** 3738 (1948).

1547 Oddo, G., and R. Indovina, *Gazz. chim. ital.*, **65,** 1037 (1935).
1548 Oddo, G., and E. Puxeddu, *Gazz. chim. ital.*, **36 II,** 1 (1906).
1549 Ogata, Y., and Y. Takagi, *J. Am. Chem. Soc.*, **80,** 3591 (1958).
1550 Okano, M., and Y. Ogata, *J. Am. Chem. Soc.*, **75,** 5175 (1953).
1551 Olah, G. A., *J. Am. Chem. Soc.*, **81,** 3165 (1959).
1552 Oliveri-Mandala, E., *Gazz. chim. ital.*, **40 I,** 123 (1908).
1553 Opolonick, N., *Ind. Eng. Chem.*, **27,** 1045 (1935).
1554 Orgel, L. E., *J. Chem. Soc.*, **1952,** 4756.
1555 Orgel, L. E., *J. Chem. Phys.*, **23,** 1004 (1955).
1556 Orton, K. J. P., *J. Chem. Soc.*, **83,** 796 (1903).
1557 Orton, K. J. P., *J. Chem. Soc.*, **87,** 99 (1905).
1558 Orton, K. J. P., and J. E. Coates, *J. Chem. Soc.*, **91,** 35 (1907).
1559 Orton, K. J. P., and R. W. Everatt, *J. Chem. Soc.*, **93,** 1021 (1908).
1560 Ospenson, J. N., *Acta Chem. Scand.*, **4,** 1351 (1950).
1561 Ospenson, J. N., *Acta Chem. Scand.*, **5,** 491 (1951).
1562 Overbeek, J. T. G., C. L. J. Vink, and H. Deenstra, *Rec. trav. chim.*, **74,** 85 (1955).
1563 Overberger, C. G., and M. B. Berenbaum, *J. Am. Chem. Soc.*, **73,** 2618 (1951).
1564 Overberger, C. G., and M. B. Berenbaum, *J. Am. Chem. Soc.*, **73,** 4883 (1951).
1565 Overberger, C. G., and M. B. Berenbaum, *J. Am. Chem. Soc.*, **74,** 3293 (1952).
1566 Overberger, C. G., and H. Biletch, *J. Am. Chem. Soc.*, **73,** 4880 (1951).
1567 Overberger, C. G., and A. V. DiGiulio, *J. Am. Chem. Soc.*, **80,** 6562 (1958).
1568 Overberger, C. G., and A. V. DiGiulio, *J. Am. Chem. Soc.*, **81,** 1194 (1959).
1569 Overberger, C. G., P. Fram, and T. Alfrey, *J. Polymer Sci.*, **6,** 539 (1951).
1570 Overberger, C. G., and H. Gainer, *J. Am. Chem. Soc.*, **80,** 4556 (1958).
1571 Overberger, C. G., and H. Gainer, *J. Am. Chem. Soc.*, **80,** 4561 (1958).
1572 Overberger, C. G., P. T. Huang, and M. B. Berenbaum, *Org. Syntheses*, **32,** 16, 50 (1952).
1573 Overberger, C. G., and M. Lapkin, *J. Am. Chem. Soc.*, **77,** 4651 (1955).
1574 Overberger, C. G., J. G. Lombardino, I. Tashlick, and R. G. Hiskey, *J. Am. Chem. Soc.*, **79,** 2662 (1957).
1575 Overberger, C. G., and J. G. Lombardino, *J. Am. Chem. Soc.*, **80,** 2317 (1958).
1576 Overberger, C. G., and J. J. Monagle, *J. Am. Chem. Soc.*, **78,** 4470 (1956).
1577 Overberger, C. G., M. T. O'Shaughnessy, and H. Shalit, *J. Am. Chem. Soc.*, **71,** 2661 (1949).
1578 Overberger, C. G., I. Tashlick, M. Bernstein, and R. G. Hiskey, *J. Am. Chem. Soc.*, **80,** 6556 (1958).
1579 Overberger, C. G., and I. Tashlick, *J. Am. Chem. Soc.*, **81,** 217 (1959).

1580 Packer, J., and J. Vaughan, *A Modern Approach to Organic Chemistry*, Clarendon Press, Oxford, 1958, p. 659.
1581 Page, M., H. O. Pritchard, and A. F. Trotman-Dickenson, *J. Chem. Soc.*, **1953,** 3878.
1582 Painter, B. S., and F. G. Soper, *J. Chem. Soc.*, **1947,** 342.
1583 Parham, W. E., and J. L. Bleasdale, *J. Am. Chem. Soc.*, **72,** 3843 (1950).
1584 Parham, W. E., and J. L. Bleasdale, *J. Am. Chem. Soc.*, **73,** 4664 (1951).
1585 Parham, W. E., and W. R. Hasek, *J. Am. Chem. Soc.*, **76,** 799 (1954).
1586 Parham, W. E., and W. R. Hasek, *J. Am. Chem. Soc.*, **76,** 935 (1954).
1587 Parham, W. E., C. Serres, and P. R. O'Connor, *J. Am. Chem. Soc.*, **80,** 588 (1958).
1588 Pascal, P., *Ann. chim. et phys.*, **25,** 372 (1912).
1589 Passerini, M., and G. Losco, *Gazz. chim. ital.*, **68,** 485 (1938).
1590 Passet, B. V., and B. A. Porai-Koshits, *Treatises of the L. T. Institute 'Lensoviet'*, **11,** 133 (1958).
1591 Pauling, L., *The Nature of the Chemical Bond*, 2nd ed., Cornell University Press, Ithaca, 1940. a) chap. III; b) p. 142; c) p. 254; d) p. 268.
1592 Pausacker, K. H., *J. Chem. Soc.*, **1953,** 1989.
1593 Pausacker, K. H., and J. G. Scroggie, *J. Chem. Soc.*, **1954,** 4003.
1594 Pearson, T. G., R. H. Purcell, and G. S. Saigh, *J. Chem. Soc.*, **1938,** 409.
1595 Pechmann von, H., *Ber.*, **25,** 3175 (1892).

1596 Pechmann von, H., *Ber.*, **25,** 3505 (1892).
1597 Pechmann von, H., *Ber.*, **27,** 1888 (1894).
1598 Pechmann von, H., *Ber.*, **28,** 855 (1895).
1599 Pechmann von, H., *Ber.*, **28,** 1874 (1895).
1600 Pechmann von, H., *Ber.*, **31,** 2950 (1898).
1601 Pechmann von, H., and E. Burkard, *Ber.*, **33,** 3590 (1900).
1602 Pechmann von, H., and L. Frobenius, *Ber.*, **27,** 651 (1894).
1603 Pechmann von, H., and L. Frobenius, *Ber.*, **27,** 672 (1894).
1604 Pechmann von, H., and L. Frobenius, *Ber.*, **28,** 170 (1895).
1605 Pechmann von, H., and L. Frobenius, *Ber.*, **28,** 173 (1895).
1606 Pechmann von, H., and K. Jenisch, *Ber.*, **24,** 3255 (1891).
1607 Pechmann von, H., and P. Manck, *Ber.*, **28,** 2374 (1895).
1608 Penney, W. G., and J. S. Anderson, *Trans. Faraday Soc.*, **33,** 1364 (1937).
1609 Peratoner, A., and E. Azzarello, *Gazz. chim. ital.*, **38 I,** 84 (1908).
1610 Perekalin, V. V., *J. Gen. Chem. U.S.S.R.*, **17,** 1788 (1947); through *Chem. Abstracts*, **42,**
      5868 c (1948).
1611 Perekalin, V. V., and L. N. Kononova, *J. Gen. Chem. U.S.S.R.*, **21,** 1150 (1951); through
      Chem. Abstracts, **45,** 10589 f (1951).
1612 Perekalin, V. V., and N. M. Slavachevskaya, *J. Gen. Chem. U.S.S.R.*, **21,** 897 (1951);
      through *Chem. Abstracts*, **45,** 8774 f (1951).
1613 Pestemer, M., and G. Scheibe, *Angew. Chem.*, **66,** 553 (1954).
1614 Pfau, A. S., and P. A. Plattner, *Helv. Chim. Acta*, **19,** 858 (1936).
1615 Pfeiffer, P., *Ann.*, **376,** 292 (1910).
1616 Pfeiffer, P., *Organische Molekülverbindungen*, 2nd ed., F. Enke Verlag, Stuttgart, 1927.
1617 Pfeiffer, P., *Ber.*, **63,** 1811 (1930).
1618 Pfeiffer, P., in *Stereochemie*, K. Freudenberg, ed., J. Deutiche, Vienna, 1933, p. 1200.
1619 Pfeiffer, P., *Angew. Chem.*, **53,** 93 (1940).
1620 Pfeiffer, P., and H. Buchholz, *J. prakt. Chem.*, **124,** 133 (1930).
1621 Pfeiffer, P., T. Hesse, H. Pfitzner, W. Scholl, and H. Thielert, *J. prakt. Chem.*, **149,** 217
      (1937).
1622 Pfeiffer, P., and S. Saure, *Ber.*, **74,** 935 (1941).
1623 Pfeiffer, P., and R. Wizinger, *Ann.*, **461,** 132 (1928).
1624 Pfeil, E., *Angew. Chem.*, **65,** 155 (1953).
1625 Pfeil, E., and O. Velten, *Ann.*, **562,** 163 (1949).
1626 Pfeil, E., and O. Velten, *Ann.*, **565,** 183 (1949).
1627 Pfitzner, H., and H. Baumann, *Angew. Chem.*, **70,** 232 (1948).
1628 Phillips, D. D., *J. Am. Chem. Soc.*, **76,** 5385 (1954).
1629 Pierrot, F., and H. Wahl, *Compt. rend.*, **240,** 879 (1955).
1630 Pierrot, F., and H. Wahl, *Compt. rend.*, **242,** 913 (1956).
1631 Pinck, L. A., *J. Am. Chem. Soc.*, **55,** 1711 (1933).
1632 Pinck, L. A., and G. E. Hilbert, *J. Am. Chem. Soc.*, **68,** 2740 (1946).
1633 Piria, R., *Ann. chim. et phys.*, (3), **22,** 160 (1848); *Ann.*, **68,** 343 (1848).
1634 Pittoni, A., *Ricerca sci. e Ricostruz.*, **17,** 1396 (1947); *Atti Soc. med. chir. Padova*, **25,** 125
      (1947); through *Chem. Abstracts*, **43,** 7368, 7835 (1949).
1635 Platt, J. R., *J. Chem. Phys.*, **17,** 484 (1949).
1636 Platt, J. R., *J. Chem. Phys.*, **18,** 1168 (1950).
1637 Platt, J. R., *J. Chem. Phys.*, **19,** 101 (1951).
1638 Plattner, P. A., *Chimia*, **4,** 260 (1950).
1639 Plattner, P. A., A. Fürst, and A. Studer, *Helv. Chim. Acta*, **30,** 1091 (1947).
1640 Plattner, P. A., A. Fürst, L. Marti, R. Süess, and H. H. Günthard, *Helv. Chim. Acta*, **34,**
      959 (1951).
1641 Plattner, P. A., A. Fürst, A. Müller, and A. R. Somerville, *Helv. Chim. Acta*, **34,** 971 (1951).
1642 Plattner, P. A., E. Heilbronner, and A. Fürst, *Helv. Chim. Acta*, **30,** 1100 (1947).
1643 Plattner, P. A., E. Heilbronner, and S. Weber, *Helv. Chim. Acta*, **35,** 1036 (1952).
1644 Plattner, P. A., and H. Roniger, *Helv. Chim. Acta*, **26,** 905 (1943).
1645 Plattner, P. A., and J. Wyss, *Helv. Chim. Acta*, **23,** 907 (1940).
1646 Plentl, A. A., and M. T. Bogert, *J. Org. Chem.*, **6,** 669 (1941).
1647 Pöhls, P., Thesis, Marburg University, 1934.
1648 Pollak, J., and E. Gebauer-Fülnegg, *Monatsh.*, **50,** 310 (1928).
1649 Pongratz, A., G. Markgraf, and E. Mayer-Pitsch, *Ber.*, **71,** 1287 (1938).
1650 Porai-Koshits, A. E., B. A. Porai-Koshits, and V. V. Perekalin, *J. Gen. Chem. U.S.S.R.*,
      15, 446 (1945); through *Chem. Abstracts*, **40,** 4885 (1946).

1651 Porai-Koshits, B. A., and I. V. Grachev, *J. Gen. Chem. U.S.S.R.*, **16,** 571 (1946); through *Chem. Abstracts*, **41,** 1215 b (1947).
1652 Porai-Koshits, B. A., and K. L. Muravich, *J. Gen. Chem. U.S.S.R.*, **23,** 1583 (1953); through *Chem. Abstracts*, **48,** 11399 c (1954).
1653 Posternak, T., *Helv. Chim. Acta*, **33,** 1597 (1950).
1654 Pray, H. A. H., *J. Phys. Chem.*, **30,** 1417 (1926).
1655 Pray, H. A. H., *J. Phys. Chem.*, **30,** 1477 (1926).
1656 Prelog, V., *Angew. Chem.*, **70,** 145 (1958).
1657 Prelog, V., M. Fausy, E. Neweihy, and O. Häfliger, *Helv. Chim. Acta*, **33,** 1937 (1950).
1658 Prelog, V., and K. Schenker, *Helv. Chim. Acta*, **36,** 1181 (1953).
1659 Prelog, V., H. J. Urech, A. A. Bothner-By, and J. Würsch, *Helv. Chim. Acta*, **38,** 1095 (1955).
1660 Preobrashenski, N. A., and M. J. Kabatschnik, *Ber.*, **66,** 1542 (1933).
1661 Prins, D. A., and T. Reichstein, *Helv. Chim. Acta*, **24,** 945 (1941).
1662 Pritchard, G. O., H. O. Pritchard, and A. F. Trotman-Dickenson, *Chemistry and Industry*, **1955,** 564.
1663 Pschorr, R., *Ber.*, **29,** 496 (1896).
1664 Pummerer, R., and J. Binapfl, *Ber.*, **54,** 2768 (1921).
1665 Pummerer, R., J. Binapfl, K. Bittner, and K. Schuegraf, *Ber.*, **55,** 3095 (1922).
1666 Pütter, R., *Angew. Chem.*, **63,** 188 (1951).

1667 Quilico, A., and E. Fleischner, *Gazz. chim. ital.*, **59,** 39 (1929).
1668 Quilico, A., and M. Freri, *Gazz. chim. ital.*, **58,** 380 (1928).

1669 Raaen, V. F., and C. J. Collins, *J. Am. Chem. Soc.*, **80,** 1409 (1958).
1670 Rabjohn, N., *Org. Syntheses*, **28,** 58 (1948).
1671 Ramart-Lucas, P., *Bull. soc. chim. France*, **11,** 75 (1944).
1672 Ramart-Lucas, P., T. Guilmart, and M. Martynoff, *Bull. soc. chim. France*, **14,** 415 (1947).
1673 Ramirez, F., and S. Levy, *J. Am. Chem. Soc.*, **79,** 6167 (1957).
1674 Ramirez, F., and S. Levy, *J. Org. Chem.*, **23,** 2035 (1958).
1675 Ramirez, F., and S. Levy, *J. Org. Chem.*, **23,** 2036 (1958).
1676 Ramsay, D. A., *J. Chem. Phys.*, **17,** 666 (1949).
1677 Ramsperger, H. C., *J. Am. Chem. Soc.*, **50,** 714 (1928).
1678 Ramsperger, H. C., *J. Am. Chem. Soc.*, **51,** 920 (1929).
1679 Ramsperger, H. C., *J. Am. Chem. Soc.*, **51,** 2134 (1929).
1680 Raschig, F., *Schwefel- und Stickstoffstudien*, Verlag Chemie, Leipzig and Berlin, 1924, p. 221.
1681 Ray, P. C., and J. N. Rakshit, *J. Chem. Soc.*, **99,** 1016 (1911).
1682 Razumovskii, V. V., and E. F. Rychkina, *J. Gen. Chem. U.S.S.R.*, **27,** 3143 (1957).
1683 Razuvaev, G. A., and E. I. Fedotova, *J. Gen. Chem. U.S.S.R.*, **21,** 1118 (1951); through *Chem. Abstracts*, **46,** 5006 g (1952).
1684 Read, J., and I. G. M. Campbell, *J. Chem. Soc.*, **1930,** 2674.
1685 Read, J., A. M. Cook, and M. J. Shannon, *J. Chem. Soc.*, **1926,** 2223.
1686 Read, J., and G. J. Robertson, *J. Chem. Soc.*, **1927,** 2168.
1687 Read, J., and C. C. Steele, *J. Chem. Soc.*, **1927,** 910.
1688 Redemann, C. E., F. O. Rice, R. Roberts, and H. P. Ward, *Org. Syntheses, Coll. Vol. III*, 244 (1955).
1689 Reilly, J., and P. J. Drumm, *J. Chem. Soc.*, **1935,** 871.
1690 Reimlinger, H., *Ber.*, **92,** 970 (1959).
1691 Relyea, D. I., and D. F. DeTar, *J. Am. Chem. Soc.*, **76,** 1202 (1954).
1692 Remington, W. R., *J. Am. Chem. Soc.*, **67,** 1838 (1945).
1693 Renaud, R., and L. C. Leitch, *Can. J. Chem.*, **32,** 545 (1954).
1694 Renouf, E., *Ber.*, **13,** 2169 (1880).
1695 Reynolds, W. B., and E. W. Cotten, *Ind. Eng. Chem.*, **42,** 1905 (1950).
1696 Reynolds, W. L., A. L. Jolusson, and R. H. Clark, *Can. J. Technol.*, **29,** 343 (1951); through *Chem. Abstracts*, **46,** 773 f (1952).
1697 Rheinboldt, H., and R. Kirberg, *J. prakt. Chem.*, **118,** 1 (1928).
1698 Riblett, E. W., and L. C. Rubin, *J. Am. Chem. Soc.*, **59,** 1537 (1937).
1699 Rice, F. O., and A. L. Glasebrook, *J. Am. Chem. Soc.*, **56,** 2381 (1934).
1700 Rice, O. K., and D. V. Sickman, *J. Chem. Phys.*, **4,** 239 (1936).
1701 Rice, O. K., and D. V. Sickman, *J. Chem. Phys.*, **4,** 242 (1936).
1702 Rice, O. K., and D. V. Sickman, *J. Chem. Phys.*, **4,** 608 (1936).
1703 Richards, R. E., and H. W. Thompson, *J. Chem. Soc.*, **1947,** 1260.

1704 Ridd, J. H., Thesis, University College, London, 1951.
1705 Ridd, J. H., *J. Chem. Soc.*, **1955,** 1238.
1706 Ridd, J. H., *J. Soc. Dyers Col.*, **75,** 285 (1959).
1707 Ried, W., *Angew. Chem.*, **64,** 391 (1952).
1708 Roberts, J. D., and M. Halmann, *J. Am. Chem. Soc.*, **75,** 5759 (1953).
1709 Roberts, J. D., C. C. Lee, and W. H. Saunders, *J. Am. Chem. Soc.*, **76,** 4501 (1954).
1710 Roberts, J. D., and R. H. Mazur, *J. Am. Chem. Soc.*, **73,** 2509 (1951).
1711 Roberts, J. D., and R. H. Mazur, *J. Am. Chem. Soc.*, **73,** 3542 (1951).
1712 Roberts, J. D., E. A. McElhill, and R. Armstrong, *J. Am. Chem. Soc.*, **71,** 2923 (1949).
1713 Roberts, J. D., and W. T. Moreland, *J. Am. Chem. Soc.*, **75,** 3165 (1953).
1714 Roberts, J. D., C. M. Regan, and I. Allen, *J. Am. Chem. Soc.*, **74,** 3679 (1952).
1715 Roberts, J. D., and C. M. Regan, *J. Am. Chem. Soc.*, **75,** 2069 (1953).
1716 Roberts, J. D., W. Watanabe, and R. E. McMahon, *J. Am. Chem. Soc.*, **73,** 760 (1951).
1717 Roberts, J. D., W. Watanabe, and R. E. McMahon, *J. Am. Chem. Soc.*, **73,** 2521 (1951).
1718 Roberts, J. D., and J. A. Yancey, *J. Am. Chem. Soc.*, **74,** 5943 (1952).
1719 Robertson, J. M., J. J. Lange, and J. Woodward, *J. Chem. Soc.*, **1939,** 232.
1720 Robertson, J. M., J. J. Lange, and J. Woodward, *Proc. Roy. Soc.*, **A 174,** 398 (1939).
1721 Robertson, P. W., P. B. D. de la Mare, and B. E. Swedlund, *J. Chem. Soc.*, **1953,** 782.
1722 Robertson, P. W., T. R. Hitchings, and G. M. Will, *J. Chem. Soc.*, **1950,** 808.
1723 Robinson, G. M., and R. Robinson, *J. Chem. Soc.*, **113,** 639 (1918).
1724 Robinson, G. M., and R. Robinson, *J. Chem. Soc.*, **125,** 827 (1924).
1725 Robinson, R., and J. Shinoda, *J. Chem. Soc.*, **1926,** 1987.
1726 Roe, A., and J. R. Graham, *J. Am. Chem. Soc.*, **74,** 6297 (1952).
1727 Roeding, A., and H. Link, *Ber.*, **87,** 971 (1954).
1728 Rogers, M. T., T. W. Campbell, and R. W. Maatman, *J. Am. Chem. Soc.*, **73,** 5122 (1951).
1729 Rondestvedt, C. S., and P. K. Chang, *J. Am. Chem. Soc.*, **77,** 6532 (1955).
1730 Rondestvedt, C. S., M. J. Kahn, and O. Vogl, *J. Am. Chem. Soc.*, **78,** 6115 (1956).
1731 Rondestvedt, C. S., and O. Vogl, *J. Am. Chem. Soc.*, **77,** 2313 (1955).
1732 Roseira, A. N., O. A. Stamm, A. Zenhäusern, and H. Zollinger, *Chimia*, **13,** 366 (1959).
1733 Rosenhauer, E., *J. prakt. Chem.*, **107,** 232 (1924).
1734 Rosenhauer, E., and H. Unger, *Ber.*, **61,** 392 (1928).
1735 Ross, W. F., and G. B. Kistiakowsky, *J. Am. Chem. Soc.*, **56,** 1112 (1934).
1736 Rostowzewa, J., *Anilinokrass. Prom.*, **5,** 199 (1935); through *Chem. Zentr.*, **1936 I,** 1965.
1737 Rostowzewa, K., *Z. anal. Chem.*, **105,** 32 (1936).
1738 Rotter, R., *Monatsh.*, **47,** 353 (1926).
1739 Rotter, R., and E. Schaudy, *Monatsh.*, **58,** 245 (1931).
1740 Rowe, F. M., *J. Soc. Dyers Col.*, **46,** 227 (1930).
1741 Rowe, F. M., W. C. Dovey, B. Garforth, E. Levin, J. D. Pask, and A. T. Peters, *J. Chem. Soc.*, **1935,** 1796.
1742 Rowe, F. M., C. Dunbar, and N. H., Williams, *J. Chem. Soc.*, **1931,** 1073.
1743 Rowe, F. M., and C. Dunbar, *J. Chem. Soc.*, **1932,** 11.
1744 Rowe, F. M., M. A. Himmat, and E. Levin, *J. Chem. Soc.*, **1928,** 2556.
1745 Rowe, F. M., and C. Levin, *J. Soc. Dyers Col.*, **40,** 218 (1924).
1746 Rowe, F. M., E. Levin, A. C. Burns, J. S. H. Davies, and W. Tepper, *J. Chem. Soc.*, **1926,** 690.
1747 Rowe, F. M., E. Levin, A. C. Burns, J. S. H. Davies, and W. Tepper, *J. Soc. Dyers Col.*, **42,** 242 (1926).
1748 Rowe, F. M., and E. Levin, *J. Chem. Soc.*, **1928,** 2550.
1749 Rowe, F. M., E. Levin, and A. T. Peters, *J. Chem. Soc.*, **1931,** 1067.
1750 Rowe, F. M., and A. T. Peters, *J. Chem. Soc.*, **1931,** 1065.
1751 Rowe, F. M., and A. T. Peters, *J. Chem. Soc.*, **1931,** 1918.
1752 Rowe, F. M., and F. J. Siddle, *J. Chem. Soc.*, **1932,** 473.
1753 Rowe, F. M., and F. S. Tomlinson, *J. Chem. Soc.*, **1932,** 1118.
1754 Roy, J. C., J. R. Nash, R. R. Williams, and W. H. Hamill, *J. Am. Chem. Soc.*, **78,** 519 (1956).
1755 Royer, R., A. Cheutin, R. Michelet, and E. Allegrini, *Bull. soc. chim. France*, **1957,** 847.
1756 Rüetschi, P., and G. Trümpler, *Helv. Chim. Acta*, **35,** 1021 (1952).
1757 Rüetschi, P., and G. Trümpler, *Helv. Chim. Acta*, **35,** 1486 (1952).
1758 Rüetschi, P., and G. Trümpler, *Helv. Chim. Acta*, **36,** 1650 (1953).
1759 Ruggli, P., and G. Bartusch, *Helv. Chim. Acta*, **27,** 1371 (1944).
1760 Ruggli, P., and E. Caspar, *Helv. Chim. Acta*, **18,** 1414 (1935).
1761 Ruggli, P., and A. Courtin, *Helv. Chim. Acta*, **15,** 75 (1932).

1762 Ruggli, P., and M. Hinovker, *Helv. Chim. Acta*, **17**, 973 (1934).
1763 Ruggli, P., and E. Iselin, *Helv. Chim. Acta*, **27**, 1711 (1944).
1764 Ruggli, P., and E. Iselin, *Helv. Chim. Acta*, **30**, 739 (1947).
1765 Ruggli, P., and C. Petitjean, *Helv. Chim. Acta*, **21**, 711 (1938).
1766 Ruggli, P., and J. Rohner, *Helv. Chim. Acta*, **25**, 1533 (1942).
1767 Ruggli, P., and M. Stäuble, *Helv. Chim. Acta*, **24**, 1080 (1941).
1768 Russell, G. A., *J. Am. Chem. Soc.*, **78**, 1044 (1956).
1769 Ruzicka, L., and H. F. Meldahl, *Helv. Chim. Acta*, **24**, 1321 (1941).

1770 Saini, G., E. Campi, and S. Parodi, *Gazz. chim. ital.*, **87**, 342 (1957).
1771 Sako, S., *Bull. Chem. Soc. Japan*, **9**, 55 (1934); through *Chem. Abstracts*, **28**, 3730 (1934).
1772 Samour, C. M., and J. P. Mason, *J. Am. Chem. Soc.*, **76**, 441 (1954).
1773 Sandmeyer, T., *Ber.*, **17**, 1633 (1884).
1774 Sandmeyer, T., *Ber.*, **17**, 2650 (1884).
1775 Sandmeyer, T., *Ber.*, **20**, 1494 (1887).
1776 Saunders, K. H., *The Aromatic Diazo-Compounds*, 2nd ed., E. Arnold & Co., London, 1949.
     a) chap. VII A; b) chap. X; c) chap. XI; d) Tables XL and XLVI (pp. 353, 387);
     e) p. 6; f) p. 50; g) p. 93; h) p. 99; i) pp. 106–115; k) pp. 126–131; l) p. 137; m)
     p. 174; n) pp. 209–217; o) p. 217; p) p. 221; q) p. 224; r) p. 238; s) pp. 268–275;
     t) p. 305; u) p. 354; v) p. 357; w) p. 378; x) p. 383; y) p. 401.
1777 Saunders, K. H., and W. A. Waters, *J. Chem. Soc.*, **1946**, 1154.
1778 Sawicki, E., *J. Org. Chem.*, **21**, 605 (1956).
1779 Sawicki, E., *J. Org. Chem.*, **22**, 365 (1957).
1780 Sawicki, E., *J. Org. Chem.*, **22**, 621 (1957).
1781 Sawicki, E., *J. Org. Chem.*, **22**, 915 (1957).
1782 Sawicki, E., *J. Org. Chem.*, **22**, 1084 (1957).
1783 Sawicki, E., *J. Org. Chem.*, **23**, 532 (1958).
1784 Sawicki, E., and D. Gerber, *J. Org. Chem.*, **21**, 410 (1956).
1785 Sawicki, E., and F. Ray, *J. Org. Chem.*, **19**, 1686 (1954).
1786 Sax, K., and W. Bergmann, *J. Am. Chem. Soc.*, **77**, 1910 (1955).
1787 Schaafsma, Y., A. F. Bickel, and E. C. Kooyman, *Rec. trav. chim.*, **76**, 180 (1957).
1788 Schaeffer, A., *SVF-Fachorgan*, **11**, 106 (1956).
1789 Scheer, M. D., and H. A. Taylor, *J. Chem. Phys.*, **20**, 653 (1952).
1790 Scheibli, K. G., Thesis, ETH, Zurich, 1952.
1791 Schenck, G. O., and H. Formanek, *Angew. Chem.*, **70**, 505 (1958).
1792 Schenck, G. O., and R. Steinmetz, *Angew. Chem.*, **70**, 504 (1958).
1793 Schenck, G. O., and H. Ziegler, *Ann.*, **584**, 221 (1953).
1794 Schetty, G., *Helv. Chim. Acta*, **32**, 24 (1949).
1795 Schetty, G., *Helv. Chim. Acta*, **35**, 716 (1952).
1796 Schetty, G., *J. Soc. Dyers Col.*, **71**, 705 (1955).
1797 Schetty, G., *Textil-Rundschau*, **11**, 216 (1956).
1798 Schetty, G., and H. Ackermann, *Angew. Chem.*, **70**, 222 (1958).
1799 Schiemann, G., and W. Winkelmüller, *Org. Syntheses, Coll. Vol. II*, 188 (1943).
1800 Schiff, R., *Ber.*, **14**, 1375 (1881).
1801 Schlittler, E., *Helv. Chim. Acta*, **15**, 394 (1932).
1802 Schlittler, E., and A. Lindenmann, *Helv. Chim. Acta*, **32**, 1880 (1949).
1803 Schlotterbeck, F., *Ber.*, **40**, 479 (1907).
1804 Schlotterbeck, F., *Ber.*, **42**, 2559 (1909).
1805 Schmid, H., *Z. Elektrochem.*, **42**, 579 (1936).
1806 Schmid, H., *Z. Elektrochem.*, **42**, 580 (1936).
1807 Schmid, H., *Z. Elektrochem.*, **43**, 626 (1937).
1808 Schmid, H., *Monatsh.*, **85**, 424 (1954).
1809 Schmid, H., and M. G. Fouad, *Monatsh.*, **88**, 631 (1957).
1810 Schmid, H., and G. Muhr, *Ber.*, **70**, 421 (1937).
1811 Schmid, H., and R. Pfeifer, *Monatsh.*, **84**, 842 (1953).
1812 Schmid, H., and A. F. Sami, *Monatsh.*, **86**, 904 (1955).
1813 Schmid, H., and A. Woppmann, *Monatsh.*, **83**, 346 (1952).
1814 Schmid, M., and R. Mory, *Helv. Chim. Acta*, **38**, 1329 (1955).
1815 Schmidlin, J., and M. Bergmann, *Ber.*, **43**, 2821 (1910).
1816 Schmidt, H., and G. Schultz, *Ber.*, **12**, 482 (1879).
1817 Schmidt, H., and G. Schultz, *Ann.*, **207**, 320 (1881).
1818 Schmidt, J., and W. Maier, *Ber.*, **64**, 767 (1931).

1819 Schmidt, J., and W. Maier, *Ber.*, **64**, 778 (1931).
1820 Schmidt, M. P., and A. Hagenböcker, *Ber.*, **54**, 2191 (1921).
1821 Schmidt, O., *Ber.*, **38**, 3201 (1905).
1822 Schmidt, R., and L. Lutz, *Ber.*, **2**, 51 (1869).
1823 Schönberg, A., and W. I. Awad, *J. Chem. Soc.*, **1950**, 72.
1824 Schönberg, A., D. Cernik, and W. Urban, *Ber.*, **64**, 2577 (1931).
1825 Schönberg, A., A. K. Fateen, and A. M. A. Sammour, *J. Am. Chem. Soc.*, **79**, 6020 (1957).
1826 Schönberg, A., H. Kaltschmitt, and H. Schulten, *Ber.*, **66**, 245 (1933).
1827 Schönberg, A., A. Moubasher, and A. Mustafa, *J. Chem. Soc.*, **1941**, 348.
1828 Schönberg, A., A. Mustafa, and W. Latif, *J. Am. Chem. Soc.*, **75**, 2267 (1953).
1829 Schönberg, A., A. Mustafa, and S. M. A. D. Zayed, *J. Am. Chem. Soc.*, **75**, 4302 (1953).
1830 Schönberg, A., and S. Nickel, *Ber.*, **64**, 2323 (1931).
1831 Schönberg, A., O. Schütz, and J. Peter, *Ber.*, **62**, 1663 (1929).
1832 Schönberg, A., and T. Stolpp, *Ber.*, **63**, 3102 (1929).
1833 Schönberg, A., and L. von Vargha, *Ann.*, **483**, 176 (1930).
1834 Schoutissen, H. A. J., *J. Am. Chem. Soc.*, **55**, 4531 (1933).
1835 Schoutissen, H. A. J., *J. Am. Chem. Soc.*, **55**, 4541 (1933).
1836 Schoutissen, H. A. J., *Rec. trav. chim.*, **54**, 381 (1935).
1837 Schoutissen, H. A. J., *J. Am. Chem. Soc.*, **58**, 259 (1936).
1838 Schoutissen, H. A. J., *Rec. trav. chim.*, **57**, 710 (1938).
1839 Schoutissen, H. A. J., *Rec. trav. chim.*, **54**, 97 (1935).
1840 Schoutissen, H. A. J., *Rec. trav. chim.*, **54**, 381 (1935).
1841 Schraube, C., and M. Fritsch, *Ber.*, **29**, 287 (1896).
1842 Schraube, C., and C. Schmidt, *Ber.*, **27**, 514 (1894).
1843 Schroeder, W., and L. Katz, *J. Org. Chem.*, **19**, 718 (1954).
1844 Schroeter, G., *Ber.*, **39**, 1559 (1906).
1845 Schroeter, G., *Ber.*, **42**, 2336 (1909).
1846 Schroeter, G., *Ber.*, **42**, 3356 (1909).
1847 Schroeter, G., *Ber.*, **49**, 2704 (1916).
1848 Schulte-Frohlinde, D., *Ann.*, **612**, 131 (1958).
1849 Schulte-Frohlinde, D., *Ann.*, **612**, 138 (1958).
1850 Schultz, R. F., E. D. Schultz, and J. Cochran, *J. Am. Chem. Soc.*, **62**, 2902 (1940).
1851 Schulz, G. V., *Naturwissenschaften*, **27**, 659 (1939).
1852 Schulz, G. V., *Z. Elektrochem.*, **47**, 265 (1941).
1853 Schulz, G. V., and G. Henrici, *Die makromol. Chem.*, **18/19**, 437 (1956).
1854 Schümann, M., *Ber.*, **33**, 527 (1900).
1855 Schwalbe, C., *Ber.*, **38**, 2196 (1905).
1856 Schwalbe, C., *Ber.*, **38**, 3071 (1905).
1857 Schwarzenbach, G., *Z. Elektrochem.*, **47**, 40 (1941).
1858 Schwarzenbach, G., *Helv. Chim. Acta*, **26**, 420 (1943).
1859 Schwarzenbach, G., *Allgemeine und anorganische Chemie*, 4th ed., G. Thieme, Stuttgart, 1952.
1860 Schwarzenbach, G., *Anal. Chim. Acta*, **7**, 141 (1952).
1861 Schwarzenbach, G., *Helv. Chim. Acta*, **35**, 2344 (1952).
1862 Schwarzenbach, G., *Die komplexometrische Titration*, F. Enke Verlag, Stuttgart, 1955.
1863 Schwarzenbach, G., and H. Ackermann, *Helv. Chim. Acta*, **31**, 1029 (1948).
1864 Schwarzenbach, G., and W. Biedermann, *Helv. Chim. Acta*, **31**, 331 (1948).
1865 Schwarzenbach, G., and W. Biedermann, *Helv. Chim. Acta*, **31**, 678 (1948).
1866 Schwarzenbach, G., M. Brandenberger, G. H. Ott, and O. Hagger, *Helv. Chim. Acta*, **20**, 490 (1937).
1867 Schwarzenbach, G., and M. Brandenberger, *Helv. Chim. Acta*, **20**, 1253 (1937).
1868 Schwarzenbach, G., and E. Felder, *Helv. Chim. Acta*, **27**, 1701 (1944).
1869 Schwarzenbach, G., and O. Hagger, *Helv. Chim. Acta*, **20**, 1591 (1937).
1870 Schwarzenbach, G., and P. Moser, *Helv. Chim. Acta*, **36**, 581 (1953).
1871 Schwarzenbach, G., G. H. Ott, and O. Hagger, *Helv. Chim. Acta*, **20**, 498 (1937).
1872 Schwarzenbach, G., and G. H. Ott, *Helv. Chim. Acta*, **20**, 627 (1937).
1873 Schwarzenbach, G., H. Senn, and G. Anderegg, *Helv. Chim. Acta*, **40**, 1886 (1957).
1874 Schwarzenbach, G., and C. Wittwer, *Helv. Chim. Acta*, **30**, 669 (1947).
1875 Seel, F., *Z. Elektrochem.*, **60**, 741 (1956).
1876 Selwood, P. W., *Magnetochemistry*, 2nd ed., Interscience Publ., New York, 1957.
1877 Semenov, D. A., E. F. Cox, and J. D. Roberts, *J. Am. Chem. Soc.*, **78**, 3221 (1956).
1878 Semenov, D. A., C. H. Shih, and W. G. Young, *J. Am. Chem. Soc.*, **80**, 5472 (1958).
1879 Severin, T., *Angew. Chem.*, **70**, 745 (1958).

1880 Seyewetz, A., and E. Chaix, *Bull. soc. chim. France*, **41,** 332 (1927).
1881 Seyewetz, A., and D. Mounier, *Compt. rend.*, **186,** 953 (1928).
1882 Seyferth, D., *Chem. Revs.*, **55,** 1155 (1955).
1883 Sheehan, J. C., and P. T. Izzo, *J. Am. Chem. Soc.*, **71,** 4059 (1949).
1884 Sheppard, N., and G. B. B. M. Sutherland, *J. Chem. Soc.*, **1947,** 453.
1885 Shikata, M., and I. Tachi, *Mem. Coll. Agr. Kyoto Imp. Univ.*, **17,** 45 (1931); through *Chem. Abstracts*, **26,** 2637 (1932).
1886 Shikata, M., and I. Tachi, *J. Agr. Chem. Soc. Japan*, **8,** 954 (1932); through *Chem. Abstracts*, **27,** 1806 (1933).
1887 Shikata, M., and I. Tachi, *J. Agr. Chem. Soc. Japan*, **9,** 207 (1933); through *Chem. Abstracts*, **27,** 2629 (1933).
1888 Shiner, V. J., *Conference on Hyperconjugation*, Pergamon Press, London, 1959.
1889 Shingu, H., *Sci. Papers Inst. Phys. Chem. Res. Tokyo*, **35,** 78 (1938); through *Chem. Zentr.*, **1939 II,** 4456.
1890 Shoppee, C. W., D. E. Evans, and G. H. R. Summers, *J. Chem. Soc.*, **1957,** 97.
1891 Siersch, A., *Ann.*, **144,** 137 (1867).
1892 Sihlbohm, L., *Acta Chem. Scand.*, **5,** 872 (1951).
1893 Sihlbohm, L., *Acta Chem. Scand.*, **7,** 790 (1953).
1894 Sihlbohm, L., *Acta Chem. Scand.*, **7,** 1197 (1953).
1895 Simamura, O., and N. Inamoto, *Bull. Chem. Soc. Japan*, **27,** 152 (1954).
1896 Simpson, J. C. E., *J. Chem. Soc.*, **1943,** 447.
1897 Simpson, J. C. E., *Condensed Pyridazine and Pyrazine Rings (Cinnolines, Phthalazines and Quinoxalines)*, Interscience Publishers, New York, 1953.
1898 Singer, L., and P. A. Vample, *J. Chem. Soc.*, **1956,** 3971.
1899 Skell, P. S., and R. M. Etter, *Chemistry and Industry*, **1958,** 624.
1900 Skell, P. S., and A. Y. Garner, *J. Am. Chem. Soc.*, **78,** 3409, 5430 (1956).
1901 Skell, P. S., and R. C. Woodworth, *J. Am. Chem. Soc.*, **78,** 4496 (1956).
1902 Skell, P. S., and R. C. Woodworth, *J. Am. Chem. Soc.*, **79,** 2542 (1957).
1903 Skita, A., *Ber.*, **45,** 3312 (1912).
1904 Slotta, K. H., and W. Franke, *Ber.*, **64,** 86 (1931).
1905 Smith, C., and C. H. Watts, *J. Chem. Soc.*, **97,** 562 (1910).
1906 Smith, F. M., Thesis, Leeds University, 1906.
1907 Smith, L. I., and H. H. Hoehn, *Org. Syntheses, Coll. Vol. III*, 356 (1955).
1908 Smith, L. I., and K. L. Howard, *J. Am. Chem. Soc.*, **65,** 159, 165 (1943).
1909 Smith, L. I., and J. H. Paden, *J. Am. Chem. Soc.*, **56,** 2169 (1934).
1910 Smith, L. I., and W. B. Pings, *J. Org. Chem.*, **2,** 95 (1937).
1911 Smith, P., and A. M. Rosenberg, *J. Am. Chem. Soc.*, **81,** 2037 (1959).
1912 Smith, P. A. S., and D. R. Baer, *J. Am. Chem. Soc.*, **74,** 6135 (1952).
1913 Smith, P. A. S., D. R. Baer, and S. N. Ege, *J. Am. Chem. Soc.*, **76,** 4564 (1954).
1914 Snavely, F. A., *Investigations of the Coordinating Tendencies of o-Substituted Aryl-azo-compounds*, Thesis, Penn. State Coll., 1952.
1915 Snavely, F. A., W. C. Fernelius, and B. P. Block, *J. Am. Chem. Soc.*, **79,** 1028 (1957).
1916 Snavely, F. A., W. C. Fernelius, and B. E. Douglas, *J. Soc. Dyers Col.*, **73,** 491 (1957).
1917 Snavely, F. A., B. D. Krecker, and C. G. Clark, *J. Am. Chem. Soc.*, **81,** 2337 (1959).
1918 Snow, C. C., *Ind. Eng. Chem.*, **24,** 1420 (1932).
1919 Söll, H., in *Houben-Weyl's Methoden der organischen Chemie*, E. Müller, ed., 4th ed., G. Thieme, Stuttgart, 1958, Vol. 11/2, p. 133.
1920 Specklin, R., and J. Meybeck, *Bull. soc. chim. France*, (5), **18,** 621 (1951).
1921 Sprengling, G. R., and C. W. Lewis, *J. Am. Chem. Soc.*, **75,** 5709 (1953).
1922 Staab, H. A., *Ber.*, **90,** 1320 (1957).
1923 Staab, H. A., *Einführung in die theoretische organische Chemie*, Verlag Chemie, Weinheim, 1959, pp. 353–361.
1924 Staedel, W., *Ber.*, **27,** 3362 (1894).
1925 Stamm, O. A., Thesis, Basle University, 1957.
1926 Stamm, O. A., and H. Zollinger, *Helv. Chim. Acta*, **40,** 1105 (1957).
1927 Stamm, O. A., and H. Zollinger, *Helv. Chim. Acta*, **40,** 1955 (1957).
1928 Stamm, O. A., and H. Zollinger, unpublished.
1929 Stammreich, H., *Experientia*, **6,** 225 (1950).
1930 Stannett, V., and R. B. Mesrobian, *J. Am. Chem. Soc.*, **72,** 4125 (1950).
1931 Staudinger, H., E. Anthes, and F. Pfenninger, *Ber.*, **49,** 1928 (1916).
1932 Staudinger, H., J. Becker, and H. Hirzel, *Ber.*, **49,** 1978 (1916).
1933 Staudinger, H., and A. Gaule, *Ber.*, **49,** 1897 (1916).

1934 Staudinger, H., and A. Gaule, *Ber.*, **49,** 1951 (1916).
1935 Staudinger, H., and J. Goldstein, *Ber.*, **49,** 1923 (1916).
1936 Staudinger, H., and H. Hirzel, *Ber.*, **49,** 2522 (1916).
1937 Staudinger, H., and O. Kupfer, *Ber.*, **44,** 2197 (1911).
1938 Staudinger, H., and O. Kupfer, *Ber.*, **45,** 501 (1912).
1939 Staudinger, H., and O. Kupfer, *Ber.*, **45,** 505 (1912).
1940 Staudinger, H., and J. Meyer, *Helv. Chim. Acta*, **2,** 608 (1919).
1941 Staudinger, H., and J. Meyer, *Helv. Chim. Acta*, **2,** 619 (1919).
1942 Staudinger, H., and J. Meyer, *Helv. Chim. Acta*, **5,** 75 (1921).
1943 Staudinger, H., and F. Pfenninger, *Ber.*, **49,** 1941 (1916).
1944 Staudinger, H., and T. Reber, *Helv. Chim. Acta*, **4,** 1 (1921).
1945 Staudinger, H., and J. Siegwart, *Ber.*, **49,** 1918 (1916).
1946 Stearn, A. E., and H. Eyring, *Chem. Revs.*, **29,** 509 (1941).
1947 Steel, C., and A. F. Trotman-Dickenson, *J. Chem. Soc.*, **1959,** 975.
1948 Steiger, M., and T. Reichstein, *Helv. Chim. Acta*, **20,** 1040 (1937).
1949 Steiger, M., and T. Reichstein, *Helv. Chim. Acta*, **20,** 1164 (1937).
1950 Stein, O., *Ber.*, **27,** 2806 (1894).
1951 Stepanov, B. I., *J. Gen. Chem. U.S.S.R.*, **28,** 2676 (1958).
1952 Stephenson, O., and W. A. Waters, *J. Chem. Soc.*, **1939,** 1796.
1953 Stephenson, O., and W. A. Waters, *J. Chem. Soc.*, **1939,** 1799.
1954 Stepukhovich, A. D., and E. G. Kaplan, *Zhur. Fis. Khim.*, **30,** 928 (1956); through *Chem. Abstracts*, **50,** 16294i (1956).
1955 Stevens, C. L., B. T. Gillis, J. C. French, and T. H. Haskell, *J. Am. Chem. Soc.*, **80,** 6088 (1958).
1956 Stiles, M., and A. J. Sisti, *J. Org. Chem.*, **24,** 268 (1959).
1957 Stoll, M., and W. Scherrer, *Helv. Chim. Acta*, **23,** 941 (1940).
1958 Stollé, R., *Ber.*, **45,** 274 (1912).
1959 Stollé, R., *Ber.*, **45,** 2680 (1912).
1960 Stollé, R., *J. prakt. Chem.*, **123,** 82 (1929).
1961 Stollé, R., and G. Adam, *J. prakt. Chem.*, **111,** 167 (1925).
1962 Stollé, R., and K. Leffler, *Ber.*, **57,** 1061 (1924).
1963 Stollé, R., and W. Reichert, *J. prakt. Chem.*, **123,** 74 (1929).
1964 Stollé, R., and W. Reichert, *J. prakt. Chem.*, **123,** 82 (1929).
1965 Strachan, A. N., and W. A. Noyes, *J. Am. Chem. Soc.*, **76,** 3258 (1954).
1966 Straubel, R., *Z. anorg. Chem.*, **142,** 133 (1925).
1967 Strecker, A., *Ann.*, **68,** 54 (1848).
1968 Strecker, A., *Ber.*, **4,** 784 (1871).
1969 Streitwieser, A., *Chem. Revs.*, **56,** 571 (1956).
1970 Streitwieser, A., *Chem. Revs.*, **56,** 583 (1956), Table 2.
1971 Streitwieser, A., *J. Org. Chem.*, **22,** 861 (1957).
1972 Streitwieser, A., and C. E. Coverdale, *J. Am. Chem. Soc.*, **81,** 4275 (1959).
1973 Streitwieser, A., and W. D. Schaeffer, *J. Am. Chem. Soc.*, **78,** 5597 (1956).
1974 Streitwieser, A., and W. D. Schaeffer, *J. Am. Chem. Soc.*, **79,** 2888 (1957).
1975 Strel'tsova, A. A., and N. D. Zelinskii, *Izv. Akad. Nauk S.S.S.R.*, **1941,** 401; through *Chem. Abstracts*, **36,** 418 (1942).
1976 Suais, E., *Bull. Soc. Ind. Mulhouse*, **77,** 75 (1907); through *Chem. Abstracts*, **5,** 3732 (1912).
1977 Suckfüll, F., and H. Haubrich, *Angew. Chem.*, **70,** 238 (1958).
1978 Sugden, S., *J. Chem. Soc.*, **1932,** 246.
1979 Suizu, K., and N. Yokozima, *J. Soc. Chem. Ind. Japan*, **19,** 32 (1926); through *Chem. Abstracts*, **20,** 2485 (1926).
1980 Süs, O., *Ann.*, **556,** 65, 85 (1944).
1981 Süs, O., *Ann.*, **579,** 133 (1953).
1982 Süs, O., M. Glos, K. Möller, and H. D. Eberhardt, *Ann.*, **583,** 150 (1953).
1983 Süs, O., and K. Möller, *Ann.*, **593,** 91 (1955).
1984 Süs, O., K. Möller, and H. Heiss, *Ann.*, **598,** 123 (1956).
1985 Süs, O., and K. Möller, *Ann.*, **599,** 233 (1956).
1986 Süs, O., H. Steppan, and R. Dietrich, *Ann.*, **617,** 20 (1958).
1987 Suter, R., and T. Häfeli, *Chimia*, **13,** 230 (1959).
1988 Swain, C. G., and A. D. Ketley, *J. Am. Chem. Soc.*, **77,** 3410 (1955).
1989 Swain, C. G., C. B. Scott, and K. H. Lohmann, *J. Am. Chem. Soc.*, **75,** 136 (1953).
1990 Swain, C. G., and C. B. Scott, *J. Am. Chem. Soc.*, **75,** 141 (1953).
1991 Swain, C. G., W. H. Stockmeyer, and J. T. Clarke, *J. Am. Chem. Soc.*, **72,** 5426 (1950).

1992 Swan, G. A., and P. Kelly, *J. Chem. Soc.*, **1954,** 416.
1993 Swann, S., C. Y. Chen, and H. D. Kerfman, *J. Electrochem. Soc.*, **99,** 460 (1952).
1994 Swern, D., *J. Am. Chem. Soc.*, **69,** 1692 (1947).
1995 Swern, D., *Chem. Revs.*, **45,** 1 (1949).

1996 Tafel, J., *Ber.*, **18,** 1739 (1885).
1997 Taft, R. W., and D. J. Smith, *J. Am. Chem. Soc.*, **76,** 305 (1954).
1998 Taft, R. W., personal communication.
1999 Taipale, K. A., *Ber.*, **56,** 966 (1923).
2000 Talat-Erben, M., and S. Bywater, *J. Am. Chem. Soc.*, **77,** 3710 (1955).
2001 Talat-Erben, M., and S. Bywater, *J. Am. Chem. Soc.*, **77,** 3712 (1955).
2002 Tamburello, A., and A. Milazzo, *Gazz. chim. ital.*, **38 I,** 95 (1908).
2003 Tassilly, M. E., *Compt. rend.*, **157,** 1148 (1913).
2004 Tassilly, M. E., *Compt. rend.*, **158,** 335, 489 (1914).
2005 Tassilly, M. E., *Bull. soc. chim. France*, **27,** 19 (1928).
2006 Taube, H., *Chem. Revs.*, **50,** 69 (1952).
2007 Taylor, H. A., and R. G. Flowers, *J. Chem. Phys.*, **10,** 110 (1942).
2008 Taylor, H. A., and F. P. Jahn, *J. Chem. Phys.*, **7,** 470 (1939).
2009 Taylor, H. A., and F. P. Jahn, *J. Chem. Phys.*, **7,** 474 (1939).
2010 Taylor, T. W. J., *J. Chem. Soc.*, **1928,** 1099.
2011 Taylor, T. W. J., *J. Chem. Soc.*, **1928,** 1897.
2012 Taylor, T. W. J., and L. S. Price, *J. Chem. Soc.*, **1929,** 2052.
2013 Tchoubar, B., *Bull. soc. chim. France*, **1949,** 164.
2014 Tedder, J. M., *J. Am. Chem. Soc.*, **79,** 6090 (1957).
2015 Tedder, J. M., *J. Chem. Soc.*, **1957,** 4003.
2016 Tedder, J. M., and G. Theaker, *J. Chem. Soc.*, **1957,** 4008.
2017 Tedder, J. M., and G. Theaker, *J. Chem. Soc.*, **1958,** 2573.
2018 Tedder, J. M., and G. Theaker, *J. Chem. Soc.*, **1959,** 257.
2019 Terentiev, A. P., *J. Gen. Chem. U.S.S.R.*, **7,** 2026 (1937); through *Chem. Zentr.*, **1938 I,** 4315.
2020 Terentiev, A. P., and A. A. Demidowa, *J. Gen. Chem. U.S.S.R.*, **7,** 2464 (1937); through *Chem. Zentr.*, **1939 I,** 640.
2021 Terentiev, A. P., G. D. Galpern, and E. V. Vinogradova, *Wiss. Ber. Mosk. Staatsuniv.*, **6,** 249 (1936); through *Chem. Zentr.*, **1937 II,** 1629.
2022 Terentiev, A. P., and L. L. Gomberg, *J. Gen. Chem. U.S.S.R.*, **8,** 662 (1938).
2023 Terentiev, A. P., and J. M. Iwanowa, *J. Gen. Chem. U.S.S.R.*, **7,** 2028 (1937); through *Chem. Zentr.*, **1938 I,** 4315.
2024 Terentiev, A. P., and J. D. Mogiljanskij, *Doklady Akad. Nauk S.S.S.R.*, **103,** 91 (1955).
2025 Terentiev, A. P., E. V. Vinogradova, and G. D. Galpern, *Doklady Akad. Nauk S.S.S.R.*, **4,** 267 (1935); through *Chem. Zentr.*, **1936 I,** 4043.
2026 Terentiev, A. P., E. V. Vinogradova, and G. D. Galpern, *Sci. Repts. Moscow State Univ.*, **6,** 235, 243 (1936); through *Chem. Zentr.*, **1937 II,** 1628.
2027 Theilacker, W., and E. C. Fintelmann, *Ber.*, **91,** 1597 (1958).
2028 Thiele, J., *Ann.*, **271,** 127 (1892).
2029 Thiele, J., *Ann.*, **271,** 134 (1892).
2030 Thiele, J., *Ber.*, **42,** 2575 (1909).
2031 Thiele, J., *Ann.*, **376,** 239 (1910).
2032 Thiele, J., *Ber.*, **44,** 2522 (1911).
2033 Thiele, J., and K. Heuser, *Ann.*, **290,** 1 (1896).
2034 Thiele, J., and O. Stange, *Ann.*, **283,** 1 (1894).
2035 Thomas, D. S., and A. Weissberger, in *The Theory of the Photographic Process*, C. E. K. Mees, ed., Macmillan, New York, 1942, p. 394.
2036 Tichwinski, M., *J. Russ. Phys. Chem. Soc.*, **35,** 673 (1903); through *Chem. Zentr.*, **1903 II,** 1271.
2037 Tiffeneau, M., and H. Calmmann, *Bull. soc. chim. France*, **2,** 1876 (1935).
2038 Tiffeneau, M., and J. Lévy, *Bull. soc. chim. France*, **49,** 1847 (1931).
2039 Tiffeneau, M., J. Lévy, and E. Ditz, *Bull. soc. chim. France*, **2,** 1871 (1935).
2040 Tishler, M., K. Pfister, R. D. Babson, K. Ladenburg, and A. J. Fleming, *J. Am. Chem. Soc.*, **69,** 1487 (1947).
2041 Tong, L. K. J., *J. Phys. Chem.*, **58,** 1090 (1954).
2042 Tong, L. K. J., and M. C. Glesmann, *J. Am. Chem. Soc.*, **78,** 5827 (1956).
2043 Tong, L. K. J., and M. C. Glesmann, *J. Am. Chem. Soc.*, **79,** 583 (1957).

2044 Tong, L. K. J., and M. C. Glesmann, *J. Am. Chem. Soc.*, **79,** 592 (1957).
2045 Tong, L. K. J., and M. C. Glesmann, *J. Am. Chem. Soc.*, **79,** 4305 (1957).
2046 Tong, L. K. J., and M. C. Glesmann, *J. Am. Chem. Soc.*, **79,** 4310 (1957).
2047 Treibs, W., W. Kirchhof, and W. Ziegenbein, *Fortschr. Chem. Forsch.*, **3,** 334 (1955).
2048 Treibs, W., and W. Schrodt, *Ann.*, **586,** 202 (1954).
2049 Treibs, W., and A. Stein, *Ann.*, **572,** 165 (1951).
2050 Treibs, W., B. Ulrici, and A. Stein, *Ann.*, **573,** 93 (1951).
2051 Treibs, W., and W. Ziegenbein, *Ann.*, **586,** 194 (1954).
2052 Troshchenko, A. T., and A. A. Petrov, *Doklady Akad. Nauk S.S.S.R.*, **119,** 292 (1958).
2053 Turner, H. S., *J. Chem. Soc.*, **1949,** 2282.
2054 Turner, S. E., and R. C. Anderson, *J. Am. Chem. Soc.*, **71,** 912 (1949).
2055 Turney, T. A., and G. A. Wright, *J. Chem. Soc.*, **1958,** 2415.
2056 Turney, T. A., and G. A. Wright, *Chem. Revs.*, **59,** 497 (1959).

2057 Ueno, K., and S. Akiyoshi, *J. Am. Chem. Soc.*, **76,** 3670 (1954).
2058 Ueno, K., *J. Am. Chem. Soc.*, **79,** 3066 (1957).
2059 Ueno, S., and F. Suzuki, *J. Soc. Chem. Japan (Suppl.)*, **36,** 615 B (1933); through *Chem. Zentr.*, **1934 I,** 849.
2060 Ugi, I., R. Huisgen, K. Clusius, and M. Vecchi, *Angew. Chem.*, **68,** 753 (1956).
2061 Ugi, I., and R. Huisgen, *Ber.*, **91,** 531 (1958).
2062 Ugi, I., H. Perlinger, and L. Behringer, *Ber.*, **91,** 2324 (1958).
2063 Ugryumov, P. G., *J. Gen. Chem. U.S.S.R.*, **10,** 1985 (1940); through *Chem. Abstracts*, **35,** 4362 (1941).
2064 Ukida, J., G. Takayama, and T. Kominami, *Chem. High Polymers (Japan)*, **11,** 233 (1954); through *Chem. Abstracts*, **50,** 113 a (1956).
2065 Ullmann, F., and C. Gross, *Ber.*, **43,** 2694 (1910).
2066 Upton, A. W. H., and G. T. Morgan, *J. Chem. Soc.*, **111,** 187 (1917).
2067 Urey, H. C., and G. I. Lavin, *J. Am. Chem. Soc.*, **51,** 3286 (1929).
2068 Urry, W. H., and J. R. Eiszner, *J. Am. Chem. Soc.*, **73,** 2977 (1951).
2069 Urry, W. H., and J. R. Eiszner, *J. Am. Chem. Soc.*, **74,** 5822 (1952).
2070 Urry, W. H., J. R. Eiszner, and J. W. Wilt, *J. Am. Chem. Soc.*, **79,** 918 (1957).
2071 Urry, W. H., and J. W. Wilt, *J. Am. Chem. Soc.*, **76,** 2594 (1954).

2072 Van Slyke, D. D., *J. Biol. Chem.*, **12,** 275 (1912).
2073 Van Vleck, J. H., *J. Chem. Phys.*, **3,** 803, 807 (1935).
2074 Vaughan, J., and L. Phillips, *J. Chem. Soc.*, **1947,** 1560.
2075 Veibel, S., *Can. J. Chem.*, **32,** 638 (1954).
2076 Veley, V. H., *J. Chem. Soc.*, **95,** 1186 (1909).
2077 Venkataraman, K., *The Chemistry of Synthetic Dyes*, Academic Press, New York, 1952, Vol. I. a) p. 428; b) p. 452; c) p. 497; d) p. 693.
2078 Veselý, V., and K. Dvořák, *Bull. soc. chim. France*, **31,** 421 (1922).
2079 Vignon, L., and A. Simonet, *Bull. soc. chim. France*, **33,** 655 (1905).
2080 Vittum, P. W., and A. Weissberger, *J. Phot. Sci.*, **2,** 81 (1954).
2081 Vladimirtsev, I. F., and I. Y. Postovskii, *Doklady Akad. Nauk S.S.S.R.*, **83,** 855 (1952); through *Chem. Abstracts*, **46,** 7904 (1952).
2082 Vloed van de, H., Thesis, Marburg University, 1946.
2083 Vogl, O., and C. S. Rondestvedt, *J. Am. Chem. Soc.*, **77,** 3067 (1955).
2084 Vogl, O., and C. S. Rondestvedt, *J. Am. Chem. Soc.*, **78,** 3799 (1956).
2085 Volman, D. H., P. A. Leighton, F. F. Blacet, and R. K. Brinton, *J. Chem. Phys.*, **18,** 203 (1950).
2086 Volpi, A., *Gazz. chim. ital.*, **77,** 473 (1947).
2087 Vorländer, D., and F. Meyer, *Ann.*, **320,** 122 (1902).
2088 Vosburgh, W. C., and G. R. Cooper, *J. Am. Chem. Soc.*, **63,** 437 (1941).

2089 Wacker, L., *Ber.*, **35,** 3922 (1902).
2090 Waentig, P., and J. Thomas, *Ber.*, **46,** 3923 (1913).
2091 Wahl, H., *Bull. soc. chim. France*, **1956,** 321.
2092 Wahl, H., and M. T. Lebris, *Bull. soc. chim. France*, **1952,** 436.
2093 Wahl, H., and M. T. Lebris, *Compt. rend.*, **234,** 631 (1952).
2094 Wahl, H., and M. T. Lebris, *Compt. rend.*, **235,** 1405 (1952).
2095 Wahl, H., and M. T. Lebris, *Compt. rend.*, **236,** 294 (1953).
2096 Wahl, H., and M. T. Lebris, *Bull. soc. chim. France*, **1954,** 587.

2097 Wahl, H., and M. T. Lebris, *Bull. soc. chim. France*, **1954,** 1277.
2098 Wahl, H., and M. T. Lebris, *Bull. soc. chim. France*, **1954,** 1281.
2099 Walker, J., *J. Chem. Soc.*, **1940,** 1304.
2100 Wallach, O., and L. Belli, *Ber.*, **13,** 525 (1880).
2101 Walling, C., *J. Am. Chem. Soc.*, **71,** 1930 (1949).
2102 Walling, C., *J. Polymer Sci.*, **14,** 214 (1954).
2103 Walling, C., *Free Radicals in Solution*, J. Wiley & Sons, New York, 1957. a) sect. 3.3;
      b) p. 514.
2104 Walther, R., *J. prakt. Chem.*, **52,** 141 (1895).
2105 Walther, R., *J. prakt. Chem.*, **53,** 433 (1896).
2106 Wang, C. H., S. H. Hsiao, E. Saklad, and S. G. Cohen, *J. Am. Chem. Soc.*, **79,** 2661 (1957).
2107 Ward, A. L., and E. E. Makin, *J. Am. Chem. Soc.*, **69,** 657 (1947).
2108 Waring, C. E., and J. R. Abrams, *J. Am. Chem. Soc.*, **63,** 2757 (1941).
2109 Warwick, G. P., *J. Soc. Dyers Col.*, **75,** 291 (1959).
2110 Waters, W. A., *Physical Aspects of Organic Chemistry*, 1st ed., Routledge, London, 1937,
      p. 181.
2111 Waters, W. A., *J. Chem. Soc.*, **1942,** 266.
2112 Waters, W. A., *Chemistry of Free Radicals*, 2nd ed., Clarendon Press, London, 1948, p. 162.
2113 Watson, E. R., *Proc. Chem. Soc.*, **29,** 348 (1913).
2114 Watson, E. R., and D. B. Meek, *J. Chem. Soc.*, **107,** 1567 (1915).
2115 Watson, J. S., *J. Chem. Soc.*, **1956,** 3677.
2116 Wegmann, J., *J. Soc. Dyers Col.*, **71,** 777 (1955).
2117 Weidenhagen, R., and H. Wegner, *Ber.*, **72,** 2010 (1939).
2118 Weil, T., B. Prijs, and H. Erlenmeyer, *Helv. Chim. Acta*, **35,** 616 (1952).
2119 Weil, T., B. Prijs, and H. Erlenmeyer, *Helv. Chim. Acta*, **36,** 142 (1953).
2120 Weinberg von, A., *Ber.*, **25,** 1610 (1892).
2121 Weininger, J. L., and O. K. Rice, *J. Am. Chem. Soc.*, **74,** 6216 (1952).
2122 Weinstein, J., and E. McIninch, *Abstr. 135th Meeting ACS*, **1959,** p. 103–O.
2123 Weissberger, A., and H. Bach, *Ber.*, **65,** 265 (1932).
2124 Weissberger, A., and R. Haase, *Ber.*, **64,** 2896 (1931).
2125 Weizmann, A., *Trans. Faraday Soc.*, **36,** 978 (1940).
2126 Werigo, A., *Ann.*, **135,** 176 (1865).
2127 Werigo, A., *Ann.*, **165,** 189 (1873).
2128 Werle, W., Thesis, Marburg University, 1937.
2129 Werner, A., *Beiträge zur Theorie der Affinität und Valenz*, Vierteljahresschrift der Zürcher
      Naturf. Ges., **36,** 1 (1891).
2130 Werner, A., *Z. anorg. Chem.*, **3,** 267 (1893).
2131 Werner, A., *Ber.*, **41,** 1062 (1908).
2132 Werner, A., *Neuere Anschauungen auf dem Gebiete der anorganischen Chemie*, 5th ed., Friedrich
      Vieweg, Braunschweig, 1923.
2133 Werner, A., and A. Miolati, *Z. physik. Chem.*, **12,** 35 (1893).
2134 Werner, A., and A. Miolati, *Z. physik. Chem.*, **14,** 506 (1894).
2135 Werner, A., and E. Stiasny, *Ber.*, **32,** 3256 (1899).
2136 Werner, A. E. A., *Nature*, **160,** 644 (1947).
2137 Werner, E. A., *J. Chem. Soc.*, **115,** 1093 (1919).
2138 Wessely, F., E. Schinzel, G. Spiteller, and G. Klezl, *Monatsh.*, **90,** 96 (1959).
2139 Wesson, L. G., *Tables of Electric Dipole Moments*, Technology Press, Cambridge, Mass.,
      1948.
2140 West, B., *J. Chem. Soc.*, **1952,** 3115.
2141 West, W., and R. B. Killingsworth, *J. Chem. Phys.*, **6,** 1 (1938).
2142 Wheland, G. W., *J. Am. Chem. Soc.*, **64,** 906 (1942).
2143 Wheland, G. W., *Resonance in Organic Chemistry*, J. Wiley & Sons, New York, 1955.
      a) p. 496.
2144 Whetsel, K. B., G. F. Hawkins, and F. E. Johnson, *J. Am. Chem. Soc.*, **78,** 3360 (1956).
2145 White, G. F., and K. H. Knight, *J. Am. Chem. Soc.*, **45,** 1780 (1923).
2146 Whitmore, F. C., and D. P. Langlois, *J. Am. Chem. Soc.*, **54,** 3441 (1932).
2147 Whitmore, F. C., and R. S. Thorpe, *J. Am. Chem. Soc.*, **63,** 1118 (1941).
2148 Wiberg, K. B., *Chem. Revs.*, **55,** 713 (1955).
2149 Wiberg, K. B., and T. W. Hutton, *J. Am. Chem. Soc.*, **78,** 1640 (1956).
2150 Wieland, H., *Ber.*, **42,** 3020 (1909).
2151 Wieland, H., *Ber.*, **45,** 492 (1912).
2152 Wieland, H., *Ann.*, **514,** 145 (1934).

2153 Wieland, H., and H. Fressel, *Ann.*, **392,** 133 (1912).
2154 Wieland, H., A. Hintermaier, and I. Dennstedt, *Ann.*, **452,** 1 (1927).
2155 Wieland, H., H. vom Hove, and K. Borner, *Ann.*, **446,** 31 (1926).
2156 Wieland, H., T. Ploetz, and H. Indest, *Ann.*, **532,** 166 (1937).
2157 Wieland, H., E. Popper, and H. Seefried, *Ber.*, **55,** 1816 (1922).
2158 Wieland, H., E. Popper, and H. Seefried, *Ber.*, **55,** 1822 (1922).
2159 Wieland, H., and O. Probst, *Ann.*, **530,** 277 (1937).
2160 Wieland, H., and C. Reisenegger, *Ann.*, **401,** 244 (1913).
2161 Wiles, L. A., *Chem. Revs.*, **56,** 329 (1956).
2162 Willard, H. H., and J. A. Dean, *Anal. Chem.*, **22,** 1264 (1950).
2163 Willstätter, R., *Ber.*, **31,** 1547 (1898).
2164 Willstätter, R., *Ber.*, **31,** 2498 (1898).
2165 Willstätter, R., and J. Parnas, *Ber.*, **40,** 3971 (1907).
2166 Willstätter, R., E. Ulbricht, L. Pogány, and C. Maimeri, *Ann.*, **477,** 161 (1929).
2167 Wilson, T. B., and G. B. Kistiakowsky, *J. Am. Chem. Soc.*, **80,** 2934 (1958).
2168 Wingler, A., *Peter Griess – Leben und Wirken eines grossen Farbstoffchemikers*, Verlag Farben-
     fabriken Bayer, Leverkusen, 1958.
2169 Winkel, A., and H. Siebert, *Ber.*, **74,** 670 (1941).
2170 Winstein, S., *Experientia Suppl. II*, 137 (1955).
2171 Winstein, S., and N. J. Holness, *J. Am. Chem. Soc.*, **77,** 5562 (1955).
2172 Wislicenus, H., *J. prakt. Chem.*, **54,** 18 (1896).
2173 Wistar, R., and P. D. Bartlett, *J. Am. Chem. Soc.*, **63,** 413 (1941).
2174 Witt, O. N., *Ber.*, **9,** 522 (1876).
2175 Witt, O. N., *Ber.*, **20,** 571 (1887).
2176 Witt, O. N., *Ber.*, **21,** 325 (1888).
2177 Witt, O. N., *Ber.*, **42,** 2953 (1909).
2178 Wittwer, C., and H. Zollinger, *Helv. Chim. Acta*, **37,** 1954 (1954).
2179 Wizinger, R., *Organische Farbstoffe*, F. Dümmler-Verlag, Bonn, 1933.
2180 Wizinger, R., *J. prakt. Chem.*, **157,** 129 (1941).
2181 Wizinger, R., *Chimia*, **7,** 273 (1953).
2182 Wizinger, R., *Zeitsch. f. Naturforschung*, **9 b,** 729 (1954).
2183 Wizinger, R., *Angew. Chem.*, **70,** 197 (1958).
2184 Wizinger, R., and K. Atakan, *Helv. Chim. Acta*, **39,** 1330 (1956).
2185 Wizinger, R., and B. Cyriax, *Helv. Chim. Acta*, **28,** 1018 (1945).
2186 Wohl, A., *Ber.*, **25,** 3631 (1892).
2187 Wolff, L., *Ann.*, **312,** 125 (1900).
2188 Wolff, L., *Ann.*, **325,** 129 (1902).
2189 Wolff, L., *Ann.*, **394,** 23 (1912).
2190 Wolff, L., and A. Hall, *Ber.*, **36,** 3612 (1903).
2191 Wolff, L., and R. Krueche, *Ann.*, **394,** 48 (1912).
2192 Wolfrom, M. L., and R. L. Brown, *J. Am. Chem. Soc.*, **65,** 1516 (1943).
2193 Wolfrom, M. L., J. D. Crum, J. B. Miller, and D. I. Weisblat, *J. Am. Chem. Soc.*, **81,**
     243 (1959).
2194 Wolfrom, M. L., and J. B. Miller, *J. Am. Chem. Soc.*, **80,** 1678 (1958).
2195 Wolfrom, M. L., S. W. Waisbrot, and R. L. Brown, *J. Am. Chem. Soc.*, **64,** 1701 (1942).
2196 Wolfrom, M. L., S. W. Waisbrot, and R. L. Brown, *J. Am. Chem. Soc.*, **64,** 2329 (1942).
2197 Work, T. S., *J. Chem. Soc.*, **1940,** 1315.
2198 Wyman, G. M., personal communication.

2199 Yates, P., *J. Am. Chem. Soc.*, **74,** 5376 (1952).
2200 Yates, P., D. G. Farnum, and D. W. Wiley, *Chemistry and Industry*, **1958,** 69.
2201 Yates, P., and E. W. Robb, *J. Am. Chem. Soc.*, **79,** 5760 (1957).
2202 Yates, P., B. L. Shapiro, N. Yoda, and J. Fugger, *J. Am. Chem. Soc.*, **79,** 5756 (1957).
2203 Yates, P., and B. L. Shapiro, *J. Org. Chem.*, **23,** 759 (1958).
2204 Yates, P., and B. L. Shapiro, *J. Am. Chem. Soc.*, **81,** 212 (1959).
2205 Yeh, S. J., and H. H. Jaffé, *J. Org. Chem.*, **24,** 717 (1959).

2206 Zahn, H., and O. Waschka, *Die makromol. Chem.*, **18/19,** 201 (1956).
2207 Zahn, H., B. Wollemann, and O. Waschka, *Z. physiol. Chem.*, **294,** 100 (1953).
2208 Zechmeister, L., O. Frehden, and P. F. Jörgensen, *Naturwissenschaften*, **26,** 495 (1938).
2209 Zelinski, R. P., and M. Jursich, *J. Am. Chem. Soc.*, **78,** 1015 (1956).
2210 Zenhäusern, A., and H. Zollinger, unpublished.

2211 Ziegler, E., *Oesterreich. Chem. Ztg.*, **53**, 31 (1952).
2212 Ziegler, E., and G. Snatzke, *Monatsh.*, **84**, 278 (1953).
2213 Ziegler, E., and G. Snatzke, *Monatsh.*, **84**, 610 (1953).
2214 Ziegler, E., and G. Zigeuner, *Monatsh.*, **79**, 363 (1948).
2215 Ziegler, E., and G. Zigeuner, *Monatsh.*, **80**, 295 (1949).
2216 Ziegler, E., G. Zigeuner, and F. Aspan, *Monatsh.*, **81**, 480 (1950).
2217 Ziegler, E., and G. Zigeuner, *Monatsh.*, **82**, 238 (1951).
2218 Ziegler, J. H., and M. Locher, *Ber.*, **20**, 834 (1887).
2219 Ziegler, K., *Brennstoff-Chemie*, **30**, 181 (1949).
2220 Ziegler, K., W. Deparade, and W. Meye, *Ann.*, **567**, 141 (1950).
2221 Ziegler, K., E. Eimers, W. Hechelhammer, and H. Wilms, *Ann.*, **567**, 43 (1950).
2222 Ziegler, K., and K. Hafner, *Angew. Chem.*, **67**, 301 (1955).
2223 Ziegler, K., H. Sauer, L. Bruns, H. Froitzheim, and J. Schneider, *Ann.*, **589**, 122 (1954).
2224 Zincke, T., and H. Bindewald, *Ber.*, **17**, 3026 (1884).
2225 Zinin, N., *J. prakt. Chem.*, **36**, 93 (1841).
2226 Zinin, N., *Ann.*, **137**, 376 (1866).
2227 Zollinger, H., *Chem. Revs.*, **51**, 347 (1952).
2228 Zollinger, H., *Helv. Chim. Acta*, **36**, 1070 (1953).
2229 Zollinger, H., *Helv. Chim. Acta*, **36**, 1723 (1953).
2230 Zollinger, H., *Helv. Chim. Acta*, **36**, 1730 (1953).
2231 Zollinger, H., *Helv. Chim. Acta*, **36**, 1732 (1953).
2232 Zollinger, H., *Helv. Chim. Acta*, **38**, 1597 (1955).
2233 Zollinger, H., *Helv. Chim. Acta*, **38**, 1617 (1955).
2234 Zollinger, H., *Helv. Chim. Acta*, **38**, 1623 (1955).
2235 Zollinger, H., *Experientia*, **12**, 165 (1956).
2236 Zollinger, H., *Helv. Chim. Acta*, **39**, 1600 (1956).
2237 Zollinger, H., *Chemie der Azofarbstoffe*, Birkhäuser Verlag, Basel, 1958.
2238 Zollinger, H., unpublished.
2239 Zollinger, H., and W. Büchler, *Helv. Chim. Acta*, **34**, 591 (1951).
2240 Zollinger, H., and W. Büchler, *Helv. Chim. Acta*, **34**, 600 (1951).
2241 Zollinger, H., W. Büchler, and C. Wittwer, *Helv. Chim. Acta*, **36**, 1711 (1953).
2242 Zollinger, H., and C. Wittwer, *Helv. Chim. Acta*, **35**, 1209 (1952).
2243 Zollinger, H., and C. Wittwer, *Helv. Chim. Acta*, **39**, 347 (1956).
2244 Zuman, P., *Chem. Listy*, **47**, 1234 (1953); through *Chem. Abstracts*, **48**, 3813 (1954).

ADDITIONAL REFERENCES

2300 Allan, Z. J., and F. Mužík, *Coll. Czech. Chem. Com.*, **23,** 1927 (1958).
2301 Andreeva, M. A., and B. I. Stepanov, *J. Gen. Chem. U.S.S.R.*, **28,** 2966 (1958).
2302 Andreeva, M. A., and B. I. Stepanov, *J. Gen. Chem. U.S.S.R.*, **28,** 2968 (1958).
2303 Bachman, G. B., and T. Hokama, *J. Am. Chem. Soc.*, **79,** 4370 (1957).
2304 Bradley, W., and J. D. Hannon, *Chemistry and Industry*, **1959,** 540.
2305 Bradley, W., and J. D. Hannon, forthcoming publication.
2306 Bradley, W., and R. Robinson, *J. Chem. Soc.*, **1934,** 1484.
2307 Brassard, P., and P. L'Écuyer, *Can. J. Chem.*, **37,** 1505 (1959).
2308 Brouwers, J. A. C. T., S. C. Bijlsma, P. E. Verkade, and B. M. Wepster, *Rec. trav. chim.*, **77,** 1080 (1958).
2309 Burawoy, A., A. Chaudhuri, and W. I. Hyslop, *J. Chem. Soc.*, **1956,** 96.
2310 Cade, J. A., and A. Pilbeam, *Chemistry and Industry*, **1959,** 1578.
2311 Capuano, L., *Ber.*, **92,** 2670 (1959).
2312 Carey, J. G., G. Jones, and I. T. Millar, *Chemistry and Industry*, **1959,** 1018.
2313 Clarke, D. A., A. M. Moore, J. Ehrlich, H. W. Dion, H. M. Crooks, R. E. Maxwell, M. S. Morgan *et al.*, *Abstracts 129th Meeting ACS*, **1956,** pp. 12 M–16 M [see also (*2317, 2318*)].
2314 Clusius, K., and F. Endtinger, *Helv. Chim. Acta*, **43,** 566 (1959).
2315 Colonna, M., A. Risaliti, and L. Pentimalli, *Gazz. chim. ital.*, **86,** 1067 (1956).
2316 Criegee, R., and A. Rimmelin, *Ber.*, **90,** 414 (1957).
2317 Dewald, H. A., and A. M. Moore, *J. Am. Chem. Soc.*, **80,** 3941 (1958).
2318 Dion, H. W., S. A. Fusari, Z. L. Jakubowski, J. G. Zora, and Q. R. Bartz, *J. Am. Chem. Soc.*, **78,** 3075 (1956).
2319 Ernest, I., and H. Jelinková, *Coll. Czech. Chem. Com.*, **24,** 3341 (1959).
2320 Fahr, E., *Ber.*, **92,** 398 (1959).
2321 Fischer, E., M. Frankel, and R. Wolovsky, *J. Chem. Phys.*, **23,** 1367 (1955).
2322 Fischer, E., and Y. F. Frei, *J. Chem. Soc.*, **1959,** 3159.
2323 Gagnon, P. E., and B. T. Newbold, *Can. J. Chem.*, **37,** 366 (1959).
2324 Gerson, F., and E. Heilbronner, *Helv. Chim. Acta*, **42,** 1877 (1959).
2325 Grashey, R., and R. Huisgen, *Ber.*, **92,** 2641 (1959).
2326 Grimison, A., and J. H. Ridd, *J. Chem. Soc.*, **1959,** 3019.
2327 Hannon, J. D., Thesis, Leeds University, 1959.
2328 Herzberg, G., and J. Shoosmith, *Nature*, **183,** 1801 (1959).
2329 Horner, L., and H. Hoffmann, *Ber.*, **91,** 45 (1958).
2330 Inscoe, M. N., J. H. Gould, and W. R. Brode, *Abstracts 134th Meeting ACS*, **1958,** p. 95 P.
2331 Jucker, H., *Anal. Chim. Acta*, **16,** 210 (1957).
2332 Kirmse, W., *Angew. Chem.*, **71,** 537 (1959).
2333 Kirmse, W., *Naturwissenschaften*, **46,** 379 (1959).
2334 Kuhn, R., and H. M. Weitz, *Ber.*, **86,** 1199 (1953).
2335 Larkworthy, L. F., *J. Chem. Soc.*, **1959,** 3116.
2336 Larkworthy, L. F., *J. Chem. Soc.*, **1959,** 3304.
2337 Lebris, M. T., and H. Wahl, *Compt. rend.*, **246,** 3472 (1958).
2338 Le Fèvre, R. J. W., R. Roper, and I. H. Reece, *J. Chem. Soc.*, **1959,** 4104.
2339 Lewis, E. S., and H. Suhr, *Ber.*, **92,** 3031 (1959).
2340 Lewis, E. S., and H. Suhr, *Ber.*, **92,** 3043 (1959).
2341 Lubs, H. A., ed., *The Chemistry of Synthetic Dyes and Pigments*, Reinhold Publishing Corp., New York, 1955.
2342 Marshall, B. A., and W. A. Waters, *J. Chem. Soc.*, **1959,** 380.
2343 Miller, F. A., and W. B. White, *J. Am. Chem. Soc.*, **79,** 5974 (1957).
2344 Miller, J. B., *J. Org. Chem.*, **24,** 560 (1959).
2345 Minisci, F., *Gazz. chim. ital.*, **89,** 1910 (1959).
2346 Minisci, F., and A. Portolani, *Gazz. chim. ital.*, **89,** 1922 (1959).
2347 Minisci, F., and A. Portolani, *Gazz. chim. ital.*, **89,** 1941 (1959).
2348 Mörikofer, A., and E. Heilbronner, *Helv. Chim. Acta*, **42,** 1909 (1959).
2349 Pentimalli, L., *Tetrahedron*, **5,** 27 (1959).
2350 Ried, W., and R. Dietrich, *Naturwissenschaften*, **46,** 474 (1959).
2351 Rosenberger, H. M., and C. J. Shoemaker, *Anal. Chem.*, **31,** 204 (1959).

2352 Rusznák, I., M. Fehérvári, L. Tölgyesi, and G. Bán, *Magyar Textiltechn.*, **2,** 73 (1957); through *J. Soc. Dyers Col.*, **75,** 268 (1959).

2353 Schulte-Frohlinde, D., *Ann.*, **622,** 43 (1959).

2354 Schulte-Frohlinde, D., *Ann.*, **622,** 47 (1959).

2355 Shoppee, C. W., R. J. W. Cremlyn, D. E. Evans, and G. H. R. Summers, *J. Chem. Soc.*, **1957,** 4364.

2356 Smith, P., and A. M. Rosenberg, *J. Am. Chem. Soc.*, **81,** 2037 (1959).

2357 Stajner, K., F. Mužik, Z. J. Allan, and J. Poskočil, *Chem. Listy*, **52,** 1304 (1958); through *J. Soc. Dyers Col.*, **75,** 468 (1959).

2358 Stedman, G., *J. Chem. Soc.*, **1959,** 2936.

2359 Stedman, G., *J. Chem. Soc.*, **1959,** 2943.

2360 Stiles, M., and A. J. Libbey, *J. Org. Chem.*, **22,** 1243 (1957).

2361 Ugi, I., H. Perlinger, and L. Behringer, *Ber.*, **92,** 1864 (1959).

2362 Ward, E. R., B. D. Pearson, and P. R. Wells, *J. Soc. Dyers Col.*, **74,** 484 (1959).

2363 Wilhelm, M., and D. Y. Curtin, *Helv. Chim. Acta*, **40,** 2129 (1957).

2364 Wittig, G., and K. Schwarzenbach, *Angew. Chem.*, **71,** 652 (1959).

2365 Wyman, G. M., *Chem. Revs.*, **55,** 625 (1959).

2366 Yeh, S. J., and H. H. Jaffé, *J. Am. Chem. Soc.*, **81,** 3283 (1959).

2367 Yeh, S. J., and H. H. Jaffé, *J. Am. Chem. Soc.*, **81,** 3287 (1959).

2368 Paul, M. A., and F. A. Long, *Chem. Revs.*, **57,** 1 (1957).

2369 Paul, M. A., and F. A. Long, *Chem. Revs.*, **57,** 935 (1957).

2370 Deno, N. C., H. E. Berkheimer, W. L. Evans, and H. J. Peterson, *J. Am. Chem. Soc.*, **81,** 2344 (1959).

2371 Dahn, H., and L. Loewe, *Helv. Chim. Acta*, **43,** 294 (1960).

2372 Dahn, H., and L. Loewe, *Helv. Chim. Acta*, **43,** 310 (1960).

2373 Dahn, H., L. Loewe, and C. A. Bunton, *Helv. Chim. Acta*, **43,** 303 (1960).

2374 Dahn, H., L. Loewe, and C. A. Bunton, *Helv. Chim. Acta*, **43,** 317 (1960).

2375 Dahn, H., L. Loewe, and C. A. Bunton, *Helv. Chim. Acta*, **43,** 320 (1960).

2376 Dahn, H., L. Loewe, E. Lüscher, and R. Menassé, *Helv. Chim. Acta*, **43,** 287 (1960).

2377 Hafner, K., Thesis, Marburg University, 1951.

2378 Benzing, E., *Ann.*, **631,** 1, 10 (1960).

2379 de Boer, T. J., and J. C. van Velzen, *Rec. trav. chim.*, **78,** 947 (1959).

2380 Chmátal, V., and Z. J. Allan, *Coll. Czech. Chem. Com.*, **25,** 210 (1960).

2381 Downes, J. E., and P. Sykes, *J. Chem. Soc.* **1960,** 963.

2382 Farnum, D. G., and P. Yates, *Chemistry and Industry*, **1960,** 659.

2383 Filler, R., and H. Novar, *Chemistry and Industry*, **1960,** 468.

2384 Finar, I. L., and B. H. Walter, *J. Chem. Soc.*, **1960,** 1588.

2385 Geller, B. A., *Ukrain. khim. Zhur.*, **25,** 196 (1959); through *J. Soc. Dyers Col.*, **76,** 46 (1960).

2386 Goerdeler, J., and H. Haubrich, *Ber.*, **93,** 397 (1960).

2387 Gompper, R., *Ber.*, **93,** 187, 198 (1960).

2388 Gremillion, A. F., H. B. Jonassen, and R. J. O'Connor, *J. Am. Chem. Soc.*, **81,** 6134 (1959).

2389 Haupter, F., and A. Pucek, *Ber.*, **93,** 249 (1960).

2390 Hesse, G., and S. Majmudar, *Ber.*, **93,** 1129 (1960).

2391 Hoegerle, K., and P. L'Écuyer, *Can. J. Chem.*, **37,** 2068 (1959).

2392 Holt, P. F., B. I. Hopson-Hill, and C. J. McNae, *J. Chem. Soc.*, **1960,** 2245.

2393 Huisgen, R., and R. Lux, *Ber.*, **93,** 540 (1960).

2394 Huisgen, R., and H. Pohl, *Ber.*, **93,** 527 (1960).

2395 Hünig, S., *et al.*, *Ann.*, **628,** 46, 56, 69, 75, 84 (1959).

2396 Inscoe, M. N., J. H. Gould, and W. R. Brode, *J. Am. Chem. Soc.*, **81,** 5634 (1959).

2397 Jarkovský, J., and Z. J. Allan, *Coll. Czech. Chem. Com.*, **24,** 3739 (1959).

2398 Khalifa, M., *J. Chem. Soc.*, **1960,** 1854.

2399 Kuhn, R., G. Krüger, and A. Seeliger, *Ann.*, **628,** 240 (1959).

2400 Lohrscheid, H. O., *Arch. Pharm.*, **293,** 181 (1960).

2401 Merian, E., personal communication.

2402 Parmerter, S. M., *Organic Reactions*, J. Wiley & Sons, New York, 1959, Vol. X, 1.

2403 Poskočil, J., and Z. J. Allan, *Coll. Czech. Chem. Com.*, **24,** 3746 (1959).

2404 Ridd, J. H., *et al.*, *J. Chem. Soc.*, **1960,** 1352, 1357, 1363.

2405 Rosenthal, A. J., and C. G. Overberger, *J. Am. Chem. Soc.*, **82,** 108, 117 (1960).

2406 Schmid, H., and C. Essler, *Monatsh.*, **90,** 222 (1959).

2407 Snavely, F. A., B. D. Krecker, and C. G. Clark, *J. Am. Chem. Soc.*, **81,** 2337 (1959).

2408 Stedman, G., *J. Chem. Soc.*, **1960,** 1702.

2409 Volpin, M. E., D. N. Kursanov, M. M. Shemyakin, V. J. Maimind, and L. A. Neyman, *Chemistry and Industry*, **1958,** 1261.

2410 Ward, E. R., C. D. Johnson, and J. G. Hawkins, *J. Chem. Soc.*, **1960,** 894.

2411 Lewis, E. S., and M. D. Johnson, *J. Am. Chem. Soc.*, **82,** 5399 (1960).

2412 Lewis, E. S., and M. D. Johnson, *J. Am. Chem. Soc.*, **82,** 5408 (1960).

2413 Lewis, E. S., and H. Suhr, *J. Am. Chem. Soc.*, **82,** 862 (1960).

2414 Bunnett, J. F., and E. Buncel, unpublished.

2415 Bunnett, J. F., E. Buncel, and G. B. Hoey, unpublished.

2416 Kresge, A. J., and Y. Chan, *J. Am. Chem. Soc.*, **81,** 5509 (1959).

2417 Melander, L., personal communication.

2418 Gold, V., and D. P. N. Satchell, *J. Chem. Soc.*, **1955,** 3609.

2419 Gold, V., and D. P. N. Satchell, *J. Chem. Soc.*, **1955,** 3619.

2420 Gold, V., and D. P. N. Satchell, *J. Chem. Soc.*, **1955,** 3622.

2421 Gold, V., and D. P. N. Satchell, *J. Chem. Soc.*, **1956,** 1635.

2422 Olah, G. A., and S. J. Kuhn, *J. Am. Chem. Soc.*, **80,** 6535 (1958).

2423 Olah, G. A., A. E. Pavlath, and J. A. Olah, *J. Am. Chem. Soc.*, **80,** 6540 (1958).

2424 Olah, G. A., and S. J. Kuhn, *J. Am. Chem. Soc.*, **80,** 6541 (1958).

2425 Gerson, F., E. Heilbronner, A. van Veen, and B. M. Wepster, *Helv. Chim. Acta*, **43,** 1889 (1960).

2426 Calvert, J. G., S. S. Thomas, and P. L. Hanst, *J. Am. Chem. Soc.*, **82,** 1 (1960).

2427 Orgel, L. E., *An Introduction to Transition-Metal Chemistry: Ligand-Field Theory*, Methuen & Co., London, 1960.

2428 Houghton, C. D., and W. A. Waters, *J. Chem. Soc.*, **1950,** 1018.

2429 Hugelshofer, P., J. Kalvoda, and K. Schaffner, *Helv. Chim. Acta*, **43,** 1322 (1960).

2430 Khalifa, M., and W. H. Linnell, *J. Org. Chem.*, **24,** 853 (1959).

2431 Seltzer, S., personal communication.

2432 Cilento, G., *J. Org. Chem.*, **24,** 2015 (1959).

2433 Yeh, S. J., and H. H. Jaffé, *J. Am. Chem. Soc.*, **81,** 3279 (1959).

2434 Lewis, G. E., *J. Org. Chem.*, **25,** 871 (1960).

2435 Lewis, G. E., *Tetrahedron*, **10,** 129 (1960).

2436 Lewis, G. E., *Tetrahedron Letters*, **9,** 12 (1960).

2437 Kauffmann, T., H. O. Friestad, and H. Henkler, *Ann.*, **634,** 64 (1960).

2438 Fischer, E., *J. Am. Chem. Soc.*, **82,** 3249 (1960).

2439 Challis, B. C., and J. H. Ridd, *Proc. Chem. Soc.*, **1960,** 245.

2440 Huisgen, R., H. Stangl, and H. Wagenhofer, unpublished.

2441 Allan, Z. J., and J. Podstata, *Coll. Czech. Chem. Comm.*, **25,** 1324 (1960).

2442 Allan, Z. J., and J. Podstata, *Coll. Czech. Chem. Comm.*, **25,** 1337 (1960).

2443 Suckfüll, F. and H. Dittmer, *Chimia*, in press (1961).

2444 Gränacher, I., H. Suhr, A. Zenhäusern, and H. Zollinger, *Helv. Chim. Acta*, in press (1961).

PATENTS[1]

2500 Belg. Pat. 562,524, Agfa Aktiengesellschaft, Leverkusen
2501 Brit. Pat. 374,498, ICI
2502 Brit. Pat. 390,029, IG
2503 Brit. Pat. 417,861, ICI
2504 Brit. Pat. 649,934, DuP
2505 Brit. Pat. 656,727, Phillips Petroleum Co.
2506 Brit. Pat. 707,990, Peboc Ltd.
2507 Brit. Pat. 726,726, S
2508 Brit. Pat. 733,452, S
2509 Brit. Pat. 740,715, S
2510 Fr. Pat. 570,268, Ciba
2511 Fr. Pat. 795,802, St. Denis
2512 Fr. Pat. 811,711, St. Denis
2513 Fr. Pat. 846,748, IG
2514 Fr. Pat. 854,330, IG
2515 Fr. Pat. 957,500, S
2516 Fr. Pat. 959,835, S
2517 Fr. Pat. 1,042,356, CN
2518 Fr. Pat. 1,064,030, Ciba
2519 Fr. Pat. 1,073,234, Ciba
2520 Fr. Pat. 1,121,646, CN
2521 Fr. Pat. 1,128,372, FBy
2522 Ger. Pat. 15,915, H. Koechlin, and O. N. Witt
2523 Ger. Pat. 34,294, BASF
2524 Ger. Pat. 40,890, B. Fischer, and H. Michaelis
2525 Ger. Pat. 65,402, FBy
2526 Ger. Pat. 78,874, BASF
2527 Ger. Pat. 81,039, P. Becker
2528 Ger. Pat. 85,387, MLB
2529 Ger. Pat. 86,367, P. Becker
2530 Ger. Pat. 89,437, MLB
2531 Ger. Pat. 89,998, P. Becker
2532 Ger. Pat. 97,933, CFM
2533 Ger. Pat. 144,640, BASF
2534 Ger. Pat. 168,273, FH
2535 Ger. Pat. 171,024, Gy
2536 Ger. Pat. 172,446, Gy
2537 Ger. Pat. 172,569, Bodenstein
2538 Ger. Pat. 172,654, FH
2539 Ger. Pat. 204,212, CFM
2540 Ger. Pat. 204,702, Calico Printers Ass.
2541 Ger. Pat. 216,246, MLB
2542 Ger. Pat. 238,841, Heilmann and Battegay
2543 Ger. Pat. 253,238, FH
2544 Ger. Pat. 253,335, R. Fischer
2545 Ger. Pat. 287,086, GrE
2546 Ger. Pat. 291,076, GrE
2547 Ger. Pat. 292,118, GrE
2548 Ger. Pat. 409,564, FBy
2549 Ger. Pat. 456,857, Rheinische Kampfer Fabrik

2550 Ger. Pat. 464,142, Ciba
2551 Ger. Pat. 502,334, IG
2552 Ger. Pat. 513,206, IG
2553 Ger. Pat. 532,562, IG
2554 Ger. Pat. 567,921, Ciba
2555 Ger. Pat. 622,306, IG
2556 Ger. Pat. 641,769, Ciba
2557 Ger. Pat. 677,663, IG
2558 Ger. Pat. 705,780, IG
2559 Ger. Pat. 711,384, IG
2560 Ger. Pat. 741,358, S
2561 Ger. Pat. 741,467, IG
2562 Ger. Pat. 807,289, BASF
2563 Ger. Pat. 818,222, FBy
2564 Ger. Pat. 832,786, FBy
2565 Ger. Pat. 842,089, Gy
2566 Ger. Pat. 889,196, BASF
2567 Ger. Pat. 893,699, BASF
2568 Ger. Pat. 900,600, BASF
2569 Ger. Pat. 901,175, CFM
2570 Ger. Pat. 905,014, CFM
2571 Ger. Pat. 909,566, Ciba
2572 Ger. Pat. 921,223, Ciba
2573 Ger. Pat. 960,205, FH
2574 Ger. Pat. 963,154, Phoenix Gummiwerke, Hamburg
2575 Ger. Pat. 1,000,119, BASF
2576 Ger. Pat. 1,005,664, Gy
2577 Ger. Pat. 1,006,553, Gy
2578 Ger. Pat. 1,013,658, Ciba
2579 Ger. Pat. 1,026,750, Ciba
2580 Ger. Pat. 1,051,272, Phrix-Werke A.G., Hamburg
2581 Swiss Pat. 302,542, Vychodočské chemické závody
2582 U. S. Pat. 2,314,196, Allied Chem. and Dye Corp.
2583 U. S. Pat. 2,350,376, Merck & Co.
2584 U. S. Pat. 2,471,959, DuP
2585 U. S. Pat. 2,520,339, DuP
2586 U. S. Pat. 2,551,003, DuP
2587 U. S. Pat. 2,551,813, DuP
2588 U. S. Pat. 2,598,077, United States Rubber Co.
2589 U. S. Pat. 2,605,260, DuP
2590 U. S. Pat. 2,675,378, DuP
2591 U. S. Pat. 2,684,358, Allied Chemical & Dye Corp.
2592 U. S. Pat. 2,711,405, DuP
2593 U. S. Pat. 2,713,576, Rohm and Haas Co.
2594 U. S. Pat. 2,773,864, General Aniline
2595 U. S. Pat. 2,828,298, General Aniline
2596 U. S. Pat. 2,828,300, General Aniline
2597 U. S. Pat. 2,832,764, BASF

---

[1] For abbreviations of dye manufacturers' names see p. 406.

2598 U. S. Pat. 2,659,719,
Eastman Kodak Co.
2599 U. S. Pat. 2,683,708,
Eastman Kodak Co.
2600 U. S. Pat. 2,790,791,
Eastman Kodak Co.
2601 Ger. Pat. 1,079,758,
Eastman Kodak Co.
2602 Ger. Pat. 1,079,759,
Eastman Kodak Co.

2700 BIOS 435
2701 BIOS 772
2702 BIOS 961
2703 BIOS 986
2704 BIOS 988, a) p. 39
2705 BIOS 1149
2706 BIOS 1363
2707 BIOS 1475
2708 FIAT 528
2709 FIAT 1313
2710 P. B. Reports 20,543, p. 5071

CODE LETTERS FOR DYE MANUFACTURERS

A complete list of code letters is published in the Colour Index (*458*). Here only those code letters are given which are used in this book. The names marked * are those of firms which are no longer in existence. The companies which formed the I. G. Farbenindustrie A. G. in 1925 and became independent on its dissolution are referred to with their new name and code letter only.

A   *Aktiengesellschaft für Anilin-Fabrikation, Berlin, Germany

BASF   Badische Anilin- und Soda-Fabrik A.G., Ludwigshafen am Rhein, Germany

C   *Leopold Casella & Co., Frankfurt am Main, Germany (see CFM)

CFM   Cassella Farbwerke Mainkur A.G., Frankfurt am Main, Germany

Ciba   Ciba Aktiengesellschaft, Basle, Switzerland

CN   Compagnie Nationale de Matières Colorantes, Paris, France

DuP   E. I. DuPont de Nemours & Co. Inc., Wilmington, Del., U.S.A.

FBy   Farbenfabriken Bayer A.G., Leverkusen, Germany

FH   Farbwerke Höchst A.G., Frankfurt am Main, Germany

GrE   *Chemische Fabrik Griesheim-Electron, Frankfurt am Main, Germany

Gy   J. R. Geigy A.G., Basle, Switzerland

ICI   Imperial Chemical Industries Ltd., Dyestuffs Division, Manchester, Great Britain

IG   *I. G. Farbenindustrie A.G., Frankfurt am Main, Germany

L   *Farbwerk Mühlheim vorm. A. Leonhardt & Co., Frankfurt am Main, Germany

LBH   L. B. Holliday & Co. Ltd., Huddersfield, Great Britain

MLB   *Farbwerke vorm. Meister Lucius & Brüning, Höchst am Main, Germany (see FH)

S   Sandoz A.G., Basle, Switzerland

AUTHOR INDEX

SUBJECT INDEX